TL
272
.5
E38
2012

D1591829

Electronic and Electrical Systems

JOHN DEERE

FUNDAMENTALS OF SERVICE

Electronic and Electrical Systems
ISBN-0-86691-382-3

FOS2009NC (2012)　(ENGLISH)

A service, testing, and maintenance guide for electronic and electrical systems in off-road vehicles, trucks, and buses

LIBRARY
NSCC, AKERLEY CAMPUS
21 WOODLAWN RD.
DARTMOUTH, NS B2W 2R7 CANADA

Deere & Company
LITHO IN U.S.A.

Introduction

Free Catalog — Call 1-800-522-7448

Check out all of our titles in the FUNDAMENTALS OF SERVICE series!

Here are a few of the titles in this series:

Air Conditioning
Service, testing, and maintenance guide for air conditioning systems in off-road vehicles, trucks, and buses.

Electronic and Electrical Systems
Service, testing, and maintenance guide for electronic and electrical systems in off-road vehicles, trucks, and buses.

Hydraulics
Service, testing, and maintenance guide for hydraulic systems in off-road vehicles, trucks, and buses.

Hydraulic Diagnostics Systems
Service, testing, and troubleshooting guide for hydraulic systems in off-road vehicles, trucks, and buses.

Identification of Parts Failures
A highly illustrated failure analysis guide for automotive and off-road vehicle parts.

Power Trains
Service, testing, and maintenance guide for power trains in off-road vehicles, trucks, and buses.

Shop Tools
A basic guide showing the right tool for each type of job and its proper use.

Welding
The fundamentals of welding, cutting, brazing, soldering, and surfacing of metals.

Our FUNDAMENTALS OF SERVICE series brings together all the technical information you need and combines it with clearly written and amply illustrated instructional aids for many types of mechanical systems, their components, the tools needed, and repair procedures.

There are many ways to order, to inquire into prices, or to receive our free catalog:

- **Call 1-800-522-7448 to order using a credit card**
- **Search online from http://www.JohnDeere.com/publications**

FUNDAMENTALS OF SERVICE (FOS)

Fundamentals of Service (FOS) is a series of manuals created by Deere & Company. Each book in the series is conceived, researched, outlined, edited, and published by Deere & Company, John Deere Publishing. Authors are selected to provide a basic technical manuscript that could be edited and rewritten by staff editors.

HOW TO USE THE MANUAL: This FOS manual can be used by anyone — experienced mechanics, shop trainees, vocational students, and lay readers. The instructions are written in simple language so that they can be easily understood.

Persons not familiar with the topics discussed in this book should begin with Chapter 1 and then study the chapters in sequence. The experienced person can find what is needed on the "Contents" page.

Each guide was written by Deere & Company, John Deere Publishing staff in cooperation with the technical writers, illustrators, and editors at Almon, Inc. — a full-service technical publications company headquartered in Waukesha, Wisconsin (www.almoninc.com).

This material is the property of Deere & Company, John Deere Publishing. All use and/or reproduction not specifically authorized by Deere & Company, John Deere Publishing is prohibited.

Engines

Engines is the definitive "how-to" book of both on- and off-road engines — from showing you how to diagnose problems and test components, to explaining how to repair each system. And when we say "show you," we mean just that! Our book is filled with illustrations to clearly demonstrate what must be done — photographs, drawings, pictorial diagrams, troubleshooting charts, and diagnostic charts.

Instructions are written in simple language so that they can be easily understood. This book can be used by anyone, from a novice to an experienced mechanic. And it can be used to work on many types of engines, from gasoline to LP-gas to diesel. By starting with the basics, the book builds your knowledge step-by-step, from how engines work to diagnosing and testing an engine. It even shows you how to perform an engine tune-up.

ACKNOWLEDGMENTS
John Deere gratefully acknowledges the following people for their contributions to this manual:

AUTHOR: *Mike Hall* is the original author. He has a B.S. degree in Industrial Technology from Pittsburg State University at Pittsburg, Kansas, and has over 25 years of experience writing and editing technical publication for agricultural equipment.

CONSULTING EDITOR: *Lon R. Shell Ed.D.*, Professor of Agricultural Systems Management, Department of Agriculture at Southwest Texas State University, is the original consulting editor. He has over 30 years of experience in research and teaching. His research specialty is tractor power delivery dealing with tractive efficiencies.

COPY EDITOR: *Tom Rader* is the original editor of the Fundamentals of Service (FOS) series of teaching materials during his career with Deere and Company. He was also a technical writer and later the manager of Technical Publications and Training for Deere in Waterloo, Iowa. He is now retired.

Continued on next page
OUO1010,0000EAC -19-10JUL09-1/2

John Deere also acknowledges the following groups:

AW Dynamometer, Inc., Dana Corporation, Allen Electric and Equipment Co., Bacharach Industrial Instrument Co., Bendix Corp., Central Tool Co., Federal-Mogul Corp., F.W. Dwyer Co., Garrett Corp., General Motors Corp., J.H. Williams and Co., Kent-Moore Corp., K.O. Lee Co., Koppers Co., L.S. Starrett Co., Marquette Manufacturing Co., Marvel-Schebler, Division of Borg-Warner Corp., MVE, Inc., National LP-Gas Assn., Nuday Co., Owatonna Tool Co., Roosa Master, Hartford Division of Standard Screw Co., Taylor Dynamometer and Machine Co., Texaco, Inc., TRW Replacement Div., Union Carbide Corp., United Tool Process Corp., Westberg Manufacturing Co.

OUO1010,0000EAC -19-10JUL09-2/2

Contents

Continued on next page

Original Instructions. All information, illustrations and specifications in this manual are based on the latest information available at the time of publication. The right is reserved to make changes at any time without notice.

COPYRIGHT © 2012
DEERE & COMPANY
Moline, Illinois
All rights reserved.
A John Deere ILLUSTRUCTION ® Manual
Previous Editions
Copyright © 1968, 1972, 1978, 1979, 1984, 1991, & 2005

Contents

Continued on next page

110112
PN=2

Contents

Contents

INTRODUCTION

DXP02701 —UN—23FEB11

1

Safety is too expensive to learn by accident. Hospital bills, doctor bills, medical supplies, and rehabilitation costs can be a big financial burden on both individuals and companies.

Because of recent dramatic increases in these costs, both company-provided and private insurance plans have begun to shift more of this burden onto the insured parties.

Accidents also result in lost time from work, and more importantly, may cause a permanent handicap or a loss of health that affects the injured party's family and earning ability. Unsafe practices also result in property damage.

Accidents are reduced by incorporating safe work practices into shop management programs. Safety must be thought of as a normal part of the management process, just as supplies, personnel, and overhead costs are.

Electricity has brought advanced technology into our homes and workplaces. From light bulbs to microcomputers, it plays a significant role in our everyday lives.

It is easy to take this unseen and somewhat mystical convenience for granted and to forget that, as wonderful as its gifts, it is a powerful and dangerous force capable of causing property damage, serious bodily injury, and even death.

OUO1082,0002BB7 -19-07MAR12-1/3

Electricity and batteries can cause fires and explosions (Fig. 1), and of course, the hazard of electrocution is always present.

People become especially complacent when working around low voltages.

However, keep in mind that a current of only one milliampere (one thousandth of an ampere) can be felt, a current of 25 milliamperes can kill, and a current of 100 milliamperes probably will kill.

If certain conditions exist, a current of only 0.006 ampere can electrocute a healthy person in less than a second.

Fig. 1 — Safety Precautions Prevent Battery Explosions

Continued on next page

OUO1082,0002BB7 -19-07MAR12-2/3

110112
PN=9

A typical battery may have two to five amperes of current flowing across its terminals (Fig. 2). Remember that this amount of current is enough to kill. Therefore, safety must be your first and most important consideration when working around and with electrical equipment.

Body resistance varies from person to person. It ranges from approximately 1000 to 500,000 ohms. The reasons for such variance depend on many factors: weight, height, body chemistry, etc.

An individual's own resistance may be lowered by perspiration, weather, wet ground conditions, and other variables.

When you learn to measure resistance, you will be able to measure your own body resistance by holding the end of a probe in each hand and taking an ohmmeter reading.

DXP02743 —UN—09FEB12

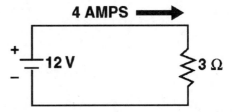

Fig. 2 — A Basic Series Circuit of a Battery

Electrical current follows the path of least resistance. Accidents happen when the human body becomes such a path.

OUO1082,0002BB7 -19-07MAR12-3/3

ELECTRICAL SYSTEM SAFETY

Avoid these hazards when servicing an electrical system:

- Fires
- Short-Circuit Start
- Bypass Start Hazard
- Battery Explosions
- Acid Burns
- Electric Shock

FIRES

Electrical systems can cause fires if not properly maintained. One of the purposes of the energy stored in the battery is to start the engine. But if a bare wire of the start system touches a metal part of the machine it will become extremely hot or may even spark and could cause a fire in dust, chaff, leaves, or oil-covered wires. Most machinery fires do not result in personal injury, but every fire is a potential source of injury. Inspect electrical systems regularly. Make sure wires are properly insulated and clean dust, chaff, leaves, and oil off wires.

Every self-propelled machine should have an all-purpose ABC dry chemical fire extinguisher on board to cover all types of fires. Everyone involved with the machine should know how to use it and its charge should be checked annually.

Fire extinguishers are classified by their ability to handle specific types of fires. The fire extinguisher has a label with symbols identifying which type of fire it can be expected to handle (Fig. 3). There are two different styles of symbols that are used: letter-shaped or pictorial. The four types of fire classifications are:

All fire extinguishers are color coded so you can see at a glance what the extinguisher is and what it contains.

- Class A—Fires involving ordinary combustible materials such as paper, wood and cloth.
- Class B—Fires involving liquids, greases, and gasses.
- Class C—Fires involving energized electrical equipment.

CLASS A

CLASS B

CLASS C

DXP03613 —UN—04JUN12

CLASS D

Fig. 3 — Fire Extinguisher Classification Symbols

- Class D—Fires involving metals such as magnesium, titanium, zirconium, sodium, and potassium.

MM61211,00012BC -19-07JUN12-1/10

Fire extinguishers with a Class C rating have a non-conductive extinguishing agent (Fig. 4). No fire extinguisher gets a Class C rating without an additional Class A and/or Class B rating. Class D fire extinguishers are not given a multipurpose rating, they are designed for Class D fires only.

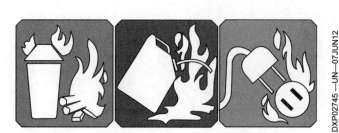

Fig. 4 — Class ABC Fire Extinguisher

Continued on next page   MM61211,00012BC -19-07JUN12-2/10

Some fire extinguishers can handle more than one type of fire (i.e. Class ABC). However, when one or more of the extinguisher symbols on the label are crossed out, the extinguisher cannot be used for the class (or classes) of fire with the symbol(s) crossed out (i.e., Class AB) (Fig. 5).

Fig. 5 — Class AB Fire Extinguisher

MM61211,00012BC -19-07JUN12-3/10

SHORT-CIRCUIT START

If insulation on electrical wires is cracked or worn, a short circuit can occur. Electricity could flow to the cranking motor and start the engine when no one is around.

If the positive and negative terminals of a cranking motor are accidentally contacted by another metal object, the current will flow between the two terminals, and accidentally start the engine.

BYPASS START HAZARD

Bypass starting of tractors and other farm equipment is a very serious safety concern.

Never short across the starter terminals with a screwdriver or other devices to start a machine. You bypass the neutral-start switch by doing so, and if the machine is in gear when the engine starts, it could suddenly lurch forward and crush you (Fig. 6). Many people have died doing it. DON'T TRY IT!

Never bypass start any tractor or other self-propelled machines and never start it while standing on the ground. Start tractors and self-propelled machines only from the operator's station and with the transmission in neutral or park.

Neutral-start switches keep the engine from starting when the transmission is engaged or when the clutch is

Fig. 6 — Avoid the Short-Circuit Starting Hazard

engaged. Check them periodically to make sure they are working properly. Neutral-start switches can be located so that starting is only possible when:

1. The clutch or inching pedal is depressed.

2. The shift lever is in neutral or park position.

3. Any combination of the above.

These switches should prevent engine cranking when the rear wheels are engaged with the engine. If they don't, they must be adjusted or replaced.

Continued on next page   MM61211,00012BC -19-07JUN12-4/10

BATTERY EXPLOSIONS

Batteries contain sulfuric acid and explosive mixtures of hydrogen and oxygen gases.

When charging and discharging, a lead-acid storage battery generates hydrogen and oxygen gas. Hydrogen will burn, and is very explosive in the presence of oxygen.

A spark or flame near the battery could ignite these gases, rupturing the battery case and splattering acid on property, clothing, skin, and eyes.

Special care must always be used around batteries:

- Wear eye protection. Also wear rubber gloves and a rubber apron when working around electrolyte.
- Keep sparks and flames away from the battery.
- Never smoke around a battery.
- Always work on batteries in a well-ventilated area.
- If the battery has been on charge or is being charged during a test procedure, blow away gases before continuing testing.
- Do not break electrical circuits near the battery top as a spark could start an explosion.

To prevent battery explosions:

1. Maintain the electrolyte at the recommended level (Fig. 7). Check this level frequently. When the level is properly maintained, less space will be available in the battery for gases to accumulate.

2. Put only distilled water in the battery.

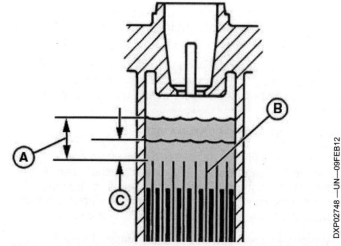

Fig. 7 — Keep Electrolyte at the Proper Level to Prevent Explosions

A—1/2 in. (13 mm) Maximum   **C—1/4 in. (6 mm) Minimum**
B—Plate Separators

3. Use a flashlight to check the electrolyte level. Never use a match or lighter. These could set off an explosion.

4. Do not short across the battery terminals by placing a metal object between them.

5. Do not charge a frozen battery. Warm the battery to 60°F (16°C).

MM61211,00012BC -19-07JUN12-5/10

---

6. Remove and replace battery clamps in the right order. This is very important.

   If your wrench touches the ungrounded (usually positive) battery post and the machine chassis at the same time, the heavy flow of current will arc across the terminals producing a dangerous spark.

   To prevent this from happening, follow these rules:

   a. When removing the battery, disconnect the grounded battery clamp first (Fig. 8).
      The ground post lead will be connected to the engine block, frame, or other metallic surface. The positive post lead will be connected to the starter relay. Some systems may have a positive ground. Although this is not common, always make sure you know which post is grounded.

   b. When installing the battery, connect the grounded battery clamp last.

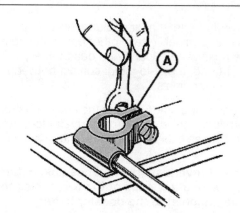

A—Ground Clamp

7. Prevent sparks from battery charger leads.

Continued on next page   MM61211,00012BC -19-07JUN12-6/10

Turn the battery charger off or pull the power cord before connecting or disconnecting changer leads to battery posts. (Fig. 9).

If you don't, the current flowing in the leads will spark at the battery posts. These sparks could ignite the explosive hydrogen gas which is always present when a battery is being charged.

CONNECTING A BOOSTER BATTERY

Improper connecting of a booster battery from one machine to the dead battery of another machine can be dangerous and can cause a battery explosion. Follow these procedures when connecting a booster battery from one machine to the dead battery of another machine.

1. Remove all cell caps of the dead battery (if so equipped).

2. Check to make sure the dead battery is not frozen. Never attempt to boost a battery with ice in its cells.

3. Be sure that booster battery and dead battery are of the same voltage.

4. Turn off all accessories and ignition of both machines.

5. Place gearshift of both vehicles in neutral or park and set the parking brake. Make sure vehicles do not touch each other.

6. Check the electrolyte level of the dead battery cells. Add distilled water to cells if low. Cover the vent holes with a damp cloth, or if caps are safety vent type, replace the caps before attaching jumper cables to the batteries.

7. Attach one end of one jumper cable to the booster battery positive terminal. Attach other end of the same cable to the positive terminal of the dead battery. Make sure of good, metal-to-metal contact between cable ends and terminals.

8. Attach one end of the other cable to the booster battery negative terminal. Make sure of good, metal-to-metal contact between the cable end and the battery terminal.

⚠ CAUTION: To prevent sparks and possible battery explosion, never allow ends of the two cables to touch while attached to the booster battery.

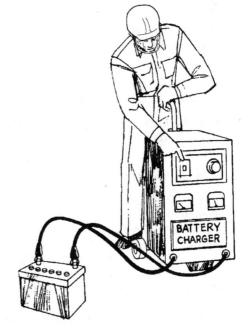

Fig. 9 — Turn Off Charger Before Connecting or Disconnecting the Charger Leads

9. Connect other end of second cable to engine block or frame of the disabled vehicle as far away from the dead battery as possible. This is to ensure that if a spark should occur at this connection, it would not ignite hydrogen gas that may be present above the dead battery.

10. Try to start the disabled vehicle. Do not engage the starter for more than 30 seconds or starter may overheat and booster battery will be drained of power. If the disabled vehicle will not start, start the vehicle with the booster battery and let it run for a few minutes with the cables attached. Try to start the disabled vehicle again.

11. Remove cables in exactly the reverse order from installation. Remove damp cloth and replace vent caps.

Continued on next page MM61211,00012BC -19-07JUN12-7/10

ACID BURNS

Battery electrolyte is approximately 36% full-strength sulfuric acid and 64% water.

Even though it is diluted, it is strong enough to burn skin, eat holes in clothing, and cause blindness if splashed into eyes.

Fill new batteries with electrolyte in a well-ventilated area, wear eye protection and rubber gloves, and avoid breathing any fumes from the battery when the electrolyte is added.

Avoid spilling or dripping electrolyte when using a hydrometer to check specific gravity readings (Fig. 10).

If you spill acid on yourself, flush your skin immediately with water for several minutes. Apply baking soda or lime to help neutralize the acid.

If acid gets into your eyes, force the lids open and flood the eyes with running water for 15 to 30 minutes. Get medical attention immediately.

If the acid is swallowed, drink large amounts of water or milk, but do not exceed 2 quarts (2 L). Get medical attention immediately.

ELECTRIC SHOCK

Injury from electric shock depends on the number of vital organs through which current passes.

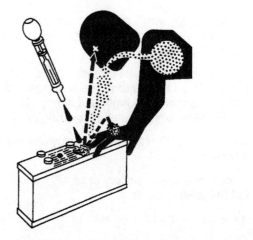

Fig. 10 — *Avoid Electrolyte Hazards When Using a Hydrometer*

Electricity travels at the speed of light, which is 186,000 miles per second, leaving no reaction time.

Further, the hand muscles contract causing a firmer grip on a current-carrying wire or component.

To prevent a current path from flowing through your heart, always keep one hand away from the voltage source when working on a circuit. Don't become part of the current path.

MM61211,00012BC -19-07JUN12-8/10

The voltage in the secondary circuit of an ignition system may exceed 25,000 volts. For this reason, don't touch spark plug terminals, spark plug cables, or the coil-to-distributor high-tension cable when the ignition switch is turned on or the engine is running (Fig. 11). The cable insulation should protect you, but it could be defective.

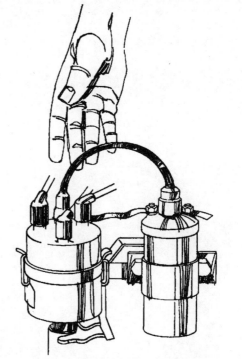

Fig. 11 — *Do Not Touch Before Turning Off Ignition Switch*

Continued on next page

MM61211,00012BC -19-07JUN12-9/10

Never run an engine when the wire connected to the output terminal of an alternator or generator is disconnected (Fig. 12).

If you do, and if you touch the terminal, you could receive a severe shock. When the battery wire is disconnected, the voltage can go dangerously high, and it may also damage the generator, alternator, regulator, or wiring harness.

Don't short across the battery terminals by placing a metal object between them.

Electric shock may cause unconsciousness and burns on the skin at the area of contact.

If necessary, use a dry rope or stick to move the victim to safety.

De-energize the power source: open the switch or cut the cable or wire using a properly insulated tool.

Keep the victim lying down and still with clothing loosened around the neck, chest, and abdomen.

If the victim is not breathing, apply cardiopulmonary resuscitation (CPR). Seek medical attention immediately.

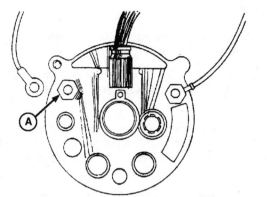

Fig. 12 — Connect the Alternator or Generator Output Terminal Lead Before Running an Engine

A—Output Terminal

MM61211,00012BC -19-07JUN12-10/10

HIGH-VOLTAGE SAFETY FOR HYBRID SYSTEMS

A high-voltage hybrid electrical system present new challenges and concerns for today's technicians when it comes to safety.

Gas-electric hybrid electrical systems can generate enough electrical energy to cause electrocution. Just a couple of amps of current can have deadly effects. Any voltage greater than 40 volts is considered potentially dangerous!

When working on an high-voltage system always wear the properly rated insulated rubber gloves such as Class 0 rated insulated gloves, which are rated to 1000 volts AC.

For Example; most hybrid electrical systems are capable of producing nearly 600 VAC and 300 VDC with the amperage in the hundreds. This current can be carried in any of the following:

- High-voltage (HV) battery packs
- Capacitors
- Motor-generators
- High-voltage cables

Always follow these important safety rules when working on high-voltage hybrid electrical system;

- Always disable drives
- Engage the high-voltage disconnect
- Remove any jewelry
- Wear heavy rubber (class 0 rated gloves)
- Wear rubber soled shoes
- Wear eye protection (goggles)
- Always have the proper fire extinguisher nearby
- Make sure the floor is dry (never work near puddles)
- No more than one hand should be holding a lead or touching vehicle ground at any time

GROUND DRIVE VOLTAGE CONSIDERATIONS

A high-voltage hybrid system will have a ground fault interrupter (GFI) that measures the system for high-voltage. This ground fault interrupter will constantly monitor the system for high-voltage, and If high-voltage loss or leakage occurs, this may happen though the chassis of the vehicle.

If high-voltage from the HV batteries or motor-generator is shorting to frame ground, the ECU will illuminate a warning and de-energize the main power to disconnect the battery pack from its drive circuit.

HIGH-VOLTAGE BATTERY CONSIDERATIONS

Always ensure the system is shut "OFF" or disconnected. All HV hybrid batteries have a safety switch or disconnect mechanism to disconnect the battery from the vehicle's electrical system. With some hybrids, you must pull out the disconnect to produce an open circuit between the battery pack and the power control module, others may need to rotate a high-voltage disconnect switch. Disconnecting the batteries should be common practice when working on HV hybrid systems.

Technicians should also follow the ten minute rule, And to wait at least ten minutes after activating the high-voltage disconnect switch before working on the high-voltage circuits. This will allow for any high-voltage capacitors in the inverter circuit to discharge fully.

Always wear the proper safety goggles, apron suitable for alkaline and thick rubber insulated gloves with a Class 0 rating. A high-voltage hybrid battery and it's components create a potential shock hazard, since it contains a tremendous amount of stored electrical energy. Precautions should always be used when handling batteries.

High-voltage hybrid batteries are completely different than a standard lead acid batteries in terms of the contents of these batteries. For example; A standard lead acid battery will have a pH level near 0 and a high-voltage hybrid battery will contain a corrosive electrolyte fluid that has a pH level of 13.5, which at this pH level is capable of dissolving human tissue.

Another important consideration is that HV hybrid battery packs are heavy and can weigh over 200 pounds (90 kg). Never attempt to remove these battery packs without the proper lifting device.

SUPPLY VOLTAGE TO ATTACHMENTS CONSIDERATIONS

Attachments can still be energized and should be treated as such. If attachments are connected to the machine, they should be disconnected and moved from the working area, to avoid contact when working on the machine.

Do not physically push or tow hybrids around the shop. Regenerative brakes can generate electricity if the vehicle is moved with all four wheels on the ground.

MM61211,00012BD -19-21JUN12-1/1

SHOP PRACTICES AND WORK HABITS

The best way to minimize hazards associated with electricity and electrical equipment is to follow proven shop practices and employ good work habits:

- Wear eye protection. Plastic goggles protect eyes from impact from the front and sides. Unvented (chemical splash) goggles offer protection against chemical vapors and liquids (Fig. 13).
- Rest regularly to avoid the effects of fatigue. Never use drugs, alcohol, or tobacco when working on equipment.
- Avoid horseplay.
- Never work on dangerous equipment when you are ill, angry, or anxious.
- Be alert.
- Work only in adequately ventilated areas.
- Make sure the work area has sufficient light.
- Be aware of common machine hazards. Don't take shortcuts. Shortcuts shorten lives, and because of the problems that they cause, cost more in time and money than they save.

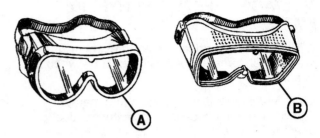

Fig. 13 — Wear Unvented Safety Goggles Around Acids

A—Unvented Goggles   **B—Vented Goggles**

- Lock out or disconnect the electrical power source from the electrical system before you begin your service procedure.
- Know your limitations: age, weight, and height all have a bearing on the jobs you are capable of doing.

Continued on next page   OUO1082,0002BB9 -19-12MAR12-1/4

- Learn the basic rules of first aid and keep a first aid kit readily available (Fig. 14).
  Apply immediate first aid to all injuries, but do not attempt any first aid procedures that you are not qualified to perform. If an injury appears severe, don't move the victim. Contact local emergency services (paramedics, emergency room, etc.) and follow their instructions.
- Know who to call for help. Keep emergency numbers for doctors, ambulance services, hospitals, and fire departments near the telephone.
- Wear rubber gloves and a rubber apron when working around electrolyte.
- Never use water on electrical fires.
- Have correct fire extinguisher available:
  - Keep a dry chemical fire extinguisher suitable for Class C fires close to but not in the fire hazard area.
  - Both Class B (burning liquids) and Class C (electrical equipment) fires require a pressurized dry chemical fire extinguisher of 20-pound capacity.
  - Shops should be equipped with at least one all-purpose ABC dry chemical fire extinguisher (Fig. 14). This extinguisher will put out Class A (combustibles like paper and wood), Class B, and Class C fires.
- Make sure that wires are properly insulated and clean and that electrical components are free of dust, chaff, leaves, and oil.

- Always read, understand and follow the instructions and manuals provided with equipment (Fig. 15). Don't guess. Keep manuals in a clean, dry, readily available place.

- Read and understand labeling on the equipment. Replace labels that are damaged or worn. Heed the safety-alert symbols on the labels and in other instructional materials (Fig. 16).

-

  Pay attention to signal words:
  Signal words like *Danger*, *Warning,* and *Caution* draw attention to potentially unsafe areas. Learn these signal words and let them become your "think trigger."
  - DANGER means that a serious potential hazards is present. Exposure to this hazard would result in a high probability of death or a severe injury if proper precautions are not taken.
  - WARNING means the hazard presents a lesser degree of risk of injury or death than that associated with Danger.
  - CAUTION is used to remind of safety instructions that must be followed and to identify property damage hazards and hazards involving minor injuries.
  Safety messages use colors as an aid to communication. Red and white are the colors used with the word Danger. Black and yellow are found on signs carrying the words Caution or Warning.
  Pay attention to pictorial representations of safety hazards. A good pictorial should identify the hazard and portray the potential consequences of failure to follow instructions (Fig. 17).

-

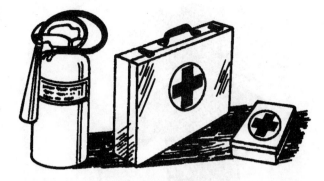

Fig. 14 — Keep a First Aid Kit and ABC Dry Chemical Fire Extinguisher Readily Available

Fig. 15 — Read and Follow Manufacturer's Instructions

Fig. 16 — This Safety-Alert Symbol Could Save Your Life

Be able to identify universal symbols used to help identify controls. Color is often used with these symbols to indicate a problem (Fig. 18).
- Never work alone. Make sure someone knows you are working in the shop and will check on you and render aid if you are injured.

Continued on next page
OUO1082,0002BB9 -19-12MAR12-2/4

110112

Fig. 17 — Pictorial = Danger of Hazardous Fumes or Dust

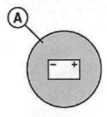

Fig. 18 — Alternator Light Turns Red When There is a Problem With Charging System

A—Alternator Light

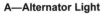

- Do not wear jewelry or other metallic objects when working on equipment. Keep metal parts of clothing, such as zippers and buttons, covered.
- Keep clothing, hands, feet, and flooring dry. Make sure floor surfaces are clean and dry.
- Use insulated tools whenever possible.

- Always select the right tool for the job and use it in the right way (Fig. 19).
  - Keep tools in good condition and store them safely when not in use.
  - Guard against eye injuries when cutting with pliers or cutters. Short and long ends of wire often fly or whip through the air when cut. Wear eye protection when cutting wire. Select a cutter big enough for the job. Keel the blades at right angles to the stock and don't rock the cutter to get a faster cut. Adjust the cutters to maintain a small clearance between the blades to prevent them from striking each other when the handles are closed.
  - Use non-metallic receptacles and funnels when working with electrolyte. Do not store electrolyte in a warm or sunny location.

- Properly store and dispose of hazardous materials such as battery acid (Fig. 20). Do not pour battery acid down a drain or into a stream, pond, or lake.

Fig. 19 — Proper Use of Tools Prevents Injury and Property Damage and Extends Tool Life

Fig. 20 — Dispose of Fluids Properly

Improper disposal of fluids can harm the environment and ecology. Check with state environmental agencies for information concerning the proper disposal of battery acid.

Used batteries must be recycled. Battery retailers are required to take one old battery for each one you buy. Manufacturers recycle batteries to produce new ones.

- Remember that you and your co-workers contribute to each other's safety. Would you want to work around someone with unsafe working habits? Would you take your machinery to a repair shop known for unsafe working conditions and practices?

Continued on next page   OUO1082,0002BB9 -19-12MAR12-3/4

OUO1082,0002BB9 -19-12MAR12-4/4

When it comes to safety, be a leader, not a follower. Safety is everybody's business (Fig. 21).

Fig. 21 — Safety: Your Life Depends on It

OUO1082,0002BB9 -19-12MAR12-5/4

NOISE PROTECTION AND SOUND LEVEL (DECIBELS)

The human ear has an enormous range of intensities. It is sensitive to that ranges from the hearing threshold to a sensation of pain. Since the range of intensity is, so wide, it is convenient to use a logarithmic scale for the measurement of sound intensities. It is referred to as the bel (B). In practice, the unit of 1B is too large. To obtain a more useful unit, we define a decibel (dB) as one-tenth of a bel.

Table 1 — Intensity Levels for Common Sounds	
Sound	Intensity Level (dB)
Hearing Threshold	0
Rustling Leaves	10
Whisper	20
Quiet Radio	40
Normal Conversation	65
Busy Street Comer	80
Tractor	90
Subway Car	100
Pain Threshold	120
Jet Engine	140—160

By using the decibel, we reduced the wide range of intensities to intensity levels from 0 to 120 dB. We must remember the scale is not linear. A 40-dB sound is 100 times more intense as a 20-dB sound. Refer to Table 1 for examples of the intensity levels for common sounds.

Experts agree continued exposure to noise above 85 dB over time will cause hearing loss. The National Institute for Occupational Safety and Health (1998) recommends the maximum exposure time at 85 dB is 8 hours. At 110 dB, the maximum exposure time is one minute and 29 seconds. Wearing ear protection for sound intensities over 85 dB will help prevent hearing loss.

OUO1082,0002BBA -19-10JAN12-1/1

TEST YOURSELF

QUESTIONS

1. Shorting across starter terminals with a screwdriver is known as the _____ _____ hazard.

2. Batteries contain _____ which make them very explosive.

3. Always wear _____ when working on a battery.

4. After jump starting a dead battery, disconnect the _____ jumper cable from the engine block first.

5. "Think" safety when you see signal words-on machinery like _____, _____ and _____.

6. When working on an electrical circuit, don't become part of the _____ .

7. If certain conditions exist, a current of only _____ _____ can electrocute a healthy person.

8. (True or False?) You can operate a tractor that emits a 90 dB sound for 8 hours with out hearing protection and suffer no hearing loss.

9. A high-voltage hybrid battery will contain a corrosive electrolyte fluid that has a pH level of ____?

(Answers are in the back of the textbook.)

OUO1082,0002BBB -19-06JUN12-1/1

Electricity—How it Works

INTRODUCTION

DXP02702 —UN—23FEB11

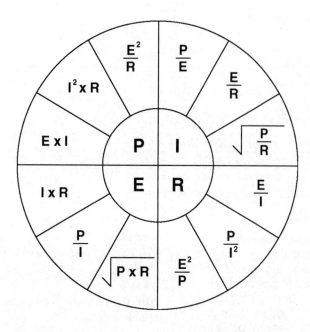

DXP02776 —UN—07JUN12

In this chapter we will cover the basics of electronics and electricity:

- SI Base Units and Prefixes
- Scientific and Engineering Notation
- Electron Theory
- Putting Electrons to Work
- Electronics vs. Electricity
- Introduction to Current, Voltage, and Resistance

- Ohm's Law
- A Basic Electronic Circuit
- Electronic Circuits—Three Types
- Power (Watts)
- Magnetism
- Electromagnetism
- Electromagnetic Induction

OUO1082,0002BC1 -19-07MAR12-1/1

SI BASE UNITS

Table 1 — SI Base Units		
Quantity	Base Unit	Symbol
Length	meter	m
Mass	kilogram	kg
Time	second	s
Electric Current	ampere	A
Thermodynamic Temperature	kelvin	K
Amount of Substance	mole	mol
Luminous Intensity	candela	cd

The engineering and scientific community commonly uses the standard international units of measure. Listed in Table 1 are the more commonly used base units. These are the units used in this text to derive all formulas.

OUO1082,0002BC2 -19-10JAN12-1/1

SI UNIT PREFIXES

	Table 2 — SI Unit Prefixes		
Prefix	**Factor to multiply root unit by**	**Letter Symbol**	**Engineering Notation**
Exa	$1\ 000\ 000\ 000\ 000\ 000\ 000 = 10^{18}$	E	Exa
peta	$1\ 000\ 000\ 000\ 000\ 000 = 10^{15}$	P	peta
tera	$1\ 000\ 000\ 000\ 000 = 10^{12}$	T	tera
giga	$1\ 000\ 000\ 000 = 10^{9}$	G	giga
mega	$1\ 000\ 000 = 10^{6}$	M	mega
kilo	$1\ 000 = 10^{3}$	k	kilo
hecto	$100 = 10^{2}$	h	Not used
deca	10	da	Not used
deci	$0.1 = 10^{-1}$	d	Not used
centi	$0.01 = 10^{-2}$	c	Not used
milli	$0.001 = 10^{-3}$	m	milli
micro	$0.000\ 001 = 10^{-6}$	μ*	micro
nano	$0.000\ 000\ 001 = 10^{-9}$	n	nano
pico	$0.000\ 000\ 000\ 001 = 10^{-12}$	p	pico
femto	$0.000\ 000\ 000\ 000\ 001 = 10^{-15}$	f	femto
atto	$0.000\ 000\ 000\ 000\ 000\ 001 = 10^{-18}$	a	atto

* The symbol for micro is the Greek letter μ (mu)

Engineering personnel use a variation of scientific notation to express numerical quantities clearly. They do this by adding an appropriate prefix onto the root unit of measurement to represent the equivalent power of ten. To create decimal multiples or submultiples of root units, SI provides the standard unit prefixes listed in Table 2. For engineering purposes, we shift the decimal point in multiples of three. Hence, the prefixes hecto, deca, deci, and centi will not be used in mathematics for electric or electronic circuits.

Root units have no prefixes. In most cases in SI, root units are also base units. The one exception is the base unit for mass, the kilogram, which historically already has the prefix kilo and is, therefore, not a root unit.

Shifting the decimal point three places at a time means some numerical values will have more than one digit to the left of the decimal point. Consequently, when using prefixes with root units, SI recommends we select prefixes, that will permit the numerical values of the quantities to be between 0.1 and 1000.

Example 2-1

Express 425000 meters in a more convenient size of unit.

Solution

Shifting the decimal point three places to the left gives a figure of 425, which we must now multiply by 1000, or 10^3 to restore its proper magnitude. Hence:

$425000m = 425 \times 10^3 m$

From Table 2, we can replace 10^3 by tacking the prefix kilo onto the root unit.

Therefore $425000m = 425 \times 10^3 m = 425km$ (kilometers)

The kilometer is 1000 times as large as the base unit the meter is.

Example 2-2

Express 1/200 second in a more appropriate form using an SI unit prefix.

Solution

Again the first step is to divide the fraction out into decimal form.

$1/200s = 0.005s$

If we shift the decimal point three places to the right to obtain the figure 5.0, we must multiply by 0.001 or 10^{-3} to restore the original magnitude. From Table 2, $1/200s = 5.0 \times 10^{-3}s = 5.0ms$ (milliseconds).

To make calculations involving quantities expressed in units with prefixes, remember that the prefixes represent powers of ten. All values must be converted to use the correct units to maintain the proper units in the answer. We can demonstrate this point with the following example:

Formula for Inductive Reactance:

$X_L = 2\pi \times$ Frequency (Hz) $\times$ Inductance (H)

Given Values:

Frequency = 455 kHz

Inductance = 750 μH

Using the Correct Values for Equation:

Frequency = $455 \times 10^3 Hz$

Inductance = $750 \times 10^{-6} H$

$X_L = 2\pi \times (455 \times 10^3 Hz) \times (750 \times 10^{-6} H)$

$X_L = 6.28318 \times 455000 \times 0.00075$

$X_L = 2144\Omega$

Using the Incorrect Values for Equation:

$X_L = 2\pi \times 455kHz \times 750\mu H$

$X_L = 6.28318 \times 455 \times 750$

$X_L = 2\ 144\ 000$

Continued on next page   OUO1082,0002BC3 -19-10JAN12-1/2

You will notice that if the incorrect units are used, the resulting answer is incorrect. If you assumed that the answer would be in ohms, the value would be off by a factor of 1000!

OUO1082,0002BC3 -19-10JAN12-2/2

ELECTRON THEORY

Because all matter contains electrons, all matter has an essential ingredient called electricity.

Let's look at the smallest unit of matter—the atom (Fig. 1). All atoms have particles called electrons in orbit around a core of protons. The simplest element is hydrogen. As shown, its atom has a single electron in orbit around a core of one proton.

One of the most complex elements is uranium. It has 92 electrons in orbit around a core of 92 protons.

Each element has its own atomic structure. Each atom has an equal number of protons and electrons.

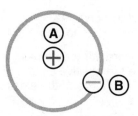

Fig. 1 — All Matter is Made Up of Atoms

A—Proton   **B—Electron**

OUO1082,0002BC4 -19-07JUN12-1/2

The element copper is widely used in electrical systems because it is a good conductor of electricity.

We can see the reasons for this in Fig. 2. The copper atom contains 29 protons and 29 orbiting electrons. The electrons are distributed in four separate orbits or rings. Those electrons beyond the second orbit are more or less free to move from one orbit to another, but still keeping the same amount of electrons per orbit.

However, notice that the outer ring has only one electron. This is the secret of a good conductor of electricity.

- Elements whose atoms have less than four electrons in their outer rings are generally good conductors.
- Elements whose atoms have more than four electrons in their outer rings are poor conductors, or insulators.

The fewer electrons in the outer ring of conductors, the more easily they are dislodged from their orbits by a low voltage to create a flow of current from atom to atom.

In summary:

- Atoms have electrons in orbit around a core of protons.
- Each atom contains an equal number of electrons and protons.
- The electrons orbit around the proton core.
- Atoms that have less than four electrons in their outer rings are good conductors of electricity, as with copper.

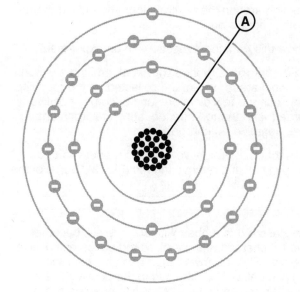

Fig. 2 — Structure of a Copper Atom

A—29 Protons

- Atoms that have more than four electrons in their outer rings are good insulators of electricity, as with plastic, glass or rubber.

OUO1082,0002BC4 -19-07JUN12-2/2

PUTTING ELECTRONS TO WORK

We have seen that atoms contain particles called protons and electrons.

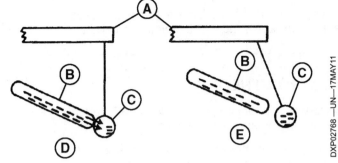

Fig. 3 — Like Charges Repel

These particles have a potential force:

- Protons = positive (+) charges
- Electrons = negative (–) charges

The protons in the core attract the electrons and hold them in orbit. Since the positive charge of the protons is equal to the negative charge of the electrons, the atom is said to be neutral.

This neutral state can be altered. If the orbiting electrons can be forced away from the atom, the atom becomes positive (+) charged and the collection of the orbiting electrons taken away become negative (–) charged. Thus:

Positive charged atoms = too few electrons

Negative charged atoms = too many electrons

The atom does not give up its orbiting electrons except by force. This force must be used to take the electrons from their position around the neutral atom and induce them into another atom's orbit.

Let's show this transfer of electrons in an experiment.

When a rubber rod is rubbed with wool, orbiting electrons from the wool are removed and collected on the rod. The wool now has too few electrons and becomes positive (+) charged, and the rod has too many electrons and becomes negative (–) charged.

Now let's touch the negative charged rubber rod to a hanging pith ball and remove the rod (Fig. 3). Some of the

A—Support   D—Rod Charges Ball
B—Rubber Rod   E—Like Charges Repel
C—Ball

extra electrons on the rod move into the orbit of the atom of the ball. The ball then becomes negative (–) charged while the rod also retains part of its negative (–) charge.

When the rod is moved toward the ball again, the ball will swing away from the rod as shown. In other words, like charges repel.

In the experiment, both charges were negative. If both charges were positive (+) the same thing would occur.

What happens if we move a positive (+) charged rod toward a negative (–) charged ball?

OUO1082,0002BC5 -19-07JUN12-1/3

When a glass rod is rubbed with silk, the silk becomes negative (–) charged and the glass rod becomes positive (+) charged. Fig. 4 shows that a negative charged hanging pith ball will be attracted to the positive charged glass rod. (In the same way, a positive charged pith ball will be attracted to a negative charged rubber rod.)

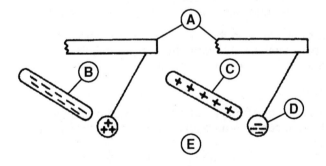

Fig. 4 — Unlike Charges Attract

In other words, unlike charges attract.

The rubbing force that causes this electron movement is called static electricity.

In summary:

- Electrons can be made to leave their atoms in some materials.
- A force such as friction is needed to cause electrons to leave their atoms.
- Like charges repel and unlike charges attract.

A—Support   D—Ball
B—Rubber Rod   E—Opposite Charges Attract
C—Glass Rod

Continued on next page   OUO1082,0002BC5 -19-07JUN12-2/3

DYNAMIC ELECTRICITY

Now let's look at another type of electron flow. Fig. 5 shows what happens with a conductor such as copper wire when it has a negative charge on one end and a positive charge at the other end. This action can be accomplished by connecting the ends of the copper wire to the positive and negative terminals of a dry cell battery. Connect the other end of the wire to some resistance and then connect the resistance to the positive terminal of the dry cell battery. (It is important some resistance, 200 to 300 ohms, is included or you will create a short circuit, and fire or an explosion of the battery could occur.)

In doing this, an electron (–) of the copper atom is forced out of its orbit and attracted to the positive (+) end of the battery through the resistor. This copper atom is now positive (+) charged because it has too few electrons. It in turn attracts an electron from its neighbor. The neighbor in turn receives an electron from the next atom and so on, until the last copper atom receives an electron from the negative (–) end of the battery.

The net result of this chain reaction movement of electrons is that the electrons move through the wire from the negative end of the battery to the positive end of the

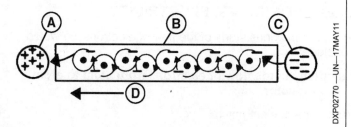

Fig. 5 — Flow of Electrons in a Conductor

A—Positive Charge   C—Negative Charge
B—Copper Wire   D—Electron Flow

battery. The resistor regulates the amount of electrons, that can flow, limiting the current flow.

This flow of electrons will continue as long as the positive and negative charges from the battery remain at each end of the wire and resistor (unlike charges attracting each other).

The use of a battery to force electrons to flow through a conductor is dynamic electricity.

OUO1082,0002BC5 -19-07JUN12-3/3

ELECTRONICS VS. ELECTRICITY

From our previous study of the flow of electrons we would conclude:

Electricity is the flow of electrons from atom to atom in a conductor.

What then is electronics?

Electronics is the control of electrons and the study of their behavior and effects..

Devices that resist, control, switch, and store the electrons accomplish this control of electrons and will be studied in a later chapter.

For a better understanding let's review the previous experiment of electron flow (electricity). The pith ball would not have reacted to the electrons in the rubber and glass rods unless the rods were rubbed with wool and silk. The rubber and glass rods, along with the respective rubbing of the wool and silk, constitute electronic devices that control electron flow.

During warm weather, clouds acquire a static charge that moves from cloud to cloud and cloud to earth. This static charge between clouds and earth may grow to more than one million volts before it is discharged as lightning (Fig. 6).

Lightning with its accompanying thunder is the result of a great number of electrons forcing their way through the atmosphere, which is normally an insulator and does not allow electrons to flow through it. The release of this much energy is what can cause vast damage during a bad electrical storm.

Fig. 6 — Lightning During an Electrical Storm

OUO1082,0002BC6 -19-10JAN12-1/1

INTRODUCTION TO DIRECT CURRENT (DC) CURRENT, VOLTAGE, AND RESISTANCE

When electricity goes to work, we are dealing with three basic factors:

• Current
• Voltage
• Resistance

These terms are basic to the understanding of electricity.

CURRENT

The flow of electrons through a conductor is called current. It is measured in amperes. Current is represented by the letter A or I.

One ampere is an electric current of 6.28 billion billion electrons passing a certain point in the conductor in one second (Fig. 7).

Thus, current is the rate of electron flow and is measured in amperes or electrons per second. You can compare

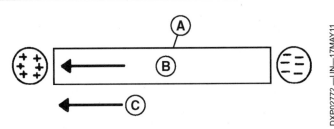

Fig. 7 — How Current Is Measured

A—Copper Wire
B—6.28 Billion Billion
   Electrons per Second
C—One Ampere

this with hydraulics, where the flow of oil in a pipe is measured in gallons per minute (gpm).

Continued on next page OUO1082,0002BC7 -19-10JAN12-1/4

There are two ways to describe current flow through a conductor (Fig. 8). The first is electron flow theory, of which we are now familiar: the electron flow or current flow through a conductor is from a negative (–) power source to a positive (+) power source.

The second theory is called the conventional flow pressure theory, where the current flow through a conductor is from a positive (+) power source to a negative (–) power source.

In the sixteenth century, long before the electron flow theory was discovered and when the basic laws of electricity were being developed, it was believed that the current flow through a conductor was due to positive carriers. Even today, the majority of educational and industrial institutions teach the conventional flow theory.

Either theory can be used, but we will use the more popular conventional flow theory (+ to –) in the remainder of this manual.

VOLTAGE

Voltage is the force that causes a flow of current in a conductor. The unit of measure for this force is the volt. V or E (electromotive force) is the letter symbol used to represent the volt. Voltage is the difference in potential (charges) between two terminals or places of a device.

Chemicals generate voltage in a storage battery and mechanical energy is converted to electrical energy to

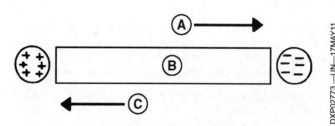

Fig. 8 — Two Theories of Current Flow Through a Conductor

A—Conventional Theory　　**C—Electron Theory**
B—Copper Wire

create voltage in a generator. Voltage is a potential force and can exist even when there is no current flow in a circuit.

A storage battery, for example, may have a potential of 12 volts between its (+) and (–) terminal posts, and this potential exists even though no current-consuming devices are connected to the posts.

Thus, voltage can exist without current, but current cannot exist without the "potential push" of voltage.

The greater the electron charges at each point, the greater the voltage.

OUO1082,0002BC7 -19-10JAN12-2/4

Look at a battery or generator as an electron pump (Fig. 9). The generator, for example, will supply a continuous flow of electrons (current) through the light bulb connected to it. The movement of electrons is continuous as the generator continues to turn. The current leaving a current source must equal the current entering that source.

A—One Ampere　　**C—One Ampere**
B—Generator

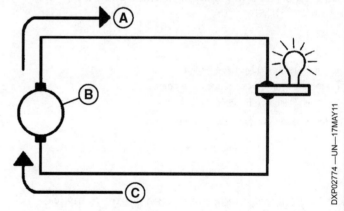

Fig. 9 — The Generator as an Electron Pump

Continued on next page　　OUO1082,0002BC7 -19-10JAN12-3/4

RESISTANCE

Resistance is the opposition of electron flow in a conductor (Fig. 10). It is represented by the capitol letter R and is measured in ohms (Ω). One ohm is the resistance that will allow one ampere to flow when the potential is one volt.

All conductors offer some resistance to the flow of current. Resistance is caused by:

1. Each atom resisting the removal of an electron due to attraction toward the core.

2. Collisions of countless electrons and atoms as the electrons move through the conductor.

The collisions create resistance and cause heat in the conductor.

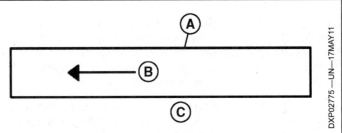

Fig. 10 — Resistance to the Flow of Current in a Conductor

A—Copper Wire
B—Current

C—Resistance and Current
    Create Heat

OUO1082,0002BC7 -19-10JAN12-4/4

OHM'S LAW

In 1827 a German, Georg Simon Ohm, established a mathematical reasoning of electronics. Then, electromotive force (volts) and electron flow (amperes) through a conductor were known entities, but no law to establish the resistance within a conductor existed. Ohm assumed that if the electromotive force and amperes could be determined from a certain length and material of a conductor, doubling the length of the same conductor would allow a passage of electrons at half the rate of the shorter conductor. This is known as Ohm's Law, whereby the ratio of the electromotive force (E) and amperes (I) can be taken as a measure of resistance (R) within a conductor. Thus:

$R = E/I$

Where:

E = the electromotive force (volts)

I = the electron flow or current in amperes

R = the resistance in ohms

The three forms of Ohm's Law are as follows:

$R = E/I$

$E = I \times R$

$I = E/R$

Fig. 11 graphically shows that when we know any two quantities, we can calculate the third.

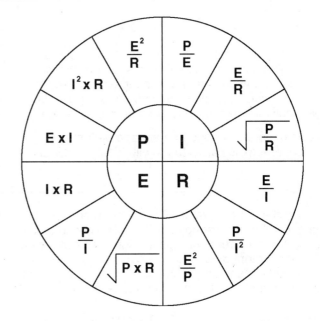

Fig. 11 — Ohm's Law Formula Circle

OUO1082,0002BC8 -19-10JAN12-1/1

A BASIC ELECTRONIC CIRCUIT

An electronic circuit is a group of electronic components connected together in a way, that allows the flow of electrons. An electrical circuit is much the same but comprises electrical components. Both electrical and electronic circuits can be represented in graphical form with a schematic. The schematic is comprises of symbols representing the various components connected together with lines representing conductors. This manual will refer to the circuits as either electric or electronic circuits depending on the particular circuit type.

A basic electronic circuit consists of three parts (Fig. 12):

- A voltage source such as a battery.
- A load (or resistor) such as a light bulb.
- Conductors such as copper wires to connect the circuit together.

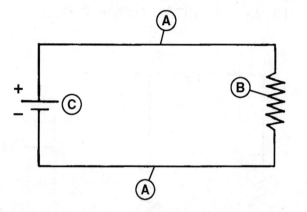

Fig. 12 — A Basic Electronic Circuit

A—Conductor   C—Battery
B—Resistor

OUO1082,0002BC9 -19-10JAN12-1/2

The basic gauges for testing an electronic circuit are these:

- An ammeter (A) to measure current flow, always connected in series.
- A voltmeter (C) to measure voltage between any two points in a circuit, always connected in parallel.

Fig. 13 shows the two basic meters and how they are connected.

A—Ammeter   C—Voltmeter
B—Resistor   D—Battery

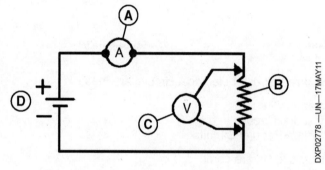

Fig. 13 — Basic Gauges for Testing a Circuit

OUO1082,0002BC9 -19-10JAN12-2/2

ELECTRICAL CIRCUITS—THREE TYPES

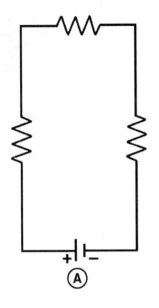 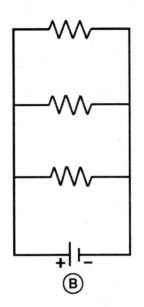 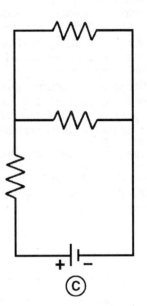

Fig. 14 — Three Types of Electrical Circuits

A—Series **C—Series-Parallel**
B—Parallel

The three types of electrical circuits are these:

• Series Circuits
• Parallel Circuits
• Series-Parallel Circuits

These circuits are compared in Fig. 14.

Series circuits have several components (resistors in this case) connected so that current can flow along only one path.

Parallel circuits have more than one path for current to flow. The components (resistors in this case) are side-by-side and provide separate routes for current.

Series-parallel circuits have some components (resistors in this case) connected in series and some in parallel.

OUO1082,0002BCA -19-07JUN12-1/4

A basic series circuit may have a three-ohm (3 Ω) resistor connected to a 12-volt battery (Fig. 15).

Example 2-1
   What is the current flowing through the 3 Ω resistor?
Solution
   I = E/R
   4A = 12V/3Ω

Example 2-2
   What is the voltage drop across the 3 Ω resistor?
Solution
   E = I x R
   12V = 4A x 3Ω

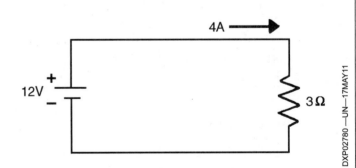

Fig. 15 — A Basic Series Circuit

After these calculations are completed, we can go measure the actual circuit values with the two meters connected as shown in Fig. 16.

Continued on next page   OUO1082,0002BCA -19-07JUN12-2/4

The series circuit in Fig. 16 has a 2 Ω resistor and a 4 Ω resistor connected to a 12-volt battery.

In a series circuit, the total circuit resistance (R_T) is equal to the sum of all the resistors.

Example 2-3

What is the total circuit resistance (R_T) in Fig. 16?

Solution

$R_T = 4Ω + 2Ω = 6Ω$

Example 2-4

What is the current in Fig. 16?

Solution

$I = E/R$

$2A = 12V/6Ω$

Example 2-5

What is the voltage drop across the resistors in Fig. 16?

Solution for the 2 Ω resistor

$E = I \times R$

$4V = 2A \times 2Ω$

Solution for the 4 Ω resistor:

$E = I \times R$

$8V = 2A \times 4Ω$

The sum of all voltage drops in the circuit (Fig. 16) must equal the source voltage, or 4V + 8V = 12V.

In order to calculate the voltage drops across the resistors, you had to first calculate the total current (I_T) of the circuit. A series circuit, like Fig. 16, can also act as a voltage divider.

The voltage divider rule equation allows us to calculate the voltage across one or a combination of series resistors without first having to solve for the current. The basic formula for the voltage division rule is:

$$(R_1 \times E)/(R_1 + R_2) = V_1$$

Where R_1 is the resistor across which you want to find the voltage drop, E is the battery source. R_2 is the other resistor in the series circuit. V_1 is the voltage drop across R_1. Use this rule to find the voltage across the 4 Ω resistor in Fig. 16.

$$(4Ω \times 12V)/(4Ω + 2Ω) = 48A/6Ω = 8V$$

Modify the voltage divider rule equation to incorporate any number of resistors into the formula as follows:

$$(R_1 \times E)/(R_1 + R_2 + R_3 + R_n) = V_1$$

Example 2-6

What is the voltage drop across R_1, Points A and B, in Fig. 17?

Solution for voltage drop (V_1) across R_1

$V_1 = (R_1 \times E)/(R_1 + R_2 + R_3 + R_n)$

$V_1 = (2Ω \times 12V)/(2Ω + 3Ω + 5Ω)$

$V_1 = 24/10Ω$

$V_1 = 2.4V$

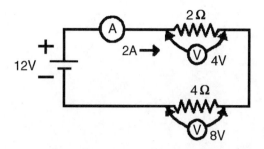

Fig. 16 — Series Circuit with Two Resistors

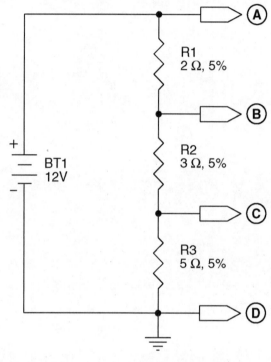

Fig. 17 — Voltage Division in a Series Circuit

A—Point A   C—Point C
B—Point B   D—Point D

Example 2-7

What is the voltage drop across R_2, Points B and C, in Fig. 17?

Solution for voltage drop (V_2) across R_2

$V_2 = I \times E$

$V_2 = (3Ω \times 12V)/(2Ω + 3Ω + 5Ω)$

$V_2 = 36/10Ω$

$V_2 = 3.6V$

Example 2-8

What is the voltage drop across R_3, Points C and D, in Fig. 17?

Solution for voltage drop (V_3) across R_3

$V_3 = (R_1 \times E)/(R_1 + R_2 + R_3 + R_n)$

$V_3 = (5Ω \times 12V)/(2Ω + 3Ω + 5Ω)$

$V_3 = 60/10 Ω$

$V_3 = 6 V$

Continued on next page   OUO1082,0002BCA -19-07JUN12-3/4

110112
PN=33

Example 2-9

What is the total circuit current (I_T)?

In a series circuit, the total resistance (R_T) is equal to the sum of the resistors.

Solution for (I_T)

$I_T = E_T/R_T$

$I_T = 12V/(2\Omega + 3\Omega + 5\Omega)$

$I_T = 12V/10\Omega$

$I_T = 1.2A$

OUO1082,0002BCA -19-07JUN12-4/4

POWER IN DC CIRCUITS (WATTS)

This is an ideal time to talk about power. Power is a measure of the rate of energy conversion of that circuit. In electronics, power is the measure of the rate at which electrical energy is converted into heat by the resistive elements within a conductor. The letter P represents this power and its measurement is in Watts, where I is amperes and E is the electromotive force (volts).

P = I x E (PIE)

I = P/E

E = P/I

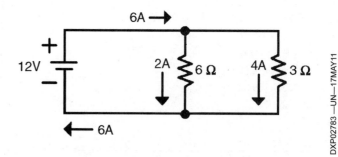

Fig. 18 — Parallel Circuit with Two Resistors

To incorporate the resistive elements (ohms) into the formula, substitute the factor of I from Ohm's Law. The power formula can now be expressed as:

$P = E/R \times E$ or $P = E^2/R$.

Example 2-10

What power ratings would our resistors in the circuit in Fig. 18 require?

Solution

Using $P = I^2 \times R$, $I_T = 1.2$ amp we can calculate the power each resistor will be required to dissipate.

Calculate the wattage ratings for the resistors as follows:

- $1.2^2 \times 2 = 2.88$W so we would use a 5 W resistor for the 2 Ω resistor.
- $1.2^2 \times 3 = 4.32$W so we would use a 5 W or a 10 W resistor for the 3 Ω resistor.
- $1.2^2 \times 5 = 7.2$W so we would use a 10 W resistor for the 5 Ω resistor.

It is apparent that with less circuit current, lower wattage components can be used. Also note that we are wasting a lot of power in heat (14.32 W). This is the main reason to spend some time in circuit design; it actually pays for itself in the long term.

In summary, series circuits have the following features:

1. The current through each resistor is the same.

2. The voltage drops across each resistor will be different if the resistance values are different.

3. The sum of the voltage drops equals the source voltage.

4. The wattage rating of the resistors varies with resistance.

PARALLEL CIRCUITS

In a parallel circuit, the voltage drop across each resistor is equal to the potential of the current source since there is a separate path for current to flow through each resistor. This means:

1. The voltage across each resistor is the same.

2. The current through each resistor will be different if the resistance values are different.

3. The sum of the separate currents equals the total current in the circuit.

The parallel circuit in Fig. 18 has a 6 Ω and a 3 Ω resistor connected to a 12-volt battery. The resistors are in parallel with each other, since the battery voltage (12 volts) flows across each resistor.

The current through each resistor or branch of the circuit can be figured using Ohm's Law.

For the 6 Ω resistor:

I = E/R

I = 12V/6Ω

I = 2 A

For the 3 Ω resistor:

I = E/R

I = 12V/3Ω

I = 4A

The total current supplied by the battery is 2 + 4 = 6 amps.

The equivalent resistance of the entire circuit has to be 2 Ω, since R = E/I = 12V/6A = 2 ohms.

Before, to find the equivalent resistance (R_T) of the entire circuit, we had to calculate the current through each resistor. The Current-Divider Rule for parallel circuits allows us to calculate the equivalent resistance of the circuit without having first to solve for the amperes. The formula for two resistors is:

$R_T = (R_1 \times R_2)/(R_1 + R_2)$

Where R_1 and R_2 are the resistors in the circuit and R_T is the equivalent resistance of the circuit. Let's calculate the equivalent resistance of the parallel circuit in Fig. 18 using the current-divider rule equation.

However, the current-divider rule formula changes when there are three or more resistors within a parallel circuit. The formula changes to:

$R_T = 1/((1/R_1) + (1/R_2) + (1/R_3) + (R..))$

Example of a two parallel resistor problem:

Continued on next page

OUO1082,0002BCB -19-07JUN12-1/4

110112

PN=35

$R_1 = 300\Omega$

$R_2 = 300\Omega$

Solution:

$R_T = 1/((1/R_1) + (1/R_2))$

$R_T = 1/((1/300\Omega) + (1/300\Omega))$

$R_T = 1/(.00333 + 0.0333)$

$R_T = 1/0.0666$

$R_T = 150\Omega$

When parallel resistors are of equal value, it becomes a matter of dividing the value of the resistor by the number of resistors in parallel. Therefore, use the following formula:

$R_T = R/\text{number of resistors}$

OUO1082,0002BCB -19-07JUN12-2/4

SERIES-PARALLEL CIRCUITS

Fig. 19 shows a series-parallel circuit. Note that the 2 Ω resistor is in series with a parallel combination (the 3 Ω and 6 Ω resistors). Since there are two resistors in parallel, we can use one of the following equations:

$I = E/R$

$R_T = 1/((1/R_1) + (1/R_2) + (1/R_3) + (R..))$

Solve the problem by using $R_T = 1/((1/R_1) + (1/R_2))$:

$R_T = 2\Omega + ((1/6\Omega) + (1/3\Omega))$

$R_T = 2\Omega + 2\Omega$

$R_T = 4\Omega$

To find the circuit current by using $I = E/R$:

$I = E/R$

$I = 12V/4\Omega$

$I = 3A$ of total circuit current

With 3 A flowing through the series 2 Ω resistor, find the voltage drop across this resistor by using $E = I \times R$:

$E = I \times R$

$E = 3A \times 2\Omega$

$E = 6V$, leaving 6 V across the parallel 6 Ω and 3 Ω resistors.

Calculating the current through the 6 Ω and 3 Ω resistor using $I = E/R$:

6 Ω Resistor:

$I = E/R$

$I = 6V/6\Omega$

$I = 1A$

3 Ω Resistor:

$I = E/R$

$I = 6V/3\Omega$

$I = 2A$

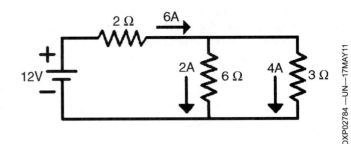

Fig. 19 — Series-Parallel Circuit

Total current must equal the sum of these two current values or 1 + 2 = 3 amps, which matches prior calculated value, so we know we have calculated correctly.

Continued on next page OUO1082,0002BCB -19-07JUN12-3/4

CURRENT FLOW IN SERIES AND PARALLEL CIRCUITS

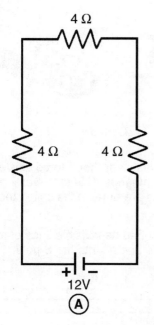 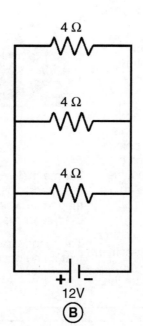 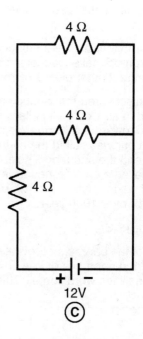

Fig. 20 — Current Flow in Series and Parallel Circuits

A—Series
B—Parallel
C—Series-Parallel

We have learned from Ohm's Law that there is a definite relationship between current, voltage, and resistance in an electrical circuit. Let's see how this applies to series and parallel circuits with a given resistance.

NOTE: All circuits shown in Fig. 20 are 12 volts. All resistors shown in Fig. 20 are 4 ohms.

Each type of circuit shown in Fig. 20 has three 4 Ω resistors. What is the total current flow in each case?

In the series circuit there is only one path for the current to flow, so the total resistance is 12 Ω. Calculate the current using $I = E/R$:

$I = E/R$

$I = 12V/12\Omega$

$I = 1A$ total current for the circuit (I_T)

In the parallel circuit, there are three different paths for current, each with a voltage drop of 12 volts across them. Calculate the current for each using $I = E/R$ as follows:

$I = E/R$

$I = 12V/4\Omega$

$I = 3A$ Total current is 3A x 3 (resistors) = 9A (I_T)

In the series-parallel circuit, the total resistance is 4 Ω plus the resistance of the parallel resistors. $4\Omega/2 = 2\Omega$, thus $4\Omega + 2\Omega = 6\Omega$. Calculate ($I_T$) using $I = E/R$ as follows:

$I = E/R$

$I = 12V/6\Omega$

$I = 2A$ (I_T)

For this example, this establishes the following general rules:

• Series circuit = high resistance, low current
• Parallel circuit = low resistance, high current
• Series-parallel circuit = medium resistance, medium current

OUO1082,0002BCB -19-07JUN12-4/4

MAGNETISM

Another form of force that causes electron flow or current is magnetism.

The effects of magnetism were first observed when fragments of iron ore called lodestone, found in nature, were seen to attract other pieces of iron (Fig. 21).

It was further discovered that a long piece of this iron ore suspended in air would align itself so that one end always pointed toward the North Pole of the earth. This end of the iron bar was called the north pole, or N pole, and the other end the south or S pole. Such a piece of iron ore was called a bar magnet. This principle became the basis for the compass, which has been used as an aid in navigation for over 1000 years.

MAGNETIC FIELDS

Further study of the bar magnet revealed that an attractive force was exerted upon bits of iron or iron filings even though the iron filings were some distance away from the

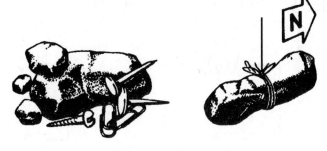

Fig. 21 — Magnetism

bar magnet. From this it was clear that a force existed in the space close to the bar magnet. This space around the magnet in which iron filings are attracted is called the field of force or magnetic field.

The magnetic field is described as invisible lines of force that come out of the N pole and go into the S pole.

OUO1082,0002BCC -19-07JUN12-1/7

The theory of magnetic lines of force can be dramatically shown by sprinkling iron filings on a piece of paper resting on top of a bar magnet. When the paper is lightly tapped by hand, the iron filings line up to form a clear pattern around the bar magnet (Fig. 22).

The pattern shows that the lines of force are heavily concentrated at the N and S poles of the magnet, and then spread out into the surrounding air between the poles. The concentration or number of lines at each pole is equal, and the attractive force on the iron filings at each pole is equal. Notice that the force of attraction on bits of metal is greatest where the concentration of magnetic lines is greatest. For a bar magnet, this area is next to the two poles.

A—South Pole   C—Bar Magnet
B—North Pole   D—Iron Filings

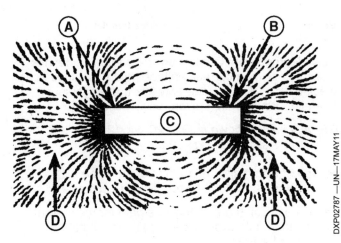

Fig. 22 — Magnetic Field of a Bar Magnet

Continued on next page   OUO1082,0002BCC -19-07JUN12-2/7

We have stated earlier, the lines of force always leave the N pole and enter the S pole of a magnet. When a small compass needle, which is a small bar magnet, is located in the magnetic field of a strong bar magnet, the compass needle will align itself so it is parallel with the lines of force of the bar magnet (Fig. 23).

This alignment takes place because the strong magnetic lines from the bar magnet must enter the S pole and leave the N pole of the compass needle.

We can also see that the unlike poles of the two magnets are attracted toward each other.

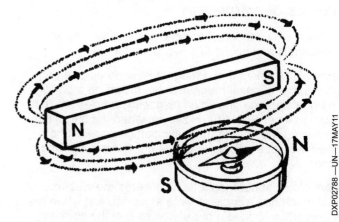

Fig. 23 — Magnetic Lines of Force Leave N Pole and Enter S Pole

OUO1082,0002BCC -19-07JUN12-3/7

To demonstrate further the force of attraction between the unlike poles of two magnets, a force of attraction is seen to exist between two bar magnets lying end to end with an N and S pole facing each other (Fig. 24). The force of attraction increases as the two magnets are moved closer together.

If, on the other hand, the magnets are aligned so the N poles or the S poles face each other, a force of repulsion is seen to exist between the two magnets, and this repulsion increases as the two magnets are moved closer together.

From these experiments, a fundamental law of magnetism can be stated:

Unlike poles attract each other, and like poles repel each other.

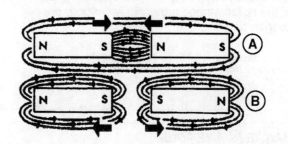

Fig. 24 — Magnetic Forces Between Poles of Bar Magnets

A—Unlike Poles Attract   **B—Like Poles Repel**

Continued on next page   OUO1082,0002BCC -19-07JUN12-4/7

THEORIES OF MAGNETISM

Either one of two theories can best explain exactly what magnetism is and how it exerts a field of force.

Theory No. 1 states that a magnet is made up of a very large number of small magnetized particles. In a bar of un-magnetized iron, the small magnetic particles are in a random manner (Fig. 25). However, when the bar of iron becomes a magnet, the magnetic particles are aligned so their individual effects add together to form a strong magnet.

Theory No. 2 about magnetism concerns the electron. The electron has a circle of force around it, and when the electron orbits align in a bar of iron so that the circles of force add together, the bar of iron is magnetized.

While iron is one of the better known magnetic materials, remember that some materials are nonmagnetic since they never exhibit any of the properties of magnetism. Some of the nonmagnetic materials are wood, paper, glass, copper, and zinc.

A—Unmagnetized Iron N—North Pole
B—Magnetized Iron S—South Pole

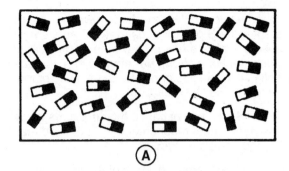
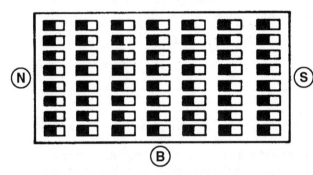

Fig. 25 — First Theory of Magnetism: Particles are Aligned

OUO1082,0002BCC -19-07JUN12-5/7

HOW MAGNETS ARE MADE

We may convert an ordinary iron bar into a magnet in a number of different ways. One method is to stroke the iron with another piece of iron, that is magnetized. The effect of inducing magnetism into the iron bar is magnetic induction.

Another method of magnetic induction is simply to place an iron bar in a strong magnetic field (Fig. 26). The lines of force in the field passing through the iron bar will cause the bar to become a magnet as long as it is located in the field. If the bar is withdrawn from the field of force, and if its composition allows it to retain some of its induced magnetism, it is then said to be permanently magnetized and is called a permanent magnet.

Most permanent magnets are made of hard metals composed of alloys, since soft metals will not retain much

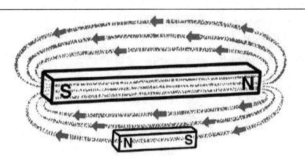

Fig. 26 — Magnetic Induction of an Iron Bar

of their magnetism. Some of the more common alloys are nickel-iron and aluminum-nickel-cobalt.

Continued on next page

OUO1082,0002BCC -19-07JUN12-6/7

Permanent magnets are found in many shapes, including the horseshoe magnet, which concentrates the lines of force at the two poles in a small area (Fig. 27).

The most effective way of inducing a high level of magnetism in a material to form a permanent magnet is by the principles of electromagnetic induction. This principle is covered in a section that follows.

SUMMARY: MAGNETISM

- Every magnet has an N pole and an S pole and a field of force surrounding it.
- Magnetic materials are acted upon when located in a field of force.

DXP02792 —UN—17MAY11

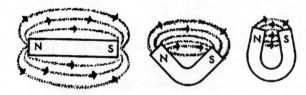

Fig. 27 — Forming a Horseshoe Magnet

- Unlike poles attract and like poles repel.
- An un-magnetized piece of iron can become a magnet through induction.

OUO1082,0002BCC -19-07JUN12-7/7

ELECTROMAGNETISM

It was not until the year 1820 that the relationship between electricity and magnetism was discovered. Before this time, it was generally believed that magnetism existed only in the lodestone or iron ore found in nature and that there was no relationship at all between electricity and magnetism.

An experiment with a compass and a wire carrying current revealed the connection between electricity and magnetism. When the compass was held over the wire, the needle turned so it was crosswise of the wire (Fig. 28). Since the only thing known that would attract a compass needle was magnetism, it was obvious that the current in the wire created a magnetic field around the wire.

A—Current-Carrying   S—South
N—North

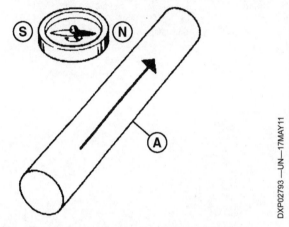

Fig. 28 — Electric Current Creates Its Own Magnetic Field

MM61211,00012BE -19-16OCT12-1/16

The nature of the magnetic field around the wire is revealed when the current-carrying wire is run through a piece of cardboard, and iron filings are sprinkled on the cardboard. The iron filings align themselves to show a clear pattern of concentric circles around the wire (Fig. 29). The circles are more concentrated near the wire than farther away. Although the iron filings on the cardboard show only the pattern in one plane, remember that the concentric circles extend the entire length of the current-carrying wire.

A—Direction of Current Flow

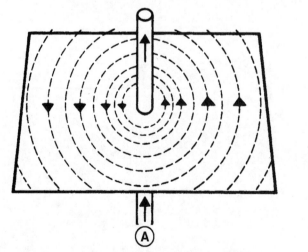

Fig. 29 — Shape of Magnetic Field Around Wire Carrying a Current

Continued on next page   MM61211,00012BE -19-16OCT12-2/16

In Fig. 30, when current is flowing in a wire in the direction indicated by the cross, the N pole of a compass needle will always point in one direction. However, when current is flowing in the wire in the opposite direction, as indicated by the dot, the north pole of the compass needle reverses and points in the opposite direction.

Since the needle always has a tendency to align itself so that magnetic lines, or flux lines, enter its S pole and leave its N pole, we can conclude:

• Magnetic lines have direction, and change direction when the current flow changes in the wire from one direction to another.
• The Right Hand Rule for straight conductors can be used to find the direction of the lines of force around the wire.

N—North   S—South

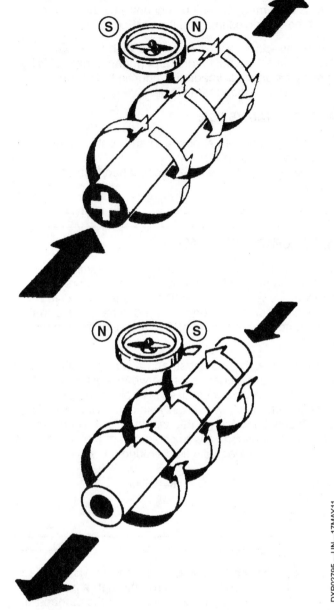

Fig. 30 — Magnetic Lines Change Direction when Current is Reversed

Continued on next page   MM61211,00012BE -19-16OCT12-3/16

To apply the rule, grasp the wire with the thumb extended in the direction of conventional current flow (positive to negative); the fingers will then point in the direction in which the lines of force surround the conductor (Fig. 31). These lines of force are always at right angles to the conductor, and the compass needle confirms the direction as determined by the Right Hand Rule.

Unlike the flow of electrons in the conductor, which actually move, the magnetic lines of force do not move or flow around the wire; instead they merely have direction as indicated by their effect upon the compass needle.

The number of lines of force, or strength of the magnetism, increases as the current through the conductor is increased.

Fig. 31 — Right Hand Rule Shows Direction of Lines of Force in a Straight Conductor

Continued on next page   MM61211,00012BE -19-16OCT12-4/16

If a compass is moved farther away from the conductor, a point finally is reached where the compass is unaffected by the field (Fig. 32). If the current is then increased, the compass needle will be affected and will again indicate the direction of the magnetic field as shown.

The number of lines of force, and the area around the conductor that they occupy, increase as the current through the conductor increases.

In other words: More current creates a stronger magnetic field.

A—One Ampere
B—Needle Unaffected
C—Three Amperes
D—Needle Aligned

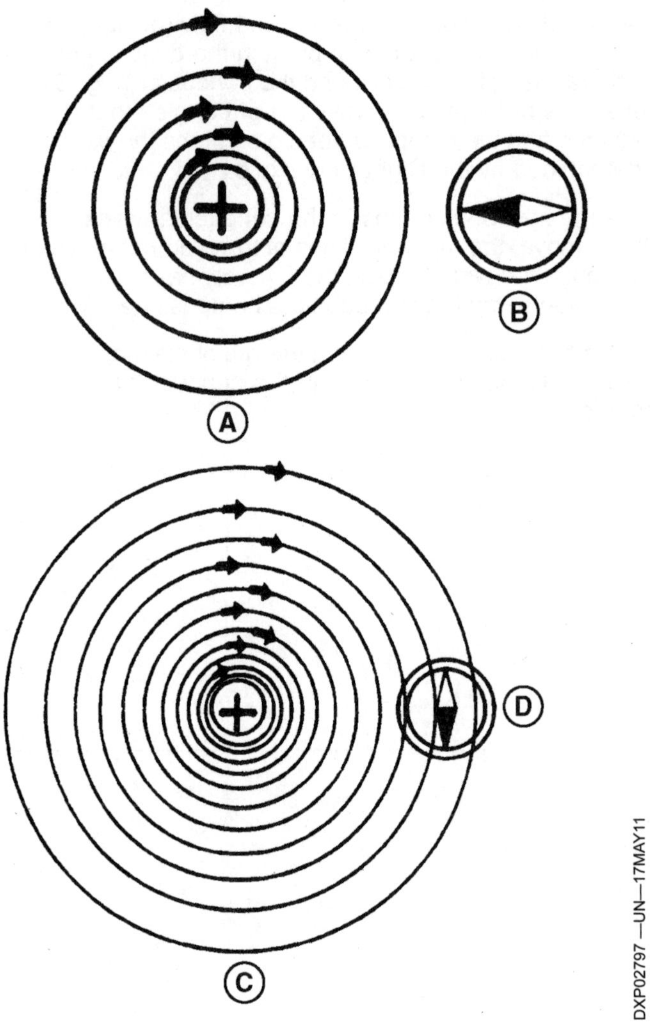

Fig. 32 — More Current Creates a Stronger Magnetic Field

Continued on next page

MM61211,00012BE -19-16OCT12-5/16

If two adjacent parallel conductors are carrying current in opposite directions, the direction of the field is clockwise around one conductor and counterclockwise around the other (Fig. 33). The lines of force are more concentrated between the conductors than on the outside of the conductors. The force lines between the two wires add together to form a strong magnetic field. Under this condition, the two wires will tend to move apart.

This leads us to conclude: A current-carrying conductor will tend to move out of a strong field and into a weak field.

A—Strong Field Between Conductors

B—Conductors Tend to Move Apart

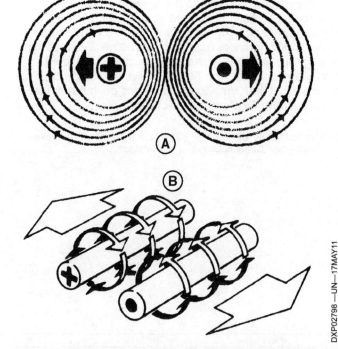

Fig. 33 — How Conductors Are Affected by Strong Magnetic Fields

MM61211,00012BE -19-16OCT12-6/16

In Fig. 34 two conductors are placed on an armature located between strong N and S poles, and the conductors are made to carry current in opposite directions. The result is that a strong and a weak field are formed on opposite sides of each conductor as shown.

By the Right Hand Rule, current flowing into the top conductor will form magnetic lines on the underneath side of the conductor that add to the lines of the N and S poles. The conductor will then tend to move upward or clockwise into the weakened field.

Similarly, current flowing out of the lower conductor forms a strong field on top and a weak field underneath, causing the conductor to move downward or clockwise.

Thus, a rotation is caused by the current flowing in the conductors. This is the principle of the starting motor (Fig. 34). For more detail on starting motors, see Chapter 7, Starting Circuits.

Fig. 34 — Principle of the Starting Motor

Continued on next page   MM61211,00012BE -19-16OCT12-7/16

A different condition exists when two parallel conductors are carrying equal currents in the same direction (Fig. 35). A magnetic field, clockwise in direction, will be formed around each conductor, with the magnetic lines between the conductors opposing each other in direction. The magnetic field between the conductor is canceled out, leaving essentially no field in this area. The two conductors will then tend to move toward each other, that is, from a strong field into a weak field.

A—Magnetic Field Between Conductors Cancels Out

B—Conductors Tend to Move Together

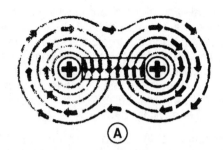

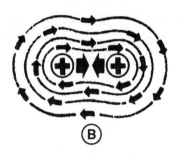

Fig. 35 — How Conductors are Affected by Weak Magnetic Fields

MM61211,00012BE -19-16OCT12-8/16

Two conductors lying alongside each other carrying equal currents in the same direction create a magnetic field equivalent to one conductor carrying twice the current (Fig. 36).

When several more conductors are placed side by side, the magnetic effect is increased as the lines from each conductor join and surround all the conductors.

Using the Right Hand Rule, we can see that all the lines of force enter the inside of the loop of wire on one side, and leave the other side as shown.

The lines of force are concentrated inside the loop. A single loop of wire carrying current is called a basic electromagnet.

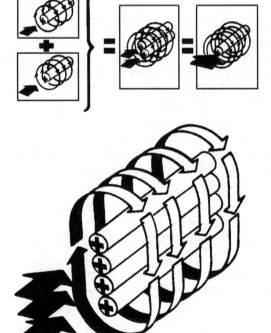

Fig. 36 — How Two or More Adjacent Conductors Increase the Magnetic Field

Continued on next page   MM61211,00012BE -19-16OCT12-9/16

A straight current-carrying wire when formed into a single loop has the same magnetic field surrounding it as when it was straight (Fig. 37).

A—Direction of Current Flow

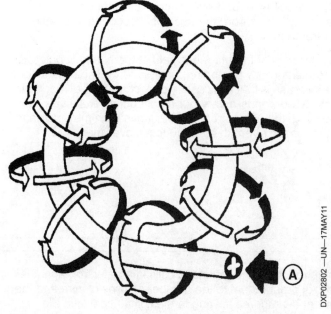

Fig. 37 — *Conductor in a Single Loop Has No Increase in Magnetic Field*

MM61211,00012BE -19-16OCT12-10/16

HOW ELECTROMAGNETS WORK

What happens when a current-carrying wire is wound into a number of loops to form a coil as shown in Fig. 38? The resulting magnetic field is the sum of all the single loop magnetic fields added together, since this is the same as several conductors lying side by side carrying current in the same direction.

With lines of force leaving the coil at one end and entering at the other end, a north and south pole are formed at the coil ends the same as in the bar magnet.

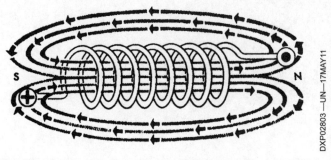

Fig. 38 — *Conductor in Several Loops Multiplies the Magnetic Field*

MM61211,00012BE -19-16OCT12-11/16

To find polarity of the coil ends, apply the Right Hand Rule for Coils by grasping the coil with the fingers pointed in the direction of current flow; the thumb will then point toward the N pole of the coil as shown in Fig. 39. If the current direction through the coil is reversed, the polarity of the coil ends will also reverse.

N—North

Fig. 39 — *Right Hand Rule for Coils*

Continued on next page

MM61211,00012BE -19-16OCT12-12/16

110112
PN=47

When a coil is wound over a core of magnetic material such as iron, the assembly becomes a usable electromagnet (Fig. 40).

The strength of the magnetic field at the N and S poles is increased greatly by adding the iron core. The reason for this increase is that air is a very poor conductor of magnetic lines, while iron is a very good conductor. Relatively speaking, the use of iron in a magnetic path may increase the magnetic strength by 2500 times over that of air.

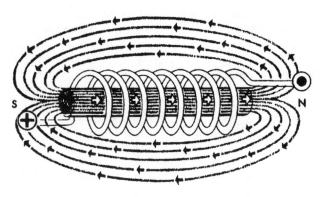

Fig. 40 — Use of Iron Core to Increase Field Strength of Coil and Form an Electromagnet

MM61211,00012BE -19- 13/16

The strength of the magnetic coils in an electromagnet is directly proportional to the number of turns of wire and the current in amperes flowing in the coil as shown in Fig. 41.

A—1 Amp
B—1000 Turns
C—10 Amps

D—100 Turns
E—1000 Ampere-Turns

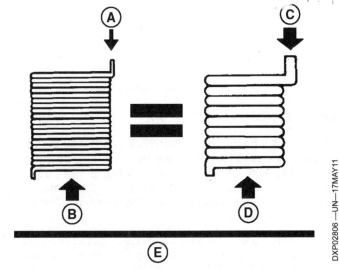

Fig. 41 — Strength of Electromagnet Depends Upon Turns of Coil

Continued on next page
MM61211,00012BE -19-16OCT12-14/16

An electromagnet having one ampere flowing through 1000 turns and another electromagnet having 10 amperes flowing through 100 turns will each create 1000 ampere-turns, which is a measure of the magnetic field strength. The attraction on magnetic materials located in the magnetic field of each of these electromagnets will be the same.

Just as electric current flows through a closed circuit, so do the lines of force created by a magnet occupy a closed magnetic circuit. Since the same number of lines that leave the N pole must also enter the S pole, a complete circuit must be present for each magnetic field.

The resistance that a magnetic circuit offers to lines of force, or flux, is called reluctance. The reluctance is comparable to resistance in an electrical circuit.

There is an equation for an electromagnetic circuit that is similar to Ohm's Law for the electric circuit. This equation is as follows:

Number of Magnetic Lines is Proportional to:

• Ampere-Turns
• Reluctance

Two facts related to this equation are important to us here:

1. The number of magnetic lines, or strength of the field, is directly proportional to the ampere-turns. In an electromagnet, more current through the coils means greater field strength.

Fig. 42 — Electromagnet Picking Up Junk Metal

2. The number of lines, or field strength, is inversely proportional to the reluctance; that is, if the reluctance increases, the field strength decreases. Since most magnetic circuits consist of iron and short air gaps, the reluctance of such a series circuit is equal to the iron reluctance added to the air gap reluctance.

MM61211,00012BE -19-16OCT12-15/16

The effect of an air gap on the total reluctance of a circuit is very pronounced. This is true because air has a much higher reluctance than iron.

To illustrate this fact, consider a magnetic circuit with a short air gap that has a field of strength of 10,000 lines of force (Fig. 43). If the length of the air gap is doubled, the reluctance will almost double, and the field strength will be reduced to approximately 5000 lines of force. Although the air gap represents only a very short segment of the total magnetic path, increasing the air gap from 0.1 inch (3 mm) to 0.2 inch (5 mm) may cut the field strength almost in half.

SUMMARY: ELECTROMAGNETISM

• Electricity and magnetism are related, because a magnetic field is established around a conductor that is carrying current.
• An electromagnet has an N pole at one end and an S pole at the other end of the iron core, much like a bar magnet.

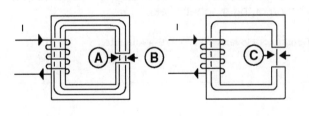

Fig. 43 — Effect of Air Gap on Reluctance of a Circuit

A—0.1 in. (3 mm)   C—0.2 in. (5 mm)
B—10,000 Lines

• Every magnetic field has a complete circuit that is occupied by its lines of force.
• An electromagnetic field gets stronger as more electrical current flows through its coils.

MM61211,00012BE -19-16OCT12-16/16

ELECTROMAGNETIC INDUCTION

When a conductor is moved across a magnetic field, a voltage is induced in the conductor. This principle is called electromagnetic induction, and is defined as the inducing of voltage in a conductor that moves across a magnetic field.

HOW VOLTAGE IS INDUCED

To show this, move a straight wire conductor across the magnetic field of a horseshoe magnet (Fig. 44). Connect a sensitive voltmeter to the ends of the wire and the needle will register a small voltage as the wire is moved across the magnetic field.

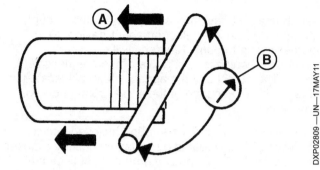

Fig. 44 — Moving Conductor Across Magnetic Field, Voltage is Induced

A—Conductor Movement   **B—Voltmeter**

MM61211,00012BF -19-16OCT12-1/14

However, if the wire is moved parallel with the lines of force, no voltage will be induced (Fig. 45). The conductor must cut across the lines of force in order to induce a voltage.

We have observed that voltage has polarity, that is, positive and negative poles. We have also stated that current flows from the positive terminal of a voltage source through the external circuit and then back to the negative terminal of the source.

A wire cutting across a magnetic field also becomes a source of electricity, and must have positive and negative ends, just like a battery.

However, we will now see that the polarity at the ends of the wire can change, unlike the battery. This polarity depends upon the relative direction of wire movement and the direction of the magnetic field.

A—Conductor Movement   **B—Voltmeter**

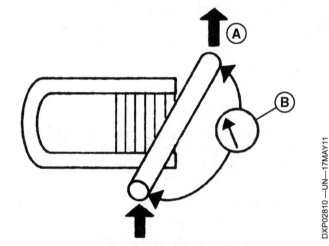

Fig. 45 — Moving Conductor Parallel to Magnetic Field, No Voltage is Induced

Continued on next page   MM61211,00012BF -19-16OCT12-2/14

To determine the polarity at the ends of a conductor and the consequent direction of current flow, consider a straight wire moving to the left across a magnetic field as shown in Fig. 46. With this direction of motion, the magnetic lines are striking the wire on the left side, and this side of the wire is called the leading side.

By applying the Right Hand Rule for an Induced Voltage, the voltage polarity and current flow direction can be determined as follows:

Grasp the conductor with the fingers on the leading side of the wire and pointed in the direction of the magnetic lines of force. The thumb will then point in the direction of current flow.

Current flows as indicated in Fig. 46. This means the polarities at the wire ends must be as shown in order to meet the condition, current flows from the positive side of a source through the external circuit and returns to the negative side of the source.

A—Current Flow

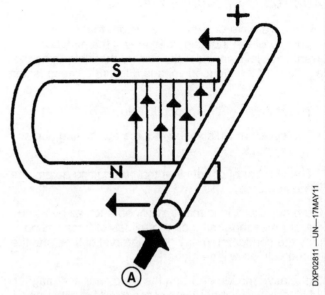

Fig. 46 — Finding Polarity at Ends of a Conductor

MM61211,00012BF -19-16OCT12-3/14

When the direction of motion of the conductor is changed to move toward the right, the right side of the conductor becomes the leading side (Fig. 47). By applying the Right Hand Rule, the current is seen to reverse its direction as in Fig. 46. This means that the voltage polarities at the wire ends have reversed.

In the previous examples, if, instead of moving the wire to the left, we move the magnetic field to the right across a stationary conductor, the same voltage and current flow are induced in the wire. The same holds true for moving the field to the left across the conductor, because in each case the leading side of the conductor and the magnetic field direction are unchanged. Therefore, we can conclude: A voltage is induced in a conductor cutting across a magnetic field when there is relative motion between the two. Either the conductor can move or the magnetic field can move.

A—Current Flow

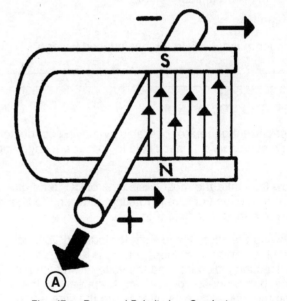

Fig. 47 — Reversed Polarity in a Conductor

Continued on next page

MM61211,00012BF -19-16OCT12-4/14

MAGNITUDES OF INDUCED VOLTAGE

Now that we have observed the factors that determine the polarity of the induced voltage and the direction of current flow, let's consider the factors that determine the magnitude of the induced voltage (Fig. 48). These factors are:

1. The strength of the magnetic field.

2. The speed at which lines of force are cutting across the conductor.

3. The number of conductors that are cutting across the lines of force.

If the magnetic field is made stronger, such as by using a larger horseshoe magnet, more lines of force will be cut by the conductor in any given interval of time and the induced voltage will be higher.

If the relative motion between the conductor and magnetic field is increased, more lines of force will be cut in any given interval of time and so the voltage will be higher.

If the straight wire conductor is wound into a coil which is then moved across the field, all the loops of wire are in series and the voltage induced in all the loops will add together to give a higher voltage.

To summarize:

• Stronger magnetic field = more induced voltage

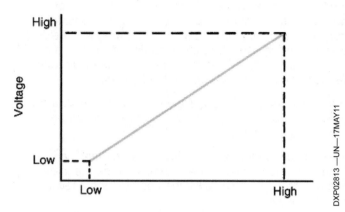

Fig. 48 — Factors That Determine the Magnitude of Induced Voltage

• Faster relative motion = more voltage
• More conductors in motion = more voltage

METHODS OF INDUCING VOLTAGE

There are three ways in which a voltage can be induced by electromagnetic induction:

• Generated Voltage
• Self-Induction
• Mutual Induction

MM61211,00012BF -19-16OCT12-5/14

GENERATED VOLTAGE

A direct-current generator operates by moving conductors across a stationary magnetic field to produce voltage and current.

To show this, take the most basic type of DC generator where a single loop of wire is rotating between the N and S poles of a magnetic field (Fig. 49).

By applying the Right Hand Rule for Induced Voltage to both sides of the wire loop, current is seen to flow in the direction indicated, and the voltages induced in the wire loop produce voltage, which appears at the two commutator segments attached to the wire ends. The current then flows through brushes riding on the commutator to the external circuit. The voltage polarities are as shown.

Another application of the principle of generated voltage is the alternating-current generator, or alternator, where the magnetic field is made to cut across stationary conductors in order to produce voltage and current.

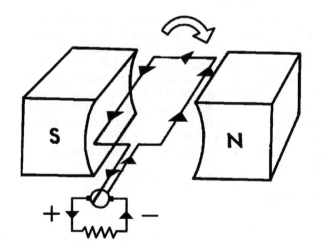

Fig. 49 — Basic DC Generator

Continued on next page   MM61211,00012BF -19-16OCT12-6/14

PN=52

Fig. 50 shows the most basic type of alternating-current generator, with a rotating magnetic field cutting across stationary conductors that are mounted on the generator frame.

By applying the Right Hand Rule, with the rotating magnetic field as shown, current flow through the conductors will alternate, thus causing an alternating current output.

The voltage induced in a conductor by physically moving the conductor or the field is referred to as generated voltage. This principle is used in DC generators and alternators, both of which are covered in detail in Chapter 6.

A—Load Circuit   C—Polarity Changed
B—Rotating Magnetic Field

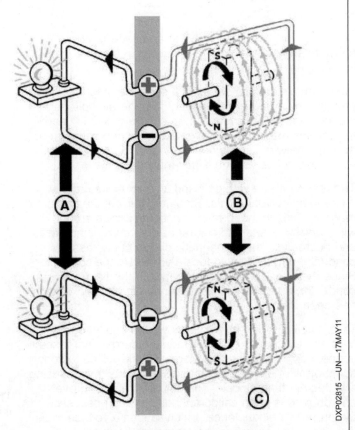

Fig. 50 — Basic Alternator Operation

Continued on next page   MM61211,00012BF -19-16OCT12-7/14

SELF-INDUCTION

Self-induction is the induction of a voltage in a current-carrying wire when the current in the wire itself is changing.

Earlier in this chapter we used a separate magnetic field provided by a horseshoe magnet to generate voltage in a conductor. In self-induction no separate field is used; instead the magnetic field created by a changing current through the wire itself is seen to induce a voltage in the wire. Hence, the voltage is self-induced.

The reason that a voltage is induced in a wire carrying a changing current is this: Since the current creates a magnetic field in the form of concentric circles around the wire, which expand and contract as the current increases and decreases, these magnetic circles cut across the conductor and thereby induce a voltage in the conductor. Since there is relative motion between the field and conductor, the condition necessary for inducing a voltage has been met.

Take a coil of wire with the turns wound tightly together over an iron core (Fig. 51). When the current increases in one loop, the expanding magnetic field will cut across some or all of the neighboring loops of wire, thus inducing a voltage in these loops. The coil of wire wound over an iron core is often called an inductor and possesses the property of inductance, which causes a voltage to be induced in the coil when the current is changing.

POLARITY OF INDUCED VOLTAGE IN A COIL

Now we can make a statement that determines the voltage polarity of the self-induced voltage in a conductor or coil of wire, and then we can explain this statement more fully.

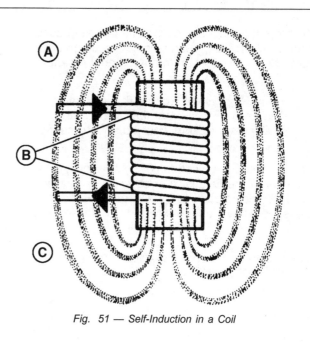

Fig. 51 — Self-Induction in a Coil

A—Current Changing   C—Magnetic Field Changing
B—Induced Voltage

The polarity of an induced voltage will oppose a change in the current that produced it.

"Change in current" refers to current that is either increasing or decreasing in value.

MM61211,00012BF -19-16OCT12-8/14

Fig. 52 shows a circuit containing a coil of wire (inductor).

After the switch is closed (Fig. 52), the current increases from zero to its maximum value of 4 amperes. During this time, a voltage will be induced in the inductor in a direction opposing the increasing current; the inductor itself becomes a source of voltage that attempts to prevent the current from increasing in the circuit.

To oppose the increasing current, the inductor will have to generate a voltage in a direction opposite to the battery current; hence, the polarity at A is positive (+) and B is negative (–). The induced voltage opposes the change in current; that is, the induced voltage tries to maintain the status quo and keep the battery current at zero when the switch is closed.

The induced voltage polarities at the coil are therefore as shown. However, the battery current in time overcomes the inductive effect of the coil, and reaches its final steady value of 4 amperes.

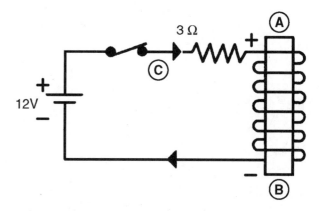

Fig. 52 — Self-Induction in a Circuit when Current Increases

A—Positve Polarity   C—Current Increasing
B—Negative Polarity

Continued on next page   MM61211,00012BF -19-16OCT12-9/14

When the switch is opened (Fig. 53), the current decreases from 4 amperes to zero. This changing current induces a voltage in the coil that again tries to maintain the status quo, or to keep the current flow at 4 amperes. The polarity of the induced coil voltage, therefore, must be as shown, because the coil attempts to supply current in the same direction as originally supplied by the battery. It attempts to keep the current flow at the 4-ampere value, and this may cause the switch to arc when it is opened.

Note that the induced voltage polarity for any direction of current flow is determined by whether the current is increasing or decreasing. For example:

	Induced Voltage	
	A	B
Current Increasing (Fig. 52)	+	–
Current Decreasing (Fig. 53)	–	+

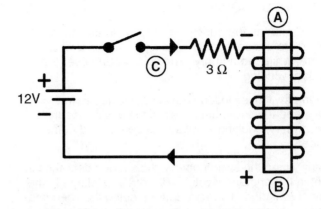

Fig. 53 — Self-Induction in a Circuit when Current Decreases

A—Negative Polarity   **C—Current Decreasing**
B—Positive Polarity

MM61211,00012BF -19-16OCT12-10/14

Although the inductive voltage tries to prevent any change in current value, the effects of the battery voltage and the closed or open switch in time cause the current to reach a constant value. The induced voltage, however, does cause a time delay while the current reaches its final value after the switch is closed or opened (Fig. 54).

Consider first the case when the switch is closed. Due to the inductive effect of the coil, the current slowly rises to its maximum value of 4 amperes. When the final current of 4 amperes is reached, there is no changing magnetic field, no induced voltage, and the resistor alone acts to establish the final current value.

There is a certain amount of energy stored in an inductive coil when current is flowing through it. This energy (W) is directly related to the amount of current (I_M) and the inductance of the coil, whose symbol is (L). The inductance of any coil is determined primarily by the number of turns of wire, their spacing, and the type of material used in the core of the coil. The amount of energy stored in a coil can be determined by using the following equation:

Energy (W) = L x I_M^2/2 = 1/2 x L x I_M^2

This equation shows that the higher the inductance and the higher the current, the greater will be the energy stored in the coil.

USE OF SELF-INDUCTION IN IGNITION CIRCUIT COILS

A standard ignition circuit operates on the principle of energy stored in the primary winding of an ignition coil. When the distributor contacts open, the current suddenly drops to zero, and from the energy equation, the energy in the coil suddenly drops to zero. Some of this energy is transferred by mutual induction (see the next section) to the secondary winding of the ignition coil, and the energy

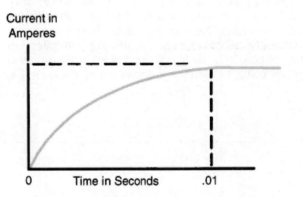

Fig. 54 — Time Delay Caused by Induced Voltage

is dissipated in the form of an arc across the spark plug. In an ignition circuit, the time delay in buildup of primary winding current when the distributor contacts close is very important.

If the contacts open before the final maximum value of current is reached, the energy stored in the coil (see the energy equation) is reduced, making less energy available to fire the plug.

Although the inductance of the ignition coil may cause a time delay of only a fraction of a second, this interval of time must be closely correlated with the time the distributor contacts are closed. (See Chapter 8 for more details on ignition circuits.)

MUTUAL INDUCTION

If a changing magnetic flux created by current flow in one coil cuts across the windings of a second coil, a voltage will be induced in the second coil. This induction of voltage in one coil because of a changing current in another coil is called mutual induction.

Continued on next page   MM61211,00012BF -19-16OCT12-11/14

MUTUAL INDUCTION IN COILS

Fig. 55 illustrates the principle of mutual induction in a circuit where the secondary winding is wound over an iron core, while the primary winding is wound over the secondary winding.

When the switch is closed, current will increase in the primary, and the expanding lines of force will cut across the secondary, causing a voltage to be induced in the secondary.

Similarly, when the switch opens, the sudden decrease in current in the primary winding will induce a voltage in the secondary winding. The secondary winding then becomes a source of voltage and will supply current to resistor R.

FINDING POLARITY OF INDUCED VOLTAGE IN SECONDARY COIL

The polarity of the induced voltage in the secondary can be determined in a number of different ways.

One of the simplest methods is to observe the direction of current in the primary and note that the current direction in the secondary must oppose any change in the primary current. Thus when the primary current is increasing, the secondary current must flow in the opposite direction around the core in order to oppose the increase, and the secondary voltage polarity is established as shown in Fig. 55.

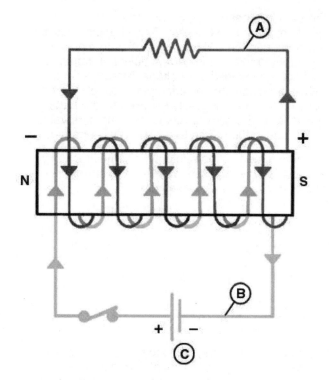

Fig. 55 — Mutual Induction in Primary and Secondary Coils

A—Secondary Winding   C—Current Increasing
B—Primary Winding

Continued on next page   MM61211,00012BF -19-16OCT12-12/14

However, if the primary current is decreasing, the secondary current must flow in the same direction around the core in order to oppose the change and to attempt to keep the flux in the core from changing. The secondary polarity is then as shown in Fig. 56.

An alternate method of finding the secondary induced voltage polarity is to use the Right Hand Rule for an Induced Voltage. Taking a lengthwise cross-sectional view of the assembly, when current increases in the primary, the circular lines of force expand and strike the secondary on the top side.

A—Secondary Winding   **C—Current Decreasing**
B—Primary Winding

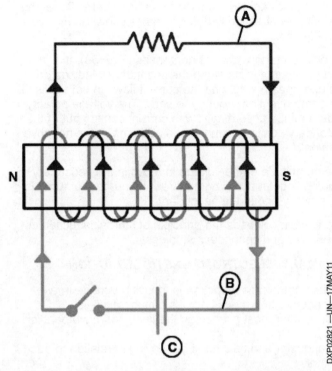

Fig. 56 — Polarity in Coils with Primary Current Decreasing

Continued on next page   MM61211,00012BF -19-16OCT12-13/14

By using the Right Hand Rule for an Induced Voltage, the current flow direction is determined as shown in Fig. 57 and Fig. 58.

When the primary current decreases (Fig. 58), the circular lines of force strike the secondary windings on the underneath side, and the current flows in both coils in the same direction around the core. The voltage polarity is determined accordingly, with current coming out of the secondary positive terminal and returning to the negative terminal.

The magnitude of the voltage induced in the secondary winding is determined primarily by the number of turns in the primary and in the secondary.

The ignition coil uses the principle of mutual induction in its primary and secondary windings.

SUMMARY: ELECTROMAGNETIC INDUCTION

- Electromagnetic induction is inducing voltage in a conductor that moves across a magnetic field.
- Conductor must cut across the field, not move parallel to it.
- Conductor and field must be moving in relation to each other.
- Faster relative motion = more voltage induced.
- More conductors in motion = more voltage.
- Stronger magnetic field = more voltage.
- Three ways of inducing voltage are generated voltage, self-induction, and mutual induction.
- Generated voltage by relative motion is used in generators and alternators.
- Self-induction creates its own voltage by a change of current in the conductor (as in the primary of ignition coils).

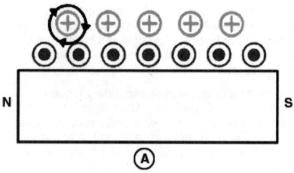

Fig. 57 — Finding Polarity of Secondary Voltage when Current is Increasing

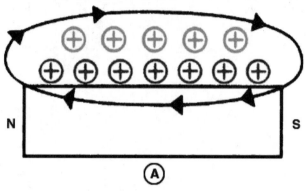

Fig. 58 — Finding Polarity of Secondary Voltage when Current is Decreasing

A—Current Decreasing

- Mutual induction occurs when changing current in one coil induces voltage in a second coil (as in the two windings of ignition coils).

MM61211,00012BF -19-16OCT12-14/14

WIRING SCHEMATICS AND DIAGRAMS

In order to understand electrical schematics and diagrams, various electrical standards organizations have tried to make diagrams and schematics more uniform. These groups include the International Electrotechnical Commission (IEC), International Organization for Standardization (ISO), Institute of Electrical and Electronics Engineers (IEEE), and American National Standards Institute (ANSI).

There are basically five electrical schematics and diagrams available to provide information to service and understand the operations of the electrical system of a machine. They are the following:

- System Functional Schematic
- Subsystem Functional Schematic
- Wire Harness Drawings
- Component Location Drawings
- Subsystem Diagnostic Wiring Diagram

SYSTEM FUNCTIONAL SCHEMATIC

SYSTEM WIRING SCHEMATIC

The system functional schematic is an electrical diagram of the complete machine and is made up of several foldouts of circuits divided into subsections. Each subsection is an electrical subsystem that contains one or more electrical

circuits and is indicated by a letter/number and circuit description. When these subsections are laid out side by side they show a logical sequence of the relationship between all the various electrical devices and show how they are connected to one another. The system functional schematic shows the operation, function, and interaction of each electrical subsystem of a machine. Each wire is identified by a number and/or color, and all electrical devices are identified by a letter/number designation and description, and are represented by an international schematic symbol. When applicable, a device will also be represented by an SAE (Society of Automotive Engineers) pictorial symbol. The System Functional Schematic contains no harness or connector information.

SYSTEM WIRING DIAGRAM

A system wiring diagram is essentially the same as the system functional schematic. The major difference is that the ends of the wires on a system wiring diagram are shown in the actual position (as on the machine), unlike a true functional schematic, which only shows the path of electricity. If a wire is terminated at a splice on the machine, the wiring diagram will show the wire terminate at a splice. If the wire is terminated at a component on the machine, the wiring diagram will show the wire terminate at that component.

Continued on next page   OUO1082,0002BCF -19-16OCT12-1/6

READING ELECTRICAL SCHEMATICS AND WIRING DIAGRAMS

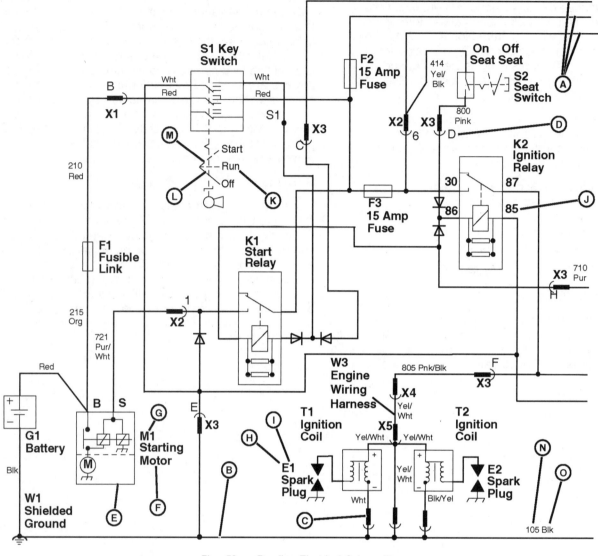

Fig. 59 — Reading Electrical Schematics

A—Power Wires	F—Name
B—Ground Wires	G—Identification Code
C—Connector	H—Identifying Letter
D—Terminal Pin Location	I—Identifying Number
E—Symbol	J—Terminal Designation

K—Switch Positions	N—Circuit Number
L—Current Switch Position (Solid Line)	O—Wire Color
M—Other Switch Position (Dash Line)	

The schematic (Fig. 59) is made up of individual circuits laid out in a sequence of related functions. It is formatted with all power wires (A) across the top and all ground wires (B) across the bottom. Current flow is generally from top to bottom through each circuit and component. All components are shown in the OFF position. The diagram does not list connector (C) information unless needed to avoid confusion. If the connector is shown, the number or letter next to it is the terminal pin location (D) in the connector.

Each component is shown by a symbol (E), its name (F), and an identification code (G). The identification code contains a device identifying letter (H) and number (I).

The identifying letter is always the same for a specific component, but the identifying numbers are numbered consecutively from upper left to lower right. The terminal designation (J) is placed directly outside the symbol next to the connecting wire path. Switch positions (K) are also placed directly outside the symbol. The solid line (L) shows the position the switch is currently in and dash lines (M) represent other switch positions.

The circuit number (N) and wire color (O) of the wires are shown directly next to the wire path.

The same component name and identification code are used consistently on all diagrams in this section. Components can be easily cross-referenced.

OUO1082,0002BCF -19-16OCT12-3/6

SUBSYSTEM FUNCTIONAL SCHEMATIC

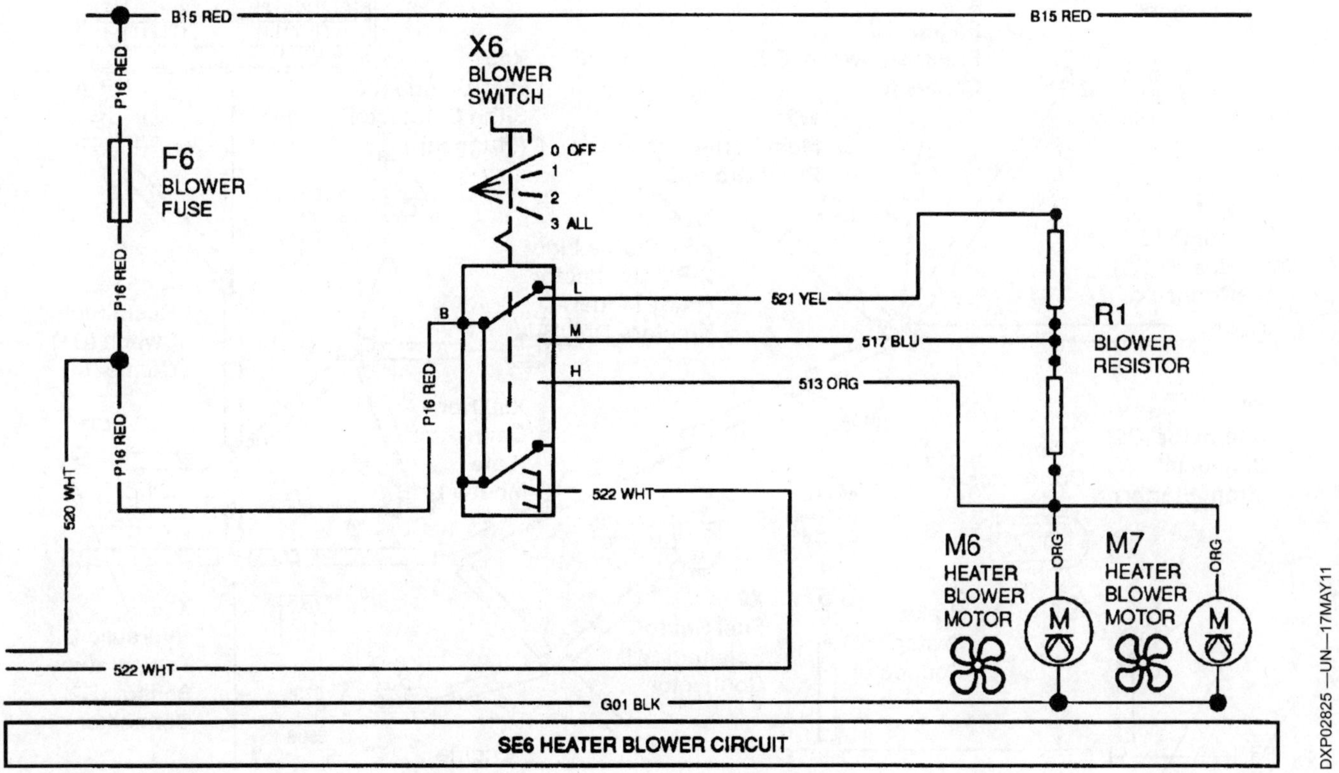

Fig. 60 — A Subsystem Functional Schematic

The subsystem functional schematic (Fig. 60) is a sectional division of the system functional schematic and shows the same letter/number designations of wires, as well as component symbols. The section division circuit is identified in a rectangle at the bottom of the schematic. In our example, a heater blower circuit is shown and it is the sixth section (SE6) of the system functional schematic.

All power supply wires are shown across the top of the drawing; the ground wires are shown across the bottom, with the components shown in between. The pictorials of the fans in our example are SAE symbols that indicate the function (blower fans) of the components (electrical motors).

Continued on next page   OUO1082,0002BCF -19-16OCT12-4/6

WIRING HARNESS DRAWINGS

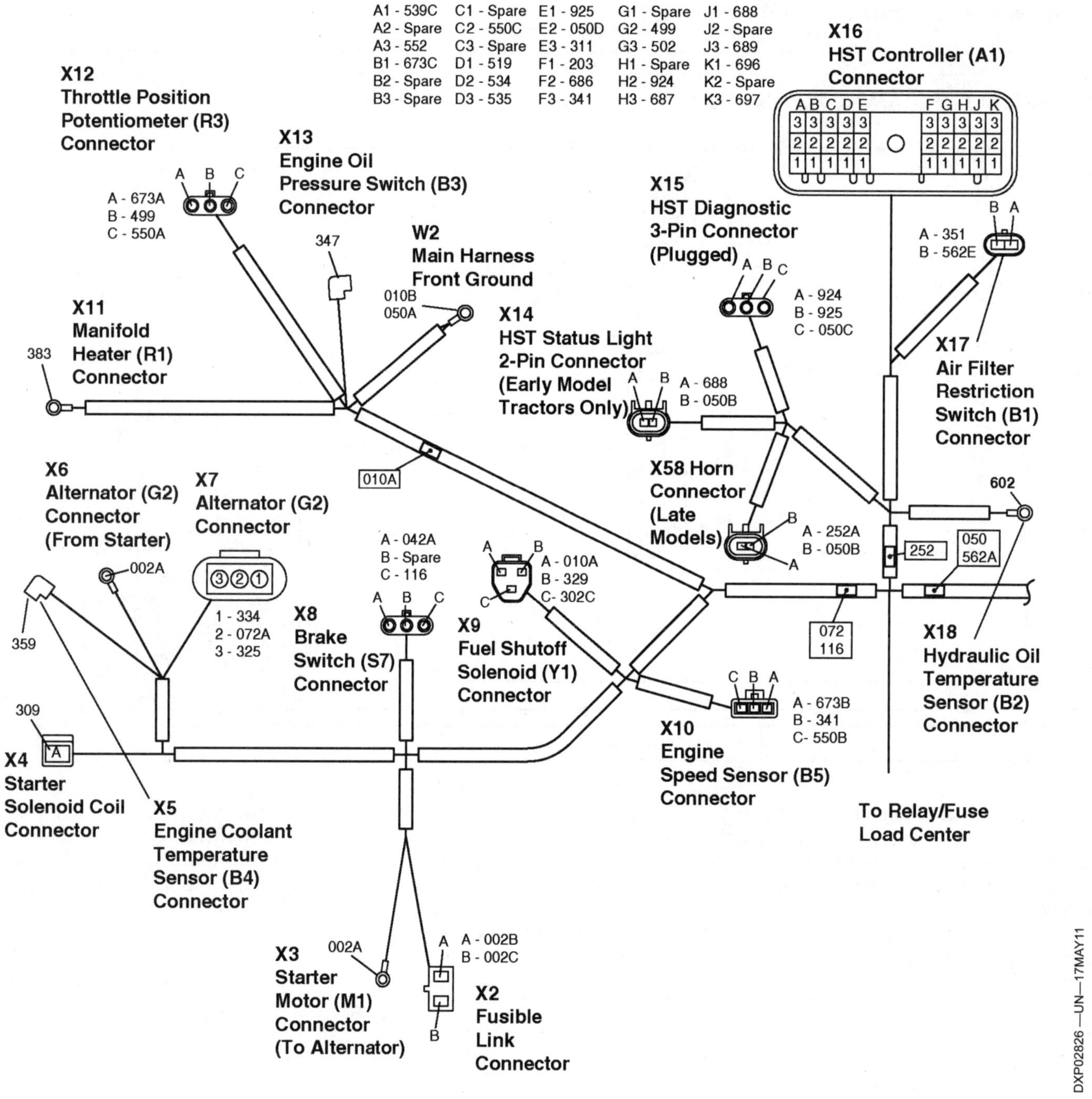

A1 - 539C C1 - Spare E1 - 925 G1 - Spare J1 - 688
A2 - Spare C2 - 550C E2 - 050D G2 - 499 J2 - Spare
A3 - 552 C3 - Spare E3 - 311 G3 - 502 J3 - 689
B1 - 673C D1 - 519 F1 - 203 H1 - Spare K1 - 696
B2 - Spare D2 - 534 F2 - 686 H2 - 924 K2 - Spare
B3 - Spare D3 - 535 F3 - 341 H3 - 687 K3 - 697

X16
HST Controller (A1)
Connector

X12
Throttle Position
Potentiometer (R3)
Connector

X13
Engine Oil
Pressure Switch (B3)
Connector

A - 673A
B - 499
C - 550A

347

W2
Main Harness
Front Ground

010B
050A

X15
HST Diagnostic
3-Pin Connector
(Plugged)

A - 924
B - 925
C - 050C

X11
Manifold
Heater (R1)
Connector

383

X14
HST Status Light
2-Pin Connector
(Early Model
Tractors Only)

A - 688
B - 050B

A - 351
B - 562E

X17
Air Filter
Restriction
Switch (B1)
Connector

010A

602

X6
Alternator (G2)
Connector
(From Starter)

X7
Alternator (G2)
Connector

002A

X58 Horn
Connector
(Late
Models)

A - 252A
B - 050B

252

050
562A

359

1 - 334
2 - 072A
3 - 325

A - 042A
B - Spare
C - 116

A - 010A
B - 329
C - 302C

X8
Brake
Switch (S7)
Connector

X9
Fuel Shutoff
Solenoid (Y1)
Connector

072
116

X18
Hydraulic Oil
Temperature
Sensor (B2)
Connector

309

X4
Starter
Solenoid Coil
Connector

X5
Engine Coolant
Temperature
Sensor (B4)
Connector

A - 673B
B - 341
C - 550B

X10
Engine
Speed Sensor (B5)
Connector

To Relay/Fuse
Load Center

002A

X3
Starter
Motor (M1)
Connector
(To Alternator)

A - 002B
B - 002C

X2
Fusible
Link
Connector

DXP02826 —UN—17MAY11

Fig. 61 — A System Wiring Diagram

A system wire harness drawing (Fig. 61) is an illustration of the actual wire harness flattened out. The wiring harness is laid out to allow identification of each connector, pin, wire number and splice location. Splices are identified by placing the associated wire numbers in a box. A leader line, attached to the box, indicates where the splice is located.

Usually separate charts give wire size, wire color, and fuse and relay information.

Continued on next page

OUO1082,0002BCF -19-16OCT12-5/6

2-40

SUBSYSTEM DIAGNOSTIC WIRING DIAGRAM

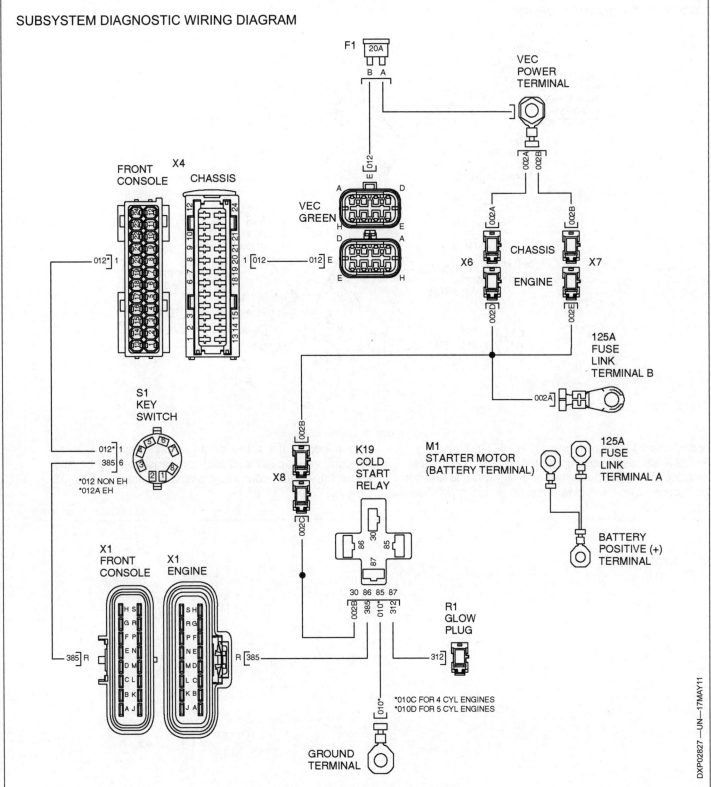

Fig. 62 — A Subsystem Diagnostic Wiring

The subsystem diagnostic wiring diagram is a diagram that combines the subsystem functional schematic with all harness connectors and pin locations to aid in diagnosing subsystems.

OUO1082,0002BCF -19-16OCT12-6/6

110112
PN=63

COMPONENT LOCATION DRAWING

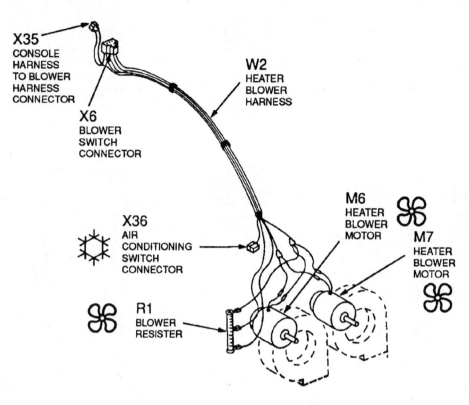

X35
CONSOLE
HARNESS
TO BLOWER
HARNESS
CONNECTOR

X6
BLOWER
SWITCH
CONNECTOR

W2
HEATER
BLOWER
HARNESS

X36
AIR
CONDITIONING
SWITCH
CONNECTOR

M6
HEATER
BLOWER
MOTOR

M7
HEATER
BLOWER
MOTOR

R1
BLOWER
RESISTER

Fig. 63 — A Component Location Drawing

A component location drawing (Fig. 63) is a pictorial view of a harness showing the location of all electrical components, connectors, harness main ground locations, and harness band and clamp locations. Each component is identified by the same identification letter/number and description used in the subsystem functional schematic. When applicable, components also are shown with SAE symbols.

OUO1082,0002BCF -19-16OCT12-7/6

DXP02828 —UN—17MAY11

COMPONENT IDENTIFICATION LETTERS

Component identification letters have been developed by standards organizations. Each electrical component and main harness connection has an identification letter assigned to it. A number is added to the letter to separate and indicate the total components and main connections within that letter group. The letters I, O, and Q are not used. The following is a list of identifying letters and some examples of what they represent.

Identification Letters	Examples
A —	ABS control units, radios, and control units
B —	All types of sensors, horns, and microphones
C —	Condensers and capacitors
D —	Digital devices, pulse counters, and integrated circuits
E —	Heaters, air conditioning, lights, distributors, and spark plugs
F —	All protection devices such as fuses and circuit breakers
G —	All power supplies such as batteries, alternators, and generators
H —	Signal devices such as alarms, buzzers, or signal lights
L —	Inductor devices such as coil windings
M —	Any electrical motor
N —	Regulators
P —	Any measuring instruments such as ammeters and tachometers
R —	Resistors
S —	Any switch
T —	Ignition coil or any transformer
U —	Converters and modulators
V —	Any semiconductors such as diodes
W —	All conductors of an electrical path
X —	All electrical connection devices
Y —	Any electrically actuated mechanical device
Z —	Any electrical filter or suppressor device

An alphabetical listing of devices and their identifying letters is given in the back of this book.

OUO1082,0002BD0 -19-16OCT12-1/1

WIRE NUMBER AND COLOR CODES

There is no set standard for wire number codes. Most major manufacturers of machines create their own number codes and list the information and show how to use these codes in their technical manuals, but most manufacturers use standard color abbreviations to identify wires in a circuit. Red-colored wires are generally used for power source wires that can be traced back to the battery. Black-colored wires are generally used for grounds. Listed here are some of the abbreviations for colors.

Color	Abbreviation
Black	BLK or BK
Brown	BRN or BN
Red	RED or R
Orange	ORG or O
Yellow	YEL or Y
Green	GRN or G
Dark Green	DK. GRN or DG
Light Green	LT. GRN or LG
Blue	BLU or B
Dark Blue	DK. BLU or DB
Light Blue	LT. BLU or LB
Purple	PUR or P
Gray	GRY or GY
White	WHT or W

If the wire is bicolored, both abbreviations are used, separated with a slash. BLK/WHT means a black wire with a white tracer.

OUO1082,0002BD1 -19-10JAN12-1/1

DIAGRAM AND SCHEMATIC SYMBOLS

Symbols for components that are used on electrical schematics worldwide.

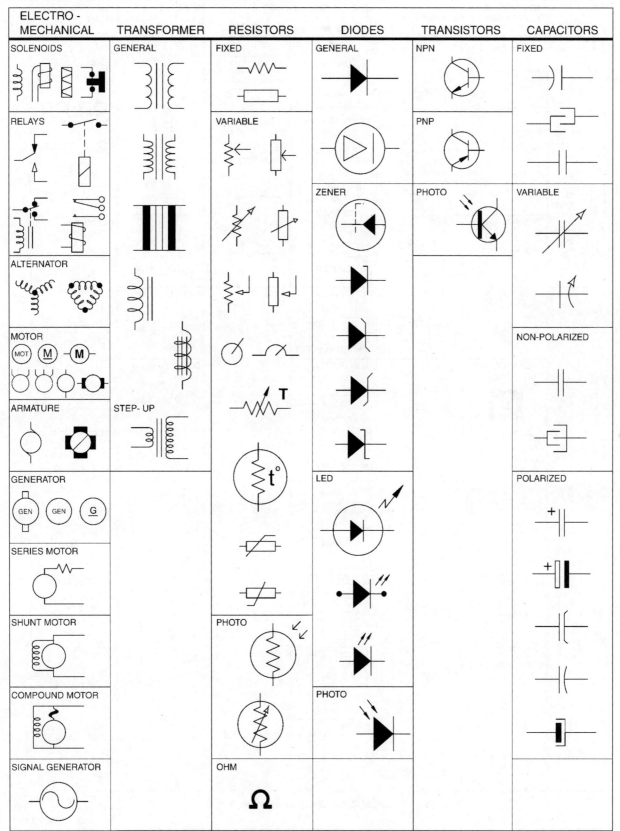

Continued on next page

OUO1082,0002BD2 -19-10JAN12-1/2

DXP02829 —UN—17MAY11

PN=67

110112

Fig. 64 — *Electrical Circuit Symbols—Section 1 of 2*

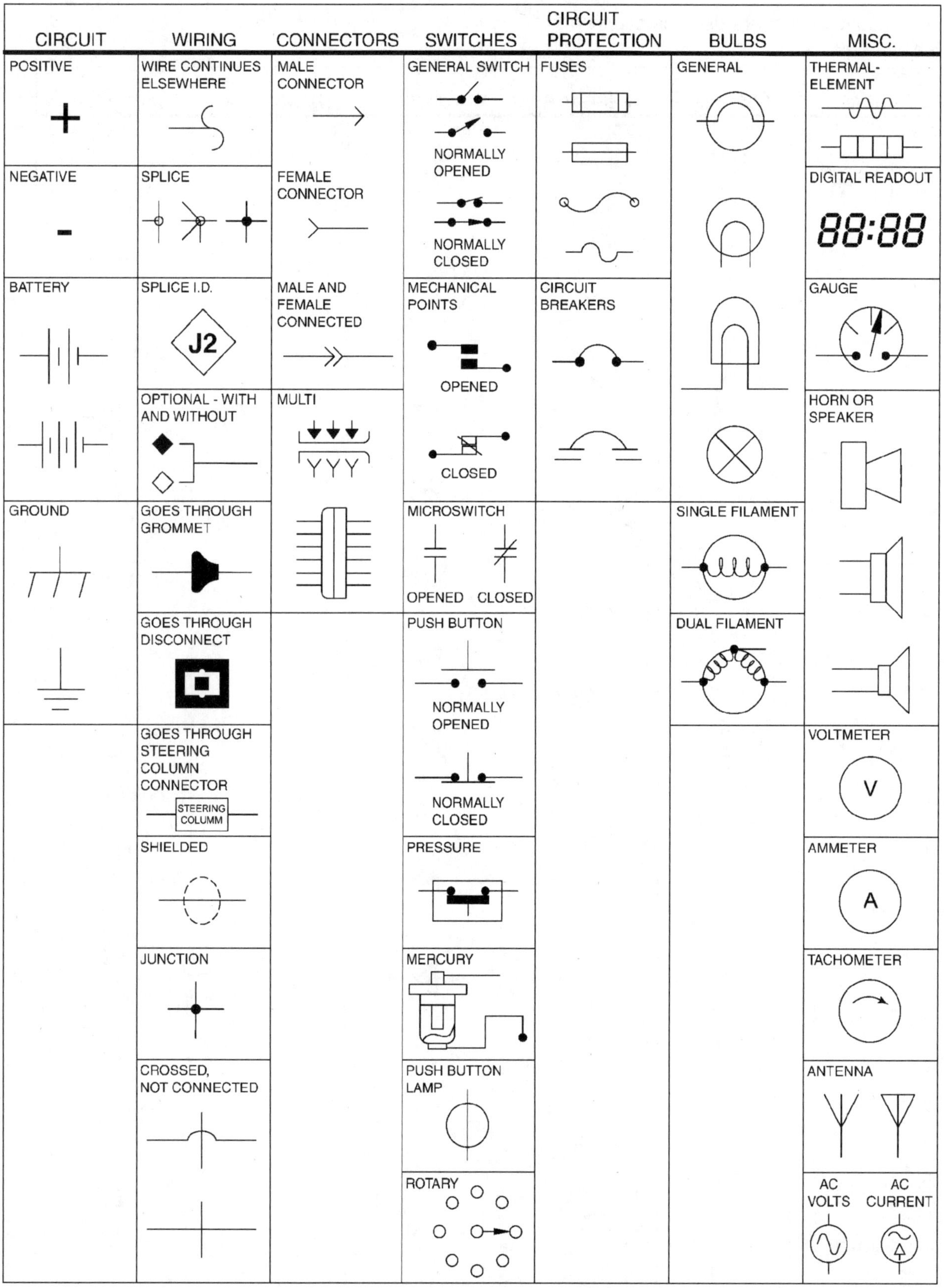

CIRCUIT	WIRING	CONNECTORS	SWITCHES	CIRCUIT PROTECTION	BULBS	MISC.
POSITIVE	WIRE CONTINUES ELSEWHERE	MALE CONNECTOR	GENERAL SWITCH NORMALLY OPENED NORMALLY CLOSED	FUSES	GENERAL	THERMAL-ELEMENT
NEGATIVE	SPLICE	FEMALE CONNECTOR				DIGITAL READOUT 88:88
BATTERY	SPLICE I.D. J2	MALE AND FEMALE CONNECTED	MECHANICAL POINTS OPENED CLOSED	CIRCUIT BREAKERS		GAUGE
	OPTIONAL - WITH AND WITHOUT	MULTI				HORN OR SPEAKER
GROUND	GOES THROUGH GROMMET		MICROSWITCH OPENED CLOSED		SINGLE FILAMENT	
	GOES THROUGH DISCONNECT		PUSH BUTTON NORMALLY OPENED NORMALLY CLOSED		DUAL FILAMENT	
	GOES THROUGH STEERING COLUMN CONNECTOR STEERING COLUMM					VOLTMETER V
	SHIELDED		PRESSURE			AMMETER A
	JUNCTION		MERCURY			TACHOMETER
	CROSSED, NOT CONNECTED		PUSH BUTTON LAMP ROTARY			ANTENNA AC VOLTS AC CURRENT

Fig. 65 — *Electrical Circuit Symbols—Section 2 of 2*

OUO1082,0002BD2 -19-10JAN12-2/2

DXP02830 —UN—17MAY11

SAE SYMBOLS

SAE symbols are boldfaced symbols designed by the
Society of Automotive Engineers (Fig. 66).

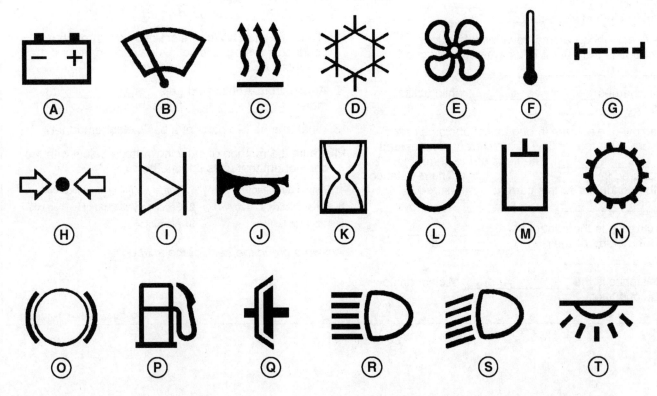

Fig. 66 — SAE Symbols—Located on Instrument Panel (Select Symbols Are Used on Some Wiring Circuit Schematics)

A—Battery	G—Filter	M—Hydraulic System	R—High Beam Lights
B—Windshield Wiper	H—Pressure	N—Transmission	S—Low Beam Lights
C—Heater	I— Level Indicator	O—Brake System	T—Interior Dome Light
D—Air Conditioning	J—Horn	P—Fuel System	
E—Fan	K—Hour Meter	Q—Clutch	
F—Temperature	L—Engine		

OUO1082,0002BD3 -19-16OCT12-1/1

TEST YOURSELF

QUESTIONS

1. The SI base unit for length is the _____.

2. Electricity is the flow of _____ from atom to atom in a _____.

3. Elements whose atoms have less than four electrons in their outer rings are generally good _____.

4. Like charges _____, while unlike charges _____.

5. The flow of electrons through a conductor is called a current. The rate of flow of the current is measured in _____. The force of the current is measured in _____. The resistance of the conductor to this current is measured in _____.

6. Electronics is the control of _____ and the study of their _____ and _____.

7. Resistance is the _____ of electron flow in a conductor.

8. The three types of circuit configurations are _____, _____ and _____.

9. (True or False?) E = I x R.

10. Every magnet has a _____ of _____ surrounding it.

11. (True or False?) When electrons flow through a conductor, a magnetic field is developed around that conductor.

12. An electromagnetic field gets _____ as more _____ flows through its coils.

13. What are the two parts of a basic electromagnet?

14. Match the method of inducing voltage below with the component that uses this method:

   a. Generated voltage   1. Primary winding of ignition coil
   b. Self-induction   2. Secondary winding of ignition coil
   c. Mutual induction   3. Alternator

(Answers are in the back of the textbook.)

OUO1082,0002BD4 -19-10JAN12-1/1

Electrical Components

INTRODUCTION

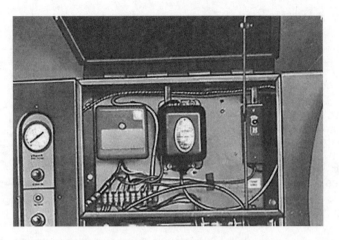

Many different types of electrical components are used to control the flow of electrons. Circuit breakers, fuses, switches, resistors, and transformers are electrical components. Of course, a wire (conductor) is an electrical component that connects the other electrical components to a power source.

OUO1082,00035F5 -19-05APR12-1/1

WIRING

Table 1 — Relative Resistance of Copper Compared to Other Metals	
SILVER	0.936
COPPER	1.000
GOLD	1.403
CHROMIUM	1.530
ALUMINUM	1.549
TUNGSTEN	3.203

Wire is used for conducting electrical current to an electrical device. Most metals are good conductors of heat and electricity. The most widely used metal for wiring is copper because of its low cost and low resistance. Copper is one of the top six metals that have the least resistance compared to other metals (Table 1). The relative resistance of copper is between silver and gold, two precious metals. Thus, copper is the best conductor in terms of cost and resistance.

Wiring is solid or is stranded (Fig. 1). Solid wire is generally called heavy duty. Household wiring is a solid type of wire conductor. Stranded wire is two or more twisted or braided conductors. All conductor wiring is insulated with a covering of plastic or rubber.

Many sizes of wires exist. The larger the number of the wire, the smaller the diameter. Therefore, a No. 12 gauge

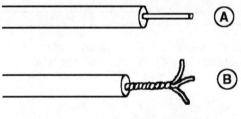

Fig. 1 — Types of Wiring

A—Solid B—Stranded

wire has a smaller diameter than a No. 10 gauge wire. This numbering system is known as the American Wire Gauge (AWG) or Brown and Sharpe Wire Gauge (B&S). The unit of measure for wire is the circular mil (0.001 in. dia.). No. 12 gauge wire is 101.9 mil (0.10 in. dia.) and No. 10 gauge wire is 0.08 in. (80.8 mil) dia.

All conductors offer some resistance to the flow of electrons. Wire must be selected that has an acceptable amount of resistance for the needs of an electrical circuit. Let's show the effect of wiring resistance on the operation of a circuit.

Continued on next page

OUO1082,00035F6 -19-08MAR12-1/6

Fig. 2 shows a circuit that has two head lamps connected to a 12-volt battery with two copper wires, each having a resistance of 0.1 ohm.

The head lamps each have a resistance of two ohms and are in parallel with the circuit. Using the current-divider rule for parallel circuits, the total resistance of the two head lamps would be:

$$R_1 \times R_2/R_1 + R_2 = 2 \times 2/2 + 2 = 4/4 = 1 \text{ Ohm}$$

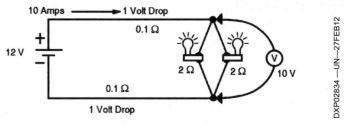

Fig. 2 — Resistance in a Conductor (Copper Wire)

OUO1082,00035F6 -19-08MAR12-2/6

The total resistance of the wires and head lamps in the circuit would be 0.1 + 1 + 0.1 or 1.2 ohms. To find the amperage of the circuit, use Ohm's Law Formula Circle (Fig. 3), where I = amps, E = volts, and R = resistance (ohms). Thus, I = E/R or 12/1.2 = 10 amperes.

The voltage drop in each wire is E = IR = 10 x 0.1 = 1 volt, or two volts total for both wires. The voltage left to operate the head lamps, or load, is 10 volts, since the sum of the voltage drops must equal the source voltage, or 1 + 10 + 1 = 12 volts.

Copper wire "robs" the head lamps of two volts, leaving 10 volts across the head lamps to provide illumination.

The wiring used in any circuit must allow sufficient voltage across the load for proper operation. The smallest wire that will not create an excessive voltage drop is normally used.

DXP02835 —UN—27FEB12

Fig. 3 — Ohm's Law Formula Circle

Resistance in a wire depends upon the wire:

- *Length*
- *Diameter*
- *Temperature*

OUO1082,00035F6 -19-08MAR12-3/6

If the length of a wire is doubled, the resistance between the wire ends is doubled (Fig. 4). In, other words, the longer the wire, the greater the resistance between the wire ends.

DXP02836 —UN—27FEB12

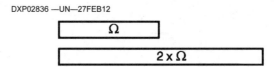

Fig. 4 — A Longer Wire Contains More Resistance

OUO1082,00035F6 -19-08MAR12-4/6

If the cross-sectional area of a wire is reduced by half, the resistance for any given length is doubled (see Fig. 5). That is, the smaller the wire, the more resistance, and the larger the wire, the less resistance.

As the temperature rises in a wire, the resistance increases.

DXP02837 —UN—27FEB12

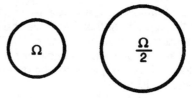

Fig. 5 — A Smaller Diameter Wire Contains More Resistance

Continued on next page   OUO1082,00035F6 -19-08MAR12-5/6

Fig. 6 shows an example of a 10-ft. (3-meter) length of wire having a resistance of 0.04 ohm at 70°F (21°C). At 170°F (77°C), the resistance is 0.05 ohm, a 25% increase.

Excessive resistance in the wiring from normal heat can hinder the performance of electrical equipment. It is for this reason why the selection of the proper wiring is so important.

Heat is developed in any wire carrying current because of the normal resistance in the wire. If the wire gets too hot, the insulation will be damaged.

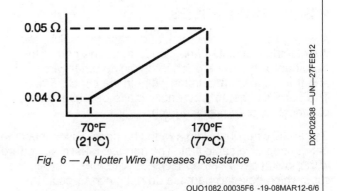

Fig. 6 — A Hotter Wire Increases Resistance

OUO1082,00035F6 -19-08MAR12-6/6

WIRING HARNESSES

A wiring harness is the trunk and branches which feed the electrical circuit. Wiring leads from one part of the circuit enter the trunk or sheath, joining other wires, and then emerge at another point in the circuit (Fig. 7). The harness sheath is normally made of rubber, cloth, electrical tape, or plastic tubing.

Be careful when installing a wiring harness. Disconnect the battery negative cable first. The harness must not interfere with moving parts of the machine. Also make certain the clips which hold the harness do not pinch through the harness and cut the wires. This can cause a short in the circuit. Make sure the harness is routed away from hot parts of the equipment and away from sharp objects.

Individual wires in a harness may be replaced by cutting off the defective wire at each end of the harness. Discard the removed ends of the wire. Run the new wire around the harness; do not try to thread the wire through the harness. Place the new wire in clips with the harness or attach to the harness with electrical tape. Avoid any sharp bends when installing the harness.

The proper gauge or size of an electrical wire depends upon:

• Total length of the wire in circuit.
• Total amperes that the wire will carry.

But when replacing a defective wire in a circuit, remember:

When replacing a defective wire in a circuit, always use the same gauge of wire for replacement. Never use an undersized wire as it will not carry the required load and will overheat.

TESTING AND DIAGNOSIS OF WIRING

An electrical circuit may fail in three ways:

• Open or Break
• Ground
• Short

The following chart tells you how to test for each of these three failures. The column on the right gives the test results you can expect if the wiring is at fault.

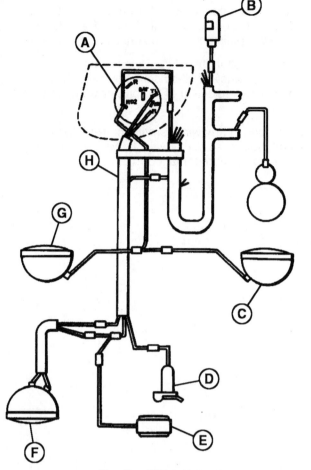

Fig. 7 — Wiring Harness

A—Light Switch
B—Dash Lamp
C—Right Headlight
D—Outlet Socket
E—Warning Lamp
F—Rear Lamp
G—Left Headlight
H—Wiring Harness

Continued on next page OUO1082,00035F7 -19-08MAR12-1/2

WIRING TEST CHART

Table 2 – Wiring Test Chart	
Type of Failure	**Test Unit and Expected Results if Faulty Wiring**
Open (Broken Wire)	Ohmmeter—Infinite resistance at other end of wire. Infinite resistance to adjacent wire. Infinite resistance to ground. Voltmeter—Zero volts at the other end of wire.
Ground (bare wire touching frame)	Ohmmeter—Zero resistance to ground. Infinite resistance to adjacent wire. May or may not be infinite resistance to the other end of the wire. Voltmeter—Instead of testing, look for blown fuse or tripped circuit breaker.
Short (rubbing of two bare wires)	Ohmmeter—Zero resistance to adjacent wire. Infinite resistance to ground. Voltmeter—Voltage will be read on both wires.

SUMMARY

- The longer the wire, the greater the resistance.
- The smaller the wire diameter, the greater the resistance.
- The hotter the wire, the greater the resistance.

OUO1082,00035F7 -19-08MAR12-2/2

ELECTRICAL CIRCUIT PROTECTION

Fuses and circuit breakers protect the electrical circuit and its electrical devices from current overload.

Fuses are inexpensive, but not reusable. They are used mainly in circuits where electrical surges from heavy loads are not common.

Circuit breakers are more expensive but can be reset without replacement. Circuit breakers are used where heavy loads, like motors, may be repeatedly placed on the circuit.

CIRCUIT BREAKERS

A circuit breaker (Fig. 8) protects an electrical circuit from current overload. The circuit breaker acts as a switch and opens when the current passing through the circuit exceeds the breaker's rated amperage. The breaker may close again automatically after a bimetallic strip or disk inside the breaker housing cools, or the breaker may need to be reset manually.

In general, circuit breakers are used when heavy loads may be instantly placed on the circuit.

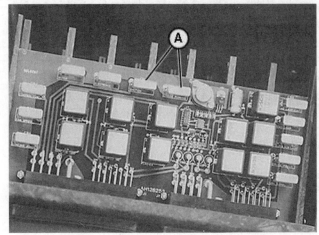

Fig. 8 — Circuit Breakers in a Circuit Board

DXP02841 —UN—27FEB12

A—Circuit Breakers

Continued on next page OUO1082,00035F8 -19-16OCT12-1/5

Some circuit breakers are equipped with a reset opening. When the breaker trips, it may be reset by inserting a small wire in the opening and pushing against the spring tension (Fig. 9).

Use an ohmmeter to check a circuit breaker. A good circuit breaker will show zero resistance. However a defective breaker will show infinite resistance. If a circuit breaker does not reset, replace it. If it does reset and trips again, determine the cause and correct it.

If a circuit breaker does not reset, replace it. If it does reset and trips again, determine the cause and correct it.

Circuit breakers are plug-in type devices and should be replaced if defective. Circuit breakers are made with a tight fit for good contact. Pull them straight out. Do not attempt to pry them out with a screwdriver or similar tool. Each circuit breaker is marked, by circuit, on the power distribution circuit board (Fig. 8).

Circuit boards can also be replaced. Make sure all lights, switches and the key switch are off before replacing a circuit board. To eliminate damage from static electricity, keep the new replacement board in its protective packaging until you are ready to install it. Hold it by its edges when installing. Circuit boards are very fragile and expensive and should be handled with care.

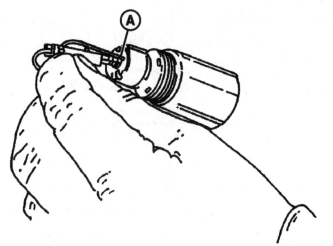

Fig. 9 — Some Circuit Breakers Require a Manual Reset

A—Reset Opening

Transfer any circuit breakers or relays to the new circuit board. Recalibrate the switches on the new board as the old ones are calibrated.

OUO1082,00035F8 -19-16OCT12-2/5

FUSES

Fuses protect an electrical circuit from current overload. When too much current passes through the circuit, the fuse blows, breaking the flow of current and preventing damage to the circuit.

A—Amperage Rating   C—Glass Tube
B—Thin Metal Strip   D—Metal End Caps

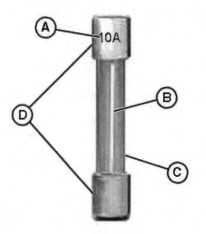

Fig. 10 — Tube-Style Fuse

Continued on next page   OUO1082,00035F8 -19-16OCT12-3/5

A fuse is a fine wire or thin metal strip enclosed in a glass cylinder with metal caps (Fig. 10), or a thermoplastic case with two metal blades (Fig. 11). The amperage rating is located on the fuse.

When amperage flowing through the fuse exceeds the amperage rating of the fuse, the wire or thin metal strip melts because of the excess heat (Fig. 11). When the fuse blows, current flowing through the circuit is stopped, preventing damage to the wiring and electrical components of that circuit.

Most fuses are located in a fuse panel or electrical load center panel (Fig. 12). The load center panel contains fuses and various other electrical components in a central location for easy access for servicing. Some machines may have several fuse panels.

⚠ CAUTION: Make sure the key switch is off when checking or changing fuses.

BLOWN FUSES ARE USUALLY CAUSED BY:

- A short circuit in the electrical circuit caused by defective wiring or a shorted component (lights, motor, etc.).
- A one-time electrical overload in the circuit caused by a surge of electricity passing through the circuit.
- Poor contacts in the electrical circuit or the components.
- Overheating in the circuit caused by electrical overloads or poor contacts.
- Incorrect amperage fuse in the circuit.
- Fuse located too close to a hot area, such as an engine or a heater.
- Vibrations near the fuse causing the contacts to come loose.

TYPES OF FUSES

Two types of fuses are widely used in machine electrical circuits:

- Quick-blowing fuse
- Slow-blowing fuse

A quick-blowing fuse blows instantly whenever amperage exceeds the amperage rating of the fuse.

A slow-blowing fuse will not blow because of a momentary electrical surge, allowing a longer time of higher-than-normal amperage before it blows.

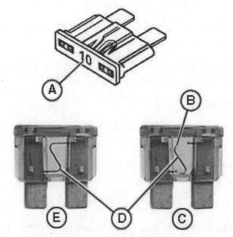

Fig. 11 — Blade-Style Fuse. A Blown Fuse Is at Right.

A—Amperage Rating　　　D—Metal Strip
B—Melted　　　　　　　　E—Good
C—Blown

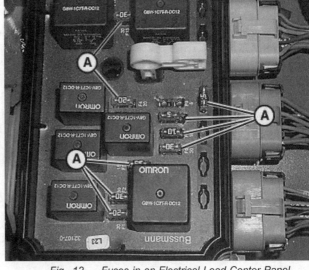

Fig. 12 — Fuses in an Electrical Load Center Panel

A—Fuses

Continued on next page

OUO1082,00035F8 -19-16OCT12-4/5

PN=77

DIAGNOSING A BLOWN FUSE

By looking at a blown fuse, you can often tell what failure in the circuit caused it to blow.

Fig. 13 shows a general check for the causes of blown-out fuses—whether from overload or from a short circuit.

Quick-Blowing Fuses

If an electrical overload—glass case will be clear because fuse link overheats and simply melts away.

If a short circuit—glass will be dark, stained by the fuse link which suddenly burns up.

Slow-Blowing Fuses

If an electrical overload—fuse link will break at solder, which has melted.

If a short circuit—fuse link will break at wires because of sudden heat.

A fuse protects against electrical overloads. While an overload is usually a one-time occurrence, a short circuit is not. Find the short circuit and repair it at once.

If a quick-blowing fuse tends to blow out frequently because of electrical surges, replace it with a slow-blowing type of the same amperage rating. If the fuse continues to blow, check the circuit for shorts or a binding motor.

If the fuse still keeps on blowing, the circuit is overloaded and is not meant to handle the loads being placed on it.

IMPORTANT: Always replace a blown fuse with one of the same amperage rating. Never use a fuse with a higher amperage rating as it may result in serious damage to the circuit it protects.

FUSIBLE LINK

A fusible link is another way to protect a wiring harness from damage by inserting a short length of smaller gauge wire in the circuit.

A fusible link is usually a 5-inch (127 mm) length of wire that is four wire gauges smaller than the wire gauge of the

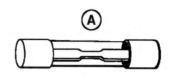
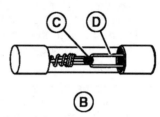

Fig. 13 — How to Tell What Caused a Fuse to Blow

A—QUICK-BLOWING FUSE
B—SLOW-BLOWING FUSE
C—If Blown from Overload—Fuse Will Be Broken at Solder Here.
D—If Blown from Short Circuit—Wires Will Be Burned Out Here.

circuit being protected. When amperage exceeds what the smaller gauge wire can safely carry, it melts. Thus, the fusible link prevents the entire wiring harness from burning.

Always position a fusible link so that it has a sagging loop. Then when the wire melts, the melted ends at the bottom of the loop will fall apart and prevent further melting of the insulation. Do not position the link vertically because the heat would travel up the wire and might cause the wire insulation to burn. See the machine's Technical Manual for fusible link locations and specifications.

FUSE AND CIRCUIT BREAKER—THE APPLICATIONS

Fuses are less expensive than circuit breakers but are not reusable. They are used mainly in circuits where "blowouts" from heavy loads are not common.

Circuit breakers are more expensive but can be reset without replacement. so they are used in heavy-duty circuits when safety or other factors justify their use.

OUO1082,00035F8 -19-16OCT12-5/5

SWITCHES

A switch is an electrical device that allow electrical current to flow freely or interrupts it. Turning a switch off opens a circuit, stopping the flow of current at the switch. Turning a switch on closes the circuit, allowing current to flow to electrical components within a circuit.

The simplest switch is the single-pole single-throw (SPST) switch (Fig. 14).

Other types of switches (Fig. 15) are single-pole double-throw (SPDT), double-pole single-throw (DPST), and double-pole double-throw (DPDT).

There are many different ways of actuating switches:

• A manually-actuated switch is controlled by an operator. It can be of a simple single-pole, single-throw (SPST) type or use multiple poles and positions.

A—Single-Pole, Double-Throw   C—Double-Pole, Double-Throw
B—Double-Pole, Single-Throw

DXP02847 —UN—27FEB12

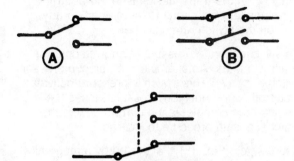

Fig. 14 — Symbol for a Single-Pole Single-Throw Switch

Fig. 15 — Symbols for Other Types of Switches

DXP02848 —UN—27FEB12

Continued on next page   OUO1082,00035F9 -19-16OCT12-1/12

• A mechanically-operated switch is actuated by a mechanical device. These switches also are called "motion complete" or "limit" switches. Such a switch is a neutral start switch (Fig. 16). The neutral start switch, generally located on the transmission, is between the key switch and starter circuit. It is mechanically operated from the transmission shifter. The switch is closed only when the transmission is in the neutral position, completing the circuit to the starter. In any other position the switch remains open.

• Pressure switches use a pressure change to open or close switch contacts. An example is an air compressor cycle switch (Fig. 17). This switch is pressure-activated and is generally open until low pressure closes the switch, which then completes the current flow to the pump clutch, causing pressure to increase.

• A magnetic switch (Fig. 18) is activated by a magnetic field that opens or closes the switch.

Switches are used for:

• Controlling circuits—Opening and closing current pathways to turn a circuit on or off.
• Selection—Multi-position switches can provide a variety of possible paths and combination of paths for current to flow.
• Sensing—These switches send a signal to some other type of device to relay information.

Some of the other major types of switches used are:

• Key
• Toggle
• Push-Pull
• Cutout
• Multiple-Contact
• Push-Button
• Twist
• Pressure
• Rocker
• Rotary
• Thermostatic Temperature Control
• Limit-Position
• Reed
• Mercury

Fig. 16 — A Neutral Start Switch

A—Neutral Start Switch

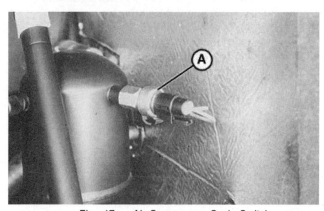

Fig. 17 — Air Compressor Cycle Switch

A—Air Compressor Cycle Switch

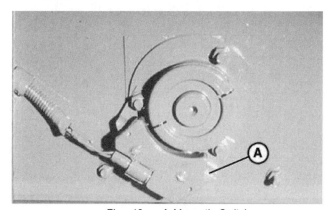

Fig. 18 — A Magnetic Switch

A—Magnetic Switch

Continued on next page   OUO1082,00035F9 -19-16OCT12-2/12

KEY SWITCHES (Fig. 19) must have a key inserted before they can be operated. Used for starting switches because of safety and to avoid theft of the machine.

A—Key Switch

Fig. 19 — Key Switch

OUO1082,00035F9 -19-16OCT12-3/12

TOGGLE SWITCHES (Fig. 20) are simple on-off flip switches. Used to control small auxiliary circuits.

PUSH-PULL SWITCHES are usually on-off switches. Used for two-way control as of a simple lighting circuit.

A—Toggle Switch

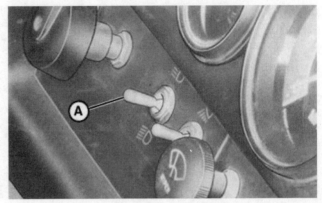

Fig. 20 — Toggle Switch

OUO1082,00035F9 -19-16OCT12-4/12

CUTOUT SWITCHES (Fig. 21) are used to break an electrical circuit as during emergencies. They may be actuated manually or automatically.

Fig. 21 — Cutout Switch

Continued on next page   OUO1082,00035F9 -19-16OCT12-5/12

MULTIPLE-CONTACT SWITCHES (Fig. 22) may use a knob or a key which is turned to various positions to make or to break contact with different circuits. Used for complex circuits such as combination lighting or for variable speed control of a fan or heater.

Fig. 22 — Multiple-Contact Switch

OUO1082,00035F9 -19-16OCT12-6/12

PUSH-BUTTON SWITCHES (Fig. 23) are moved in only one direction to open or close a circuit. Used for simple jobs such as sounding a horn or bright headlamps.

TWIST SWITCHES give the same on-off control as push-pull types, except that they give a rotary action. Used for two-way or two-speed control of simple circuits such as windshield wipers.

A—Push-Button Switch

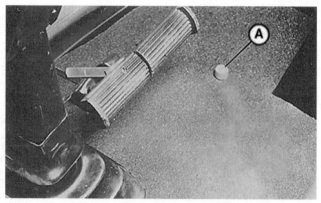

Fig. 23 — Push-Button Switch

OUO1082,00035F9 -19-16OCT12-7/12

PRESSURE SWITCHES (Fig. 24) are operated by an outside force from oil, water, air, or gas. Usually they are spring-type units which open or close a circuit automatically in response to pressure. Often these switches are used as sending units for oil pressure lamps, etc.

A—Pressure Switch

Fig. 24 — Pressure Switch

Continued on next page   OUO1082,00035F9 -19-16OCT12-8/12

ROCKER SWITCHES (Fig. 25) are usually two-way control switches. They may or may not have LED lighting.

A—Rocker Switches

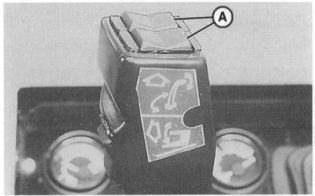

Fig. 25 — Rocker Switches Used to Lower a Harvesting Unit

OUO1082,00035F9 -19-16OCT12-9/12

The ROTARY SWITCH is a variation on the twist switch. This switch is often used with a fan to complete a circuit when the fan reaches a certain speed. It also shuts off when the fan drops below this speed.

A good example of a rotary switch is one that is used with the fan on a crop dryer (Fig. 26). When the fan reaches a predetermined speed, the rotary switch will activate, completing an electrical circuit to the gas burner. This ensures that the fan is always running before the burner starts. When the fan slows down, it will again activate the switch, shutting off the burner. Thus the switch is a protective device against possible failure of the fan and consequent heat build-up.

Fig. 26 — Rotary Switch on a Fan

OUO1082,00035F9 -19-16OCT12-10/12

A THERMOSTATIC TEMPERATURE CONTROL SWITCH (Fig. 27) is a gas-filled temperature sensing tube. It inserts in the evaporator core of the air conditioner. The switch end of the sending tube uses a diaphragm to control two external contacts wired to the compressor clutch. When the cab air needs to be cooled, the gas in the sensing tube expands the diaphragm, completing the circuit in the switch and engaging the compressor clutch. The compressor continues to operate until the preselected cab temperature is reached.

Fig. 27 — Thermostatic Temperature Control Switch

Continued on next page

OUO1082,00035F9 -19-16OCT12-11/12

Another special type of switch is the LIMIT-POSITION SWITCH (Fig. 28), sometimes referred to as a microswitch. It is a miniature unit activated by a light pressure with a small amount of travel. It usually has three terminals: a "C" common terminal to which one wire is connected; an "NO" or normally open terminal to which the other wire is connected if the circuit is open except when the bale is depressed; and an "NC" or normally closed terminal for another wire if the circuit is closed except when the bale is depressed.

The REED SWITCH is a thin pair of separated metal contacts in an airtight glass envelope positioned near a rotating or moveable magnet. When the magnet nears the contacts, the magnetic field pulls the two contacts together, completing an electrical circuit. When the magnet moves away, the contacts separate, breaking the electrical current flow.

MERCURY SWITCHES. Mercury is a liquid and was chosen for use in this type of switch because of its extreme temperature operating range, with a freezing point of -38°F (39°C) and boiling point of 674°F (357°C). A small amount of mercury is poured into a sealed glass tube with a metal electrode at each end of the tube. When this switch is level, the mercury completes the electrical circuit between the two metal electrodes. Tilting the glass tube moves the liquid mercury away from one of the electrodes, interrupting the electrical circuit. These switches are silent in operation and have long lives, including when used with high current loads.

SERVICING OF SWITCHES

If a switch is defective, always replace it with a new switch. Do not void the safety of a defective switch by disassembling and trying to repair it.

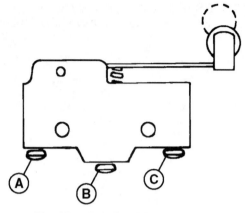

Fig. 28 — Bale Size Limit-Position Switch

A—COMMON
B—NO

C—NC

SUMMARY

• Switches control circuits by opening and closing current pathways to turn circuits on and off.
• Most switches are manually and mechanically operated. Some switches are activated by pressure, temperature, a magnetic field, or a rotary motion.

OUO1082,00035F9 -19-16OCT12-12/12

RESISTORS

A resistor reduces voltage output by resisting current flow or amperage. Resistors create heat when current begins to flow through a circuit. They then transfer this heat to the surrounding area. Therefore, ambient temperature and humidity must be considered before putting a resistor in a circuit. Ambient temperature is that atmosphere immediately surrounding a given component. There are two types of resistors: fixed and variable.

FIXED RESISTORS

A fixed resistor is a resistor with a specified resistance that under normal circumstances never varies. It can be made of wirewound resistance wire, metal film, carbon film, or molded carbon powder. Carbon resistors are labeled with a wattage value which indicates how much power they can dissipate.

Wirewound resistors (Fig. 29) consist of a tubular form wrapped with coils of resistance wire. They can withstand lots of heat.

Metal film resistors use a thin film of metal or metal particle mixture to achieve various resistances. These resistors are laser trimmed for accuracy.

Carbon film resistors use carbon film on a small ceramic cylinder. A spiral groove cut into the film controls the length of the carbon and thus the resistance.

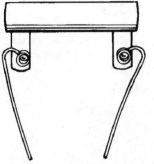

Fig. 29 — A Wirewound Resistor

Molded powder carbon resistors are known as carbon composition resistors. Such a resistor consists of carbon powder mixed with a glue-like binder and molded with a protective housing. The ratio of carbon powder and binder determines its resistance.

Resistors are marked with their value in ohms. For example: 5 ohms, 25 kilohms (25,000 ohms), or 3 megaohms (3 million ohms). Some resistors are so small that they can't be marked with any numerical value. These small resistors are color coded with bands for their value.

Continued on next page

OUO1082,00035FA -19-16OCT12-1/8

RESISTOR COLOR CODES

A—First Digit of Resistance
   Value
B—Second Digit of Resistance
   Value
C—Number of Zeros Following
   the First Two Digits

D—Tolerance Value
E—Failure Rate

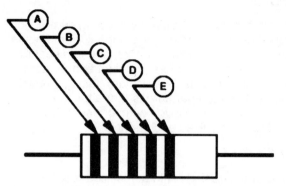

Fig. 30 — Resistor Color Codes

| | | Table 3–Resistor Color Codes | | |
| | | Bands | | |
Color	First (Digit)	Second (Digit)	Third (Multiplier)	Fourth (Tolerance)	Fifth (Failure Rate)
BLACK	0	0	10		
BROWN	1	1	10		1.0%
RED	2	2	100		0.1%
ORANGE	3	3	1000		0.01%
YELLOW	4	4	10,000		0.001%
GREEN	5	5	100,000		
BLUE	6	6	1,000,000		
VIOLET	7	7	10,000,000		
GREY	8	8	100,000,000		
WHITE	9	9	NONE		
GOLD				±5%	
SILVER				±10%	
NONE				±20%	

Continued on next page   OUO1082,00035FA -19-16OCT12-2/8

Small carbon composition resistors are marked with color bands that indicate their resistance value (Table 1). These bands are located on one end of the resistor. Always read the resistor values with the bands placed to your left.

A resistor can have up to five color bands around it. The first band shows the first digit of the resistor's value from zero to nine. The second band indicates the second digit of the resistor's value from zero to nine. The third band is a multiplier value that is multiplied by the first and second band digits together. The first three bands will give the resistors value in ohms.

What would be the resistance value of a resistor with bands of red, yellow, and red around it? Looking at the chart Table 1, the resistance digit for the color red is 2 and the resistance value for yellow is 4. The multiplier for red is 100. Therefore, the resistance is 24 x 100 or 2400 ohms resistance.

The fourth band, which is not always included on the resistor, indicates tolerance or how close the resistor actually comes to its rated value. This band will be either gold or silver in color. The gold band indicates a plus or minus 5% value of its resistance. The silver band indicates a plus or minus 10% value of its resistance. If there is no fourth color band on the resistor it indicates a plus or minus 20% value of its resistance.

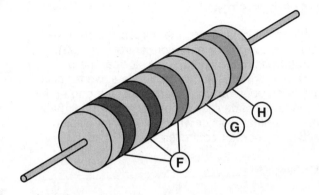

Fig. 31 — Example Resistor 22.3 Ohm ± 1%

F—22000 or 22.3 Ohms   **H—1% Failure Rate**
G—± 5% Tolerance

In the previous example, no fourth band existed. So the resistance tolerance value would be 2400 plus or minus 20%, or 1920 to 2880 ohms.

The fifth band, if present, indicates the tested percentage of failure per one thousand hours of use. A brown band would be 1.0%, a red band would be 0.1%, an orange band would be 0.01%, and a yellow band would be 0.001%.

OUO1082,00035FA -19-16OCT12-3/8

The symbol for fixed resistors is shown in Fig. 32.

DXP02865 —UN—27FEB12

Fig. 32 — Symbol for a Fixed Resistor

Continued on next page   OUO1082,00035FA -19-16OCT12-4/8

VARIABLE RESISTORS

A variable resistor varies its internal resistance based
on temperature, light, or operator control (Fig. 33).
An operator-controlled variable resistor can be a
potentiometer or rheostat. A rheostat is a two-terminal
resistor, or an operator-controlled slider and one end
of a three-terminal device. A potentiometer (Fig. 34)
is a three-terminal resistor where the center, sliding
connection is operator controlled.

A—Potentiometers

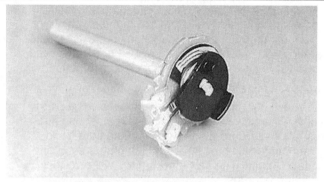

Fig. 33 — An Operator-Controlled Variable Resistor

Fig. 34 — Manually Operated Potentiometers for Hitch Control

OUO1082,00035FA -19-16OCT12-5/8

Operator-controlled variable resistor symbols are shown
in Fig. 35.

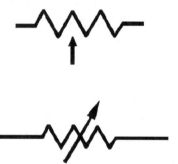

Fig. 35 — Operator-Controlled Variable Resistor Symbols

OUO1082,00035FA -19-16OCT12-6/8

A photoresistor (Fig. 36) varies its resistance based on
the amount of light hitting the resistor. Its consists of a
high resistance semiconductor material that decreases in
resistance with increasing light intensity.

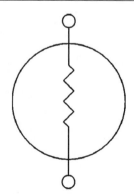

Fig. 36 — A Symbol for a Photoresistor

Continued on next page OUO1082,00035FA -19-16OCT12-7/8

A thermistor (Fig. 37) varies its resistance based on the temperature in the immediate area of the thermistor. Most thermistors sense ambient temperature. The schematic symbol for a thermistor is shown in Fig. 38.

Fig. 37 — A Thermistor

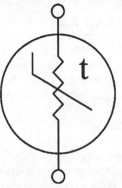

Fig. 38 — A Symbol for a Thermistor

OUO1082,00035FA -19-16OCT12-8/8

CAPACITORS

Capacitors come in many sizes and shapes (Fig. 39), but they all do the same thing. They store electrons.

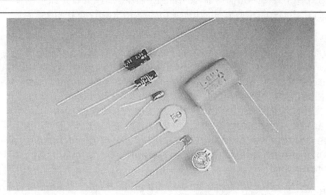

Fig. 39 — Capacitors

Continued on next page   OUO1082,00035FB -19-16OCT12-1/6

HOW CAPACITORS ARE MADE

The construction of a capacitor has two metal plates separated with a thin insulating material called a dielectric. The dielectric can be paper, plastic, mica, or air. The metal plates can be aluminum foil or a thin film of metal (Fig. 40). After pressing the plates and dielectric together, the capacitor is rolled into a cylinder or oval, or it is left flat.

When we connect the two metal plates to a source of DC voltage, the capacitor will store energy. The symbol for capacitance is C, and the unit of measure is the farad (F), microfarad (μF) (0.000001 F), or picofarad (pF) (0.000000000001 F). The greater the area of the plates and the shorter the distance between them, the greater will be the capacitance.

Fig. 40— Capacitor Construction

A—Insulation   **B—Metal Plates**

OUO1082,00035FB -19-16OCT12-2/6

HOW CAPACITORS WORK

Like a battery, a capacitor has two terminals. Fig. 41 explains the action of a capacitor in a circuit. With the plates being insulated from each other, it would seem no current would flow in this circuit. This is true, except at the instant of time when the switch is closed. At that instant, the voltage across the plates will suddenly change from zero to 12 volts.

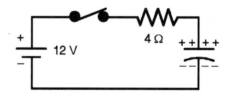

Fig. 41— Capacitor in a Circuit with Switch Closed

This is how it works:

When the switch is closed, electrons will leave the battery and gather on the capacitor negative plate as shown in Fig. 41. This plate will then have an excess of electrons. At the same time, electrons will leave the other plate and cause this plate to become positively charged. It is important to note that the electrons flow through the circuit but not through the insulating material separating the two plates.

As the two plates become negatively and positively charged, a voltage appears across the plates. Remember, a voltage between two points is the direct result of a difference in charge between the two points. As more and more electrons accumulate on the negative plate and leave the positive plate, the voltage across the plates approaches the battery voltage. When the capacitor voltage equals the battery voltage, the flow of electrons will stop. The equation giving the amount of charge on a capacitor is:

Charge = Capacitance x Voltage

Thus the higher the capacitance and applied voltage, the greater will be the charge on the capacitor.

At the very instant the switch is closed, the initial current is determined by the resistor R in the circuit:

$I = E/R = 12/4 = 3$ amperes

Initially the capacitor acts like a short circuit, since only the resistor (R) limits the initial current flow. As the capacitor voltage increases, the current decreases. Finally, the current flow stops completely when the capacitor voltage is equal to the battery voltage.

The time needed for the current to reach a zero value may be only a fraction of a second. Although this time interval may seem very short, it can be of major importance in electrical systems where voltages are changing at extremely rapid rates.

Continued on next page   OUO1082,00035FB -19-16OCT12-3/6

The flow of current into and the voltage across the capacitor plates are shown in Fig. 42.

A—Volts   C—Time in Seconds
B—Amps

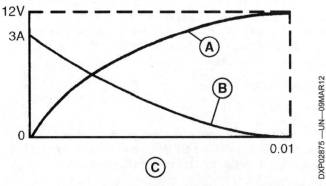

Fig. 42 — Curves Showing Current and Voltage for Capacitor Plates

OUO1082,00035FB -19-16OCT12-4/6

When the switch opens suddenly, the charge of the capacitor will remain (Fig. 43). The accumulated charge represents stored energy, and a capacitor has the ability to store a charge. The amount of energy stored may be calculated by the formula:

Energy = (Capacitance x Voltage x Voltage)/2

Or:

$W = 1/2(CV^2)$

Where:

W = Watts

C = Capacitance

V = Applied Voltage

Thus, the higher the capacitance and voltage, the higher the energy stored in the capacitor. In time, the charge

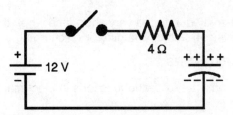

Fig. 43 — Capacitor in a Circuit with Switch Open

will leak off the plates through the insulating material and surrounding air, reducing the charge to zero.

Continued on next page
OUO1082,00035FB -19-16OCT12-5/6

By adding another switch to the circuit, the energy stored in the capacitor is used to send a current through the resistor (Fig. 44). When the switch is closed, a momentary surge of current will flow through the resistor until the charge on the two plates is equal.

The initial current will be:

$I = E/R = 12/4 = 3A$

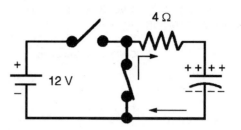

Fig. 44 — Capacitor in Circuit with Two Switches

As the electron flow continues, the voltage across the plates decreases until the current value is zero. Again, the time interval may be only a fraction of a second.

The operation of capacitors is summarized:

- A capacitor, as it builds up a charge, develops a voltage across its plates.
- The capacitor has the ability to store a charge, or to store energy.
- Current flows only during the very short time when the capacitor plates are either charging or discharging.

USES OF CAPACITORS

Capacitors perform the following functions in electrical circuits:

- Isolate (block) DC current between circuit stages.
- Store harmful energy for a moment (as to prevent arcing of distributor points).
- Smooth out changing voltages (as in regulators).

RESISTOR AND CAPACITOR (RC) CIRCUITS

Resistor and capacitor circuits are of the following major types and will be covered in detail in Chapter 14:

- Integrator circuit—Converts a square wave to a triangle wave.
- Differentiator circuit—Converts a square wave input to a spike output.
- Filter circuits—Passes signals only below a certain frequency.

SUMMARY

- A capacitor (or condenser) is made of two metal plates separated by thin insulation.
- A capacitor can store energy.
- A capacitor can build up a counter voltage across its two plates.
- Current flows between the plates only at the moment when the plates are either charging or discharging.
- A resistor and capacitor circuit that controls frequency is called a filter circuit.
- A resistor and capacitor circuit that transforms square wave input to a spike output is called a differentiator circuit.

OUO1082,00035FB -19-16OCT12-6/6

SEMICONDUCTORS

In Chapter 2 we learned that conductors have less than four electrons in the outer rings of their atoms, while insulators have more than four electrons in their outer rings.

Semiconductors are elements that have just four electrons in the outer rings of their atoms. They are neither good conductors nor good insulators. The most common semiconductor elements are silicon and germanium. Silicon is the most common element used for semiconductors. Since silicon makes up 27.7% of the earth's crust, availability is high and cost is low.

Semiconductors are used to make diodes and transistors and integrated circuits.

Let's first see how the basic silicon element is made into semiconductors, then we'll talk about diodes and transistors. We will cover integrated circuits in Chapter 15.

HOW SEMICONDUCTORS ARE MADE

Silicon crystal for semiconductors is made by covalent bonding (Fig. 45). This means that the electrons in the outer ring of one silicon atom join the electrons of other

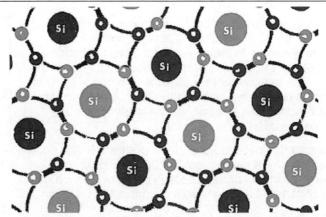

Fig. 45 — Silicon Formed as Insulator by Covalent Bonding

silicon atoms so that the atoms share electrons in their outer rings. Now each atom really has eight electrons in its outer ring as shown. This creates a very good insulator since there are now more than four electrons in the outer ring.

The silicon crystal is then doped (selectively contaminated to control its conductivity) by adding other materials.

OUO1082,00035FC -19-16OCT12-1/6

Two elements commonly used to dope the silicon are phosphorus and antimony. Both of these elements have five electrons in their outer ring. Covalent bonding occurs, but there is one electron left over (Fig. 46). This electron is called a free electron, which can be made to move through the material very easily. Any material having an extra electron is called a negative or "N" type material.

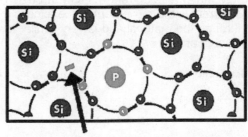

Fig. 46 — Use of Phosphorus to "Dope" Silicon for "N" Type Material

Continued on next page   OUO1082,00035FC -19-16OCT12-2/6

Two other elements commonly used to dope the silicon crystals are boron and indium. These elements have only three electrons in their outer ring. Covalent bonding occurs but there is a shortage of one electron for complete bonding. The resulting void is called a hole (Fig. 47). This hole can be considered as a positive charge of electricity. Materials lacking this electron and having this hole are called positive or "P" type material.

To understand semiconductors, think of this hole as a positive (+) current carrier, just like the electron in a negative (−) current carrier. The hole can move from atom to atom, just as an electron can move from atom to atom.

SUMMARY

- Semiconductors are made by covalent bonding.
  - This is joining atoms, which then share electrons.
  - The result is a good insulator.

- Doping silicon crystals results in a free electron ("N" type material) or a voided electron, or hole ("P" type material).

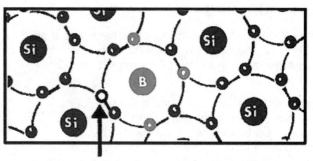

Fig. 47 — Use of Boron to "Dope" Silicon for "P" Type Material

- Either "N" or "P" material is a current carrier, moving electrons from atom to atom.
- Semiconductors have special uses in diodes and transistors.

OUO1082,00035FC -19-16OCT12-3/6

HOW SEMICONDUCTORS OPERATE

The current flow (electron movement) in "N" type material is shown in Fig. 48. By connecting a voltage source such as a battery to the material, a current will flow through the circuit. This current is the movement of the excess of free electrons through the material and is very similar to what occurs in a copper wire.

A—Electron Movement

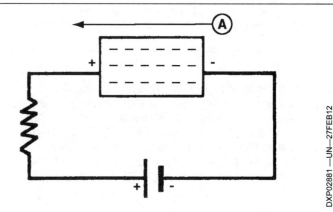

Fig. 48 — Electron Movement in Circuit with "N" Type Material

OUO1082,00035FC -19-16OCT12-4/6

The current flow in "P" type material is shown in Fig. 49. The current is a movement of the positively charged holes. This hole movement works as shown in Fig. 50.

A—Electrons   C—P Material
B—Holes

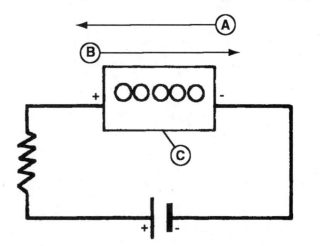

Fig. 49 — Movement of Holes in Circuit with "P" Type Material

Continued on next page   OUO1082,00035FC -19-16OCT12-5/6

Notice how the positive (+) battery terminal in No. 1 attracts the electrons (–) in the material (unlike charges attracting). Similarly, the negative (–) battery terminal will repel the electrons. So an electron from one of the covalent bonds will move to the left toward the positive (+) terminal, and will fill one of the holes near the terminal. This movement of an electron leaves behind a hole. The positively charged hole, then, has moved to the right, toward the negative (–) battery terminal. This process continues and the hole keeps moving to the right until it nears the negative (–) connection at the semiconductor. At this time, the hole is filled by an electron, which leaves the (–) wire connected to the semiconductor, and the positive (+) wire removes an electron from the semiconductor at the other end (see No. 5 in Fig. 50). The process is then ready to repeat itself.

The continuous movement of holes from the positive (+) terminal to the negative (–) terminal can be looked upon as current flow in "P" type material, and occurs when the battery voltage causes the electrons to shift around in the covalent bonds.

The hole movement occurs only within the semiconductor, while electrons flow through the entire circuit.

The hole movement theory will help us to understand how diodes and transistors operate, which follows.

SUMMARY

- Outside voltage causes a current flow in the "N" or "P" material of semiconductors.
- In "N" material, current flow is the movement of "free" negative (–) electrons.
- In "P" material, current flow is the movement of positive (+) charged holes.

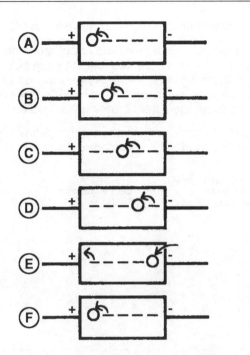

Fig. 50— Hole Movement in "P" Type Material

A—1   D—4
B—2   E—5
C—3   F—6

Next we will show how semiconductors are used in diodes and transistors.

OUO1082,00035FC -19-16OCT12-6/6

DIODES

A diode is an electrical device that will allow current to pass through itself in one direction only.

HOW DIODES ARE MADE

A diode is formed when two semiconductor materials are joined (Fig. 51), one of "N" type material, the other of "P" type. In diodes, the "N" material is usually phosphorus-doped silicon, while the "P" material is usually boron-doped silicon.

A—Current Flow   B—Diode Symbol

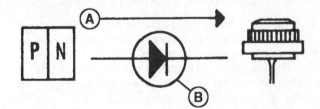

ELEMENT	ATOMIC NUMBER	NUMBER OF PROTONS	NUMBER OF ELECTRONS	VALENCE RING ELECTRONS
Boron (B)	5	5	5	3
Silicon (Si)	14	14	14	4
Phosphorus (P)	15	15	15	5

Fig. 51— Diode

Continued on next page   MM61211,00012C0 -19-16OCT12-1/6

The basic construction of a diode is shown in Fig. 52.

"N" and "P" materials attract each other but are kept stabilized by positive and negative ions on each side. (An ion is an atom having a shortage or an excess of electrons.) The ions "pull back" on the free electrons and the holes to prevent them from crossing the junction.

The net result is a stabilized condition with a deficiency of electrons and holes at the junction area.

A—Unlike Charges Attract
B—Free Electrons
C—Positive Ions
D—Junction
E—Negative Ions
F—Holes

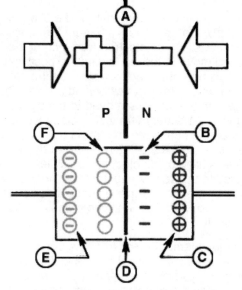

Fig. 52 — Construction of a Diode

MM61211,00012C0 -19-16OCT12-2/6

HOW DIODES OPERATE

Now let's activate the diode by connecting a battery to it (Fig. 53). The negative battery voltage will repel the electrons in the "N" material, while the positive battery voltage will repel the holes in the "P" material. With sufficient voltage, electrons will move from the negative terminal of the battery across the junction to the positive battery terminal and so create a flow of current. Also, the positive holes will move through the "P" material and through the junction as previously described.

The battery maintains the current flow, but for current to flow through the semiconductor, there must be holes present at the junction into which electrons can move.

In Fig. 51 is shown a forward bias connection of the semiconductor. The battery negative (–) to diode negative "N" and battery positive (+) to diode positive "P" connection creates the repelling action. This causes the electrons and holes to congregate at the junction in the large numbers necessary for current to flow through a diode.

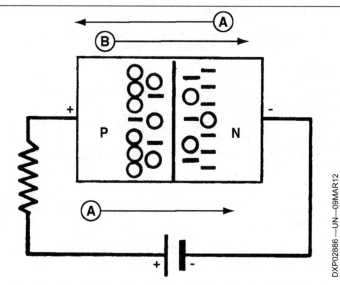

Fig. 53 — Diode: Allowing Current Flow (Forward Bias)

A—Electrons

B—Holes

Continued on next page

MM61211,00012C0 -19-16OCT12-3/6

Now let's see what happens when we reverse the battery connections (Fig. 54). The positive (+) side of the battery attracts electrons away from the junction, while the negative (–) side of the battery attracts the holes away from the junction. The result is that no current will flow.

This type of battery connection is called reverse bias, which causes the diode to block current flow.

SUMMARY

- The diode will allow current to flow if the voltage across the diode causes electrons and holes to congregate at the junction area (Forward Bias).
- The diode will not allow current to flow if the voltage across the diode causes the junction area to be void of electrons and holes (Reverse Bias).

Let's repeat a statement already made in this chapter:

- For electrons to move into the "P" material, there must be holes present in the "P" material near the junction into which the electrons can move.

The reasons for the hole theory now become more apparent, as this theory provides a convenient means of explaining how a diode blocks or prevents current flow.

A complete description of diodes as used in alternators is given in Chapter 6.

DIODE LEAKAGE CURRENT

When a reverse bias voltage is connected to a diode, it may be true that a small current will flow through the diode in the reverse direction, but the reverse current is very, very small.

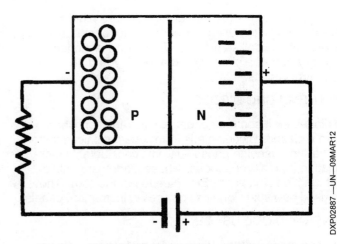

Fig. 54 — Diode Blocking Current Flow (Reverse Bias)

If the voltage across the diode is increased, a value eventually will be reached called the maximum reverse voltage or peak reverse voltage of the diode. At this voltage, the covalent bond structure will break down and a sharp rise in reverse current will occur. If the reverse current is sufficient in magnitude and duration, the diode will be damaged due to excessive heat.

Diodes are selected, of course, with an adequate maximum reverse voltage or peak reverse voltage rating so that damaging reverse currents will not normally occur during operation.

MM61211,00012C0 -19-16OCT12-4/6

DIODE TYPES AND USES

ZENER DIODE

The Zener diode is a specially designed type of diode that will conduct current in the reverse direction at a particular voltage. The primary feature of this type of diode is that it is very heavily doped during manufacture—the large number of extra current carriers (electrons and holes) allows the Zener diode to conduct current in the reverse direction without damage if proper circuit design is used. The Zener diode symbol is shown in Fig. 55.

What makes the Zener diode unique is that it will not conduct current in the reverse direction below a certain predetermined voltage (called reverse bias voltage). As an example, a certain Zener diode may not conduct current if the reverse bias voltage is below 6 volts, but when the reverse bias voltage becomes 6 volts or more, the diode suddenly conducts reverse current. This type of diode is used in control and protection circuits.

POWER RECTIFIER DIODES

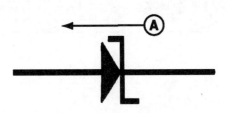

Fig. 55 — Zener Diode Symbol

A—Reverse Current

Power rectifier diodes can handle high current. They are insulated in metal packages that act as heat sinks to dissipate excess heat. They are used mainly in power supplies such as alternators.

SMALL SIGNAL DIODES

Continued on next page MM61211,00012C0 -19-16OCT12-5/6

Small signal diodes (bottom of Fig. 56) are used to transform low alternating current to direct current and absorb voltage spikes within a circuit. These diodes are generally part of a circuit board assembly and are used for control circuits.

LIGHT-EMITTING DIODES

All diodes emit some electromagnetic radiation when forward biased. Diodes made from certain semiconductors like gallium arsenide phosphide emit considerably more radiation than silicon diodes. These diodes are called light-emitting diodes or LEDs (see top of Fig. 56). They are used as visual signalling devices in instrument panels.

GENERAL DIODE USAGE

One common use for a diode is for protection in electric clutch applications. When power is cut off to the clutch, a reverse voltage spike is created by the collapse of the coil

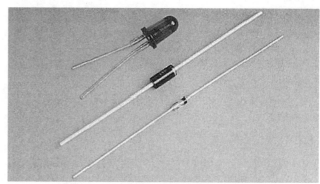

Fig. 56 — Light-Emitting and Small Signal Diodes

magnetic field. This reverse voltage spike travels back in the opposite direction, toward the system or switch. A diode is used to short this spike to ground, thus protecting the system and switch.

MM61211,00012C0 -19-16OCT12-6/6

TRANSISTORS

A transistor is a solid-state electronic device that is used in circuits to control the flow of current. It acts like a relay where a small current controls a larger current load and operates by either allowing current to flow or not allowing it to flow.

HOW TRANSISTORS ARE MADE

A transistor is usually formed by adding a second section of "P" type material to the PN junction used for diodes. This results in the PNP transistor (Fig. 57). This type of transistor is known as bipolar.

The "P" material on the left is called the emitter, the "N" material in the center is the base, and the "P" material on the right is called the collector.

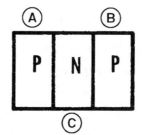 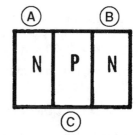

Fig. 57 — Basic Parts of Transistors

A—Emitter
B—Collector

C—Base

Continued on next page

OUO1082,00035FE -19-16OCT12-1/8

The base of a transistor is very thin (Fig. 58). A metallic ring is attached around the base and this is connected to the circuit. By this design, the distance between the emitter and the collector is shorter than the distance between the emitter and the base ring. This gives the transistor its unusual operation as we'll see now.

A—Emitter   C—Collector
B—Ring   D—Base

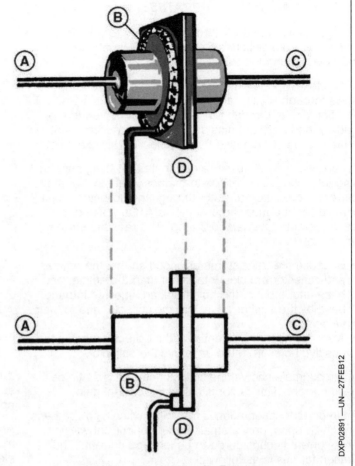

Fig. 58 — Construction of a Transistor

Continued on next page
OUO1082,00035FE -19-16OCT12-2/8

HOW A TRANSISTOR OPERATES

In Fig. 59, we have connected a battery to a PNP transistor. With switches S_1 open and S_2 open, no current will flow through the transistor.

If we close S_1, there will be a small base current that flows through R_1, R_2, and S_1. The circuit is a simple PN junction diode, through emitter-base, connected to the battery in the forward bias direction. We'll assume that the emitter-base current is 200 milli-amps for this example.

When switch S_2 is closed, a rather startling thing happens. The total current increases to 5 amps. But most of the current leaves the transistor through the collector circuit. The current through the collector is 4.8 amps and the base current remains at 0.2 amp. The reasons for this are as follows:

- Because the transistor is arranged so that the emitter and collector are closer together than the emitter and base ring, most of the holes that are injected into the base by the emitter travel into the collector due to their velocity.
- Also, the negative potential at the collector attracts the positive holes from the base into the collector.

In the example shown, the collector current is 24 times the base current. This factor is called the current gain.

An important observation is that with switch S_2 closed and switch S_1 open, only a small amount of current will flow. This current is considered to be leakage current. The reason for this is as follows:

- With the base circuit open, there are no holes being injected into the base from the emitter, and so there are no holes in the base that can be attracted by the negative battery potential into the collector.

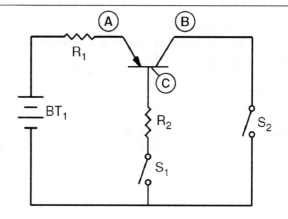

Fig. 59 — Transistor in Circuit with Switch S_2 Open

A—Emitter   C—Base
B—Collector

- Furthermore, the negative battery potential at the collector attracts the holes in the collector away from the base-collector junction area and the resistance across the base-collector junction becomes very high.

Although the emitter and collector are joined, opening switch S_1 effectively "shuts off" the transistor so that no appreciable current flows.

An NPN transistor operates in the same way as a PNP transistor, with current flow consisting of a movement of electrons (instead of holes) from the emitter to the base and collector.

The significant thing about a transistor is that by controlling a small base current, a much larger collector current can also be controlled.

OUO1082,00035FE -19-16OCT12-3/8

BIPOLAR TRANSISTORS

There are many types of bipolar transistors (Fig. 60). Small signal transistors are used to amplify low-level signals, or one can be made to act as an on-off switch. Some small transistors can be made to both amplify and switch on and off within the same unit.

The bipolar power transistor is used in high-power applications. Its large size and exposed metal casing act as a heat sink to keep it cool.

A—Small Signal Transistor   B—Power Transistor

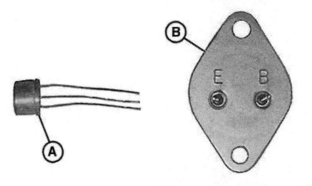

Fig. 60— Signal and Power Bipolar Transistors

Continued on next page   OUO1082,00035FE -19-16OCT12-4/8

SYMBOLS FOR BIPOLAR TRANSISTORS

The symbols for bipolar resistors are shown in Fig. 61. The line with the arrow is the emitter, the heavy line is the base, and the line without an arrow is the collector. Note that the arrow points in the direction of conventional current flow, that is, from positive to negative in the external circuit.

As we said, it is convenient to look upon current flow in the PNP transistor as a movement of holes, and in the NPN transistor as a movement of electrons. Although the electrons move against the arrow in the NPN transistor, this is not contradictory as it is easier to visualize the current carriers (electrons) as being emitted by the emitter into the base and collector.

FIELD EFFECT TRANSISTOR

Field effect transistors (FETs) use a small amount of voltage to vary a high flow of current. Connections are the

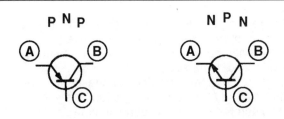

Fig. 61— Symbols for Bipolar Transistors

A—Emitter
B—Collector

C—Base

source (input), drain (output), and gate (control). There are two major types of FETs in use today: the junction and the metal oxide semiconductor.

JUNCTION FIELD-EFFECT TRANSISTOR

OUO1082,00035FE -19-16OCT12-5/8

There are two types of junction field-effect transistors (JFETs). They are N-channel and P-channel (Fig. 62). The channel acts like a silicon resistor that conducts current when in operation from the source to the drain. At zero volts to the gate, maximum current is obtained from the source to the drain. As voltage is applied to the gate, two high-resistance regions or fields are created around the channel, slowing the current flow. As more voltage is applied to the gate, the fields will completely block the current flow. This gate-channel resistance is very high because in operation the gate-channel junction is a reverse biased diode. Voltage to the gate generally varies from zero to one volt for an operational range.

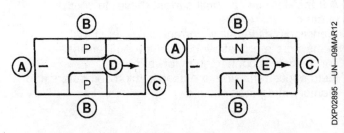

Fig. 62 — N-Channel and P-Channel Type Junction FETs

A—Source
B—Gate
C—Drain

D—N Channel
E—P Channel

OUO1082,00035FE -19-16OCT12-6/8

JFETs are used at the input stage of amplifiers to provide a high-resistance input. They can produce high-frequency signals and can also be used as switches. The symbols for JFETs are shown in Fig. 63.

METAL OXIDE SEMICONDUCTOR FIELD-EFFECT TRANSISTORS

Metal oxide semiconductor field-effect transistors (MOSFETs) have become an important transistor in use today. Most microcomputers and memory-integrated circuit devices are made up of thousands of MOSFETs on a very small piece of silicon. This is because their design is easily produced in integrated form. Integrated circuits are discussed in Chapter 15.

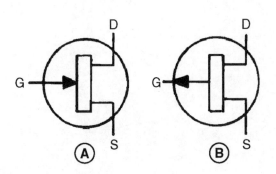

Fig. 63 — Junction FET Symbols

A—N Channel

B—P Channel

Continued on next page
OUO1082,00035FE -19-16OCT12-7/8

All MOSFETs are N-type or P-type FETs (Fig. 64). Unlike the JFET, the gate of the MOSFET does not have any electrical contact with the source and drain. An insulating silicon oxide glass-like layer separates the metal contact of the gate from the channel. Applying voltage to the gate causes electrons to be attracted to the region below the gate, creating a thin N- or P-type channel in between the source and drain, allowing current to flow through the channel. The amount of gate voltage determines the resistance of the channel.

MOSFETs have almost infinite gate-channel resistances. They use virtually no current and can switch at very high speeds. They are, however, very sensitive to static electricity. High voltage can easily pierce the insulation layer. MOSFETs are sometimes referred to as insulated gate field-effect transistors or IGFETs. The symbols for MOSFETs are shown in Fig. 62.

SUMMARY

- Transistors control the current in a circuit.
- A transistor uses a small current (base) to control a larger current (emitter).
- Transistors either allow current to flow or stop it.
- Transistors are destroyed when the emitter-base current flow is connected in forward bias.
- Field-effect transistors are used in microcomputers and memory-integrated circuits.

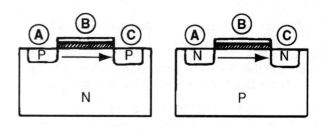

Fig. 64 — N- and P-Type MOSFETs

A—Source　　　　　　　　　C—Drain
B—Gate

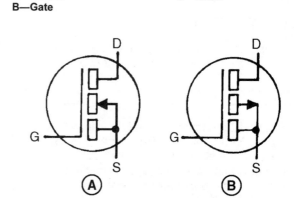

Fig. 65 — MOSFET Symbols

A—N MOSFET　　　　　　　　B—P MOSFET

OUO1082,00035FE -19-16OCT12-8/8

TRANSFORMERS

A transformers convert incoming voltage and current to a higher or lower voltage and current output. They are also used in a 1:1 ratio as an isolation device. Transformers have two or more windings around a metal core and use induction in the transformation process.

To transform voltage and current from one winding to another, the current must be fluctuating or alternating current. A steady or direct current will not transform voltage and current from one winding to another.

Transformers do not create an output power change from nothing. They are dependent upon the voltage and current input and the number of windings of each coil. The output of a transformer cannot exceed the power of its input.

If the input windings are less then the output windings, or stepped-up, the output voltage increases from the input voltage. However, the output current decreases from the input current.

If the input windings are more than the output windings or stepped-down, the output voltage decreases. However, the output current increases.

HOW A TRANSFORMER WORKS

A transformer steps-up or steps-down voltage and current by the amount of windings in each coil. The incoming voltage and current is connected to the winding known as the primary winding. The output winding is called the secondary winding.

STEP-UP VOLTAGE TRANSFORMER

A step-up voltage transformer (Fig. 66) increases the input voltage. The windings of the output or secondary windings are greater than the input or primary windings.

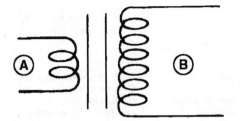

Fig. 66 — Step-Up Voltage Transformer Symbol

A—Input   B—Output

Thus, the voltage output is increased by the turn ratio of the primary coil to the secondary coil and the current is decreased. For example, if the turn ratio of the coil is 1:5, then for every turn of the primary coil there are five turns at the secondary coil. If the incoming voltage is 12 volts, the output voltage would be 60 volts (12 x 5).

Continued on next page   OUO1082,00035FF -19-16OCT12-1/4

In mobile machinery an example of a step-up transformer is an ignition coil (Fig. 67). See Chapter 8 on "Ignition Circuits" for more information.

A—Rubber Boot
B—Coil Tower
C—High Tension Terminal
D—Primary Terminal
E—Secondary Winding
F—Primary Winding
G—Iron Core
H—Lamination
I— Porcelain Insulator

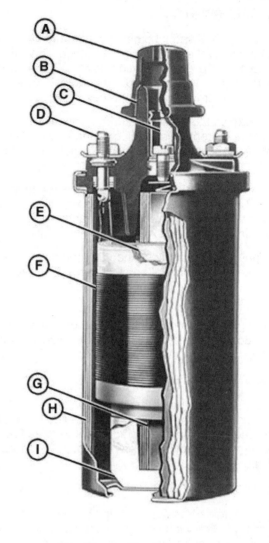

Fig. 67 — Ignition Coil

OUO1082,00035FF -19-16OCT12-2/4

Another type of step-up voltage transformer is used in crop dryers (Fig. 68), where it is used to increase the voltage to jump a spark across electrodes to ignite the dryer's gas. This type of transformer is also known as an ignition transformer.

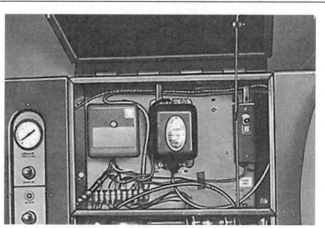

Fig. 68 — Transformer for Ignition on a Crop Dryer

Continued on next page

OUO1082,00035FF -19-16OCT12-3/4

STEP-DOWN VOLTAGE TRANSFORMER

A step-down voltage transformer decreases the input voltage (Fig. 69). The secondary windings (output) are less than the primary windings (input). Thus, in a 5:1 turn ratio the voltage will drop 60 volts at the primary windings to 12 volts at the secondary windings. Most step-down transformers are used by utility companies to reduce power line voltage and increase current to a usable level to our homes.

SUMMARY

- Transformers have the ability to transform incoming AC voltage and current to a higher or lower output AC voltage and current.
- Transformers will not work with DC voltage.
- The step-up voltage transformer has more secondary windings than primary windings.

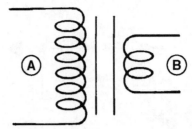

Fig. 69 — Step-Down Voltage Transformer Symbol

A—Input   B—Output

- The step-down voltage transformer has more primary windings than secondary windings.

OUO1082,00035FF -19-16OCT12-4/4

INVERTER/CONVERTER

An Inverter/Converter is one unit that contains both the inverter and the converter.

The inverter is an electrical device that will convert DC (Direct Current) to AC (Alternating Current) to provides electricity to the motor/generator for vehicle propulsion, or operate devices that require an AC (Alternating Current). To convert AC (Alternating Current) back to DC (Direct Current) that is needed to supply current back to the battery pack for recharging during regenerative braking or in the battery recharge mode a rectifier is used (Fig. 70).

Hybrids systems often have several voltage level requirements that differ from the supply voltage. Using a DC to DC converter will increase (step-up or boost converter) or decrease (step-down or buck converter) the supply voltage supplying the correct voltage to these devices.

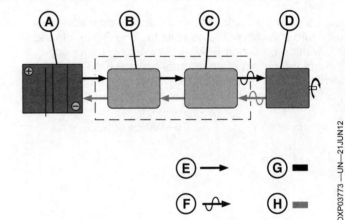

Fig. 70— Basic Working Operation of an Inverter

A—Battery Pack   E—Direct Current
B—DC to DC Converter   F—Alternating Current
C—Inverter/Rectifier   G—Battery Recharging Mode
D—Electric Motor   H—Regenerative Braking Mode

Continued on next page   MM61211,00012C5 -19-16OCT12-1/3

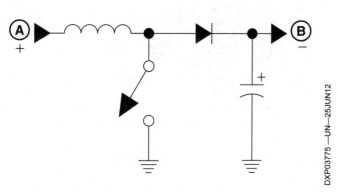

Fig. 71 — Basic Step-Up or Boost Converter

A—Voltage IN (V$_{IN}$)   **B—Voltage IN (V$_{OUT}$)**

The step-up or boost converter uses a transistor switch, typically a MOSFET, to pulse width modulate the voltage into an inductor. Rectangular pulses of voltage into an inductor result in a triangular current waveform. (Fig. 71).

MM61211,00012C5 -19-16OCT12-2/3

The step-down or buck converter will convert a voltage source into a lower regulated voltage. The DC input uses pulse-width modulation (PWM) of switching frequency to control the output of an internal power MOSFET. An external diode, together with external inductor and output capacitor, produces the regulated dc output. (Fig. 72).

A—Voltage IN (V$_{IN}$)   **B—Voltage IN (V$_{OUT}$)**

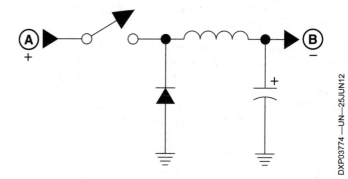

Fig. 72 — Basic Step-Down or Buck Converter

MM61211,00012C5 -19-16OCT12-3/3

TEST YOURSELF

QUESTIONS

1. What metal is less resistive than copper?

2. What element is used for most wiring?

3. What is the difference between a circuit breaker and a fuse? Which is used where heavy loads are instantly placed on the circuits? Which is normally replaced after it activates?

4. Switches are used for _____ _____ and _____.

5. A number 12 gauge wire's diameter is smaller than a number 10 gauge wire's diameter. True or false?

6. Resistors reduce voltage by resisting _____.

7. The bands on some resistors indicate their _____ value as measured in _____.

8. What value would a Brown, Black, Orange, and Gold resistor be? ____.

9. Capacitors are electronic components that _____ electrons.

10. Name two electronic components which use semiconductors.

11. Diodes allow current to pass in _____only.

12. Factors that affect a wire's resistance:

a. Length of the wire.

b. Diameter of the wire.

c. Temperature of the wire.

d. All of the above.

e. None of the above.

13. If a quick-blow fuse is blown and the glass is clear, the fuse was blown because of an:

a. Electrical short-circuit.

b. Electrical overload.

c. Both a and b.

d. None of the above.

14. The difference between a fuse and a circuit breaker is:

a. The fuse can be reset and used again while a circuit breaker cannot.

b. The circuit breaker can be reset and used again while a fuse cannot.

c. Both a and b.

d. None of the above.

15. An ignition coil is an example of a step-up transformer. True or false?

16. What type of converter will convert a voltage source into a lower regulated voltage?

(Answers are in the back of the textbook.)

OUO1082,0003600 -19-11JUL12-1/1

Electromechanical Components

INTRODUCTION

DXP02704 —UN—23FEB11

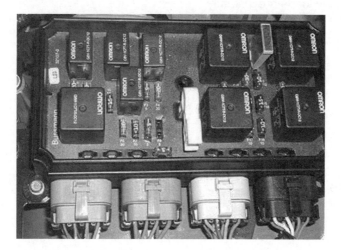

4

DXP02906 —UN—09JAN12

BB87125,000415B -19-11JUN12-1/1

ELECTROMECHANICAL COMPONENTS

An electromechanical component converts electrical energy into mechanical energy, or mechanical energy into electrical energy. Relays, solenoids, electrical generators, alternators, and motors are all electromechanical components.

OUO1082,0002C0D -19-10JAN12-1/1

RELAYS

A relay uses low amperage to create an electromagnetic switch that controls another low-amperage circuit or a high-amperage circuit (Fig. 1). An electromagnet is an iron core surrounded by a coil of wire through which electrical current flows to create a strong magnetic field. Thus, a relay converts electrical energy into mechanical energy. A relay can control electrical current to several electrical devices simultaneously.

DXP02903 —UN—09JAN12

Fig. 1 — A Relay with Cover Removed

Continued on next page OUO1082,0002C0E -19-16OCT12-1/9

RELAY CONSTRUCTION

A relay consists of a coil winding around an iron core, a spring, a stationary metal contact point, and a movable metal armature with a contact point. The armature is mounted over the iron core and winding (Fig. 2). When the coil winding is energized, the iron core becomes magnetized and, thus, an electromagnet. The magnetic force causes the metal armature to move.

A—Armature
B—Spring
C—Stationary Contact Point
D—Coil Winding
E—Iron Core

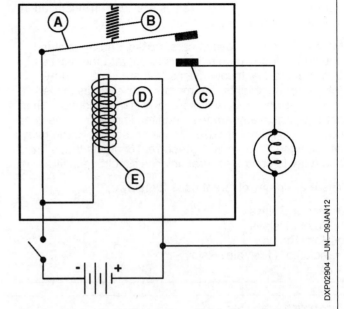

Fig. 2 — Typical Relay: Switch Open, Points Normally Open

OUO1082,0002C0E -19-16OCT12-2/9

A relay's contact points can be designed to be normally open or normally closed (Fig. 2). If the points are normally open, closing the switch completes the electrical circuit. Current now flows in the coil winding surrounding the iron core and becomes an electromagnet. The magnetic force now created pulls the metal armature toward the stationary contact point. Once both points come together, electrical current flows to the light bulb and it is lit (Fig. 3). If the points are normally closed, the magnetic force pulls the metal armature away from the stationary contact point. That interrupts the electrical current to the light bulb, turning it off.

A—Points Closed
B—Switch Closed

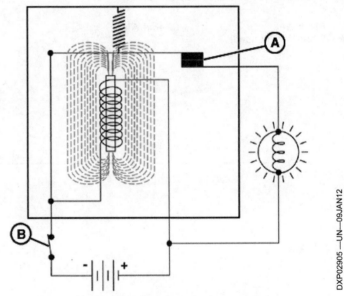

Fig. 3 — Switch closed allows current to flow through coil winding, creating a strong magnetic field that acts on armature to close contact points.

Continued on next page

OUO1082,0002C0E -19-16OCT12-3/9

For ease of service, most relays are currently installed in the fuse box (Fig. 4).

Most electrical devices in cars, trucks, and agricultural equipment today require relays to operate the devices. Some of the electrical devices that are controlled by relays are headlights, fan motors, fuel shutoffs, wiper motors, power window motors, and starter motors. When extremely high amperage is required to power an electrical device, two relays are usually used in series. Some relays are designed with multi-high-current contacts that allow one relay to control several devices simultaneously.

There are many different uses for relays:

- Starter Relays
- Cutout Relays
- Horn Relays
- Indicator (Tell-Tale) Relays

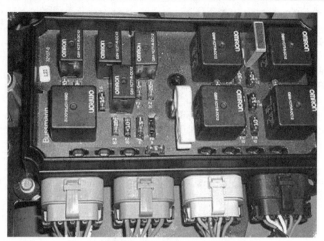

Fig. 4 — Relays Located in a Fuse Box

OUO1082,0002C0E -19-16OCT12-4/9

STARTER RELAYS

A starter relay (Fig. 5) is an electromagnetic switch that controls the high-amperage circuit to the starter solenoid only when the transmission is in neutral.

A—Black Wire   C—Red Wire
B—White Wire (2 used)

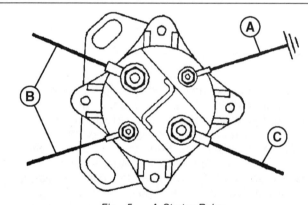

Fig. 5 — A Starter Relay

Continued on next page   OUO1082,0002C0E -19-16OCT12-5/9

OPERATIONThe coil windings of the starter relay terminal A (Fig. 6) cannot be activated until the transmission is in neutral and the ignition switch is in the start position. With the transmission in neutral, the neutral start switch is closed, closing the circuit from the ignition switch to terminal A of the starter relay. Turning the ignition switch to the start position energizes the coil windings of the starter relay, causing the relay contacts to close. With the contacts closed, battery voltage is delivered to the solenoid windings. The solenoid plunger moves, causing the contact disk to engage the solenoid's battery and starter motor connections. This action allows high-amperage current to the starter motor so it can operate. Once the engine is started, the ignition switch is released from the start position to the run position, disabling the starter relay and starter motor.

A—Ignition Switch
B—Neutral Start Switch
C—Starter Relay
D—Battery
E—Solenoid
F—Starting Motor

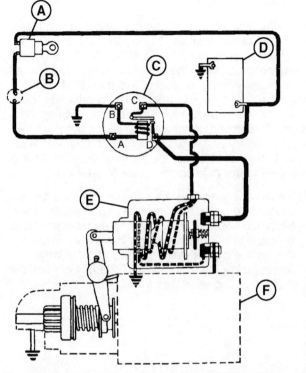

Fig. 6 — Starter Relay Operation in a Typical Starting Circuit

OUO1082,0002C0E -19-16OCT12-6/9

CHECKING

1. Remove the wire connection from terminal C (Fig. 7) of the starter relay to prevent accidental engagement of starter motor during checkout.

2. Using a multimeter set to read DC voltage, check voltage at terminal D by placing the red lead of the meter on terminal D and the black lead of the meter to ground or frame of the unit. Reading should be battery voltage. If no voltage is noted, there is an open or high resistance in the wire to the battery. Clean connections at the battery and starter relay or replace wire.

3. If voltage is okay in step 2, place a jumper wire to terminals A and D. Check voltage at terminal C to ground with a multimeter. Reading should be battery voltage, indicating the contacts of the starter relay have closed properly. If no voltage is noted, the starter relay is defective and should be replaced.

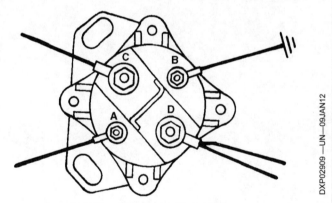

Fig. 7 — Checking a Starter Relay

Continued on next page OUO1082,0002C0E -19-16OCT12-7/9

HORN RELAY

A horn relay is an electromagnetic switch that completes the electrical circuit from the battery to the horn when pressing the horn button (Fig. 8). When the horn button is pressed, the circuit from the battery is completed through the horn relay winding to ground and then back to the battery. The magnetism created in the winding by the current pulls the armature toward the core, closing the contacts. This action completes the circuit between the horns and battery and causes the horn to operate. When the horn button is released, the flat spring on the back of the relay armature pulls the contacts apart.

NOTE: A light-duty horn relay may also be used as an indicator lamp relay. A normally open sensor takes the place of the horn button and an indicator lamp is connected to terminal H of the relay. When the sensor closes (failure), the indicator lamp lights, telling the operator a failure has occurred and indicating what has failed.

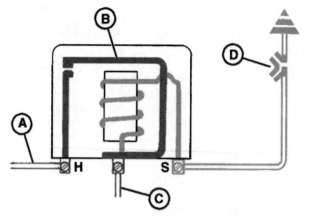

Fig. 8 — Horn Relay Circuit

A—To Horn
B—Horn Relay
C—To Battery
D—Horn Button

Continued on next page

OUO1082,0002C0E -19-16OCT12-8/9

CHECKING

To check the horn relay (See Fig. 8), connect a voltmeter from the relay horn terminal H to ground, and use a jumper wire to terminal S and to ground. The voltmeter will read battery voltage if the points are closed. However, if the voltmeter reads zero volts, the contacts are not closed and the relay is defective.

INDICATOR (TELL-TALE) RELAY

An indicator (tell-tale) relay is an electromagnetic switch that controls electrical current to a dash light, which informs the driver if a tail light or turn signal light is burned out. An indicator (tell-tale) relay is generally used on trucks and buses where indicator lamps are lit on an instrument panel for normal operation and then go out when a failure occurs.

OPERATION

When an electrical load of predetermined value is connected through the indicator (tell-tale) relay winding to the battery, current flows through the relay winding (Fig. 9). This situation creates a magnetic field that pulls the armature toward the core so that the relay contact points close. This connects the indicator lamp to the battery and so the lamp lights up.

If any part of the load circuit is not functioning properly, such as a burnt out taillight, a reduced current flow through the relay winding allows the relay contact points to open. As a result the indicator lamp will go out, telling the operator that something is wrong in the circuit.

NOTE: *Some indicator (tell-tale) relays are designed so that the indicator lamp lights up when the electrical units are not working, rather than when they are.*

Some indicator (tell-tale) relays require the following adjustments: air gap, point opening, and operating amperage of the contact points. The air gap and point opening are checked and adjusted the same as in the cutout relay (Chapter 6).

TESTING

To measure the amount of current required to operate the indicator (tell-tale) relay, connect an ammeter into the circuit at the terminal of the relay that is connected to the unit being operated. Also connect a variable resistor

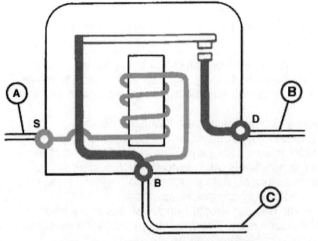

Fig. 9 — Indicator (Tell-Tale) Relay Circuit

A—To Electrical Load   C—To Battery
B—To Indicator Lamp

in series at the terminal of the relay which is connected to the battery. Close the signal lamp switch and slowly reduce the resistance until the relay operates, noting the ammeter reading.

If necessary, adjust the operating amperage by bending the armature spring post. Bend it up to increase the spring tension and the operating amperage, and bend it down to decrease the amperage.

NOTE: *Each indicator (tell-tale) relay is designed for use with a specific number of bulbs and bulb types. Using higher candlepower bulbs or more bulbs than specified causes the relay's contact points to burn. Using smaller candlepower bulbs or fewer bulbs than specified may not close the relay points. Thus, the indicator lamps will not glow.*

SUMMARY: RELAYS

- A relay uses low amperage to create an electromagnetic switch that controls another low-amperage circuit or a high-amperage circuit.
- A relay can control several electrical devices simultaneously.

OUO1082,0002C0E -19-16OCT12-9/9

SOLENOIDS

Two definitions can be used to accurately define a solenoid:

1. A solenoid uses low amperage to create an electromagnetic field to cause a rod (plunger) to move in a linear motion so that the rod (plunger) can act on a device.
   Some solenoids have an additional function:
2. A solenoid uses low amperage to create a magnetic field to move a rod in a linear motion. One end of the rod (plunger) acts on a device while the other end of the rod (plunger) acts as an electromagnetic switch that controls a high-amperage circuit.
   A solenoid is constructed and operates in a similar fashion as a relay. Thus, a solenoid converts electrical energy into mechanical energy.

STARTER SOLENOIDS

A starter solenoid is an electromagnetic switch that causes the plunger to move in a linear motion to engage the starter pinion with the flywheel while simultaneously acting as an electromagnetic switch for the high-amperage circuit to the starter motor. Before turning the ignition switch on, the plunger remains seated because spring pressure exerts a force on it. Because the contact disk is attached to the plunger, the contact disk is disengaged from both terminals.

Turning the switch on, current flows to the solenoid windings (Fig. 10). Because the solenoid coils are wound

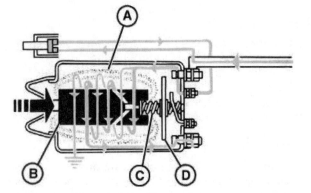

Fig. 10 — Solenoid Plunger Starting to Move, Switch Turned On

A—Magnetic Field C—Spring
B—Plunger D—Contact Disk

in the same direction, current flows in the same direction, creating a strong magnetic field. The magnetic force overrides spring pressure, forcing the plunger off its seat.

OUO1082,0002C0F -19-08JUN12-1/6

Thus, the plunger forces the contact disk against both terminals to allow the high amperage current to flow from the battery to the starter motor (Fig. 11).

A—From Battery C—To Starter
B—Contact Disk

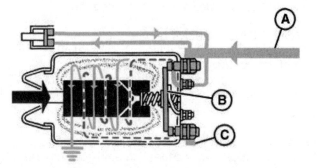

Fig. 11 — Contact disk engages BOTH terminals to allow high amperage current to flow from the battery to the starter.

Continued on next page OUO1082,0002C0F -19-08JUN12-2/6

Turning the switch off, several things happen quickly (Fig. 12). First, current through the switch to the solenoid is cut off. Because the magnetic field is de-energized, the return spring pushes the contact disk away from both terminals, breaking the current from the battery to the starter motor.

A—Key Switch Released

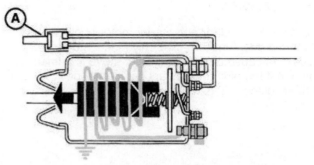

Fig. 12 — Contact Disk as Switch Is Released

OUO1082,0002C0F -19-08JUN12-3/6

CONSTRUCTION

The solenoid has two coils of wire wound in the same direction: the pull-in winding and the hold-in winding.

The pull-in winding is made up of heavy wire connected to the motor terminal of the solenoid and through the motor to ground.

The hold-in winding has an equal number of turns of fine wire with one end connected to ground.

Inside the solenoid, the contact disk closing shorts out the heavy pull-in winding. That leaves only the fine hold-in winding energized during the starting period. The initial current flow through the pull-in winding is of very short duration. The current flow through the hold-in winding continues as long as the control circuit is closed.

The current then flows in a reverse direction in the pull-in winding. But the current flow continues in the same direction as before through the hold-in winding because it is grounded. Because the number of turns in the two windings are equal, the ampere flow is equal. Thus, the direction of flow is opposite and the magnetic field of one coil opposes that of the other. This action causes an immediate collapse of the magnetic field. Therefore, spring tension forces the plunger back to its original position.

A starter solenoid also provides a shift lever. A contact disk is attached at one end of plunger and a shift lever at the other end of the plunger. Turning the switch on forces the plunger forward, causing the contact disk against both terminals while simultaneously forcing the shift lever to move the starting motor's pinion to mesh with the flywheel ring gear (Fig. 13).

TESTING

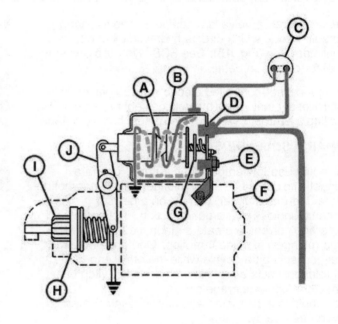

Fig. 13 — Solenoid Circuit

A—Hold-In Winding	F—Starting Motor
B—Pull-In Winding	G—Contact Disk
C—Key Switch	H—Overrunning Clutch
D—Battery Terminal	I—Pinion
E—Starter Motor Terminal	J—Shift Lever

Solenoids are tested by removing the solenoid from the circuit and testing the windings for resistance with an ohmmeter. The specified resistance reading of a solenoid will be listed in the machine's technical manual.

Continued on next page OUO1082,0002C0F -19-08JUN12-4/6

OTHER SOLENOIDS

Solenoids constructed for non-starter motor applications do not have a dual function. The only function of these solenoids is to cause a rod (plunger) to move in a linear motion so that the plunger may act on another device. A fuel shutoff solenoid (Fig. 14) is an example.

Fig. 14 — A Fuel Shutoff Solenoid

OUO1082,0002C0F -19-08JUN12-5/6

An electrohydraulic valve is a solenoid used to control a hydraulic valve, which directs hydraulic oil to other hydraulic devices (Fig. 15). See FOS Hydraulic Systems Manual for operation details.

A microprocessor-controlled electrohydraulic valve uses a microprocessor that varies the voltage sent to a solenoid in controlling a hydraulic valve instead of just battery voltage.

SUMMARY: SOLENOIDS

- Solenoids use low amperage current to create a magnetic field to move a rod (plunger) in a linear motion so that the rod (plunger) can act on a device.
- Some solenoids have a dual function: To use low amperage current to create a magnetic field to move a rod (plunger) in a linear motion. One end of the rod (plunger) acts on a device while the other end of the rod (plunger) acts as an electromagnetic switch that controls a high-amperage circuit.
- A solenoid is constructed and operates in a similar fashion as a relay.

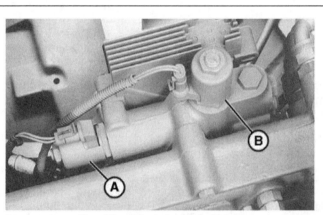

Fig. 15 — Electrohydraulic Valves

A—Electrohydraulic Valves   B—Electrohydraulic Valves

OUO1082,0002C0F -19-08JUN12-6/6

GENERATOR

A generator, when driven by an external source, rotates an armature through a stationary electromagnetic field to create alternating current that is rectified to direct current by the commutator and carbon brushes. Thus, a generator converts mechanical energy into electrical energy.

The basic generator (Fig. 16) has two parts:

- Armature: rotating wire loop (the conductor).
- Magnetic Poles: stationary magnetic field.

A—Magnetic Poles   B—Armature

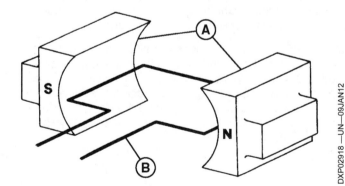

Fig. 16 — The Basic Parts of a Generator

Continued on next page   OUO1082,0002C10 -19-11JUN12-1/6

As the armature rotates through the magnetic field of the poles, voltage is generated (Fig. 17). Using the Right-Hand Rule, we can see that the voltage comes toward us on the left side in Fig. 17, and flows away from us on the right side. By the Conventional Theory, this means that the left end of the armature loop is positive (+) while the right end is negative (–).

A—Rotation   C—Current Flow
B—Magnetic Field

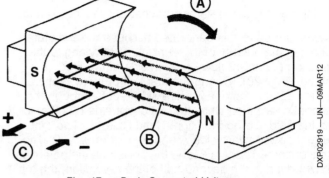

Fig. 17 — Basic Generated Voltage

OUO1082,0002C10 -19-11JUN12-2/6

For current to flow, we must add three more parts (Fig. 18). A commutator connects the ends of the armature loop to a split ring. Carbon brushes allow electrical current to flow to and from the commutator. Wires connect the carbon brushes to a load. The circuit is now complete and electrical current will flow.

A—Commutator   D—Load
B—Rotation   E—Carbon Brushes
C—Wires

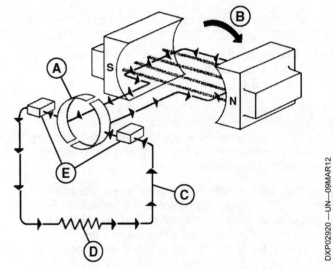

Fig. 18 — Basic Current Flow in Generator

OUO1082,0002C10 -19-11JUN12-3/6

To ensure a strong current and proper flow, we must add one more feature (Fig. 19).

The magnets by themselves are weak and create a weak magnetic field. The result is that the voltage induced is low. To remedy this situation, a field circuit is needed.

A field circuit is a current-carrying wire wrapped around a magnet to create an electromagnet that produces a strong magnetic field (Fig. 19).

Three factors decide how much voltage is generated:

- The strength of the magnetic field.
- The number of wire conductors in the armature.
- The speed of the armature.

A—Field Circuit   B—Rotation

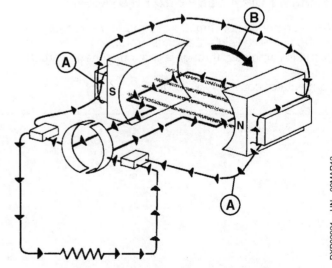

Fig. 19 — Complete Parts of Basic Generators

Continued on next page   OUO1082,0002C10 -19-11JUN12-4/6

HOW THE GENERATOR CONVERTS AC TO DC

So far, the basic generator produces alternating current.

Alternating current is generated because the armature reverses the polarity of the current. That changes the direction of current flow on each side of the loop as it rotates (Fig. 20). During the first half of its revolution in Fig. 20, the top of armature side A cuts through the magnetic field first, while the bottom of side B is first to cut the field. Using the Right-Hand Rule, we find that current flows toward side A and away from side B. The Conventional Theory (+ to –) then gives us the polarities shown. During the second half of the revolution, the top of side B is the leading edge while the bottom of side A is leading. B is now (+), while A is (–). Therefore, the armature loop ends reverse polarity during each revolution. The result: alternating current (AC).

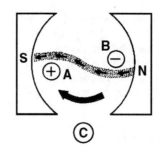 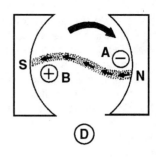

Fig. 20 — How the Polarity of the Armature Changes During Each Revolution

C—First Half of Revolution   **D—Second Half of Revolution**

OUO1082,0002C10 -19-11JUN12-5/6

Getting this alternating current to flow to the load in the same direction, or direct current, is the job of the commutator and brushes (Fig. 21).

The static neutral point is when the armature is vertical to the magnetic field. Twice during each rotation, the armature is vertical to the magnetic field. The armature loop is not passing through the field and so no voltage is generated at this instant.

The commutator is split into two parts with the open areas matching the neutral point of the armature. Thus, a gap exists as the commutator passes the brushes. Past this point, the other half of the commutator contacts the brushes. Because the coil is in the same position as during the preceding one-half revolution, current flow to the brush stays in the same direction. This action is how the generator converts alternating current to direct current. The final result: direct current (DC).

SUMMARY: HOW A GENERATOR WORKS

- Moving a conductor (armature) through a stationary electromagnetic field = basic generator.
- Circuit is completed through a commutator and carbon brushes.
- Commutator converts AC to DC.

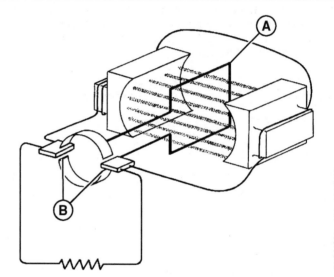

Fig. 21 — How Generator Converts AC to DC Current

A—At Static Neutral Point No Voltage Generated   **B—Gaps Between Commutator Halves**

OUO1082,0002C10 -19-11JUN12-6/6

ALTERNATORS

A direct current generator cannot supply adequate voltage at low and idle speeds to meet the demands of the ignition system and electrical accessories. Thus, the alternator was introduced in the early 1960s to meet that demand.

An alternator, when driven by an external source, rotates an electromagnet through stationary windings to create alternating current that is rectified to direct current by the diodes.

Although an alternator is similar to a generator in that it converts mechanical energy into electrical energy, two major differences exist: the way voltage is generated, and the way alternating current is converted to direct current.

BASIC OPERATION

- Alternators—rotating an electromagnetic field across stationary conductors = induced voltage.
- Alternators—convert AC to DC with diodes.

Fig. 22 — Alternator on a Modern Tractor

OUO1082,0002C11 -19-29OCT12-1/21

CONSTRUCTION

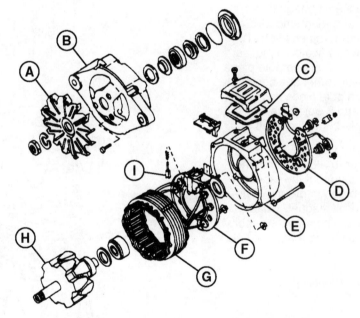

Fig. 23 — Exploded View of Typical Alternator

A—Fan
B—Front Housing
C—Voltage Regulator
D—Rear Cover
E—Rear Housing
F—Rectifier Bridge
G—Stator
H—Rotor
I—Brush

Alternators have three main parts (Fig. 23):

- Rotor assembly—rotating electromagnet.

- Stator assembly—stationary electrical conductors.
- Rectifier assembly—diodes that change AC to DC.

Continued on next page   OUO1082,0002C11 -19-29OCT12-2/21

ROTOR ASSEMBLY

The rotor assembly is a revolving electromagnet (Fig. 24). A wire coil wraps around a soft iron core. Pole pieces (A) made of soft iron encase the coil assembly. The ends of the coil winding are connected to two slip rings (B) mounted on one end of the rotor's shaft.

Two carbon brushes ride on top of the slip rings. One carbon brush connects to ground. The other carbon brush connects to the coil winding, which is also connected to the voltage regulator.

A—Pole Pieces   B—Slip Rings (2 used)

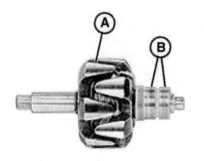

Fig. 24 — A Typical Rotor

OUO1082,0002C11 -19-29OCT12-3/21

The rotor consists of the shaft, coil winding (B), slip rings (A), and two pole pieces (C). The coil winding, when energized, becomes an electromagnet. Because the coil winding is located inside both pole pieces, the pole pieces become magnetized.

Each pole piece is made of soft iron. Soft iron is used because it does not become permanently magnetized like hard metals do once exposed to a magnetic field. Once the soft iron is removed from a magnetic field, it loses it magnetic properties. And when two pole pieces enter a magnetic field opposite each other, one pole piece becomes a north pole magnet while the other one becomes a south pole magnet. Because each pole piece is made in the shape of fingers, alternating N and S poles are created when both pole pieces are assembled onto the shaft.

The voltage regulator senses battery voltage. If it is low, voltage flows from the regulator to a carbon brush, through a slip ring, into the coil winding, out the other slip ring and through the other carbon brush to ground. The coil assembly now becomes an electromagnet, which magnetizes the soft iron pole pieces. The rotor assembly is now one big electromagnet with a strong magnetic field acting on the stator windings.

A—Slip Rings   C—Coil Winding
B—Pole Pieces (2 used)

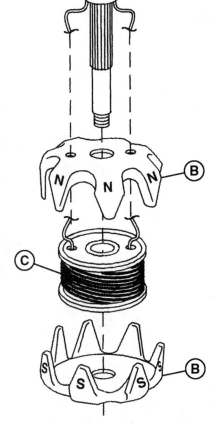

Fig. 25 — Exploded View of a Rotor

Continued on next page   OUO1082,0002C11 -19-29OCT12-4/21

STATOR ASSEMBLY

The stator assembly is a stationary group of three coil windings mounted in a laminated soft iron ring (Fig. 26). Because a stator has three separate windings, it is called a three-phase stator. Each group of windings is made up of from 8 to 16 coils, depending on the design. One end of each stator winding is connected to a positive and a negative diode.

A—End Frame   **C—Iron Laminate**
B—Stator Windings

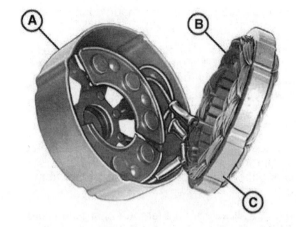

Fig. 26 — Stator Assembly

OUO1082,0002C11 -19-29OCT12-5/21

The other ends of the stator windings can be connected by either one of two ways (Fig. 27):

- Y-connected stator windings.
- Delta-connected stator windings.

The delta-connected alternator may be used for heavy-duty operations where high amperage is needed.

The Y-connected alternator usually provides moderate amperage.

An alternator is rated by its maximum amperage output. Thus, a 100-amp alternator is capable of creating a maximum of 100 amps.

A—Y-Connected Stator   **B—Delta-Connected Stator**

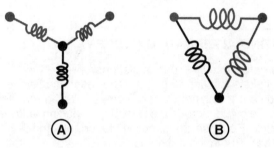

Fig. 27 — Two Connections of 3-Phase Stator Windings

OUO1082,0002C11 -19-29OCT12-6/21

RECTIFIER ASSEMBLY (DIODES)

To convert AC to DC current, rectifiers or diodes are used.

A diode is a semiconductor device that allows electrical current to flow in one direction only. A semiconductor is an insulator, but can be transformed into an electrical conductor. In a three-phase alternator, six diodes (C) are used (Fig. 28). Three negative diodes are mounted in the end frame or in a heat sink bolted to the end frame. Three positive diodes are mounted in the heat sink, which is insulated from the end frame.

A—Negative Diode Assembly   **C—Diode (6 used)**
B—Positive Diode Assembly

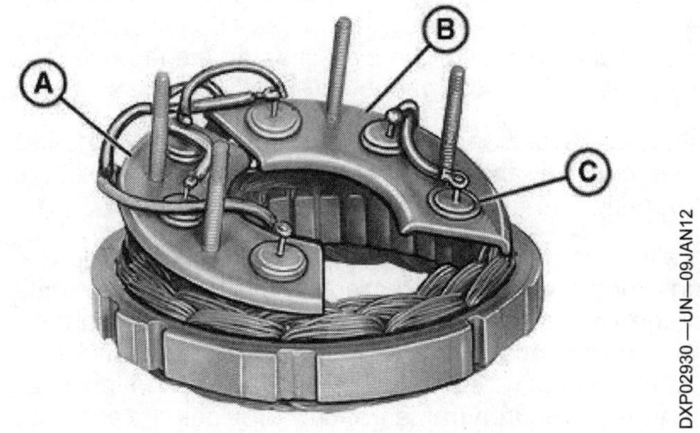

Fig. 28 — Diode Assemblies in Alternator

Continued on next page   OUO1082,0002C11 -19-29OCT12-7/21

Some alternators have all six diodes mounted in one assembly, a rectifier bridge (Fig. 29).

NOTE: On negative-grounded alternators, the positive diodes are mounted in the insulated heat sink. On positive-grounded alternators, the negative diodes are mounted in the insulated heat sink.

ISOLATION DIODE

An isolation diode is a semiconductor device that prevents electrical current from leaving the battery when the alternator is not operational, preventing the battery from discharging.

An isolation diode allows for an alternator charge indicator lamp without the use of a relay. The charge indicator lamp on the dash panel is connected in parallel with the isolation diode. Because all alternator output current passes through this diode, high temperatures can be expected. For this reason, the diode is mounted in a heat sink metal frame where plenty of air surrounds it.

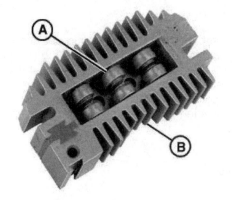

Fig. 29 — Rectifier Bridge

A—Diode   B—Heat Sink

OUO1082,0002C11 -19-29OCT12-8/21

GENERATING ALTERNATING CURRENT

In an alternator, the wire loop is stationary, while the magnetic field is rotating (Fig. 30). The magnetic field is supplied by a bar magnet (N and S poles). As the magnet rotates, its field cuts across the wire loop, inducing voltage into the wire. Because the circuit is closed, electrical current flows. But in what direction?

In the first half revolution (upper diagram in Fig. 30) the S pole induces voltage in the wire loop. Current flows in the direction indicated by the arrows. The same direction of current flow is induced by the lower N pole on the bottom side of the wire loop. Thus, current flows from positive to negative, the upper loop is (+) and the lower end is (−).

In the second half of the revolution (lower diagram in Fig. 30) the bar magnet has reversed poles. Therefore, the direction of current flow has reversed. This action changes the polarity of the loop ends as the top one is now (−) while the bottom one is (+).

With each revolution, current flows from loop to load, first in one direction and then in the other. This action creates alternating current.

An alternator made with a bar magnet rotating inside a single loop of wire is not practical. That's because very little voltage and current are produced with just a bar magnet and one wire loop. The performance is improved when both the loop of wire and the magnet are placed inside an iron frame. The iron frame not only provides a place onto which the loop of wire can be assembled, but also acts as a conducting path for the magnetic lines of force.

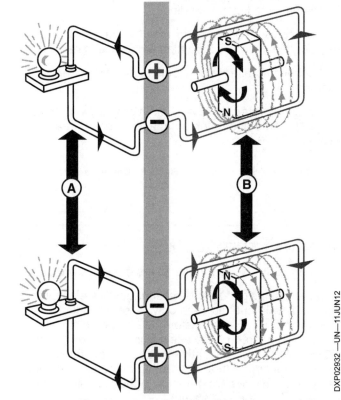

Fig. 30 — Basic Alternator Operation

A—Load Circuit   B—Rotating Magnetic Field

Continued on next page   OUO1082,0002C11 -19-29OCT12-9/21

Without the iron frame, magnetism leaving the N pole (C) of the rotating bar magnet must travel through air to get to the S pole (E) (Fig. 31). Iron conducts magnetism very easily. Adding the iron frame greatly increases the number of lines of force between the N pole and the S pole. Thus, more lines of force will be cutting across the conductor that lies between the bar magnet and the frame.

A large number of magnetic lines of force are at the center of the magnet tip. However, only a few lines of force are at the leading and trailing edges of the tips. Therefore, there is a strong magnetic field at the center and a weak magnetic field at the leading and trailing edges. This condition results when the distance, an air gap, between the magnet and field frame is greater at the leading and trailing edges than at the center of the magnet.

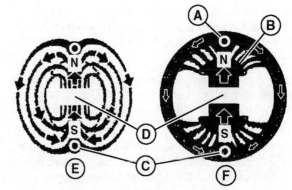

Fig. 31 — Magnetic Lines of Force

A—Strong Field
B—Weak Field
C—Conductor
D—Rotor
E—Air Path—High Reluctance
F—Iron Frame—Low Reluctance

OUO1082,0002C11 -19-29OCT12-10/21

Three methods exist for increasing voltage generated by the alternator (Fig. 32).

• Increasing the speed that the magnet (rotor) turns. The faster the magnet turns, the more times the lines of force will cut across the wire.
• Increasing the number of conductors (wires). The more wires the stator has, the greater the voltage and current output.
• Increasing the strength of the magnetic field. For example, doubling the number of magnets the rotor has doubles the output voltage. And because the rotor is an electromagnet, increasing the voltage to the rotor's coil increases the alternator's output voltage and current.

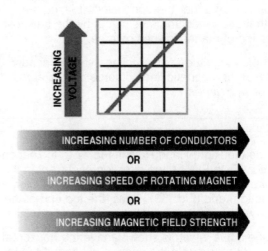

Fig. 32 — Increasing Voltage

Continued on next page

OUO1082,0002C11 -19-29OCT12-11/21

Fig. 33 shows the different positions of the rotor as it rotates at constant speed. At the top is a curve showing the magnitude of the voltage that is generated in the loop of wire as the rotor revolves.

The voltage curve shows the generated voltage (A) or electrical pressure which can be measured across the ends of the wire, just as voltage can be measured across the terminal posts of a battery.

With the rotor in the first position 0° (E). No voltage being generated in the loop of wire. That's because there are no magnetic lines of force cutting across the conductor.

As the rotor turns and approaches the second position 90° (F). The rather weak magnetic field at the leading edge of the rotor starts to cut across the conductor, and the voltage increases.

When the rotor reaches second position 90° (F). The generated voltage has reached its maximum value (C), as shown above the horizontal line in the illustration.

The maximum voltage occurs when the rotor magnetic poles are directly under the conductor. It is in this position that the conductor is being cut by the heaviest concentration of magnetic lines of force.

Note that the magnitude of the voltage varies because the concentration of magnetic lines of force cutting across the loop of wire varies.

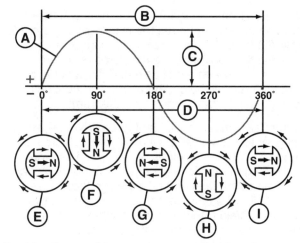

Fig. 33 — Pattern of Generated Voltage during Each Revolution

A—Generated Voltage
B—One Cycle
C—Maximum Value
D—Degree of Rotor Rotation
E—First Position 0°
F—Second Position 90°
G—Third Position 180°
H—Fourth Position 270°
I— Fifth Position 360°

The voltage curve shown is not the result of a change in rotor speed, because in the illustration the rotor is considered to be turning at a constant speed.

OUO1082,0002C11 -19-29OCT12-12/21

By applying the Right-Hand Rule in Fig 34 to the second position 90° (F) in Fig 33, the direction of current in the loop of wire will be out of the top end of the conductor, and into the bottom end (Fig. 33). Thus, the top end of the conductor will be positive, and the bottom end negative.

The voltage curve which is shown above the horizontal line in Fig. 33 represents the positive voltage at the top end of the wire loop which is generated as the rotor turns from the first position 0° (E) to the third position 180° (G).

As the rotor turns from second position 90° (F) to third position 180° (G), the voltage decreases until at of the third position 180° (G), it again becomes zero.

As the rotor turns from third position 180° (G) to fourth position 270° (H), the N pole of the rotor is now passing under the top part of the wire loop, and the S pole under the bottom part. From the Right-Hand Rule, the top end of the loop of wire is now negative, and the bottom end is positive. The negative voltage at the top end of the loop is pictured in the illustration by the curve which is below the horizontal line.

Fig. 34 — Right-Hand Rule

The voltage again returns to zero when the rotor turns from fourth position 270° (H) to fifth position 360° (I).

The voltage curve in the illustration represents one complete turn or cycle of the rotor. With the rotor making 60 complete turns in one second, there will be 60 such curves, one coming right after the other, resulting in 60 cycles per second. The number of cycles per second is called the frequency. Because the generator speed often varies, the frequency also varies.

Continued on next page   OUO1082,0002C11 -19-29OCT12-13/21

In Fig. 35, the single loop of wire acting as a stator winding (B), and the bar magnet acting as the rotor (A), show how an AC voltage is produced in a basic alternator. When two more separate loops of wire, spaced 120 degrees apart, are added to our basic alternator, two more separate voltages will be produced.

With the S pole of the rotor directly under the AA conductor, the voltage at AA will be maximum in magnitude and positive in polarity.

After the rotor turns 120 degrees, the S pole will be directly under the BB conductor and the voltage at BB will be maximum positive. Similarly, 120 degrees later, the voltage at CC will be maximum positive. This situation means that the peak positive voltages at AA, BB, and CC in each loop of wire occur 120 degrees apart (Fig. 35).

A—Rotor
B—Stator

C—One Cycle

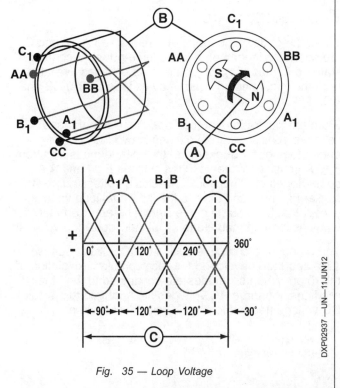

Fig. 35 — Loop Voltage

DXP02937 —UN—11JUN12

OUO1082,0002C11 -19-29OCT12-14/21

DELTA-CONNECTED STATOR

When the ends of the loops of wire marked A_1, B_1, and C_1, Fig. 36 are connected to the ends marked B, C and A respectively, a basic three-phase delta-connected stator is formed. The three AC voltages available from the delta-connected stator are identical to the three voltages previously discussed, and may now be denoted as the voltages from B to A, C to B, and A to C, or more simply BA, CB and AC. Inspect the illustration to see the logic of this. Example: the voltage formerly called A_1B is now called BA.

A—Delta Stator
B—Stator Winding

C—One Cycle

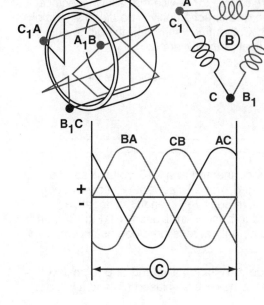

Fig. 36 — Phase Voltage (Delta Stator)

DXP02938 —UN—11JUN12

Continued on next page

OUO1082,0002C11 -19-29OCT12-15/21

Y-CONNECTED STATOR

When the ends of the loops of wire marked A, B, and C, are connected together, a basic three-phase Y-connected stator is formed (Fig. 37). The three voltages available from the Y-connected stator may be labeled BA, CB and AC.

From the illustration you can see that each of these voltages consists of the voltages in two loops of wire added together. For example, the voltage measured from B to A consists of the voltages in loops B, B_1 and A, A_1 added together. This addition yields a voltage curve BA similar in shape and form to the individual loop voltages, except that the voltage curve BA will be approximately 1.7 times as large in magnitude as an individual loop voltage.

Three separate complete cycles of AC voltage spaced 120° apart are developed for each complete revolution of the rotor. When six diodes are connected to the stator windings, the three AC voltages are changed to a single DC voltage needed for the DC electrical system.

A—Y-Stator   **C—One Cycle**
B—Stator Winding

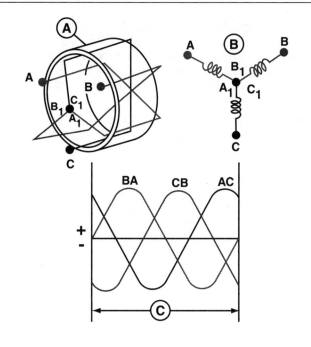

Fig. 37 — Phase Voltage (Y-Stator)

OUO1082,0002C11 -19-29OCT12-16/21

HOW DIODES CHANGE AC TO DC

A diode is a semiconductor device that allows electrical current to flow in one direction only. The diode's symbol (B) is in Fig. 38. Current flows through the diode only in the direction indicated by the arrow.

A—Current Flow   **B—Diode Symbol**

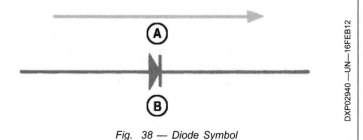

Fig. 38 — Diode Symbol

OUO1082,0002C11 -19-29OCT12-17/21

When a diode is connected to an AC voltage source having ends marked A and B, current will flow through the diode when A is positive (+) and B is negative (–). The diode is said to be forward-biased (A) (Fig. 39), and with the voltage polarity across the diode as shown, it will conduct current.

When the voltage at A is negative and at B is positive, the diode is said to be reverse-biased (B) and it will not conduct current.

A—Forward Bias   **C—No Current Flow**
B—Reverse Bias   **D—Current Flow**

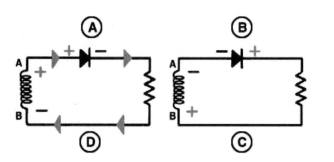

Fig. 39 — Forward and Reverse Bias

Continued on next page   OUO1082,0002C11 -19-29OCT12-18/21

The current flow that would be obtained from this arrangement is illustrated in Fig. 40. Because the current flows only half the time, the diode provides half-wave rectification (Fig. 40). A generator having only one diode would provide very limited output.

A—Current   **B—Time**

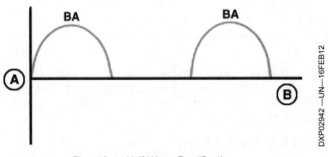

Fig. 40 — Half-Wave Rectification

OUO1082,0002C11 -19-29OCT12-19/21

The output is increased when four diodes are used to provide full-wave rectification (Fig. 41). Note that the current is more continuous than with one diode, but that the current varies from a maximum value to a zero value.

It is particularly important to observe that the current flow through the external load resistor is in one direction only. The AC voltage and current have therefore been rectified to a unidirectional or DC voltage and current.

C—Current   **D—Time**

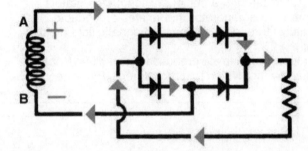

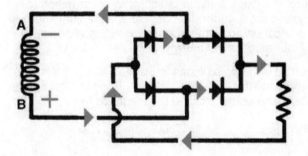

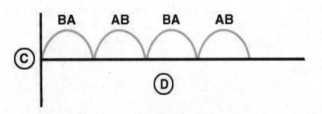

Fig. 41 — Full-Wave Rectification

Continued on next page   OUO1082,0002C11 -19-29OCT12-20/21

In order to obtain a higher output and a smoother voltage and current, a three-phase stator is connected to six diodes which forms a three-phase full-wave bridge rectifier (Fig. 42).

An alternator is used to charge a battery. Although an alternator produces more current at low and idle speeds, an alternator does not produce as much current at high speeds compared to a generator.

SUMMARY: ALTERNATORS

- An alternator is an alternating current generator.
- Alternator = rotor (moving) + stator (fixed) + rectifier (diodes).
- An alternator generates voltage by rotating a magnetic field (rotor) through a stationary conductor (stator) compared to a generator that rotates a conductor (armature) through a stationary magnetic field (field circuit).
- The alternating current produced by an alternator is rectified by the diodes to direct current. DC is needed

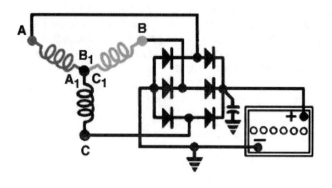

Fig. 42 — Three-Phase, Full-Wave Rectification

to maintain the battery charge and power the electrical devices.
- An alternator is more compact and produces more current at low and idle speeds compared to a generator.

OUO1082,0002C11 -19-29OCT12-21/21

MOTORS

A motor produces continuos rotary motion to drive a device as long as electrical current flows into the motor's armature. Although a motor is similar in construction to a DC generator, a generator converts mechanical energy into electrical energy while a motor converts electrical energy into mechanical energy.

First consider the pole pieces in the field frame assembly of the motor as the ends of a magnet (Fig. 43). The space between these poles is called the magnetic field.

A—Pole Pieces   B—Magnetic Field

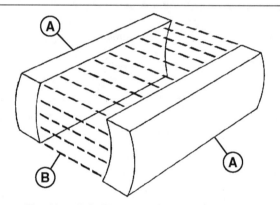

Fig. 43 — Pole Pieces and Their Magnetic Field

OUO1082,0002C12 -19-18JUN12-1/7

A field winding is a current-carrying wire wrapped around each pole piece. The strength of the magnetic field between the pole pieces increases (Fig. 44).

A—Field Winding

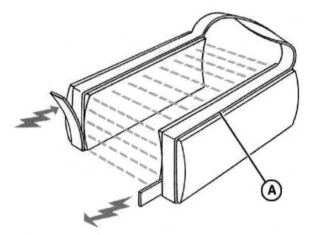

Fig. 44 — Field Winding Added to Pole Pieces

Continued on next page   OUO1082,0002C12 -19-18JUN12-2/7

Now let's consider a loop of wire (Fig. 45). When we feed electrical energy from the battery into this loop, a magnetic field is also formed around the wire.

A—Magnetic Field   **B—Battery Current**

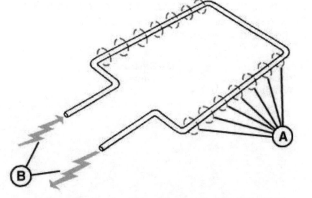

Fig. 45 — Loop of Live Wire and Its Magnetic Field

OUO1082,0002C12 -19-18JUN12-3/7

If we place the loop of wire in the magnetic field between the pole pieces and pass current through the loop, we have the makings of a simple armature (Fig. 46). The magnetic field around the loop and the field between the pole pieces repel each other, causing the loop to turn.

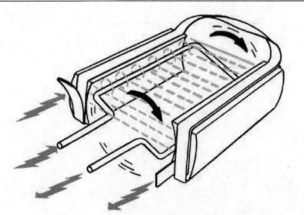

Fig. 46 — Loop of Wire Placed in Field between Poles

OUO1082,0002C12 -19-18JUN12-4/7

In an actual armature, the number of loops is increased (Fig. 47). A commutator has separate metal segments attached to the ends of each wire loop. When electrical current goes through carbon brushes to the commutator and then the armature, a repelling or kicking action causes a continuous rotation of the armature. All starting motors use this basic principle to develop useful mechanical energy.

A—Commutator   **B—Brushes**

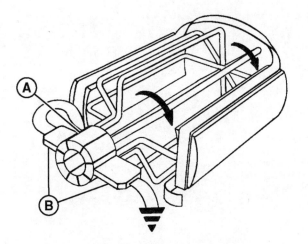

Fig. 47 — Armature for Starting Motor

Continued on next page   OUO1082,0002C12 -19-18JUN12-5/7

Every motor is constructed with an armature, commutator, carbon brushes, and electromagnets (magnets surrounded by field windings) (Fig. 48).

A—Armature
B—Pole Pieces
C—Field Windings
D—Brushes
E—Commutator

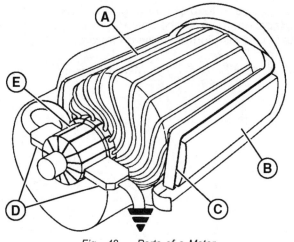

Fig. 48 — Parts of a Motor

Continued on next page

OUO1082,0002C12 -19-18JUN12-6/7

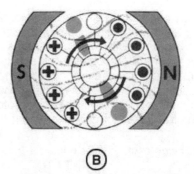

Fig. 49 — Static Neutral Point of Rotating Armature

A—Static Neutral   **B—Operational Neutral**

As the armature rotates (Fig. 49) the sides of its loops reach a point shown when they are as far out of the magnetic field as possible. This is the static neutral point and is always halfway between the pole pieces of the motor. Current must be changed at this point to keep the same turning force.

The reversal of current is done every half-turn by the commutator. It works as follows: When the armature moves, so does the commutator. By the time the left-hand side of the armature has swung around to the north pole, the commutator segments will have reversed their connections with the brushes. Current will then flow in the opposite direction in the armature windings. This change of current flow would cause the armature to reverse, but since the windings have made a half-turn while the commutator changed connections, the force exerted on the armature will continue its rotation.

To keep rotating the motor, the current flow must be reversed every half-turn of the armature. This keeps the magnetic lines of force acting in the same direction.

The static neutral point is always halfway between the pole shoes and is the point where the direction of current must be changed to maintain a turning force in the same direction. This situation is true whether the motor has two, four, or six poles. However, when current flows through the armature windings creating another magnetic field, the normal field between the pole shoes is distorted. Since

lines of force may be assumed not to cross each other, the neutral point is therefore shifted. The motor brushes are shifted back from the static neutral point to an operational neutral (against the direction of rotation) to prevent excessive arcing and to obtain more efficient operation.

The main point is that the magnetic field of the armature distorts the field of the pole shoes and shifts the neutral point to a new position. To match this position, the motor brushes are mounted back at the new position.

SUMMARY: MOTORS

- A current-carrying conductor formed in a loop and mounted on a shaft will cause the shaft to rotate when placed inside a magnetic field. The result: a basic motor.
- If the direction of current flow in the loop is reversed as the loop passes the neutral position, the loop and shaft continue to rotate. This action is how a motor remains running.
- To increase the power of the motor, more loops of conductors connected in series with an equal number of commutator segments are needed.
- Increasing the strength of the magnetic field will affect the turning power of the motor, and will be directly related to the number of field poles and the number of ampere turns on each pole.
- Most motors have two, four, or six field poles with windings, a wound armature with a commutator, and two, four, or six brushes.

OUO1082,0002C12 -19-18JUN12-7/7

MOTOR/GENERATORS

Hybrids use electric motors to assist their internal combustion engines, that consist of a motor/generator. A motor/generator is a device that can be used as either an electric motor or a generator, converting electrical energy to another form, such as mechanical energy, and vise versa. This is accomplished by mechanically coupling an internal combustion engine to an electric motor and generator or a motor/generator can be one unit (Fig. 50).

A—Mechanical Energy Input   D—Mechanical Energy Output
B—Generator   E—Batteries
C—Motor

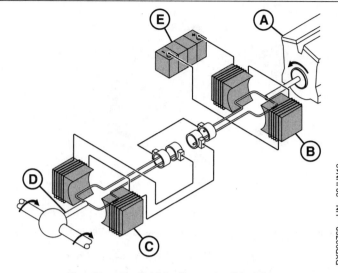

Fig. 50 — Basic Motor/Generator Principle

MM61211,00012C2 -19-11JUL12-1/2

This allows a motor/generator to run in two opposite modes or change the direction of electricity. As a motor it consumes electricity to make mechanical energy, and as a generator, it consumes mechanical energy to produce electricity (Fig. 51).

SUMMARY: MOTOR/GENERATORS

As the motor is turning, it also acts as a generator and generates a electromotive force (emf), that represents energy per unit charge (voltage). A motor/generator set may consist of motor and generator coupled together, or a single unit motor/generator will have both rotor coils of the motor and the generator wound around a single rotor, and both coils share the same outer field coils or magnets. The motor will run on the electrical input current while the generator creates the electrical output current. So if the motor is not under a load, the generator is creating a voltage supply back to the batteries (regenerative braking). See Regenerative Braking for more information.

A—Electricity Produced from   B—Voltage to Motor
    Motor

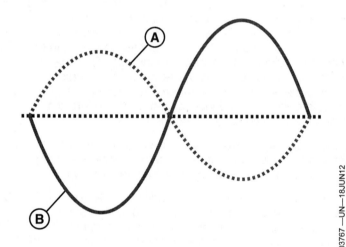

Fig. 51— Motor/Generator in Two Opposite Modes

MM61211,00012C2 -19-11JUL12-2/2

REGENERATIVE BRAKES

Regenerative braking is a system in which the electric motor that normally drives a hybrid vehicle is essentially operated in reverse (electrically) during braking or coasting.

This energy is reclaimed during braking by recharging the batteries and used to power the motor when the vehicle calls for an electric power source.

Instead of consuming energy to propel a vehicle, the motor acts as a generator that charges the on-board batteries with electrical energy that would normally be lost as heat through traditional mechanical friction brakes.

Regenerative brakes reclaim energy through the fundamentals of physics, Newton's Second Law (Force = mass X acceleration, or F=ma);

- F = Force
- m = mass
- a = acceleration

The faster you want an object to accelerate, the more force you have to apply, thus the same effect when stopping an object, creating friction, which equals energy. Regenerative brakes can reclaim some of this energy that would normally be lost.

In regenerative braking mode, the motor/generator acts as an electric generator whenever the brakes are applied causing the motor/generator to create a drag or torque to the drivetrain and counteracts the forward momentum, thus stopping the vehicle. As this happens it will also create energy (Voltage) back to the battery pack (Fig. 52).

NOTE: *In some cases where hybrids have no traditional energy storage, regenerative braking can be*

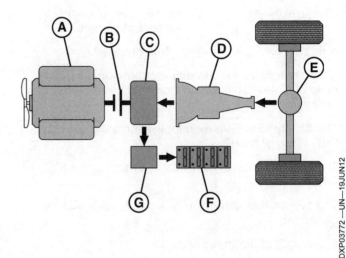

Fig. 52 — Example of Regenerative Braking

A—Internal Combustion Engine is "OFF"
B—Clutch is Disengaged
C—Motor/Generator Receiving AC Voltage
D—Transmission
E—Input
F—Battery Pack (DC Voltage IN)
G—Inverter (Converting AC to DC Voltage)

used to send energy back to the generator assisting with hydraulic operations.

MM61211,00012C3 -19-16OCT12-1/1

TEST YOURSELF

QUESTIONS

1. Relays allow a _____ amount of current to control a _____ amount of current.

2. A relay is basically a switch. True or false?

3. Electromagnetic devices that use the strength of the magnetic field generated in a coil to move a metal core are called _____.

4. The final result of a generator is alternating current (AC). True or false?

5. The final result of an alternator is direct current (DC). True or false?

6. The factors that determine how much voltage is generated:

   a. Strength of magnetic field

   b. Number of wire conductors.

   c. Speed of the armature or rotor.

   d. All of the above.

   e. None of the above.

7. The difference between an alternator and a generator is:

   a. The alternator has a stationary conductor while a generator has a rotating conductor.

   b. The alternator has a rotating magnetic field while a generator has a stationary magnetic field.

   c. Both a and b.

   d. None of the above.

8. A DC generator has all BUT one of the following:

   a. Armature.

   b. Field winding and magnets.

   c. Carbon brushes.

   d. Diodes.

9. Although a motor and generator are similar in construction, the difference is the:

   a. Generator converts mechanical energy into electrical energy.

   b. Motor converts electrical energy into mechanical energy.

   c. Both a and b.

   d. None of the above.

10. Solenoids and relays both convert electrical energy into mechanical energy. True or false?

11. What converts electrical energy to another form of energy?

12. What reclaims energy through the fundamentals of physics?

(Answers are in the back of the textbook.)

OUO1082,0002C13 -19-11JUL12-1/1

Storage Batteries

Introduction

DXP02964 —UN—12JAN12

BB87125,000415A -19-10FEB12-1/1

WHAT A BATTERY DOES

The battery stores energy for the complete electrical system.

On demand, the battery produces a flow of direct current for the devices connected to its terminals.

Battery current is produced by a chemical reaction between the active materials of the plates and the sulfuric acid in the battery fluid, or electrolyte.

After a period of use, the battery becomes discharged and will no longer produce a flow of current. However, it can be recharged by making an outside direct current flow through it in the opposite direction from the way current flows out.

In normal operation, the battery is kept charged by current input from the generator or alternator.

For good operation, the battery must do three jobs:

- It supplies current for starting the engine.
- It supplies current when the demand exceeds the output of the charging system.
- It stabilizes the voltage in the system during operation.

OUO1082,0002C1B -19-10FEB12-1/1

HOW A BATTERY IS CONSTRUCTED

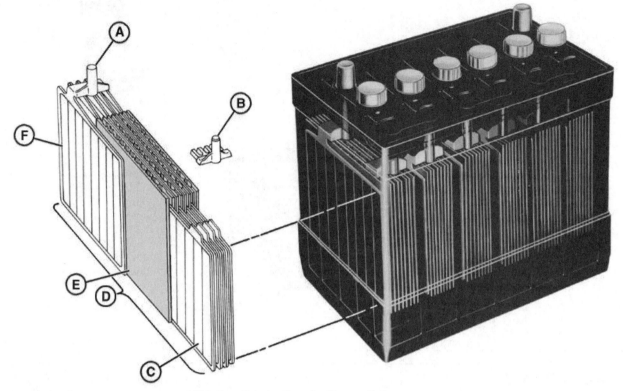

Fig. 1 — Construction of a Storage Battery

A—Terminal Post
B—Plate Strap Casting
C—Positive Plate Group
D—Element
E—Separator
F—Negative Plate Group

The battery is made up of a number of individual cells in a hard rubber case (Fig. 1). The basic units of each cell are the positive and negative plates.

These plates hold the active materials in flat grids. Charged negative plates contain spongy lead (Pb), which is gray in color. Charged positive plates contain lead peroxide (PbO_2), which has a chocolate brown color.

A plate group is made by welding a number of similar plates to a plate strap. (See Fig. 1).

Plate groups of opposite polarity are interlaced so the negative and positive plates alternate. Negative plate groups normally have one more plate than the positive groups. This keeps negative plates exposed on both sides of the interlaced group.

Each plate in the interlaced plate group is kept apart from its neighbor by porous separators as shown in Fig. 1. The separators allow a free flow of electrolyte around the active plates. The resulting assembly is called an element.

After the element is assembled, it is placed in a cell compartment of the battery case.

On a soft-top battery, cell covers are installed next. Then the cell connectors are welded between the intermediate terminal posts of adjoining cells. In this way the cells are connected in series. Finally the top of the battery case is sealed.

Continued on next page

OUO1082,0002C1C -19-11JUN12-1/3

Hard-top batteries have one-piece cell covers that reduce the formation of corrosion on top of the case (Fig. 2). These batteries have cell connectors that pass through the partitions between cells. The connectors and partitions are sealed so that electrolyte will not transfer between cells. This improves battery performance, since the cell connections are shorter and the cover is more acid-tight.

The main battery terminals are the positive (+) and negative (–) terminals. The positive (+) terminal is larger to help prevent the danger of connecting the battery in reverse polarity.

Reversing the polarity may damage some components and wiring in the system.

There is usually a red cable connected to the battery positive terminal and a black cable connected to the battery negative terminal. The negative battery cable will be connected to the engine block or other metal surface. The positive battery cable will be connected to the starter.

Always disconnect the negative battery cable first and connect it last. Otherwise a dangerous spark could occur. Never disconnect a battery with the key switch on or the engine running.

Do not lay metal tools or other objects across the battery because this may create a short circuit.

Vent caps are located in each cell cover. The caps have two purposes:

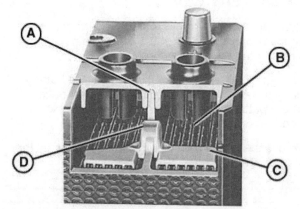

Fig. 2 — Hard-Top Battery with One-Piece Cover

A—Partition   C—Plate Strap
B—Element   D—Connector

- They close the openings in the cell cover through which the electrolyte level is checked and water is added.
- They provide a vent for the escape of gases formed when the battery is charging.

Electrolyte can cause acid burns, and the gases formed in batteries are very explosive. Review the battery safety information in Chapter 1, and be sure to follow proper precautions when working around or near batteries.

OUO1082,0002C1C -19-11JUN12-2/3

Each cell in a storage battery has a potential of about 2 volts. Six-volt batteries contain three cells connected in series, while 12-volt batteries have six cells in series (Fig. 3, top diagram).

For higher voltages, combinations of batteries are used. An example is where two 12-volt batteries are connected in series to serve a 24-volt system (Fig. 3, bottom diagram).

In summary:

- The battery is made up of cells.
- Each cell has positive and negative plates.
- Similar plates are welded into plate groups.
- The plate groups are interlaced but separated.
- This allows a free flow of electrolyte around the active plates.
- The resulting assembly is an element—one for each battery cell.
- Each cell is connected in series.
- Main terminals—(+) and (–)—connect all cells.
- Six-volt batteries have three cells in series.
- Twelve-volt batteries have six cells in series.

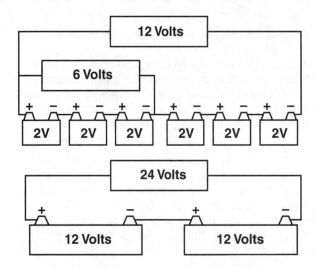

Fig. 3 — Battery Cells and Batteries Connected in Series

- For higher voltages, two or more batteries are connected.

OUO1082,0002C1C -19-11JUN12-3/3

HOW A BATTERY WORKS

The battery produces current by a chemical reaction between the active materials of the unlike plates and the sulfuric acid of the electrolyte (Fig. 4).

While this chemical reaction is taking place, the battery is discharging. After almost all active materials have reacted, the battery is discharged. It must then be recharged before use.

We'll discuss these two cycles, but first let's see what the electrolyte is made of.

Electrical Current Produced by Dissimilar Metal Plates in an Electrolyte Solution

Fig. 4 — How a Battery Produces Current Flow

OUO1082,0002C1D -19-16OCT12-1/5

ELECTROLYTE SOLUTION

The electrolyte in a fully charged battery is a solution of concentrated sulfuric acid in water (Fig. 5). Carefully follow all safety warnings in Chapter 1. It has a specific gravity of about 1.270 at 80°F (27°C) — which means it weighs 1.270 times as much as water. The solution is about 36% sulfuric acid (H_2SO_4) and 64% water (H_2O) as shown.

The voltage of a battery cell depends upon the chemical difference between the active materials and also upon the concentration of the electrolyte.

DISCHARGE CYCLE OF BATTERY

When the battery is connected to a complete circuit, current begins to flow from the battery. The discharge cycle begins.

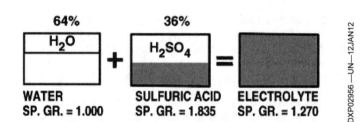

64%		36%		
H_2O	+	H_2SO_4	=	ELECTROLYTE
WATER SP. GR. = 1.000		SULFURIC ACID SP. GR. = 1.835		ELECTROLYTE SP. GR. = 1.270

Fig. 5 — Battery Electrolyte

This current is produced by a chemical action as follows:

OUO1082,0002C1D -19-16OCT12-2/5

The lead peroxide (PbO_2) in the positive plate is a compound of lead (Pb) and oxygen (O_2). Sulfuric acid is a compound of hydrogen (H_2) and the sulfate radical (SO_4), which, in turn, is a compound of sulfur (S) and oxygen. Oxygen in the positive active material combines with hydrogen from the sulfuric acid to form water (H_2O). At the same time, lead in the positive active material combines with the sulfate radical, forming lead sulfate ($PbSO_4$). See Fig. 6.

A similar reaction takes place at the negative plate, where lead (Pb) of the negative active material combines with the sulfate radical to form lead sulfate ($PbSO_4$). Thus, lead sulfate is formed at both plates as the battery is discharged, while the sulfuric acid in the electrolyte is replaced by water.

Note that the material in the positive plates and negative plates becomes chemically similar during discharge, as the lead sulfate accumulates. This condition accounts for the loss of cell voltage, since voltage depends upon the difference between the two materials.

CHEMICAL CHANGES IN BATTERY DURING DISCHARGE

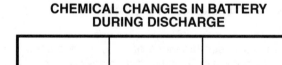

$Pb O_2$	$H_2 SO_4$	Pb

Fully Charged

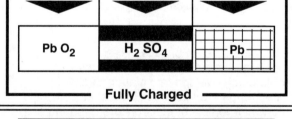

$Pb O_2$ $Pb SO4$	H_2O $H_2 SO_4$	Pb $Pb SO_4$

Completely Discharged

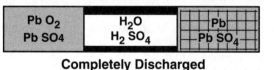

Fig. 6 — Chemical Action of the Battery

Continued on next page   OUO1082,0002C1D -19-16OCT12-3/5

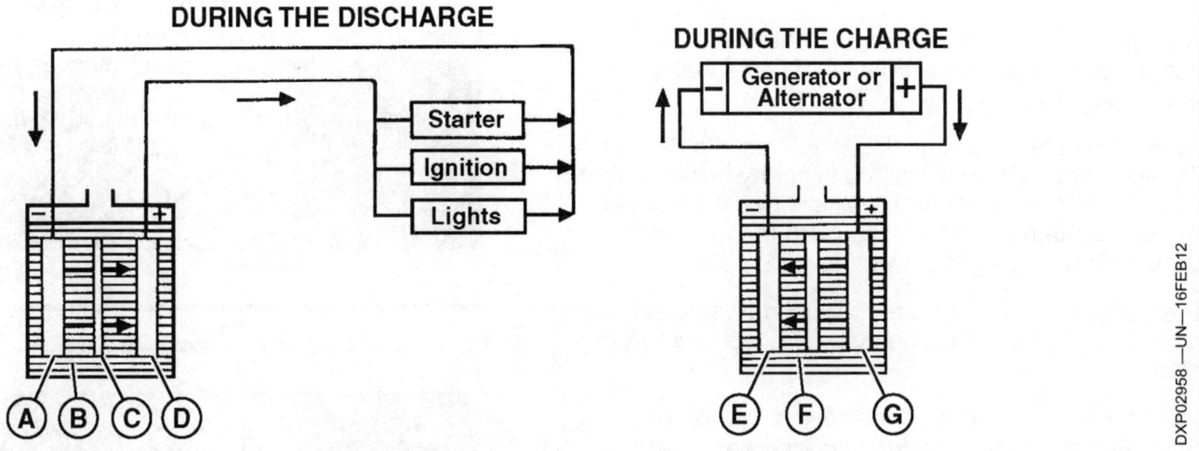

DURING THE DISCHARGE

DURING THE CHARGE

Generator or Alternator

Starter

Ignition

Lights

Ⓐ Ⓑ Ⓒ Ⓓ

Ⓔ Ⓕ Ⓖ

Fig. 7 — Chemical Action in Battery During Discharge and Charge Cycles

A—Negative Plate—Sponge lead changing to lead sulfate.

B—Electrolyte—The sulfate of sulfuric acid unites with active materials on plates leaving weaker acid solution. Hydrogen of acid and oxygen of lead peroxide combine to form water, diluting the solution.

C—Separator

D—Positive Plate—Lead peroxide changing to lead sulfate

E—Negative Plate—Lead sulfate changes to sponge lead. Sulfate returns to electrolyte.

F—Very dilute electrolyte made stronger by return of sulfate from plates

G—Positive Plate—Lead sulfate changes to lead peroxide. Sulfate returns to electrolyte.

As the discharge continues, the dilution of the electrolyte and the accumulation of lead sulfate in the plates eventually brings the reactions to a stop. For this reason the active materials never are completely exhausted during discharge. At low rates of discharge the reactions are more complete than at high rates, since more time is available for the materials to come in contact. When the battery can no longer produce the desired voltage, it is said to be discharged. It must be recharged by a suitable flow of direct current from some external source before it can be put back in service.

In summary, refer to Fig. 7 for a diagram of the complete discharge cycle of the battery.

Continued on next page

OUO1082,0002C1D -19-16OCT12-4/5

DXP02958 —UN—16FEB12

CHARGING CYCLE OF BATTERY

The chemical reactions that go on in the battery cell during charge are essentially the reverse of those that occur during discharge. (See Fig. 7 and Fig. 8).

The lead sulfate on both plates is split up into Pb and SO_4 while water (H_2O) is split up to get hydrogen to form H_2SO_4, or sulfuric acid. At the same time, the oxygen enters into chemical combination with the lead at the positive plate to form PbO_2, or lead peroxide.

These reactions demonstrate the important fact that water actually takes part in the chemistry of a lead-acid storage battery.

It is interesting to note that the specific gravity of the electrolyte decreases during discharge for two reasons—sulfuric acid (which is "heavier" than water) is used up and water is formed. Conversely, when the battery is charged, the specific gravity of the electrolyte increases—sulfuric acid is formed and water is used up.

When checking the specific gravity of the electrolyte after the battery has been fast charged, the reading may continue to rise for some time because the newly-formed acid requires time to diffuse from the plates into the electrolyte. Therefore, a specific gravity reading taken while the electrolyte is full of gas will be erroneously low. Conversely, higher specific gravity readings will be obtained as the gas is dissipated from the electrolyte. This situation often leads to the mistaken impression that specific gravity is still rising after charging has been discontinued, when this is not always true.

We have noted that water plays an important part in the chemical action of a storage battery. The purity of water for battery use has always been a controversial subject, but always resolves to the fact that distilled water is the best. Water with impurities hurts the life and performance of a battery.

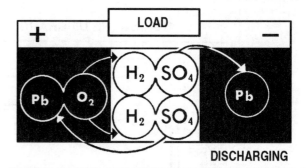

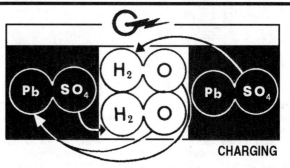

Fig. 8 — Chemical Action in the Battery While Discharging and Charging

SUMMARY: HOW A BATTERY WORKS

- The battery produces current by chemical action.
- This chemical action discharges the battery.
- As chemical action fails, the battery discharges.
- Charging the battery reverses the chemical action.
- Chemical action is between lead plates and electrolyte fluid.
- Electrolyte is sulfuric acid in water. Be careful.
- More acid in electrolyte = higher charge.
- Higher charge = heavier electrolyte.
- "Specific gravity" measures weight of electrolyte.

OUO1082,0002C1D -19-16OCT12-5/5

THE BATTERY AND THE CHARGING CIRCUIT

The battery is the heart of the electrical system. It plays its role in the operation of the starting, charging, ignition, and accessory circuits.

However, the battery is really part of the charging circuit.

In operation, the battery works in cycle with the generator or alternator (Fig. 9). This happens as follows:

1. The battery supplies current to the system and becomes discharged.

2. The generator sends reverse current to the battery, recharging it.

3. The voltage regulator limits the voltage from the generator to a safe value that does not over-charge the battery at high speeds.

The charging cycle is different at various engine speeds.

When the engine is shut off, the battery alone supplies current for the accessory circuits.

At low speeds, both the battery and generator may supply current.

At higher speeds, the generator may take over and supply enough current to operate the accessories and also recharge the battery.

This charging cycle is more fully explained in Chapter 6, "Charging Circuits."

A—Load
B—Battery
C—Generator

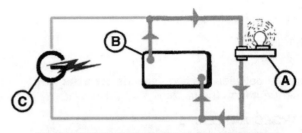

BATTERY SUPPLYING LOAD CURRENT

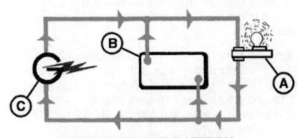

**GENERATOR AND BATTERY
SUPPLYING LOAD CURRENT**

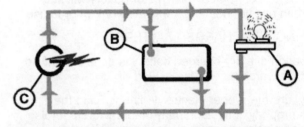

**GENERATOR AND BATTERY SUPPLYING LOAD
CURRENT AND CHARGING THE BATTERY**

Fig. 9 — The Battery and the Charging Circuit

DXP02960 —UN—12JAN12

OUO1082,0002C1E -19-10FEB12-1/1

TYPES OF BATTERIES

There are two types of batteries:

• Dry-Charged
• Wet-Charged

The difference between the two depends upon the way they are sent out from the factory.

DRY-CHARGED BATTERIES

A dry-charged battery contains fully-charged elements. But it contains no electrolyte until it is activated for service in the field. Therefore, it leaves the factory in a dry state. Once activated in the field, it is essentially the same as a wet-charged battery.

At the factory, the battery elements are specially charged as follows: A direct current is passed through the plates while immersed in an electrolyte of dilute sulfuric acid. The fully-charged plates are then removed from the electrolyte, washed in water, and completely dried. The battery is then assembled.

A dry-charged battery retains its state of full charge as long as moisture is not allowed to enter the cells. If stored in a cool, dry place, this type of battery will stay factory-fresh and will not become "shelf worn" prior to use.

ACTIVATING DRY-CHARGED BATTERIES

The activation of a dry-charged battery is done in the field by either the warehouse or the dealer.

To make sure the proper electrolyte is used and the battery is properly activated, many manufacturers furnish a packaged electrolyte for their dry-charged batteries along with instructions for placing the battery into service. These instructions must be carefully followed.

Under normal conditions, activate dry-charged batteries as follows:

1. Wear safety goggles and rubber gloves. Keep sparks and flame away from the battery. Make sure the work area is well ventilated.

2. Remove the seals from the battery cell openings and remove the vent caps (Fig. 10).

3. Carefully fill each cell with the approved electrolyte to the proper level (usually at the bottom of the filler neck). Examine the vent caps to be sure they are open and install the caps (Fig. 10).

4. Check the specific gravity with a hydrometer and record the corrected reading. (See "Battery Testing.")

5. Using a date code ring, gently stamp the date code on the battery. (See Fig. 22).

6. Allow the battery to stand for a few minutes, then recheck the level of electrolyte in each cell. If necessary, add electrolyte—not water.

7. As a precaution, check the open-circuit voltage of the battery. (See "Battery Testing.") As a general rule,

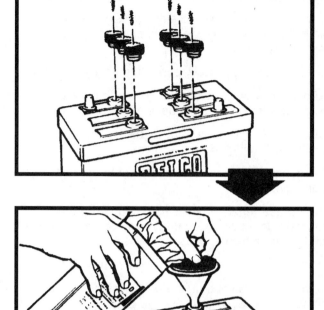

Fig. 10 — Activating Dry-Charged Batteries

place a 12-volt battery in service if it tests 12 volts or more, charge it first if it tests 10–12 volts, and consider it defective if it tests less than 10 volts.

8. As a final test, check the specific gravity of the electrolyte again. If the reading shows more than a 30-point drop (0.030) from the previous reading, charge the battery.

9. Slow charge a freshly-activated battery to ensure that the user receives a fully-charged battery. Always charge a newly-activated battery if the machine will not be run for at least one hour.

10. After the battery has been in service, add only approved water. Do not add acid.

11. Once in use, keep the battery serviced and charged just like a conventional wet-charged battery.

Dry-charged batteries should be stored in a cool, dry place with low humidity. Also be sure the temperature is between 60° and 90°F (16° and 32°C). Under these conditions, a battery can be stored for several years and keep a good charge. Under bad conditions, the battery may lose its charge in several weeks.

What is the advantage of dry-charged batteries? The prime advantage is that they do not sulfate and corrode during long storage like wet-charged batteries.

One disadvantage is that acids must be handled. Also, it is difficult to give the battery a good quality check before shipment.

Continued on next page   OUO1082,0002C1F -19-11JUN12-1/3

WET-CHARGED BATTERIES

Wet-charged batteries contain fully-charged elements and are filled with electrolyte at the factory. A wet-charged battery will not maintain its charged condition during storage, and it must be recharged periodically.

During storage, even though the battery is not in use, slow reaction takes place between the chemicals inside the battery, which causes it to lose charge. This reaction is called self-discharge.

The rate at which self-discharge occurs varies directly with the temperature of the electrolyte. A fully-charged battery stored at a room temperature of 100°F (38°C) will be almost completely discharged after a storage period of 90 days. The same battery, stored at 60°F (16°C) will be only slightly discharged after 90 days.

Wet-charged batteries, therefore, should be stored in as cool a place as available, as long as the electrolyte does not freeze.

A wet-charged battery that is kept fully charged will not freeze, while a discharged battery can freeze. For example, a discharged battery with a specific gravity of 1.100 will freeze at 18°F (–8°C) whereas a fully-charged battery with a specific gravity of 1.260 is never in danger of freezing, unless the temperature is –75°F (–59°C). See Table 1 below.

CHART SHOWING WHEN ELECTROLYTE FREEZES AT VARIOUS SPECIFIC GRAVITIES

Table 1 — When Electrolyte Freezes at Various Specific Gravities			
Condition of Battery	Specific Gravity of Electrolyte	When Electrolyte Freezes (Temp.)	
		(°F)	(°C)
Discharged	1.100	+18°	–8°
	1.140	+ 8°	–13°
	1.180	–6°	–21°
	1.220	–31°	–35°
Fully-Charged	1.260	–75°	–59°

SULFATED BATTERIES

Wet-charged batteries that are stored for long periods of time without recharging may be permanently damaged by the oxidation of the positive plate grid wires and the formation of lead sulfate crystals in the plates, which become dense and hard.

If the sulfate crystals are not too dense and hard, the battery may be restored to normal service by applying a slow charge rate for a longer-than-normal period. However, if the sulfate crystals are excessively hard and dense, the battery can never be restored to a normal operating condition, regardless of the rate or time of the charge.

Sulfation is caused by the chemical reaction in the battery discharge and was discussed earlier in this chapter. Both plates become lead sulfate ($PbSO_4$), and the acid is converted to H_2O; no further reactions can take place and a discharged battery results.

Continued on next page

OUO1082,0002C1F -19-11JUN12-2/3

If this condition is allowed to exist for a long enough period of time (30–90 days), the lead sulfate will harden and cause a sulfated battery (Fig. 11).

The hard sulfate deposit on the plates is extremely difficult to break down. Charging at high rates will only cause extreme heating, because the plates will tend to reject much of the current. Even the normal rate of charge is high for sulfated batteries. For sulfated batteries, therefore, recharge at 1/2 the normal rate, or approximately 1/2 ampere per positive plate per cell.

For example, a typical 6-volt battery has 12 negative and 11 positive plates per cell. If the battery is sulfated, recharge at a slow rate.

How long will it take to recharge a sulfated battery? This depends on the degree of sulfation, the state of battery charge, and the battery age. Charge at a rate that will not allow the electrolyte temperature to exceed 120°F (49°C), and charge until the specific gravity of all cells indicates a fully-charged battery.

This may take 60–100 hours when sulfation is extremely bad. If the specific gravity has not reached the normal full charge in this time, replace the battery.

While in storage, wet-charged batteries should be brought to full charge every 30 days, to guard against sulfation. Batteries removed from equipment during the winter should receive the same care or be stored under cool conditions.

Trickle-type chargers have been developed to produce a charging rate measured in milli-amperes, which is just sufficient to offset the losses due to self-discharge.

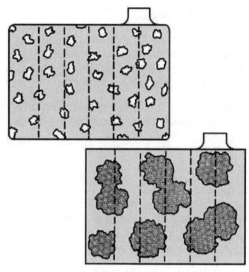

Fig. 11 — Sulfation of Battery Plates

NOTE: *Do not use trickle chargers for more than 60 days. Very low charging rates for long periods can cause permanent damage to the positive plate grids.*

A word about "warm" storage of batteries: Remember, you don't do a wet battery a "favor" by keeping it warm during storage; in fact, the best bet is to store the battery in as cold a place as possible, as long as the electrolyte doesn't freeze. In general, store batteries in a cool, dry place.

OUO1082,0002C1F -19-11JUN12-3/3

CHECKING ELECTROLYTE LEVEL IN BATTERY CELLS

Carefully follow the safety warnings in Chapter 1.

Periodically check the level of the electrolyte in the battery cells. This should be done at least every week during steady operation of the system.

Proper level is 1/4 inch (6 mm) to 1/2 inch (13 mm) above plate separators (so that the tops of the battery plates are covered). (See Fig. 12). Do not overfill or acid may spew out of caps.

Use only distilled water in the battery. If not available, be sure to use clean, soft water. Avoid hard water.

Never add acid to the battery unless electrolyte is lost by spilling.

Always wait until after checking specific gravity before you add water to the battery. This will ensure a true reading. If level is too low to check specific gravity, add water, operate in circuit for a few minutes to mix water and electrolyte, then check.

In freezing weather, never add water to the battery unless it will be operated immediately to allow proper mixing of water with electrolyte.

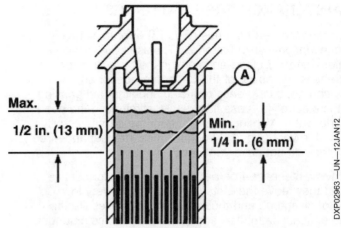

Fig. 12 — Proper Level of Electrolyte in Battery Cells

A—Plate Separators

OUO1082,0002C20 -19-11JUN12-1/1

MAINTENANCE-FREE BATTERIES

Maintenance-free batteries (Fig. 13) operate similarly to conventional style batteries. The use of lead-calcium plates instead of lead-antimony in their construction increases the ability of the battery to accept an overcharge, thus greatly reducing bubbling and gassing of the electrolyte. Less fluid is lost, eliminating the need to add water. Venting of gases from the cells is usually through a vent (Fig. 14) because most maintenance-free batteries do not have vent caps.

Most maintenance-free batteries are ready for service when they leave the factory. They have a very low rate of discharge and thus have a longer shelf life than conventional batteries—sometimes 12 months or longer, depending on storage temperature.

Fig. 13 — Maintenance-Free Battery

VISUAL INSPECTION

A simple visual inspection of the battery will often prove valuable in locating a possible cause of failure.

For example, many conditions are easily noted, such as damage due to excessive tightness or looseness of the hold-down clamps, distorted, cracked, or leaky case or cell vent caps, evidence of overflowing electrolyte, or heavy deposits of dust on the top of the battery. Any of these can contribute to battery failure.

If necessary, check out your visual diagnosis with further battery tests.

SPECIFIC GRAVITY TEST

The state of battery charge is indicated by the specific gravity or weight of the battery electrolyte.

The strength of the electrolyte varies directly with the state of charge of each cell.

To find out how much energy is available from the battery, you need only find out what percentage of sulfuric acid remains in the electrolyte. One of the simplest and most reliable ways to do this is to measure the specific gravity or weight of the solution.

Specific gravity can be measured very quickly by means of a battery hydrometer with a thermometer for temperature correction.

Hydrometers are calibrated to measure specific gravity correctly at an electrolyte temperature of 80°F (27°C).

Fig. 14 — Location of Vent on Maintenance-Free Battery

A—Vent

To determine a corrected specific gravity reading when the temperature of the electrolyte is other than 80°F (27°C): Add to the hydrometer reading four gravity points (0.004) for each 10°F (5.5°C) above 80°F (27°C). Subtract four gravity points (0.004) for each 10°F (5.5°C) below 80°F (27°C).

This compensates for expansion and contraction of the electrolyte at temperatures above or below the standard.

Continued on next page OUO1082,0002C21 -19-20JUN12-1/5

For example, a specific gravity reading of 1.234 is obtained at 120°F (49°C). Since this reading was taken with the electrolyte temperature 40°F (4°C) above the standard, a total of 16 (4 x 4) gravity points (0.016) is added, giving a corrected reading of 1.250 (Fig. 15).

As a further example, suppose a reading of 1.282 is obtained at 0°F (18°C). This reading was taken with the electrolyte temperature 80°F (27°C) below the standard. Therefore, a total of 32 (8 x 4) gravity points (0.032) is subtracted, giving a corrected reading of 1.250.

Batteries used in tropical or arctic regions are special cases. In tropical areas, use 1.225 as a full charge adjusted reading. In arctic regions, use 1.280 as a full charge reading. This allows for the special operating conditions and ensures maximum performance under stress of heat or cold.

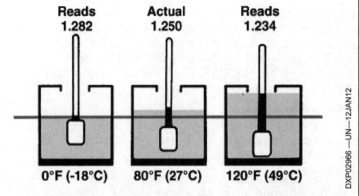

Fig. 15 — Correcting Specific Gravity Readings to Allow for Temperatures

Continued on next page

OUO1082,0002C21 -19-20JUN12-2/5

Using the hydrometer, test the specific gravity of each cell (Fig. 16). Be sure the hydrometer float is suspended freely in the liquid, not touching the walls, top, or bottom of the tube. Also be sure that your eye is at the level of the liquid when the reading is taken. Readings taken at a sharp angle are generally inaccurate.

If the liquid level is too low to check, add distilled or filtered water to the cells and charge the battery long enough to ensure complete mixing of the water and electrolyte; then check with the hydrometer.

When checking specific gravity of a battery which has been gassing freely, allow sediment to settle or gas to escape from the sample before taking the reading.

- Specific gravity should read from 1.225 to 1.280 (corrected for 80°F (27°C) electrolyte temperature).
- The variation in readings between cells should be not more than 0.050.

If the readings are not within the specified range, do the following:

IF SPECIFIC GRAVITY IS LESS THAN 1.225

When the specific gravity reading is less than 1.225 (after correction for temperature), the battery may be in satisfactory condition although its state of charge is low. Charge the battery before making further tests. (See later in this chapter for details.)

IF SPECIFIC GRAVITY IS ABOVE 1.280

When the specific gravity reading is above 1.280 (after correction for temperature), the battery may be in satisfactory condition although it is above full charge. In use, its specific gravity should return quickly to the normal 1.225–1.280 range. Make further tests to be more certain of the battery condition.

IF MORE THAN 0.050 VARIATION BETWEEN CELLS

A difference of more than 50 specific gravity points (0.050) between cells indicates an unsatisfactory battery condition. This may be due to unequal consumption of electrolyte in the cells caused by an internal defect, short circuit, improper activation, or deterioration from extended use. The battery should normally be replaced.

NOTE: *Specific gravity readings do not always give a true indication of the state of charge of a battery. If water has been added recently or acid has been lost through accident or leakage, the reading will indicate a lower state of charge than is actually the case. Therefore, never use specific gravity readings alone to decide the condition of a battery.*

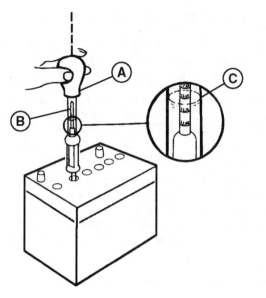

Fig. 16 — Checking Specific Gravity of Battery with Hydrometer

A—Hold Hydrometer Vertical   C—Read Scale at Eye Level
B—Float Must Be Free

Table 2 — State of Charge of a Typical Battery at Various Specific Gravity Readings	
Specific Gravity Reading (Adjusted)	**State of Charge**
1.260 Sp. Gr.	100% Charged
1.230 Sp. Gr.	75% Charged
1.200 Sp. Gr.	50% Charged
1.170 Sp. Gr.	25% Charged
1.140 Sp. Gr.	Very Little Useful Capacity
1.110 Sp. Gr.	Discharged

Table 2 above shows the state of charge of a typical battery at various specific gravity readings.

PREDICTING BATTERY LIFE

When the battery is new, all cells are in good condition and the voltage difference between cells is about zero or is negligible.

But as the battery gets months or years of service, the voltage difference between cells is greater. This is normal, for all batteries are perishable.

However, when the maximum difference in cell voltages reaches 0.05 volt, the battery is worn out and should be replaced.

HIGH-RATE DISCHARGE TEST

When a battery is known to be in good condition, its discharge performance can be measured by the specific gravity test. However, this check gives no hint of other factors that may cause a battery to perform badly.

Continued on next page

OUO1082,0002C21 -19-20JUN12-3/5

To be sure of a battery's ability to deliver current under load, give it a high-rate discharge test. This test shows the internal conditions that might not otherwise be detected.

Continued on next page

OUO1082,0002C21 -19-20JUN12-4/5

The test is made by using a high-rate discharge battery tester (Fig. 17).

This instrument is primarily a high-capacity fixed or variable resistance through which the battery may be discharged at a known rate, voltmeter readings taken, and comparisons made. Terminal voltage under load is used as the standard of performance.

The following conditions must exist before this test is made:

1. Battery specific gravity must not be less than 1.225 at 80°F (27°C). Otherwise, erratic or unreliable readings will result.

2. Battery temperature must be between 70° and 90°F (21° and 32°C). Terminal voltage does not remain constant but actually decreases as the temperature of the battery drops below range. For example, the terminal voltage of a 12-volt battery at 80°F (27°C) under load might be as high as 10.8 volts, while the terminal voltage of the same battery under the same load at 0°F (−18°C) would be only 8.4 volts.

Note the ampere-hour capacity of the battery, which is normally printed or stamped on the case. For a 6-volt battery, apply a fixed load in the test of twice this capacity. For a 12-volt battery, apply a fixed load of three times this capacity.

Connect the high-rate discharge tester to the battery as shown in Fig. 17. Be sure to follow the manufacturer's instructions.

Discharge the battery under the fixed load for approximately 20 seconds, then read the terminal voltage.

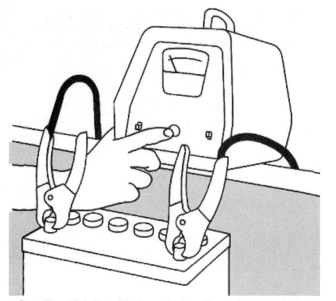

Fig. 17 — High-Rate Discharge Battery Tester Connected to Battery

If the battery is in satisfactory condition, the terminal voltage reading should remain above 4.8 volts for a 6-volt battery or above 9.6 volts for a 12-volt battery.

If the terminal voltage falls below this value, the battery is defective or it is not as fully charged as the specific gravity reading indicated in the specific gravity test.

To be sure of the battery condition, carefully charge it and repeat the test.

Replace the battery if it is defective.

Table 3 — Battery Testing Chart		
BATTERY TESTING CHART		
TEST RESULTS	**CONDITION**	**CORRECTIVE PROCEDURE**
SPECIFIC GRAVITY TEST		
SPECIFIC GRAVITY BETWEEN 1.225 AND 1.280	CHARGED	PERFORM HIGH-RATE DISCHARGE TEST
SPECIFIC GRAVITY BELOW 1.225	DISCHARGED	RECHARGE; PERFORM HIGH-RATE DISCHARGE TEST
MORE THAN 50 GRAVITY POINTS (0.050) VARIATION BETWEEN CELLS	(A) SHORTED CELL (B) ACID LOST (C) OLD BATTERY	REPLACE
HIGH-RATE DISCHARGE TEST[a]		
MIMIMUM TERMINAL VOLTAGE: 4.8 VOLTS FOR 6-VOLT BATTERY 9.6 VOLTS FOR 12-VOLT BATTERY	(A) DISCHARGED (B) OLD BATTERY	RECHARGE REPLACE

[a]*Ampere load should equal 2 x amp-hr rating for 6-volt batteries and 3 x amp-hr rating for 12-volt batteries.*

The chart in Table 3 shows the basic test results from the specific gravity and high-rate discharge tests.

OUO1082,0002C21 -19-20JUN12-5/5

CHARGING THE BATTERY

The amount of electrical current a battery can produce is limited by the amount of chemical reaction that can take place within it.

When chemical reaction in a battery has ended through defect or long use, the battery is discharged and can no longer produce a flow of electrical current.

The battery can be recharged, however, by causing direct current from an outside source to flow through it in a direction opposite from the way it flowed out of the battery.

During discharge, current flows from the positive (+) terminal of the battery, through the circuit, and back into the battery at the negative (−) terminal (Fig. 18). Within the battery, current flow is from the negative to the positive terminal.

To recharge the battery, this flow of current is reversed as shown, restoring the chemicals in the battery to their active state.

The battery then becomes charged and ready to produce electrical current again. The chemical action that takes place within a battery during discharging and charging is explained earlier in this chapter.

Batteries can be recharged in two ways:

• Fast Charging
• Slow Charging

A battery that is in satisfactory condition but requires recharging will accept a large amount of charging current without undesirable effect. This type of battery may be charged quickly at a high rate with a battery FAST CHARGER.

A battery that becomes sulfated, however, will not accept a high rate of charging current without possible damage. Its sulfated condition provides increased resistance to current flow within the battery. Flow of a high rate of charging current through this resistance creates heat, which can result in warping of the plates, boiling of the electrolyte, and eventual damage to the separators. Cell caps and covers and the battery case may be damaged or distorted.

A battery in this condition must be charged over a long period at a low rate. In this manner, sulfate formation on the plates will be gradually broken down and the battery returned to its normal charged state.

The reaction of the battery itself to fast charging will indicate the amount of charging current it can accept without damage. Never allow the battery electrolyte to heat up above 120°F (49°C).

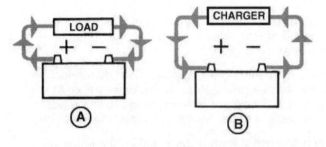

Fig. 18 — Current Flow During Discharge and Charge of Battery

A—Discharging   B—Charging

If the battery is sulfated, use a fast charger and reduce the charging rate or SLOW CHARGE it. For details, see "Sulfated Batteries" earlier in this chapter.

Wear safety goggles and rubber gloves when charging a battery. Keep sparks and flames away from the battery. Make sure the work area is well ventilated. When charging and discharging, a lead-acid storage battery generates harmful fumes and gas. This gas is very explosive.

Batteries connected in series can be charged together if their voltages are within 0.1 volt for 6-volt batteries or 0.2 volt for 12-volt batteries, of if their specific gravity is within 20 points. Otherwise, batteries must be charged individually.

When charging several batteries in series, charge at the rate of the lowest capacity battery in the line.

Batteries connected in parallel must be disconnected and the surface charge removed before checking the voltage of each battery.

To remove the surface charge, ground each battery negative terminal one at a time and turn a machine light switch on for one minute. Then turn the light switch off and wait one minute and check battery for proper voltage using a voltmeter.

Batteries connected in parallel can be charged together without disconnecting them when the battery voltage is 6 volts or above for 6-volt batteries and 12 volts or above for 12-volt batteries.

If battery voltage is below these specifications, the batteries may be sulfated. Charging each battery individually will break down the oxide and revive the batteries quicker than charging all batteries together in parallel connection.

Continued on next page   OUO1082,0002C22 -19-11JUN12-1/3

FAST CHARGING

Fast charging gives the battery a high charging rate for a short period of time. Never use a fast charger as a booster to start an engine.

Disconnect the battery ground cable. Then disconnect the battery positive cable. Remove the battery from the machine and, if necessary, fill the cells with distilled water to the level recommended by the load tester manufacturer.

Connect a charger or load tester of a 30–300 ampere rating to the battery. Be sure to follow the manufacturer's instructions for using the charger. A portable-type charger is shown in Fig. 19.

Set the charging rate at 30–60 amperes for a 6-volt battery or at 15–30 amperes for a 12-volt battery.

Start the charger at a slow or low charging rate. Increase the charging rate one selection at a time. Observe the ammeter after one minute at each selection for a 10-amp charging rate. If necessary, select boost.

After the charger has operated for at least three minutes, note the electrolyte. If it gasses excessively, the battery is sulfated and the charging rate must be reduced to prevent possible damage. Reduce the charging rate until the electrolyte produces comparatively few bubbles but gassing has not stopped entirely. Replace the cell caps.

The maximum charging time at the boost selection is 10 minutes for one conventional battery and 20 minutes for a maintenance-free battery. Allow an additional five minutes charging time for each -12°C (10°F). If the battery is not accepting the required 10-ampere charging rate by the specified time, replace the battery.

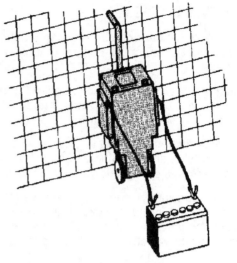

Fig. 19 — Fast Charging

If the battery is accepting the charge, check specific gravity after 30 minutes for a conventional battery or 60 minutes for a maintenance-free battery.

Charge battery to a specific gravity reading of 1.230 to 1.265 points.

The charging rate for conventional batteries may require 2–4 hours. The charging rate for maintenance-free batteries may require 4–8 hours.

After replacing a battery or after cleaning battery terminals, use an electrical sealant around the base of the terminals.

Continued on next page   OUO1082,0002C22 -19-11JUN12-2/3

SLOW CHARGING

A battery that is badly sulfated will not accept fast charging without possible damage. So these batteries must be charged at a slow rate.

Be sure to follow the manufacturer's instructions for using the charger.

Charge the battery at a low rate (7% of the battery ampere-hour rating or less) for an extended period of time until fully charged.

A battery is considered fully charged when three consecutive hydrometer readings, taken at hourly intervals, show no rise in specific gravity.

The normal slow-charging period is 12–24 hours.

If a battery's specific gravity has not reached the normal full-charge range (1.225–1.280) within 48 hours of slow charging, replace the battery.

Badly sulfated batteries, however, may take 60–100 hours to recharge completely.

SUMMARY: CHARGING OF BATTERIES

Remember these key facts when charging batteries:

- Batteries are charged by reversing their flow of current using an outside power source.

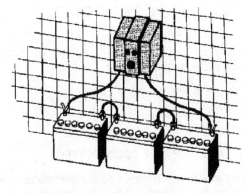

Fig. 20 — Slow Charging

- There are two ways to recharge batteries: fast charging and slow charging.
- If a battery is sulfated, use a fast charger but reduce the charging rate.
- If the battery is badly sulfated and will not accept a fast charge, use the slow-charging method.
- If fast charging is used, never exceed 30 amps for a 12-volt battery or 60 amps for a 6-volt battery. Avoid heating up the battery electrolyte above 120°F (49°C).
- To ensure a fully charged battery, follow the fast charge with a slow charge.
- After charging, always make sure the electrolyte is at the proper level in each cell.

OUO1082,0002C22 -19-11JUN12-3/3

BALANCING BATTERIES (24-VOLT SPLIT-PHASE SYSTEMS)

Four 6-volt batteries or two 12-volt batteries are sometimes connected in series to furnish 24 volts to the starting system. The lights and other electrical equipment then operate on two 12-volt circuits. Each circuit uses half of the batteries. These circuits are connected so the electrical load is nearly balanced between the batteries.

An unbalanced condition may occur when more than a normal load is imposed on one half of the batteries through a power outlet.

The method used to connect the batteries places them in balance; that is, the rate of discharge from all batteries is approximately the same, provided that accessories used with the power outlet, such as auxiliary lights, do not draw more than, say, 3 amperes. Thus the life of all batteries will be approximately the same. Auxiliary lights or other electrical equipment that draws up to 7 or 8 amperes can be used for short periods of time without materially affecting the batteries.

However, if auxiliary electrical equipment that draws more amperes is used for long periods, the batteries will be thrown out of balance and the life of those on one side will be affected. This is because the current drawn from this side is greater than that from the other, which results in failure to maintain the batteries at proper charge.

One method of correcting this condition is to install an extra power outlet to the other side.

The outside electrical load should then be alternated between the two outlet sockets as the battery charges demand, or when the first pair of batteries becomes low in charge, disconnect the outlet socket wire from one pair and connect it to the other pair.

Under these unusual conditions, pay strict attention to the charge of the batteries at all times so the load can be switched when one pair of batteries becomes low in charge.

OUO1082,0002C23 -19-10JAN12-1/1

CAPACITY RATINGS OF BATTERIES

The Society of Automotive Engineers (SAE) and Battery Council International have developed capacity ratings for batteries, these ratings are:

- Cold Cranking Ampere Rating
- Reserve Capacity

Let's look at each one.

COLD CRANKING AMPERE (CCA) RATING

This rating tells the power for starting on cold days when the going gets tough. It gives the number of amperes the battery at 0°F (-18°C) can deliver over 30 seconds and not fall below a voltage of 1.2 volts per cell, the minimum voltage required for dependable starting.

This is the most important rating because it tells how much power the battery can deliver for its No. 1 job—starting. The tougher the engine is to start, the more amperes it takes to get it started. Many low-priced batteries can deliver only 200 amps. The more powerful batteries will deliver 600 amps under the same conditions. A battery capable of delivering 200 amperes isn't likely to start an engine that needs 400.

RESERVE CAPACITY

The second rating is called reserve capacity. It tells "the number of minutes a new fully charged battery at 80°F (27°C) will deliver 25 amperes while maintaining a voltage of 1.75 volts per cell."

A simple translation is, if the charging system of your machine failed suddenly, how much time would you have to find help? The load of 25 amperes is equivalent to the needs of ignition, lights, and normal accessories.

In other words, 25 amperes is the power drain required to keep your machine operating. Reserve capacity is always expressed in minutes, the time available to seek help. The greater number of minutes, the greater the margin of safety.

COLD WEATHER AND BATTERY SIZE

For cold-weather starting, the battery must be big enough for the cranking job.

Fig. 21 shows how the load on the battery gets bigger when it is colder. At –20°F (-29°C), the battery has only 30% of its full cranking capacity. At the same time, a greater load is put on the battery by the colder engine when starting.

In effect, at cold temperatures the battery is "smaller" while the engine is "larger".

If the replacement battery is smaller than the original, the engine will surely be harder to start in cold weather.

HOT WEATHER AND BATTERY SIZE

In hot climates, hot starts often require as much or more battery power than cold starts. They may occur hard

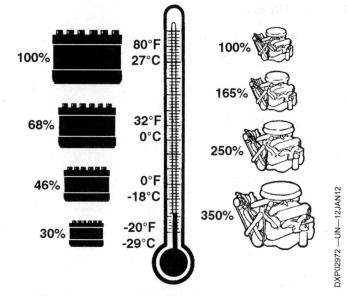

Fig. 21 — How Cold Weather Affects the Battery and the Engine When Starting

during hot weather, after the machine has been worked and the engine is hot. Hot starts are more common with the big high-compression engines and are aggravated when the machine is equipped with air conditioning.

There are many times in the heat of summer when engines are just as hard to start as in the winter. Therefore, use the same system of matching battery power to the engine in the hot climates as you do in cold climates.

OTHER FACTORS IN BATTERY SELECTION

When replacing batteries, be sure to replace the battery with one at least equal in size to the original.

A larger battery than the original may be needed if added accessories such as air conditioning put a larger load on the battery.

An extra-output generator may be the answer in cases where electrical loads are excessive or when operating mostly at idle speeds. This will help keep the battery charged and increase its service life.

The cheapest battery is not always the best buy for replacement. For example, three batteries in the same group size may vary in price, but they also vary in cold power rating, in construction, and in warranty period. Divide the price by the months of warranty, and you may find the most expensive batteries are really the cheapest, per month of expected service.

A final word on replacing batteries: One out of every four batteries returned for warranty has nothing wrong with it except that it is discharged. Be sure to troubleshoot the battery before you replace it.

Continued on next page   OUO1082,0002C24 -19-10JAN12-1/2

OUO1082,0002C24 -19-10JAN12-2/2

BATTERY REMOVAL AND INSTALLATION

Remove the battery as follows:

1. Record the location of the positive (+) terminal so that the battery is installed in the same way.

2. Disconnect the ground terminal first. Use only a box end wrench to loosen clamps on terminals. Remove clamps using a screw-type puller. Do not hammer on the battery posts.

3. Remove the battery and inspect the battery tray and hold-downs for dirt or corrosion. Clean any corroded part with ammonia solution or baking soda (1/4 pound added to a quart of water).

4. Check cables for worn or frayed insulation. Replace cable or bolts if corroded.

Install the battery as follows:

1. Be sure the battery is fully charged.

2. On new batteries with a warranty tag (Fig. 22), punch the tag to show the date of purchase and also when the guarantee expires. For example, if battery is purchased in November 2005 and has a pro rate warranty of 24 months, punch out dates as shown in Fig. 22.

3. On new batteries without a warranty tag, gently stamp the date on the top of the battery using a date coding ring (Fig. 22, upper). As shown, the 12 letters in the outer part of the ring are for the months, while the 10 figures in the inner part of the ring identify the year. Example: L5 = November 2005.

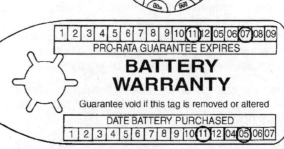

Fig. 22 — Date Coding for New Batteries

4. Set the battery in place, using a lifting strap if necessary. Make sure the battery is resting level in its tray.

5. Tighten the hold-down nuts evenly until the battery is secure. Do not overtighten because this will distort or crack the battery case.

6. Clean the battery terminals and cable clamps with a wire brush before attaching the clamps. This will ensure a good contact. Coat the terminals with petroleum jelly to prevent corrosion. Never paint the terminal posts.

Continued on next page   OUO1082,0002C25 -19-11JUN12-1/2

7. Check for the correct polarity of the battery (Fig. 23). The ground may be to the positive or negative pole, depending upon the system. Reversed polarity can damage the system. Note that the positive battery terminal post is larger than the negative post—match it with the larger cable clamp. Wait until last to connect the grounded cable or strap to avoid short circuits. On alternator-equipped machines, before connecting the last cable or ground strap, momentarily touch it against the battery post. With all switches and accessories off, no spark should occur. If it does occur, check for reversed battery polarity, improper alternator connections, or defective electrical equipment.

8. Tighten the clamps on the battery terminals. Use a box end wrench carefully to avoid twisting the battery terminal posts.

9. On generator-equipped machines, after the battery is connected and before starting the engine, polarize the dc generator. (See Chapter 6.) Never attempt to polarize alternator-equipped machines.

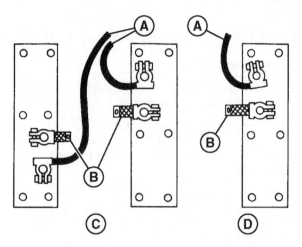

Fig. 23 — Installation of Typical Batteries

A—To Starter
B—To Ground
C—Dual Batteries
D—Single Battery

OUO1082,0002C25 -19-11JUN12-2/2

WHAT AFFECTS BATTERY LIFE

Periodic service has the best effect on battery life. In contrast, neglect and abuse will shorten the life of the battery (Fig. 24).

Besides periodic cleaning of the battery top, posts, and cable clamps, the four key factors in battery life are these:

- Electrolyte Level
- Overcharging
- Undercharging
- Cycling

Let's discuss each of these factors briefly.

ELECTROLYTE LEVEL

Keeping up the level of electrolyte in each battery cell is the most basic step in long battery life.

Underfilling causes the electrolyte to become too concentrated, making the plates deteriorate more rapidly. The low level also exposes the tops of the plates, which harden and become chemically inactive.

Overfilling causes electrolyte to spill out, corroding the battery posts and cell covers. Normally water is the only part lost from the battery electrolyte. This loss of water is due to evaporation, especially in hot weather and while charging the battery. Be sure to use distilled water if available. Otherwise, use only clean, soft water.

The correct level of electrolyte is always above the tops of the cell plates, which is usually to the bottom of the cell filler neck.

OVERCHARGING

Overcharging causes a loss of water in the cells by separating the electrolyte into hydrogen and oxygen gases. The gas bubbles wash active materials from the plates and reduce the battery capacity.

If the battery uses too much water, check it for overcharging.

Overcharging also causes the battery to heat up inside and oxidates the positive plate grids, resulting in a loss of cell capacity and early failure.

UNDERCHARGING

A battery that stays undercharged will become sulfated. The sulfate normally formed in the plates will become dense, hard, and chemically irreversible if allowed to remain in the plates for long periods. The lowered gravity levels then make the battery more likely to freeze.

In cold weather, undercharged batteries often fail to crank the engine because of their lack of reserve power.

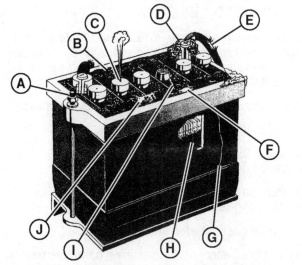

Fig. 24 — Things That Affect the Life of the Battery

A—Loose Hold-Down	F—Sealing Compound Defect
B—Dirt	G—Cracked Case
C—Overfilling	H—Low Electrolyte
D—Corrosion	I— Cracked Cell Cover
E—Frayed or Broken Cable	J— Cell Connector Corrosion

CYCLING

A cycle consists simply of a discharge and recharge. If operating conditions subject the battery to heavy and repeated cycling, its life will be shortened because cycling causes the positive plate's active material to shed and fall to the sediment tray in the bottom of the battery.

While the battery is perishable and will eventually wear out, be sure to remember that its life can be prolonged with a reasonable amount of care.

OTHER FACTORS IN BATTERY LIFE

If the battery hold-downs are loose, the battery will bounce around in its tray. This may cause the case to crack or cause internal damage to the elements.

If the hold-downs are too tight, this can also damage the battery by warping the case.

Dirt and corrosion will damage the battery case and may cause a dangerous short circuit.

Frayed or broken battery cables may also create a short circuit.

OUO1082,0002C26 -19-09MAR12-1/1

BATTERY LOAD TESTING

Before load testing a battery, follow proper safety precautions and read the instructions provided by the load tester manufacturer. Wear safety goggles and rubber gloves. Keep sparks and flame away from the battery.

Always visually inspect the battery prior to load testing.

Batteries can be load tested in two ways:

- Fixed Load Test
- Adjustable Load Test

If the battery has been on charge, blow away gases before continuing testing.

Load test batteries one at a time.

After replacing a battery or after cleaning battery terminals, use an electrical sealant around the base of the terminals.

FIXED LOAD TEST

1. Take a hydrometer reading of each cell. If there are more than 50 points variation between cells, replace the battery. If less than 50 points variation, proceed to step 2.

2. Test the specific gravity of the battery. It must be at least 1.225 at 80°F (27°C). If specific gravity is lower than this, charge the battery. If the specific gravity does not come up to this level, replace the battery.

   If the battery tests above this level, test it for internal shorts. Do this by connecting a 300-ampere load across the battery terminals for 15 seconds. If the battery starts to smoke or gas, replace it.

   If the battery tests at 1.225, proceed to step 3.

3. Make sure all electrical switches and accessories are off to reduce the possibility of arcing when the ground cable is disconnected. Disconnect the battery ground cable. Then disconnect the battery positive cable.

4. Clean corrosion from the battery and battery terminals.

5. Measure the temperature in the center cell of the battery.

6. Connect the voltmeter and load test leads to the proper battery terminals.

7. Apply a test load equal to 50% of the cold cranking ampere (CCA) rating of the battery.

   Another way to determine the correct load to apply to the battery is to note the ampere-hour capacity of the battery, which is normally printed or stamped on the case. For a 6-volt battery, apply a fixed load of twice this capacity. For a 12-volt battery, apply a fixed load of three times this capacity.

Apply the load for 15 seconds. Read the battery voltage, then immediately remove the load from the battery.

8. If the test voltage is below the minimum required (4.8 volts or above for a 6-volt battery; 9.6 volts or above for a 12-volt battery), replace the battery. If test voltage is at or over the minimum required, return the battery to service.

ADJUSTABLE LOAD TEST

1. Set the battery tester selector to the correct battery or engine size. The battery size selector must be set to a range which will include 50% of the cold cranking amp (CCA) rating of the battery. This range is three times the 20 ampere-hour capacity of the battery.

2. Connect the voltmeter and load test leads to the proper battery terminals.

3. Apply the load for 15 seconds. Read the battery voltage on the meter. Immediately disconnect the load from the battery.

4. Compare the battery voltage and temperature to the proper chart following.

Table 4 — Load Test Temperature Chart—6-Volt Battery		
LOAD TEST TEMPERATURE CHART (6-volt battery)		
°F	°C	Volts
70 and above	21 and above	4.8
60	16	4.75
50	10	4.7
40	4	4.65
30	–1	4.55
20	–7	4.45
10	–12	4.35
0	–18	4.25

Table 5 — Load Test Temperature Chart—12-Volt Battery		
LOAD TEST TEMPERATURE CHART (12-volt battery)		
°F	°C	Volts
70 and above	21 and above	9.6
60	16	9.5
50	10	9.4
40	4	9.3
30	–1	9.1
20	–7	8.9
10	–12	8.7
0	–18	8.5

5. If voltage is less than that shown in the chart, replace the battery. If reading is equal to or greater than that on the chart, the battery is good and can be returned to service.

OUO1082,0002C27 -19-10JAN12-1/1

CONNECTING A CHARGING BATTERY

Improper jump-starting of a dead battery can be dangerous. Follow these procedures when jump-starting a battery from a charging battery.

1. Check for a frozen battery. Never attempt to jump-start a battery with ice in the cells.

2. Make sure the charging battery and dead battery are of the same voltage.

3. Turn off accessories and both machine ignitions.

4. Place the gearshift of each machine in neutral or park and set the park brake. Make sure the machines do not touch each other.

5. Check electrolyte level in both batteries. Add, if low. Make sure the vent caps are secure and level. Cover the vent caps with a damp cloth.

6. Attach one end of one jumper cable to the charging battery positive terminal. Attach the other end of the same cable to the positive terminal of the dead battery (Fig. 25 and Fig. 26).

   Make sure there is good, metal-to-metal contact between the cable ends and the terminals.

7. Attach one end of the other cable to the charging battery negative terminal.

   Make sure there is good, metal-to-metal contact between the cable end and the battery terminals.

   Never allow the ends of the two cables to touch while attached to the batteries.

8. Connect the other end of the second cable to the engine block or machine metal frame below the dead battery and as far away from it as possible.

   That way, if a spark should occur at this connection, it would not ignite hydrogen gas that may be present above the dead battery.

9. Try to start the machine with the dead battery.

   Do not engage the starter for more than 30 seconds or the starter may overheat and the charging battery will be drained of power.

   If the machine with the dead battery will not start, start the other machine and let it run for a few minutes with the cables attached. Try to start the second machine again.

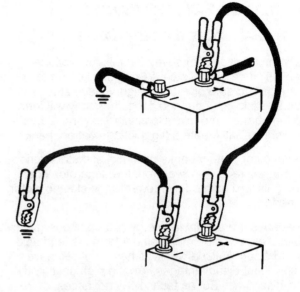

Fig. 25 — Jump-Starting 12-Volt Batteries in a Single-Battery Application (Charging Battery Is at Bottom)

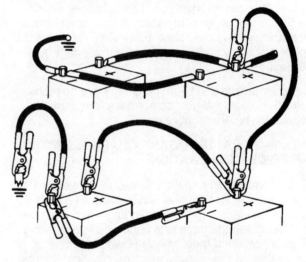

Fig. 26 — Jump-Starting 12-Volt Batteries in a Two-Battery Application (Charging Battery Is at Bottom)

10. Remove cables in exactly the reverse order from installation, disconnecting the grounded cable from the engine block or other metallic ground first, then the other grounded cable from the charging battery.

    Disconnect cables at positive terminals last.

11. Remove the damp cloth from the vent caps.

OUO1082,0002C28 -19-20JUN12-1/1

DXP02976 —UN—12JAN12

DXP02977 —UN—12JAN12

HIGH-VOLTAGE BATTERY BANKS

ABOUT HIGH-VOLTAGE BATTERY BANKS

A battery bank consists of several small, low-voltage batteries called cells; these cells when stacked on top of each other with create one larger high-voltage stick. And when these sticks are connected together, they will form a high-voltage battery module. Combining several of these battery modules will create a high-voltage battery bank.

Some hybrid car battery banks used nickel metal hydride (NiMH) that will receive power from the generator when recharging as well as produce power to the electric motor when needed.

NiMH batteries are a reliable energy source of energy for hybrids and are a major improvement from the lead acid battery most conventional vehicles have, but still have some significant disadvantages, like the high cost, and high self-discharge. But as technology advances, there is greater need for a more powerful and lighter battery, Li-ion batteries for hybrids are being developed. Lithium ion or (Li-ion) batteries which can have a power density of close to three times in comparison with a nickel-metal hydride battery, and is capable of producing higher output, and higher efficiency make it a great improvement over the NiMH battery.

Another advantage is that Li-ion batteries have no memory effect, which means that you do not have to completely discharge them before recharging.

HIGH-VOLTAGE BATTERY BANK CHARGING WITH ENGINE POWER GENERATION

An internal combustion engine is linked to an electric motor or (motor/generator) that is capable to run as a generator or an electric motor, depending what mode the vehicle is in. When the vehicle is under less-demanding scenarios, a portion of the engine's power is converted into energy though the motor/generator, creating voltage or charge to the battery bank.

The on-board computer sends a signal to stop sending electricity and start receiving it electricity, the motor/generator simultaneously stops receiving electricity for powering the vehicle and starts sending current back to the battery for charging (Fig. 27).

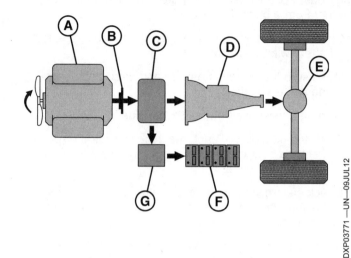

Fig. 27 — Battery Charging Mode

A—Internal Combustion
   Engine Is Running
B—Clutch Is Engaged
C—Motor/Generator Working
   as a Generator
D—Transmission

E—Output
F—Battery Bank (DC Voltage
   In)
G—Inverter (Converting AC to
   DC Voltage)

Continued on next page

MM61211,00012C4 -19-16OCT12-1/2

HIGH-VOLTAGE BATTERY BANK CHARGING WITH REGENERATIVE BRAKING

Regenerative braking will not only assist in slowing down the vehicle, it uses a motor/generator to create otherwise lost energy into renewable energy. As brakes are applied the electric motor reverses and it's roll now becomes a generator, creating current that is sent back to the high-voltage battery bank, thus recharging these batteries.

Although the voltage or energy collected while braking will not recharge the batteries completely it will greatly improve overall efficiency (Fig 28).

A—Internal Combustion Engine Is Off
B—Clutch Is Disengaged
C—Motor/Generator Receiving AC Voltage
D—Transmission
E—Input
F—Battery Bank (DC Voltage In)
G—Inverter (Converting AC to DC Voltage)

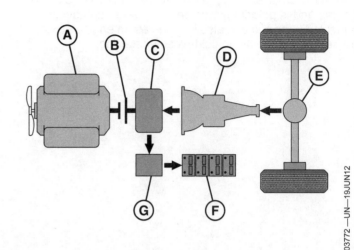

Fig. 28 — Regenerative Braking Mode

MM61211,00012C4 -19-16OCT12-2/2

BATTERY AND BATTERY ACID DISPOSAL

Improper disposal of batteries and battery acid can harm the environment and ecology. Check with environmental agencies for information concerning the proper disposal of these items (Fig. 29). Do not pour battery acid down a drain or into a stream, pond or lake.

Fig. 29 — Dispose of Fluids Properly

OUO1082,0002C29 -19-21JUN12-1/6

BATTERY TEST EQUIPMENT AND TOOLS

The testing equipment shown here will give you a balanced group of aids in testing and troubleshooting. But only one example from the many models available is shown. Also remember that this is not a complete listing; many other tools are useful for auxiliary tests.

HYDROMETER

The hydrometer (Fig. 30) checks the specific gravity of the battery electrolyte. All the good hydrometers have a built-in thermometer.

DXP02979 —UN—12JAN12

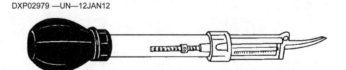

Fig. 30 — Hydrometer

Continued on next page

OUO1082,0002C29 -19-21JUN12-2/6

BATTERY CHARGER

The battery charger in Fig. 31 provides both fast and slow charges and is polarity protected to prevent damage if connected wrong. It can also be used as an engine starter for short periods to aid in cold-weather starting.

Fig. 31 — Battery Charger

OUO1082,0002C29 -19-21JUN12-3/6

BATTERY SERVICE KIT

The battery service kit shown in Fig. 32 is equipped with safety goggles, rubber gloves, battery carrier, post/clamp cleaner, clamp remover, clamp spreader/cleaner, side terminal adapter, hydrometer, and an apron. It services both side terminal and top post batteries. It is used to remove battery clamps, clean terminals and clamps, and test electrolyte.

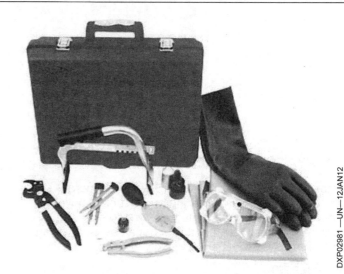

Fig. 32 — Battery Service Kit

Continued on next page   OUO1082,0002C29 -19-21JUN12-4/6

BATTERY TESTER

The solid state battery load tester shown in Fig. 33 electronically checks condition, power, and state of charge of both 6 and 12-volt batteries. It can also be used to compare batteries in multiple hookups and to check alternator regulated voltage.

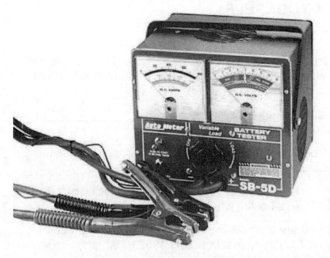

Fig. 33 — Battery Load Tester

DXP02982 —UN—12JAN12

OUO1082,0002C29 -19-21JUN12-5/6

CURRENT GUN

The current gun shown in Fig. 34 has an LCD readout that indicates both DC and AC currents. It measures current flow of each component from one location. It also measures alternator output, starting current, and battery charging levels.

Fig. 34 — Current Gun

DXP02983 —UN—12JAN12

OUO1082,0002C29 -19-21JUN12-6/6

TEST YOURSELF

QUESTIONS

1. (True or False?) The specific gravity of a fully charged battery is the same, regardless of the temperature of the electrolyte.

2. Battery electrolyte is made up of _____ and _____ .

3. (True or False?) Dry-charged batteries are activated at the factory.

4. If you test a battery and find that the specific gravity is 1.200 in all cells, what should you do?

5. If you are load testing a 6-volt battery and get cell specific gravity readings of 1.196, 1.193, and 1.194, what should you do?

6. The two methods of charging batteries are _____ charging and _____ charging.

7. Which method of charging should be used on badly sulfated batteries?

8. Batteries connected in _____ can be charged together if their specific gravity is within _____ points.

9. When performing a fixed load test on a battery, apply a test load equal to _____ of the _____ rating of the battery.

10. A battery pack consists of what?

11. How are high-voltage battery packs recharged?

(Answers are in the back of the textbook.)

OUO1082,0002C2A -19-11JUL12-1/1

DXP02706 —UN—23FEB11

DXP02924 —UN—09JAN12

Continued on next page OUO1082,0002C3B -19-12JUN12-1/2

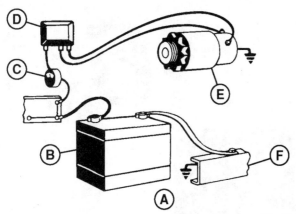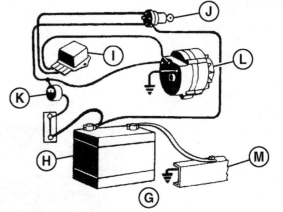

Fig. 1 — Charging Circuits—Two Types

A—DC CHARGING CIRCUIT
B—Battery
C—Ammeter
D—Regulator

E—Generator
F—Ground
G—AC CHARGING CIRCUIT

H—Battery
I— Regulator
J—Ignition Switch
K—Ammeter

L—Alternator
M—Ground

The charging circuit does two jobs:

• It recharges the battery.
• It generates current to power electrical, electromechanical, and electronic components during operation.

There are two kinds of charging circuits:

• DC Charging Circuits (Generators)
• AC Charging Circuits (Alternators)

Both circuits generate an alternating current (AC). The difference is in the way they rectify the AC current to the direct current (DC).

DC CHARGING CIRCUITS (A) have a generator and a regulator (Fig. 1).

The generator supplies the electrical power and rectifies its current mechanically by using commutators and brushes.

The regulator has three jobs: 1) opens and closes the charging circuit; 2) prevents overcharging of the battery; 3) limits the generator's output to safe rates.

AC CHARGING CIRCUITS (G) have an alternator and a regulator (Fig. 1).

The alternator is really an AC generator. Like the generator, it produces AC current but rectifies it electrically using diodes. Alternators are generally more compact than generators of equal output, and supply a higher current output at low engine speeds.

The regulator in AC charging circuits limits the alternator voltage to a safe, preset value. Transistorized models are used in many of the modern charging circuits.

OUO1082,0002C3B -19-12JUN12-2/2

OPERATION OF CHARGING CIRCUIT

All charging circuits operate in three stages:

- During starting—battery supplies all load current.
- During peak operation—battery helps generator (or alternator) supply current.
- During normal operation—generator (or alternator) supplies all current and recharges battery.

In both charging circuits, the battery starts the circuit when it supplies the spark to start the engine. The engine then drives the generator (or alternator), which produces current to take over the operation of the ignition, lights, and accessory loads in the whole system.

The battery also helps out during peak operation when the electrical loads are too much for the generator (or alternator).

But once the engine is started, the generator (or alternator) is the "work horse" that gives current to the ignition and accessory circuits.

The generator (or alternator) supplies this current as long as the engine is running. When the engine slows down or stops, the battery takes over part or all of the load.

Operation of the charging circuits during the three stages is illustrated in Fig. 2.

The top illustration shows operation while starting the engine.

The middle diagram shows what happens during peak electrical loads when the battery helps the generator.

The bottom diagram shows the system during normal operation when the generator supplies all power for loads and also recharges the battery.

In the rest of this chapter, let's look at each charging circuit by itself, first the parts of DC circuits.

A—Generator
B—Battery
C—Load
D—BATTERY SUPPLYING LOAD CURRENT
E—GENERATOR AND BATTERY SUPPLYING LOAD CURRENT
F—GENERATOR AND BATTERY SUPPLYING LOAD CURRENT AND CHARGING THE BATTERY

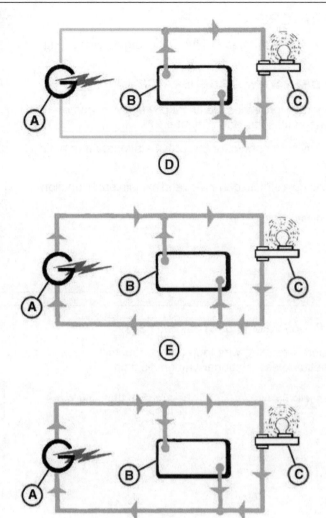

Fig. 2 — Charging Circuit in Operation—Three Stages

OUO1082,0002C3C -19-12JUN12-1/1

GENERATORS

The generator is the heart of the DC charging circuit (Fig. 3).

BASIC OPERATION OF GENERATOR

The generator produces electrical power by means of electromagnetic induction (Chapter 2).

This is moving a conductor through a stationary magnetic field.

Let's build up a simple generator and explain each function.

A—Generator

Fig. 3 — Generator Is the Heart of the DC Charging Circuit

OUO1082,0002C3D -19-16OCT12-1/39

The basic generator (Fig. 4) has two parts:

- Armature—rotating wire loop (the conductor)
- Magnetic Poles—stationary magnetic field

A—Magnetic Poles   B—Armature (Rotating Wire Loop)

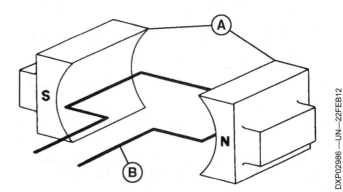

Fig. 4 — The Basic Parts of a Generator

OUO1082,0002C3D -19-16OCT12-2/39

Now let's set the basic generator in motion (Fig. 5).

As the armature rotates through the magnetic field of the poles, voltage is generated.

Using the Right Hand Rule, we can see that the voltage comes toward us on the left side in Fig. 5, and flows away from us on the right side.

By the Conventional Theory, this means that the left end of the armature loop is positive (+) while the right end is negative (–).

A—Direction of Rotation   C—Direction of Current Flow
B—Magnetic Field

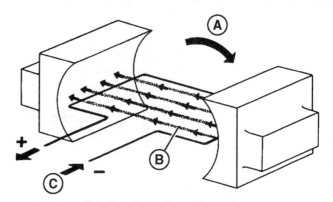

Fig. 5 — Basic Generated Voltage

Continued on next page   OUO1082,0002C3D -19-16OCT12-3/39

For current to flow, we must add three more parts (Fig. 6).

Let's connect the ends of the armature loop to a split ring called a commutator.

Next we need some brushes to contact the commutator and some wires to connect the brushes to a load.

Now we have completed the circuit and current will flow.

A—Commutator   C—Load
B—Circuit Wires   D—Brushes

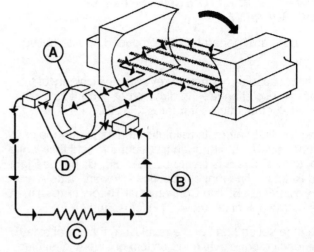

Fig. 6 — Basic Current Flow in Generator

OUO1082,0002C3D -19-16OCT12-4/39

To ensure a strong current and proper flow, we must add one more feature (Fig. 7).

The magnets by themselves are weak and create a weak field. The result is that the voltage induced is low.

To remedy this, let's wind the wire conductors around the magnets as shown in Fig. 7.

Now by attaching the wires to the brushes, the current is used to strengthen the magnetic field between the poles. This wiring is called the field circuit of the generator.

This completes our basic generator.

A—Field Circuit

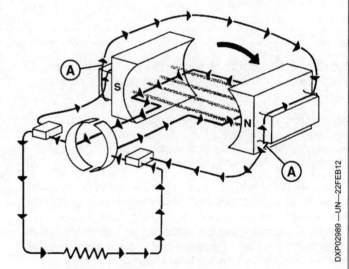

Fig. 7 — Complete Parts of Basic Generators

Continued on next page   OUO1082,0002C3D -19-16OCT12-5/39

HOW THE GENERATOR CONVERTS AC TO DC CURRENT

So far, our basic generator has produced an alternating current.

This is because the armature reverses the polarity of the current and so changes the direction of current flow on each side of the loop as it rotates (Fig. 8).

During the first half of its revolution in Fig. 8, the top of armature side A cuts through the magnetic field first, while the bottom of side B is first to cut the field. Using the Right Hand Rule, we find that current flows "toward" side A and "away from" side B. The Conventional Theory (+ to −) then gives us the polarities shown: (+) for A, and (−) for B.

During the second half of the revolution, the top of side B is the leading edge, while the bottom of side A is leading. Again using the rules, we find that B is now (+), while A is (−).

So we see that the armature loop ends reverse polarity during each revolution.

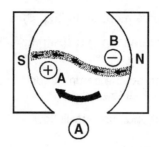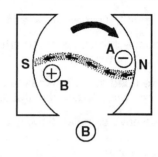

Fig. 8 — How the Polarity of the Armature Changes During Each Revolution

A—FIRST HALF OF
REVOLUTION

B—SECOND HALF OF
REVOLUTION

The result: alternating current (AC).

How do we convert this AC current to DC?

OUO1082,0002C3D -19-16OCT12-6/39

Getting this AC current to flow to the load in the same direction (DC) is the job of the commutator and brushes (Fig. 9).

Twice during each rotation, the armature is vertical to the magnetic field as shown. Here the armature loop is not passing through the field and so no voltage is generated at this instant. This is the static neutral point.

The commutator is split into two parts with the open areas matching the neutral point of the armature as shown. This means that there is a gap as the commutator passes the brushes. Past this point the other half of the commutator contacts the brushes. Since the coil is in the same relative position as during the preceding one-half revolution, current flow to the brush stays in the same direction.

The result: direct current (DC).

This is how the generator converts AC current to DC current.

As we saw in Chapter 2, three factors decide how much voltage is generated:

- The strength of the magnetic field
- The number of wire conductors on the armature
- The speed of the armature

SUMMARY: HOW A GENERATOR WORKS

- Moving a conductor through a stationary field = basic generator.
- Basic generator = armature (rotating) + magnetic poles (fixed).

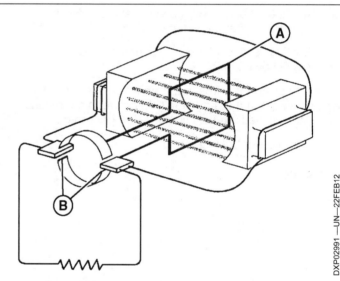

Fig. 9 — How Generator Converts AC to DC Current

A—At Static "Neutral Point" No
Voltage Is Generated

B—Gaps Between Commutator
Halves

- Circuit is completed through commutator and brushes.
- Field circuit windings strengthen the magnetic poles.
- Commutator converts AC to DC current.

Now let's look at the generator parts in more detail.

Continued on next page   OUO1082,0002C3D -19-16OCT12-7/39

ARMATURE

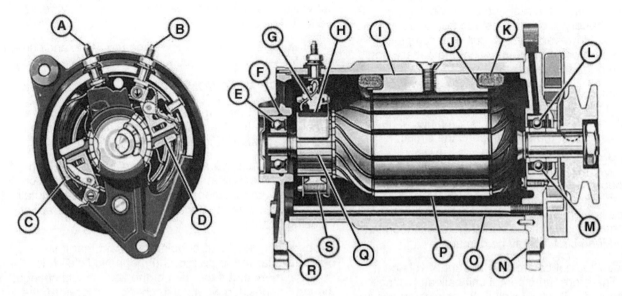

Fig. 10 — DC Generator in Cutaway View

A—Field Terminal	E—Ball Bearing	K—Field Coil	P—Armature
B—Armature Terminal	F—"O" Ring Clamp	L—Ball Bearing	Q—Commutator
C—Grounded Brush Holder	G—Brush Arm	M—Felt Retainer Plate	R—Spring
D—Insulated Brush Holder	H—Brush	N—Drive End Frame	S—Commutator End Frame
	I— Pole Shoe	O—Thru Bolt	
	J—Insulation		

The armature is not just one wire loop or conductor, but many wire conductors. This means that a greater voltage is developed.

These conductors are wound around a core of soft laminated iron sections as shown in Fig. 10. The sections are then attached to the armature drive shaft.

The laminated iron sections are used in place of a solid core of iron to reduce heat. A solid iron core would generate unwanted voltage within itself. This would result in current flow called "eddy currents or foucault currents", which create excessive heat.

COMMUTATOR

The commutator must have a section to match each wire section of the armature.

So the commutator ring is composed of many sections or bars (Fig. 10). Mounted on the end of the armature drive shaft, each section or bar is held together and separated from the adjacent bar by an insulating material. The ends of each wire conductor are connected to two adjacent commutator bars.

BRUSHES

The brushes are made of various materials, depending on the output needs of the generator. Fixtures in the generator hold the brushes so that their ends rub or ride on the commutator ring. Usually, spring pressure forces the brushes against the ring as the brushes wear.

POLE SHOES

The pole shoes are permanent magnets, fixed to the inside of the generator housing. Set directly across from each other, the two opposing poles set up a weak magnetic field.

FIELD CIRCUIT

The field circuit is composed of one wire conductor wound around both field poles many times. One end of the wire is attached to the brush; the other end to the field circuit terminal.

HOUSING

All generator components are enclosed in a metal housing. Most generator housings have openings at both ends. This allows air to pass through and cool the generator. On the pulley end of the drive shaft, there is usually a fan to force the air to circulate.

AUXILIARY UNITS

Three external units are an important part of generator operation.

We will briefly discuss these units now and cover them more extensively later in this chapter.

CUTOUT RELAY

Continued on next page

OUO1082,0002C3D -19-16OCT12-8/39

As you know, the generator recharges the battery as well as supplies current to the rest of the electrical system. To recharge the battery, a circuit must run from the generator to the battery. However, if this circuit was complete when the generator was not operating, the battery would discharge through the generator.

To prevent this, an automatic switch called a cutout relay is installed in the circuit. While the generator is operating, the switch is closed and the circuit is complete. When the generator is stopped, the switch opens the circuit.

VOLTAGE REGULATOR

Voltage induced by the generator will go as high as necessary to overcome any resistance in the circuit. If resistance is high, voltage will be high, while low resistance means low voltage. But if voltage is too high, the field and load circuits may be damaged.

The generator cannot control the amount of voltage it produces. Therefore, an external unit called a voltage regulator is used in the field circuit. It has a shunt coil and contact points to control the strength of the magnetic field, thus limiting the voltage generated.

CURRENT REGULATOR

Excessive current flow is caused by too little resistance and can also cause heat damage to the armature.

A current regulator is installed in the load circuit to control this current flow. This unit is very similar to the voltage regulator above.

Both the voltage regulator and current regulator are used, but while one is working, the other is not. They never work at the same time.

All three units—cutout relay, voltage regulator, and current regulator—are usually housed together in one assembly.

ARMATURE REACTION

We have said that commutation takes place when the armature is in the "neutral" position. This is true of a one-loop armature (Fig. 9).

However, an actual armature has more than one loop. In this case, "one loop at a time" is in the neutral position. Therefore, commutation occurs between the commutator sections connected to that loop. The other loops are still inducing voltage.

In describing the "neutral point," we said that it is perpendicular to the path of the magnetic field. It is obvious, then, that if the path of the field should change, the neutral position would also change. Therefore, the brush position would also have to be changed.

To see why, let's return to the basic operation for a moment.

Remember that when the generator is producing voltage and current, the brush is in contact with the commutator section. This contact is like a completed circuit.

To get commutation, the commutator section beneath the brush is replaced by the section following it. In a sense, the circuit between the first section and the brush is broken—an open circuit.

Continued on next page   OUO1082,0002C3D -19-16OCT12-9/39

During normal operation (Fig. 11), no voltage is induced in the loop attached to the commutator section at the time the connection is broken. However, if the voltage and current flow are still in that loop at this time, a spark or arc will appear between the brush and commutator section (Fig. 12).

This arcing is caused by the current that is attempting to cross between the section and brush. The duration of the arc is quite short because of the low voltage and rapidly expanding distance between brush and section. However, severe arcing will damage the brushes and commutator.

However, the brushes are set directly over the open area at the moment when the armature loop is in neutral position (Fig. 12).

But if the magnetic field path is distorted, the armature loop will conduct current during the commutation. The result: arcing.

Distortion of the magnetic field as shown really exists. This distortion is caused by the magnetic field set up around the armature conductors acting with the magnetic field of the poles. It is called armature reaction.

A—Brush
B—Armature Loop
C—Commutator

D—Armature Loop Inducing Voltage at "Old" Neutral Point
E—Arcing

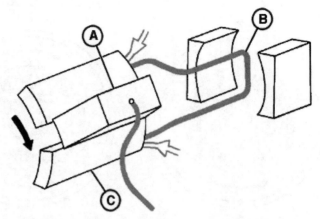

Fig. 11 — Brush-Commutator Circuit (Normal Operation)

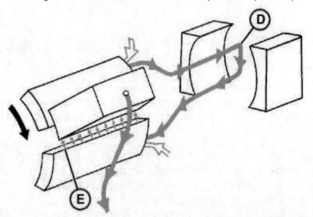

Fig. 12 — Arcing Occurs When Neutral Point Is Changed

Continued on next page   OUO1082,0002C3D -19-16OCT12-10/39

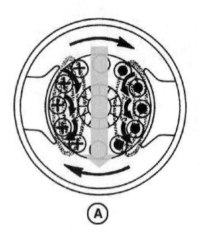 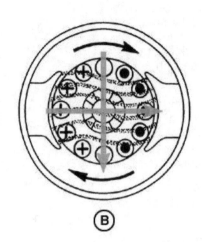 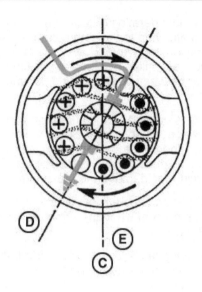

Fig. 13 — Armature Reaction

A—ARMATURE MAGNETIZING   B—RESULTING FLOW   D—Load Neutral
   FORCE   C—BRUSH PLACEMENT   E—Mechanical Neutral

Fig. 13 shows the sequence of the armature reaction that distorts the field and how the brushes are placed to counteract it.

The illustration at left shows the magnetic field surrounding the coils of the armature that results when current flow is established in these coils. Remember that all the load current flows through the conductors of the armature, and the greater the current flow the greater will be the strength of the surrounding magnetic field.

The center diagram in Fig. 13 shows the magnetic field formed after combining the magnetic field of the armature with the field of the pole pieces. The change in the path of the magnetic field changes the neutral position to a new position under load.

To counteract this, the brushes must be located at the load neutral rather than at the mechanical neutral. This is shown at right in Fig. 13. The load neutral is located after the mechanical neutral during rotation as shown. At a constant speed and load, the new load neutral is the ideal

commutating point. However, with varying speeds and loads, the load neutral point is constantly changing. For this reason a brush position is selected which will be the best average location that will create the least arcing at the brush under normal operating conditions.

TYPES OF GENERATORS

Basically, all generators are alike. They all use the basic parts we have described.

However, there are variations, each using the basic components in different ways or quantities.

The different types of generators are these:

• Shunt—standard for most uses
• Third Brush—needs no current regulator
• Interpole—provides better commutation
• Bucking Field—for changing loads and speeds
• Split Field—for low speeds but high loads

Let's discuss each type of generator.

Continued on next page   OUO1082,0002C3D -19-16OCT12-11/39

SHUNT GENERATOR

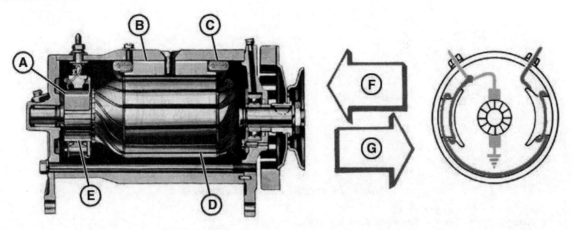

Fig. 14 — Shunt Generator

A—Brush
B—Pole Piece
C—Field Coil
D—Armature
E—Commutator
F—Cross Sectional View
G—Electrical Diagram

The shunt generator is similar to the basic generator we described earlier. It is a two-pole, two-brush unit with an armature, a commutator, and field and load circuits (Fig. 14).

Operation is also the same: voltage is induced by an armature rotating through a magnetic field, and current is sent through the commutator into the field and load circuits, via the brushes.

A shunt generator uses an external voltage regulator to control the field circuit. The name "shunt" refers to the field coil that is in parallel with the armature.

OUO1082,0002C3D -19-16OCT12-12/39

The generator field circuit is shown in Fig. 15.

In this circuit the voltage regulator points are located after the field coils. The field circuit is grounded on one end at the generator regulator. The other end is attached to the insulated brush inside the generator. This circuit is called an "A" circuit.

NOTE: *Some generators have field circuits in which the regulator points are located before the field coils and the field coils are grounded inside the generator. These models are called "B" circuit generators. They are not used on farm and industrial machines at the present time. In this chapter we will cover only the common "A" circuit generators.*

The third brush generator has three brushes instead of two, and uses another means of controlling the flow of current.

The two main brushes, insulated and grounded, are positioned at the neutral point on the commutator to obtain the maximum voltage. The third brush is placed between the other two, which means that it picks up less than maximum voltage.

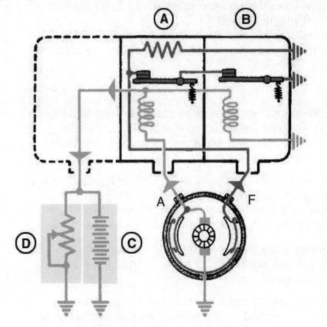

Fig. 15 — Generator Field Circuit

A—Current Reg
B—Voltage Reg
C—Battery
D—Vehicle Load

Continued on next page

OUO1082,0002C3D -19-16OCT12-13/39

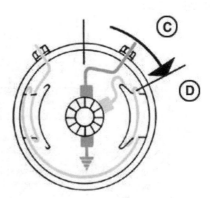

Fig. 16 — Third Brush Generator Output Adjustments

A—Higher Output
B—Field — Increased Voltage,
   Increased Current, Greater
   Magnetic Strength

C—Lower Output
D—Field — Reduced Voltage,
   Decreased Current, Less
   Magnetic Strength

As you can see in Fig. 16, the two main brushes (shown in dark gray) are in the load circuit. The third brush (shown in light gray) is connected to the field coil.

On most units the third brush position is adjustable as shown. By moving the brush toward the insulated brush, voltage is increased across the field circuit. Moving it away from the main brush decreases the voltage.

When a third brush is used, current is controlled in two ways:

• The third brush picks up less voltage; therefore, less current flows through the field circuit. This means a weaker magnetic field.
• At greater loads and speeds, the magnetic field is more distorted so fewer lines of force are cut by the armature.

This means that less voltage and current are developed in the field circuit and coils.

At one time, the third brush generator was widely used in the automotive industry. It is relatively simple in design and by shifting the third brush, its output can be controlled. It can also reach its peak output at medium speed.

Today, however, the demands of electrical power have increased. Often the third brush generator cannot meet these demands. Though it reaches its peak at medium speed, power begins to decrease at higher speeds. For this reason it is now used primarily on slow speed equipment that has a low power requirement.

OUO1082,0002C3D -19-16OCT12-14/39

The interpole generator is quite similar to the shunt model, but has an extra magnetic pole shoe (Fig. 17). This changes the operation and solves a problem of locating the brushes at load neutral on the shunt generator.

Earlier we explained that the best commutation took place when the armature was at the "neutral point." We also told how, because of magnetic field distortion, an ideal commutation point for all loads could not be reached.

This is true except when using the interpole generator. By adding another pole shoe, the distortion of the magnetic field is corrected.

By installing this extra magnet between the other two shoes, the distorted magnetic field created by the current flow through the armature is neutralized.

The interpole is wound with heavy copper wire since all armature current flow goes through this coil. The number of coil turns is calculated to produce enough ampere

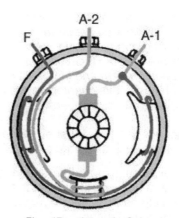

Fig. 17 — Interpole Generator

turns in the opposite direction to offset the magnetic field created by the armature.

Continued on next page   OUO1082,0002C3D -19-16OCT12-15/39

6-12

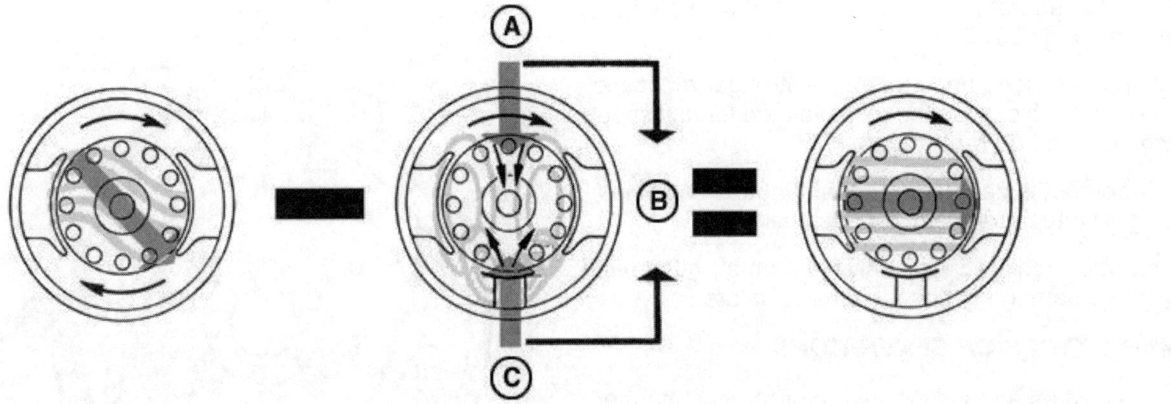

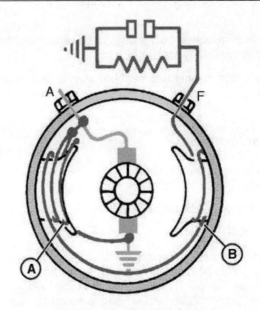

Fig. 18 — Interpole Generator in Operation

A—Armature Magnetizing Force   B—Cancel
C—Interpole Magnetizing Force

Now the magnetic field lines are again in a straight line as shown in Fig. 18. The best commutation point is again at the "neutral" or "mechanical neutral point," and the brush position is matched to this.

Besides providing the ideal commutation point, the interpole generator can greatly increase the brush life over a non-interpole generator.

The bucking field generator is another variation on the standard shunt generator. But it can develop the voltage for high current at very low speeds.

Actually, getting a high current at low speeds is comparatively easy. The problem is to control excessively high voltage at high speeds.

OUO1082,0002C3D -19-16OCT12-16/39

To control the high voltage, a "bucking" field coil is used (Fig. 19). This coil is a high-resistance conductor wound around one pole shoe and connected across the brushes as shown. The coil is connected in reverse of the main field circuit.

This produces a magnetic effect which opposes the normal magnetic field.

At low speeds, the bucking field has little or no effect on the magnetic field and the generator is able to produce high voltage and current.

As speed increases, the bucking field magnetism becomes greater and reduces the magnetic field lines of force. With a reduced field, the armature's voltage is lowered and the voltage output of the generator drops.

In effect, the bucking field circuit helps the voltage regulator to control voltage. It reduces the residual magnetism in the pole shoes while the regulator controls the magnetism and current flow in the field circuit.

Although the bucking field generator is able to provide adequate electrical power at low speeds, its primary use is in a system that has a wide variation in speed.

Some generator uses require a high power output at slow speeds for long periods of time.

These systems are usually on buses, farm machines, etc., that operate at low speeds or sit with the engine idling.

Fig. 19 — Bucking Field Generator

A—Bucking Field   B—Normal Field

The split field generator works for these operations.

Continued on next page   OUO1082,0002C3D -19-16OCT12-17/39

The split field generator has an extra set of pole shoes and brushes (Fig. 20).

By doubling the shoes and brushes, a stronger magnetic field is created. This gives the extra voltage for low-speed charging and load current.

Generator output is doubled by separating the two fields and using a voltage regulator for each field.

Yet, each field circuit receives only the normal voltage and current so no damage is done to the regulators.

SUMMARY: TYPES OF GENERATORS

- Shunt—used as a standard generator for most normal operations.
- Third Brush—eliminates the use of a current regulator. Is relatively easy to change third brush position and control the output. Used in systems with low speed and low load requirements.
- Interpole—provides a better commutation point and extends brush life.
- Bucking Field—used where there is a wide variation of load and speed requirements.
- Split Field—used in systems with low speed, but high load requirements.

USES OF GENERATORS

Why is one generator used for one application, but not in another?

We have already touched on the uses of generators when discussing the various types.

Now let's go a little deeper and see the "why" of generator applications.

Here are the key factors in selecting a generator:

- Power Requirements
- Operating Conditions
- Service and Maintenance Needs
- Drive Ratio—Pulley to Generator

Below we'll discuss each of these factors.

POWER REQUIREMENTS

One of the most important factors to consider is the power requirements. The best rule is to select a generator that can provide 10 to 20% more than the total load requires. The extra output can be used to recharge the battery even when full load output is required. Also, the

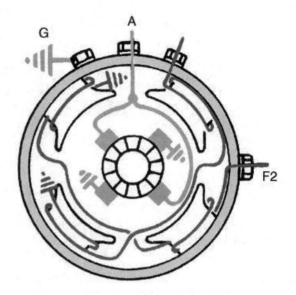

Fig. 20 — Split Field Generator

total load requirements would not take into consideration momentary load demands such as starter motor, cigarette lighter, and other accessories.

OPERATING CONDITIONS

Operating conditions are another prime consideration in generator selection.

Extremely dirty or damp conditions often require that the generator be fully enclosed, and the output of an enclosed generator is sharply reduced compared to a ventilated one of the same size.

High temperatures around the generator can add to the heat developed within the generator and reduce the output as well.

SERVICE AND MAINTENANCE NEEDS

The type of service required of the generator and the type of maintenance on it are important factors, too.

The generator may be subject to long use at high, low, or variable speeds and loads.

The cost of repair parts, the length of service they give, and the ease with which they can be replaced are also important.

DRIVE RATIO—PULLEY TO GENERATOR

Continued on next page   OUO1082,0002C3D -19-16OCT12-18/39

The drive ratio between the engine pulley and generator is also quite critical (Fig. 21). Armature speed is determined by this ratio.

A high armature speed may cause damage by developing more voltage than the regulator can handle. A low speed may not provide the necessary voltage output.

The drive ratio also affects the operation of the cutout relay switch. Due to varying idle speeds, the relay should be actuated at speeds of 100 rpm below or above idle speeds.

If the relay is set to operate at a precise idle speed, the relay points will constantly open and close due to this variation. The relay points would soon burn up in this kind of operation.

SUMMARY: USES OF GENERATORS

- Total load + 10 to 20 percent = required generator size.
- Dirty or damp conditions = enclosed generator required.
- Heat conditions = ventilated generator required.
- Engine-to-generator pulleys = critical drive ratio.
- Drive ratio = speed of generator rotation.
- Too fast rotation = too much voltage for regulator.
- Too slow rotation = not enough voltage output.

TESTING AND SERVICING OF GENERATORS

Like any other piece of equipment, generators are subject to failures and disorders.

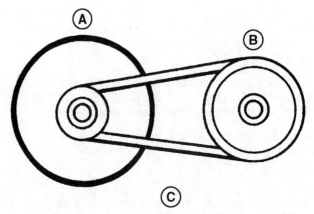

Fig. 21 — Example of Drive Ratio—Engine to Generator

A—Generator 3 in. Diameter   C—2-TO-1 RATIO
B—Engine 6 in. Diameter

To discover just what in particular ails them, there are several tests that can be made on the basic generator.

First, you should always test the complete circuit before removing the generator to the bench. This will ensure that the generator is actually the "sick" member of the charging circuit team.

OUO1082,0002C3D -19-16OCT12-19/39

TYPES OF FAILURES

The four basic electrical failures are these:

- Short Circuits—These are unwanted connections, usually copper-to-copper, that allow current to bypass all or part of the circuit. (See Fig. 22, top.)
- Open Circuits—These are breaks in the circuit which cause extremely high resistance. Usually no current will flow through an open circuit.
- Grounded Circuits—These are unwanted connections that bypass all or part of the circuit from the insulated side to the grounded side of the circuit; usually a copper-to-iron connection.

A—Bypass
B—Short
C—Increased Electrical Flow
D—Open
E—No Electrical Flow
F—Ground
G—Acts as Shorted Circuit
H—No Electrical Flow
I—Increased Electrical Flow

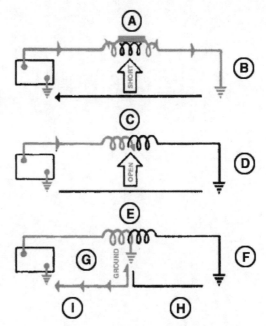

Fig. 22 — Basic Failures of Electrical Circuits

Continued on next page   OUO1082,0002C3D -19-16OCT12-20/39

• High-Resistance Circuits—These are usually caused by poor or corroded connections, and frayed or damaged wires, all of which create greater resistance in the circuit. (See Fig. 23.)

After you have isolated the cause of the problem as a "sick" generator, test it thoroughly out of the circuit. The tests can tell you which component in the generator is failing.

To perform these tests, several types of testing units are necessary. Each test may require just one or a combination of these units.

However, one item is necessary for nearly all the tests—the manufacturer's Technical Manual for the machine. This manual is kept up-to-date and lists all the generator specifications plus servicing and repair procedures. If in doubt, always consult the Technical Manual. We will only give general specifications here.

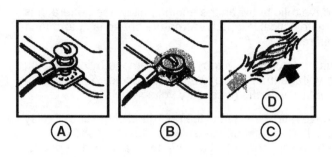

Fig. 23 — Causes of High Resistance

A—POOR OR LOOSE CONNECTIONS
B—CORRODED CONNECTIONS
C—DAMAGED WIRES
D—Lost Energy Through Heat

Continued on next page

OUO1082,0002C3D -19-16OCT12-21/39

GENERATOR OUTPUT TEST

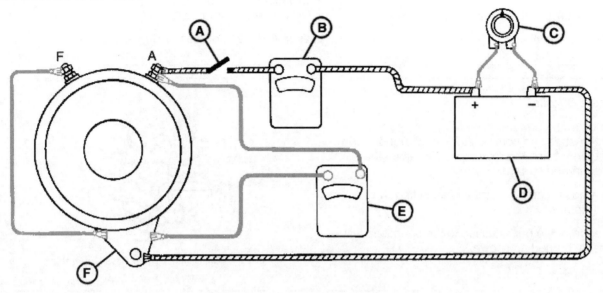

Fig. 24 — Testing the Generator Output

A—Switch
B—Ammeter

C—Variable Resistor

D—Battery
E—Voltmeter

F—Generator

A generator output test is an overall test that generally tells which internal component is malfunctioning.

To test the output, connect the units as shown in Fig. 24.

1. Connect an ammeter and switch in series with a battery to the generator output terminal.

2. Connect a voltmeter from the generator output terminal to ground as shown.

3. Connect a carbon pile resistor across the battery.

4. Connect a jumper lead to the generator field terminal.

5. Operate the generator to obtain battery voltage and close the switch.

6. Speed up the generator to its rated value, adjust the carbon pile resistor to obtain the specified voltage, and compare the current output with the generator specifications.

7. If the generator output is below par, disassemble it for further testing.

NOTE: The output test shown in Fig. 24 is for the common "A" circuit generator. For "B" circuit models, a different test hookup is used.

GENERATOR TROUBLESHOOTING CHART

Below is a general list of generator failures and their possible causes:

No Output

• Sticking brushes
• Dirty or corroded commutator
• Loose connections
• Grounded, shorted, or open armature

• Grounded, shorted, or open field circuit
• Grounded terminals

Excessive Output

• Grounded or shorted field circuit

Variable Or Low Output

• Loose or worn drive belts
• Low brush spring tension
• Dirty or burned commutator
• Eccentric or worn commutator
• Partial grounded, shorted, or open armature
• Partial grounded, shorted, or open field circuit

Noisy Generator

• Loose mounting
• Loose pulley
• Worn or dirty bearings
• Improperly seated brushes

From this list, make the easy checks first. A good visual check of all the components may help you to catch the more obvious causes of failures such as these:

Loose or broken lead wires; dirty or worn brushes; improperly seated brushes; broken brush springs; worn or glazed commutator; loose pulley; copper-to-copper contact of conductors in either the armature or field circuit (shorted); broken conductors in the armature or field circuits (open); copper-to-iron contact of conductors in either the armature or field circuit (grounded).

If these failures are not visible or cannot be corrected, then make detailed tests on each component.

These component tests are given on the following pages.

Continued on next page   OUO1082,0002C3D -19-16OCT12-22/39

DXP03594 —UN—12MAR12

ARMATURE TESTS

Four possible failures of the armature are these:

• Open Armature Circuits

• Shorted Armature Coils
• Grounded Armature
• Dirty or Worn Commutator

Let's review each of these failures.

OUO1082,0002C3D -19-16OCT12-23/39

Open Armature Circuits

An open circuit in the armature coil will cause severe arcing at the brushes and commutator. Another indication is when it requires twice the rated speed to attain the specified voltage and current.

The broken winding can be found by inspecting the commutator (Fig. 25).

The trailing edge of the bar attached to the open loop will usually be badly burned as shown.

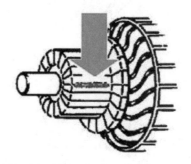

Fig. 25 — Checking for Open Circuit in Armature

OUO1082,0002C3D -19-16OCT12-24/39

Another method of finding the broken loop is with a combination test unit and growler (Fig. 26).

Place the test prods of the unit on two adjacent commutator bars. Rotate the armature to get the highest meter reading and record the reading.

Then turn the armature slightly and check two other bars. If one reading is lower than the others, that circuit is open.

A—Compare Readings

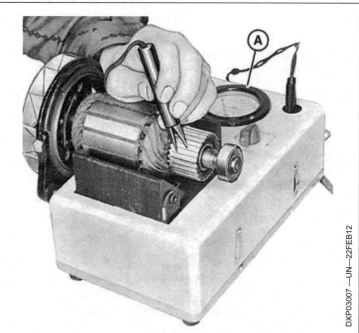

Fig. 26 — Testing Armature for Open Circuit

Continued on next page   OUO1082,0002C3D -19-16OCT12-25/39

Shorted Armature Coils

Another cause of low generator output is a short-circuited armature coil. If the armature loops are touching each other, they set up a closed circuit and very little current can get to the external load circuit. The more loops shorted, the higher the speed required to obtain voltage and current. Long use of a shorted armature can create damage from overheating.

Shorted windings can be found with the growler test unit (Fig. 27). The growler has an oscillating magnetic field that cuts across the armature loops, creating voltage and current flow through the shorted loops.

By holding a strip of metal such as a hacksaw blade over the armature and slowly rotating the armature in the growler, the magnetic field set up by the shorted windings will attract and release the metal strip. This will tell you that the armature coil is shorted.

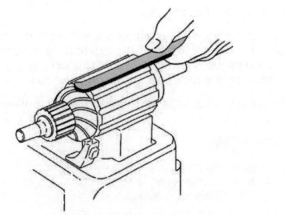

Fig. 27 — Testing for Shorted Windings

OUO1082,0002C3D -19-16OCT12-26/39

Grounded Armature

A grounded armature is another source of current loss. The armature is grounded when the winding is in contact with the ground. This bypasses the external load circuit and, since the grounded connection has low resistance, the remaining voltage is very low.

To find a grounded armature, use the test lamp on the growler, if equipped (Fig. 28). Or use a separate test lamp.

Place one test prod on the metal of the armature and the other prod on the commutator. If the lamp lights, the winding is grounded.

Dirty Or Worn Commutator

A dirty or oxidized commutator can cause symptoms that appear as if the armature were shorted or grounded.

Foreign material packed between the commutator bars can offer a path for current flow, thus shorting the armature loops.

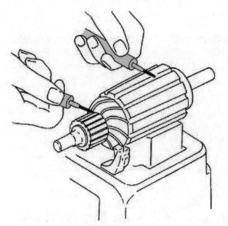

Fig. 28 — Testing for Grounded Armature

A corroded commutator can prevent brush contact, thus prohibiting voltage development.

Continued on next page   OUO1082,0002C3D -19-16OCT12-27/39

Reconditioning The Commutator

To correct this, turn down the commutator with an armature turning tool (Fig. 29). Also be sure to undercut the material between each bar as shown in Fig. 29. This will prevent rapid brush wear due to bouncing or arcing brushes.

Use a strip of No. 00 sandpaper to polish the commutator. Do not use emery cloth.

ARMATURE REPAIR

The commutator can be turned down with the proper tools. The armature, however, is seldom rewound in cases of shorts, opens, or ground.

Normally, it is replaced with another armature. Of course, if the proper tools and qualified personnel are available, then it can be repaired.

FIELD CIRCUIT TESTS

Like the armature, the field circuit can fail due to open, grounded, or shorted coils. It can also fail because of high resistance.

A—TURNING DOWN THE
COMMUTATOR

B—UNDERCUTTING MICA ON
COMMUTATOR

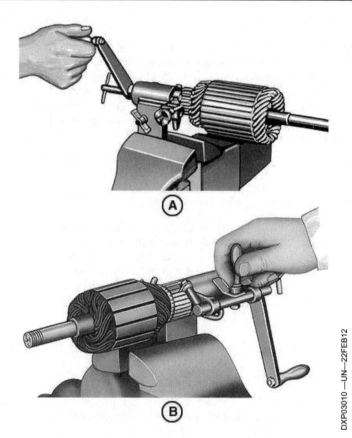

Fig. 29 — Reconditioning the Commutator—Tool for Turning Down Commutator and Undercutting Mica

OUO1082,0002C3D -19-16OCT12-28/39

Open Field Circuits

A broken coil or open circuit in the field circuit stops current flow.

This means the magnetic field cannot be strengthened and the amount of developed voltage is dependent on residual magnetism. This voltage is too low to supply the battery.

Use a test lamp to find an open field circuit. Touch the prods of the lamp to the generator as shown in Fig. 30. If the lamp does not light, the field circuit is open. In this case, look for a broken wire in the coils or leads.

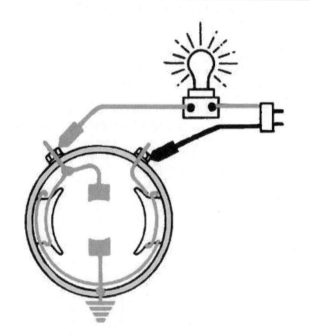

Fig. 30 — Testing for an Open Field Circuit

Continued on next page

OUO1082,0002C3D -19-16OCT12-29/39

Grounded Field Circuit

A grounded field circuit will have a different effect on generator output, depending on where the ground is located (Fig. 31).

Let's assume that all circuits start at the insulated brush.

If the circuit is grounded before the coils, there will be no current flow through them. Therefore, the magnetic field will not be strengthened and no voltage will develop. In this case the armature will also be grounded since the field circuit is connected to the armature circuit.

If the field is grounded at the middle, the circuit will still build up voltage. However, with less resistance in the field circuit, more current will flow. The ground will bypass the regulating points and regulator resistance and there will be no control over voltage or current.

If the circuit is grounded after the coils, the circuit will react similar to the ground at the middle and there will be no control over voltage.

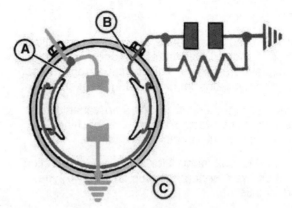

Fig. 31 — Locating a Grounded Field Circuit

A—Start   C—Middle
B—End

OUO1082,0002C3D -19-16OCT12-30/39

Testing For A Grounded Field Circuit

A test lamp is used to find out if the field circuit is grounded. All intended ground connections of the field circuit must be disconnected.

Place the prods of the test lamp as shown in Fig. 32.

If the lamp lights, the field circuit is grounded. Add this information to what is known about the effect a grounded circuit has on generator output, and you should be able to locate the grounded wire.

For a grounded circuit, either replace the field windings or repair them by reinsulating, revarnishing, and retaping.

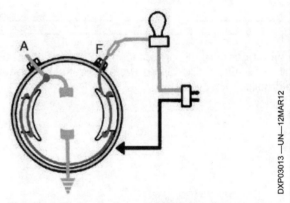

Fig. 32 — Testing for Grounded Field Circuit

Continued on next page
OUO1082,0002C3D -19-16OCT12-31/39

Shorted Field Circuit

A shorted field circuit may cause excessive current flow. The number of shorted coils cuts resistance and so creates a higher current flow. This higher current can burn and oxidize the regulator points, creating an open circuit.

Use a volt-ampere tester with a 100-amp variable resistance unit for this test. Refer to the machine Technical Manual for the proper test readings.

1. Follow the test unit manual for the proper connections. (Fig. 33 shows a general hookup for the two types of field circuits.)

2. Adjust the variable resistance unit so that the voltmeter reads the specified voltage as given by the Technical Manual specifications.

3. Measure the current flow by the ammeter. It should be the same as the Technical Manual specifications. Any difference between the reading and specifications, either way, indicates a bad field circuit.

If the current flow is more than specified, the field circuit is shorted.

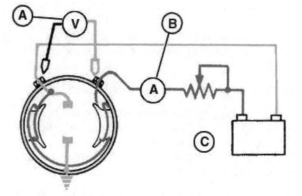

Fig. 33 — Locating a Shorted Field Circuit

A—V   C—Load
B—A

If the current flow is less than specified, there is high resistance (a damaged wire or loose connection) in the field circuit. This high resistance cuts the magnetic field strength and so reduces the generator output.

OUO1082,0002C3D -19-16OCT12-32/39

In either case, repair or replacement of the field circuit coils is required. Fig. 34 shows a typical set of generator field coils.

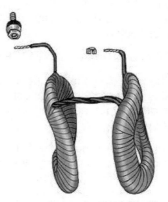

Fig. 34 — Field Circuit Coils

Continued on next page

OUO1082,0002C3D -19-16OCT12-33/39

BRUSH TESTING

During normal operation a copper oxide film is formed on the commutator (Fig. 35). This film reduces the friction between the brushes and commutator. At low or no current loads, the film can be worn away by the brushes and the brushes will then chatter.

Continual brush chatter can loosen the brush lead, forming a high-resistance connection. Current will then follow an easier path through the brush surface and brush holders. This can eventually lead to burned brushes, brush holders, and brush arms.

A brush arm stop prevents the brush arm from pressing on the brush when the brush is worn away (Fig. 36). However, the main purpose of the stop is to prevent the arm from scoring the commutator.

But if the brushes are checked regularly for wear, this should never happen.

A—Pressure of Spring Arm Against the Direction of Rotation
B—Spring Arm Stop
C—Spring
D—Spring Arm Stop
E—Commutator Rotation
F—Brush
G—Brush Holder

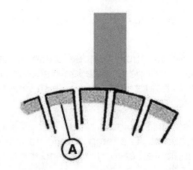

Fig. 35 — Copper Oxide Film on Commutator

A—Copper Oxide Film

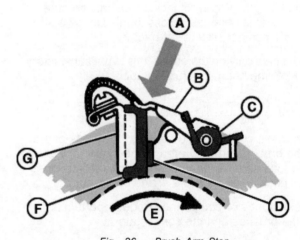

Fig. 36 — Brush Arm Stop

OUO1082,0002C3D -19-16OCT12-34/39

Brush arm spring tension should be checked during generator repair (Fig. 37). The Technical Manual can give you the proper tension specifications. Be sure to measure tension at a point as close to the middle of the brush as possible.

Too little tension will cause the brushes to bounce and arc at high speeds. Too strong a tension will cause excessive friction and brush wear.

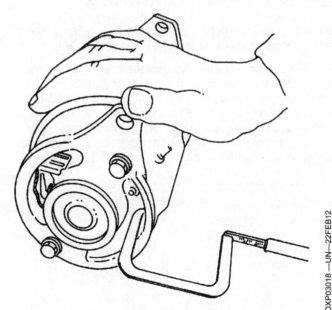

Fig. 37 — Checking Brush Spring Tension

Continued on next page

OUO1082,0002C3D -19-16OCT12-35/39

To check for grounds, or opens on the brush holders, use a test lamp (Fig. 38).

Place the test prods across the grounded brush holder and the frame to check for opens. The lamp should light. If it does not, the brush holder is insulated from the frame and the circuit is open.

Place the lamp across the insulated brush holder and frame to check for grounds. The lamp should not light. If it does, a ground is indicated at the frame and the brush holder is grounded at this point.

REPLACING BRUSHES

Replace the brushes when they have worn to one-half of their original length. When replacing brushes, be sure that a brush seat is obtained across the thickness of the brush. A 25% contact area is satisfactory.

If the brush seats only on the edges, this is not satisfactory, regardless of whether it is a 25% contact.

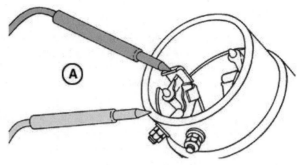

Fig. 38 — Electrical Check of Brush Holders

A—Insulated Brush Holder
 Test for Ground

OUO1082,0002C3D -19-16OCT12-36/39

Fig. 39 shows in color the bad heel and toe seats at the edge of the brush. The gray area at the center of the brush is a good seat. Seating on the edges will change the neutral position, and severe arcing can occur.

Use seating stones or compounds to get a perfect fit between the brushes and the commutator.

GENERATOR POLARITY

Polarity is the direction of current flow through the generator. It is determined by the magnetic pole shoes. If the polarity of the pole shoes is changed, current flow will also change, regardless of whether other conditions change or not. Therefore, by changing pole polarity the generator can supply load current in either direction.

Pole shoe polarity is determined by the magnetism of the field coils the last time current passed through the coils. Anytime a current flows through the field coils, it sets the pole shoe polarity until the next time current flows. This action sets up a potential trouble spot. When working on or testing the generator, you can accidentally change pole polarity. Just a slight current through the coils can do it.

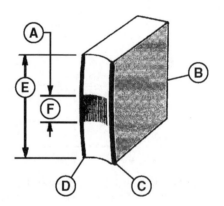

Fig. 39 — Seating of Brush for Good Contact

A—Normal Seat
B—Brush
C—Heel Seat
D—Toe Seat
E—Area "A"
F—1/4 "A"

Continued on next page OUO1082,0002C3D -19-16OCT12-37/39

The damage does not occur until the generator, with a polarity opposite that of the battery, is put back into the charging circuit (Fig. 40).

When this is done, the generator builds up voltage and closes the cutout relay points. This, in effect, puts the battery in series with the generator, and their voltages are added together. This high voltage across the points (about twice the system voltage) can create high current and enough heat to weld the points together as shown.

However, this damage does not happen immediately. The instant the points close, voltage is about the same on both sides of the relay coil. Since there is little difference in voltage, very little current will flow and spring tension opens the points.

But generator voltage will again close the points and the cycle is repeated. Because this action repeats very rapidly, heat and arcing will finally cause the points to weld together.

When the points do weld together, the battery and the generator are connected at all times. The low resistance

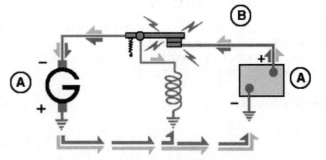

Fig. 40 — How Reverse Polarity in Generator Damages the Charging Circuit

A—12 Volts　　　　　**B—24 Volts**

in the generator allows the battery to continue to discharge into the generator. This develops a high current that creates enough heat to burn the armature, ruining it.

In summary, after any service, polarize the DC generator.

OUO1082,0002C3D -19-16OCT12-38/39

Polarize the generator by connecting a jumper lead from the insulated side of the battery to the armature terminal as shown in Fig. 41. The battery, generator, and regulator grounds must be connected. Just a touch of the generator lead between the "BAT" and "GEN" terminals of the regulator will cause current to flow in the proper direction in the field coils. A flash or arc will be noted when the lead is removed.

On high-voltage generators it is best to insulate the brushes. This will allow current to flow only through the field coils.

SUMMARY: POLARITY OF GENERATORS

The correct polarity of the DC generator is very important. A good rule to follow is to pass a current through the field coils in the direction that will have the grounded side of the coils connected to the grounded side of the battery.

A—Jumper

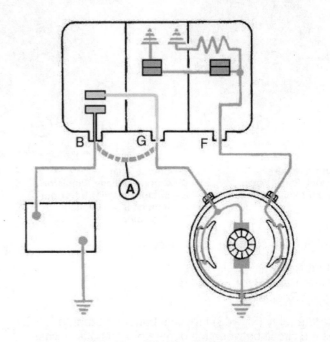

Fig. 41 — Polarizing the Generator

OUO1082,0002C3D -19-16OCT12-39/39

GENERATOR REGULATORS

The DC regulator (Fig. 42) is the control for the generator. Otherwise, the generator would produce too much current and voltage at high speeds. Or the battery would discharge back through the generator at low speeds.

A—Generator Regulator

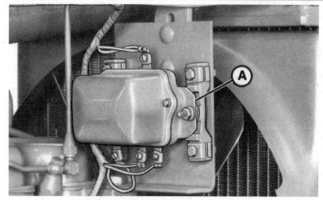

Fig. 42 — Contact Point Generator Regulator on a Tractor

OUO1082,0002C3E -19-16OCT12-1/20

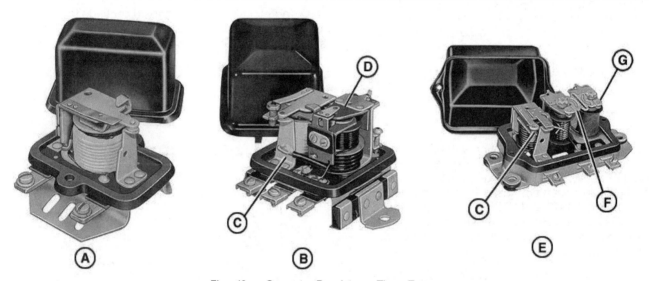

Fig. 43 — Generator Regulators—Three Types

A—Cutout Relay
B—Cutout Relay With Current-Voltage Regulator

C—Cutout Relay
D—Current-Voltage Regulator
E—Cutout Relay With Current Regulator And Voltage Regulator

F—Current Regulator
G—Voltage Regulator

A regulator can combine three functions:

• Cutout Relay
• Voltage Regulator
• Current Regulator

The cutout relay (Fig. 43) prevents battery discharge. It closes the circuit between the generator and battery when the generator starts charging, and breaks the circuit when the generator stops charging.

The last two regulators work at separate times as we'll see later. Both control the generator's output by varying the strength of its magnetic field.

Regulators may have one, two, or three of these features combined in one unit (Fig. 43).

All three of these devices operate by electromagnetism and are very similar in operation and appearance.

Let's see how each specific function works in the charging circuit.

CUTOUT RELAY

The main purpose of the cutout relay is to open and close the circuit between the generator and the battery.

The cutout relay operates, as do all the regulator units, by electromagnetic induction. What happens is that current flow through a coil of wire wound around an iron core magnetizes the core. The strength of this magnetism is determined by the strength of the current and the number of turns in the coil.

NOTE: The voltage and current regulators also operate on this same principle.

Continued on next page   OUO1082,0002C3E -19-16OCT12-2/20

Fig. 44 illustrates the physical features of the cutout relay. The relay consists of two windings (one heavy and one fine), one iron core, a hinged flat metal piece called the armature, and a stationary contact point.

The heavy winding, called the current or series winding, is wound around the core. One end is attached to the relay armature and the other end is connected to the charging circuit.

The fine winding is the voltage or shunt winding. One end is also attached to the relay armature. The other end is connected across the generator so that generator voltage is impressed on it at all times.

The relay armature is mounted above the core, but does not touch it. It is hinged at the back and is held away from the core by spring tension.

A contact point on the armature is aligned directly above the stationary contact point, which is connected to the battery by wire.

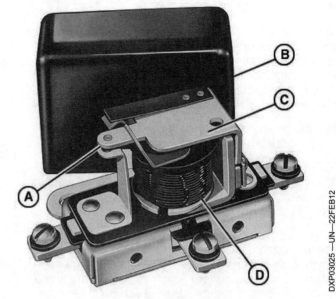

Fig. 44 — Cutout Relay

A—Points
B—Cover
C—Armature
D—Winding

Continued on next page

OUO1082,0002C3E -19-16OCT12-3/20

OPERATION OF CUTOUT RELAY

As the generator builds voltage, current flows through the cutout windings, creating a magnetic field in the core. This magnetism pulls the armature toward the core and the two contact points close. The circuit between battery and generator is completed. Current then flows through the series winding to the battery (Fig. 45).

When the generator slows or stops, battery voltage becomes greater than generator voltage. Current then begins to flow from the battery to the generator.

With current flow reversed, polarity of the series winding is reversed. The shunt winding polarity remains the same, however.

The two opposing fields reduce the strength of the magnetism, and the armature point is released from the stationary contact point by spring action. This opens the circuit and stops current flow from the battery to the generator, and so prevents battery discharge.

VOLTAGE REGULATOR

As we said earlier in this chapter, the voltage regulator's main function is to regulate the generator magnetic field. In this way, the voltage buildup in the generator is controlled.

The appearance of the voltage regulator is similar to that of the cutout relay. Like the relay, it has an iron core, flat hinged armature, and stationary contact point.

However, the position of some of these components is different, as are the type and number of windings on some models.

The armature is hinged on top, and the armature contact point is directly below the stationary contact point. Spring tension holds the points together when the regulator is not operating, and is provided by an adjustable spiral spring at the back of the regulator.

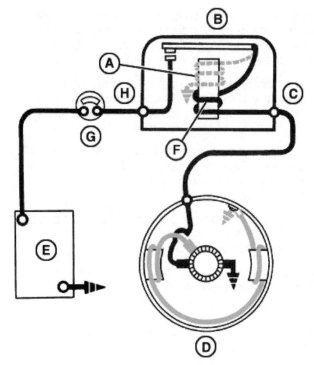

Fig. 45 — Cutout Relay in Charging Circuit

A—Shunt Winding
B—Cutout Relay
C—GEN
D—Generator
E—Battery
F—Series Windings
G—Ammeter
H—BAT

The hinge on the voltage regulator armature is made of two thermostatic materials to allow for changing temperatures. This causes the regulator to regulate at a higher voltage when cold.

Continued on next page   OUO1082,0002C3E -19-16OCT12-4/20

TYPES OF VOLTAGE REGULATORS

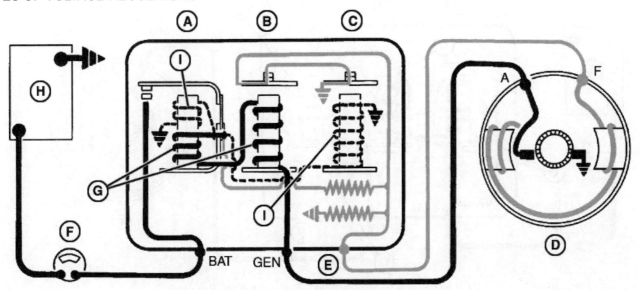

Fig. 46 — Voltage Regulator with Single Winding

A—Cutout Relay
B—Current Regulator
C—Voltage Regulator
D—Generator
E—Field
F—Ammeter
G—Series Windings
H—Battery
I— Shunt Winding

Two types of windings are used on standard voltage regulators:

• Single Winding
• Accelerator Winding

The single winding type has only a shunt winding of fine wire (Fig. 46). This winding is connected across the generator. When the generator reaches a specified voltage as determined by the regulator, the magnetic field created by current flow through the winding draws the armature contact point away from the stationary contact. This opens the contact circuit and inserts resistance into the generator field circuit. The result is a reduction of voltage and current output in the generator.

Reducing the voltage and current reduces the magnetic attraction in the shunt winding. This allows the spring to pull the armature point back into contact with the stationary point. The generator field circuit is then grounded, and voltage and current increases to the preset point.

The cycle then starts over again and is repeated many times a second. This is the method used in regulating generator voltage to a predetermined value.

Continued on next page
OUO1082,0002C3E -19-16OCT12-5/20

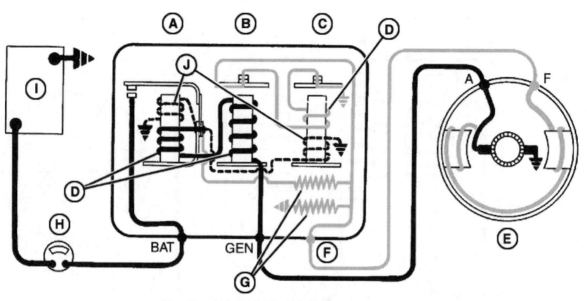

Fig. 47 — Voltage Regulator with Accelerator Winding

A—Cutout Relay
B—Current Regulator
C—Voltage Regulator

D—Series Windings
E—Generator
F—Field

G—Resistances
H—Ammeter
I— Battery
J—Shunt Winding

The second type of regulator is the accelerator winding type (Fig. 47). It is equipped with the same components as the first type and has an added winding called an accelerator winding. This is a series winding of heavy wire.

Operation is basically the same as the first type except at a faster rate of speed.

In a sense, the series winding or coil, connected to the generator field circuit, helps the shunt winding create a stronger magnetic field faster. This draws the two points out of contact quicker.

The same speed causes the series coil magnetic field to collapse faster. When the armature point is suddenly released, it closes the circuit with the stationary point. The cycle is again repeated at a fast rate.

Voltage regulated in this manner allows the generator to supply varying amounts of current as needed by the battery and load circuits.

CURRENT REGULATOR

The current regulator controls the current output of the generator.

The current regulator looks the same as the single-winding voltage regulator. However, the current regulator winding is a series coil of heavy wire. The coil is connected into the generator armature or load circuit and carries the entire generator current output.

During a heavy load, such as a discharged battery and use of electrical accessories, voltage may not increase enough to actuate the voltage regulator. In these cases, the generator output will continue to increase to meet this demand. To limit this output to a safe point, the current regulator steps in.

As the output reaches a point as determined by the regulator, the magnetism of the regulator series coil draws the armature point toward the coil assembly. This breaks the contact between the two points. Resistance is then inserted into the generator field circuit and so the generator output is reduced.

This reduced output cuts the magnetism in the current regulator coil. Spring tension then draws the points back into contact and the generator field is directly connected to ground. The output again increases and the cycle is repeated as long as there is a heavy load.

As soon as the load is reduced (the battery is fully charged or the accessories are turned off) the voltage will increase. The voltage regulator then operates and gradually reduces the output. With the voltage regulator operating, there is no need for current regulation and the current regulator points remain in contact.

When one regulator is working, the other is not. Both will not operate at the same time.

Continued on next page   OUO1082,0002C3E -19-16OCT12-6/20

HOW THE THREE REGULATORS WORK TOGETHER

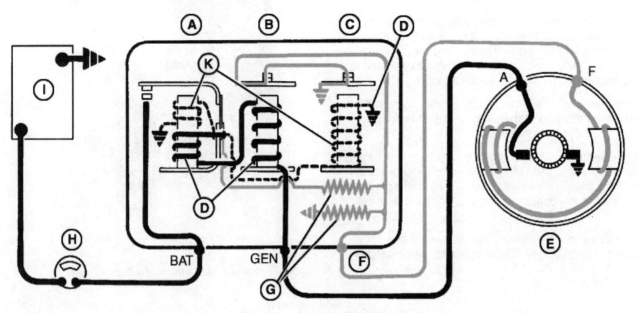

Fig. 48 — Operation of All Three Generator Regulator Units

A—Cutout Relay
B—Current Regulator
C—Voltage Regulator
D—Series Windings
E—Generator
F—Field
G—Resistances
H—Ammeter
I— Battery
K—Shunt Winding

Now that we have described the three generator regulators separately, let's take a look at the three operating as a unit.

Fig. 48, shows the three regulators in one unit operating in the charging circuit.

Shown in black are the series windings of the cutout relay and current regulator. In dashed lines are the shunt windings in the cutout relay and voltage regulator. And in gray are shown the field circuit and the resistors.

When the generator begins to operate, it must recharge the battery. Two of the three units, the cutout relay and current regulator, perform in this operation.

The current flows from the generator armature into the series coil of the current regulator. From there it flows into the series coil of the cutout relay, through the closed relay contact points, and into the battery.

As the battery becomes charged, its resistance increases and the generator voltage rises. Then the voltage regulator goes into action, controlling generator field current and voltage.

When the engine stops, current from the battery flows back through the cutout series winding and reverses the polarity of its magnetic field. This causes the cutout points to open and disconnect the generator from the battery.

REGULATOR RESISTORS

The regulator also uses two common resistors. Both are fixed beneath the base of the regulator.

One resistor is inserted into the field circuit when either current or voltage regulator is used.

The second resistor is placed between the regulator field terminal and cutout relay frame.

The resistors are used to reduce a sudden voltage surge in the field coils caused by opening contacts. This prevents excessive arcing at the contact points.

VARIATIONS ON BASIC REGULATORS

As we said earlier, the three regulators are combined as units in some uses.

Let's discuss the major variations.

Continued on next page

OUO1082,0002C3E -19-16OCT12-7/20

CURRENT-VOLTAGE REGULATOR

This unit combines the current and voltage regulators into one regulating unit (Fig. 49). It is an economical means of controlling both generator voltage and output simultaneously. However, the current-voltage regulator is limited to machines having low electrical load.

As you can see in Fig. 49, this regulator also has a cutout relay. Basically this is a standard type cutout relay we discussed earlier in this chapter.

In many respects, the current-voltage regulator unit of this regulator is similar to the voltage regulator in a standard three-unit regulator. It is equipped with a hinged armature, iron core, stationary contact point, and adjustable spiral spring.

The major differences between this unit and other regulators are the number of windings and their operation.

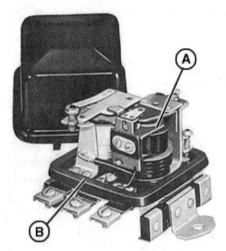

Fig. 49 — Current-Voltage Regulator

A—Current-Voltage Regulator   **B—Cutout Relay**

Continued on next page   OUO1082,0002C3E -19-16OCT12-8/20

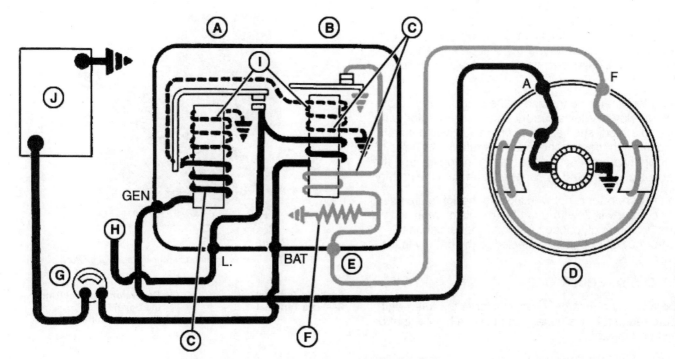

Fig. 50 — Current-Voltage Regulator Operation

A—Cutout Relay
B—Regulator
C—Series Winding
D—Generator
E—Field
F—Resistance
G—Ammeter
H—To Light Load
I—Shunt Winding
J—Battery

The current-voltage regulator employs three windings, a shunt and two series (Fig. 50). The shunt winding is of fine wire and is connected across the generator to receive generator voltage at all times. One winding is of heavy wire and is connected in series with the charging circuit. The other series winding is of a relatively heavy wire and is connected in series with the generator field circuit when the regulator contact points are closed.

In Fig. 50, the shunt winding in the cutout relay and the current-voltage regulator unit are shown in dashed lines. The charging circuit series windings are shown in solid black. The field circuit series winding is shown in gray.

Operation Of Current-Voltage Regulator

As generator voltage builds, it causes current to flow through the cutout relay and into the regulator charging circuit winding and on into the battery. At the same time, voltage sensed in the regulator shunt winding causes some current to flow in it.

The two magnetic fields created by this current draw the regulator armature toward the iron core and open the contact points. Field current is now diverted to ground through a resistor. This causes a drop in generator voltage and output.

A voltage drop, of course, reduces current flow through the windings, and the magnetic field is weakened. Spring tension is then able to pull the armature point back into contact with the stationary point. This completes the field circuit, and again the generator voltage and current output

increase. This cycle is repeated many times a second as long as the generator and regulator are operating.

The field current series winding acts as an accelerator winding in that it helps to speed up the regulating cycle. When the regulator points are closed, field current flows through this winding, creating another magnetic field.

This added magnetic force helps to open the points faster. However, when the points open, field current flow stops and this field suddenly collapses. This, in turn, reduces the total magnetism enough to close the points quickly. The result is a faster regulator armature action rate.

In this way, the regulator controls both the generator voltage and current output.

One feature of current-voltage regulator operation is that as the charging rate increases, regulated voltage drops. This means that the higher the current flow to the battery, the lower the regulated voltage and vice versa.

Current-Voltage Regulator Terminals

We have mentioned that this unit is limited to use in low-output, low-load systems. An example is a diesel engine whose load requirements are only for battery recharging and occasional starting.

However, we don't want to rule out the ability of the current-voltage regulators to control more load than this. Because of another feature, it can handle some extra load such as lights or ignition.

Continued on next page   OUO1082,0002C3E -19-16OCT12-9/20

The added feature is the extra terminal that this unit has (Fig. 51). It is a load terminal, mounted on the base of the regulator, where the battery terminal is on a three-unit regulator. The "L" stamped on the terminal stands for "load."

The load terminal is connected to the stationary point of the cutout relay. It allows current from the generator to be diverted to a load, such as lights or ignition, without first passing through the current-voltage regulator. As a result, this current has no effect on the operating voltage and the regulator is only affected by current to and from the battery.

When the generator is not working and the lights are used, battery current will flow through the regulator winding and the "L" terminal to load. Any load that exceeds the generator output must be connected to the battery in the system.

HEAVY-DUTY REGULATORS

The heavy-duty regulator is very similar to the three-unit standard regulator. It is usually used with a high output or split field generator.

This type of installation is usually found on heavy equipment, such as trucks, where high loads in a wide range of speeds are required.

Heavy-duty regulators have special features such as double contact points, fiber insulating brackets on the stationary points, and added resistors for better control.

DOUBLE CONTACT GENERATOR REGULATOR

The cutout relay and current regulator parts of this unit are the same as used on the standard three-unit regulator.

However, the voltage regulator is different from the standard voltage regulator. It has an extra set of contact points. One of the points is on an extra armature that is over one of the stationary contact points. The other point is on the top of stationary contact point frame.

During normal operation the lower set of contact points operate like those on a standard voltage regulator.

But during high generator speeds and low loads, the voltage control shifts to the upper set of points. This connects the normally grounded end of the field circuit to the generator output circuit, shorting out the coils to control the generator voltage.

TESTING AND ADJUSTING THE DC REGULATOR

Before testing and adjusting the DC regulator, take these preliminary steps:

1. Check out the whole charging circuit to isolate the component that is failing.

2. Start with a visual check of the circuit components, lead wires, and connectors.

3. Then make an electrical check, using a voltmeter, ammeter, tachometer, and resistance unit.

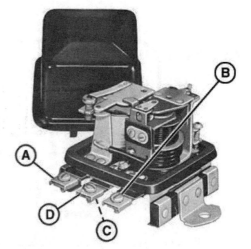

Fig. 51 — Terminals on a Current-Voltage Regulator

A—Load Terminal
B—Field Terminal

C—Generator Terminal (Under the Base)
D—Battery Terminal

NOTE: *In many cases it is cheaper to replace a regulator rather than repair it. However, tests must be made to find out if the regulator is defective.*

PRELIMINARY TEST PROCEDURES

Once the problem has been traced to the regulator, take the following preliminary steps and precautions:

1. First make sure that the specified regulator is being used, one that is of the proper polarity. Most regulators are stamped on the base with a "P" for positive or "N" for negative.

2. Clean the contact points and make any minor adjustments outlined by the regulator or machine Technical Manual. Quite often this will correct the regulator problem.

3. Mechanical tests and adjustments should be made with the battery disconnected and the regulator out of the circuit.

⚠ CAUTION: Never close the cutout relay points by hand while the battery is connected. High current flow from the battery can damage the regulator.

4. Electrical checks and adjustments can be made with the regulator in or out of the circuit. However, the checks must be made with the regulator in operating position and the regulator cover in place.

5. Be sure to warm up the regulator to normal operating temperature before making the electrical tests. Do this by operating the regulator for 15 minutes with a 1/4-ohm resistance in series with the battery. The regulator cover must also be in place. No electrical load other than ignition should be used during testing.

Continued on next page

OUO1082,0002C3E -19-16OCT12-10/20

6. Speeds during the tests should be as specified by the Technical Manual.

7. The circuit must be polarized after each test or adjustment and before the engine is started. To do this, connect a jumper wire, momentarily, between the battery and generator regulator terminals.

8. Be sure to use the regulator service manual or the machine's Technical Manual. It will list all the necessary specifications and testing and adjustment procedures. A complete knowledge of the regulator components and operation is also necessary. Quite often an improper adjustment will do more damage than no adjustment at all.

9. Though the regulator can be electrically adjusted on the machine, it is better to remove it and its generator to the bench for servicing.

The first part of this chapter listed some general problems caused by a malfunctioning generator. Unfortunately, a faulty regulator can also create these same problems.

Let's assume that we have checked and found the generator and battery operating properly. Now we'll see how the regulator can cause these problems.

REGULATOR TROUBLESHOOTING CHART

Low Charging Rate—Fully Charged Battery

Regulator operation is normal.

Low Or No Charging Rate—Low Battery

Low regulator setting. Burned or oxidized contact points, or open series circuit in the regulator.

High Charging Rate—Fully Charged Battery

Improper voltage regulator setting. Defective voltage regulator unit, or grounded generator field circuit in the regulator.

High Charging Rate—Low Battery

Regulator operation is normal.

SEQUENCE OF TESTING REGULATOR UNITS

The generator regulator should be tested and adjusted in the following sequence:

• Check the voltage regulator first.
• Next check the cutout relay.
• Check the current regulator last of all.

Always remember to bring the regulator units up to operating temperature. This gives the best testing results.

VOLTAGE REGULATOR TESTS AND ADJUSTMENTS

Two tests—air gap distance and voltage setting—are performed on the voltage regulator.

Air Gap Test

The air gap between the regulator armature and windings is an important mechanical adjustment. Remember that the air gap in a magnetic circuit acts as a resistance. Therefore, the greater the gap between armature and windings, the more magnetic force and so current needed to draw the armature down.

To measure the air gap, push down on the armature until the points are just touching. Then measure the gap between the armature and the core. The distance should be as specified by the Technical Manual.

Continued on next page

OUO1082,0002C3E -19-16OCT12-11/20

Adjust the gap as shown in Fig. 52. On some regulators, a screw post at the top of the unit is adjusted to lengthen or shorten this distance.

Voltage Setting Test

There are two methods for checking the voltage setting:

• Fixed Resistance Method
• Variable Resistance Method

A—Voltage Regulator
B—Proper Size Gauge
C—Standard Voltage Regulator

D—Turn Contact Support Nut to Set Air Gap
E—Air Gap (Check with Points Just Touching)
F—Post-Type Voltage Regulator

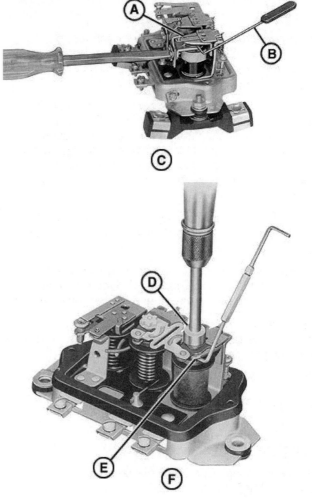

Fig. 52 — Checking and Adjusting Air Gap in Voltage Regulators

Continued on next page   OUO1082,0002C3E -19-16OCT12-12/20

Fig. 53 shows how to make either check. Detailed procedures follow.

Fixed Resistance Method

1. Insert a 1/4-ohm fixed resistor into the charging circuit at the battery terminal. (Fig. 53, top.)

2. Connect a voltmeter from the battery terminal to ground.

3. Operate the circuit for 15 minutes at specified speed to warm it up. See step 5 of "Preliminary Test Procedures."

4. Cycle the generator by one of two methods:

    a. Slow it down until voltage drops to about 1/4 of rated value. Then increase speed and note the voltage reading.

    b. Or cycle the generator by inserting a variable resistance into the field circuit. Slowly increase resistance until voltage drops to about 1/4 of rated value. Decrease the resistance and note the voltage reading.

A—Fixed Resistance Method	F—Connect to Ground
B—Regulator	G—Variable Resistance Method
C—1/4-Ohm Fixed Resistance	H—Ammeter
D—Generator	I—Variable Resistance
E—Voltmeter	

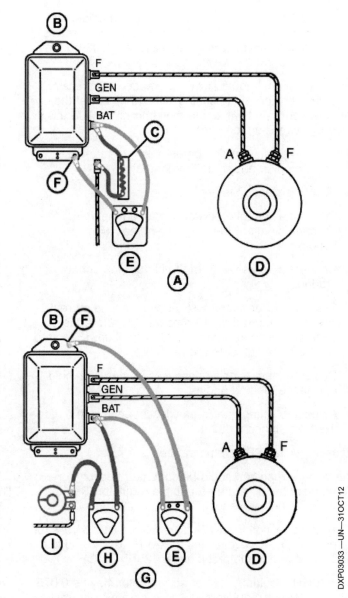

Fig. 53 — Checking the Voltage Setting of Voltage Regulator

DXP03033 —UN—31OCT12

Continued on next page

OUO1082,0002C3E -19-16OCT12-13/20

5. Adjust the voltage setting by turning the adjusting screw as shown in Fig. 54. If the adjusting screw is turned to its limits, it may be necessary to bend the spring support. However, do this very carefully.

Final adjustment should always be made by increasing the spring tension. If the setting is too high, adjust the unit below the specified value and then bring it back to this value by increasing the spring tension.

After each adjustment and before taking a reading, replace the cover and cycle the generator.

Variable Resistance Method

1. Connect a variable resistor and an ammeter into the charging circuit at the battery terminal. (Fig. 53, bottom.)

2. Connect a voltmeter from the battery terminal to ground.

3. Start generator and adjust resistor to get a current flow of not more than 10 amperes. Operate the generator at specified speed to warm it up. (See step 5, "Preliminary Test Procedures.")

4. Cycle the generator as described in step 4 of fixed resistance method above.

5. Adjust the voltage setting as described in step 5 of the fixed resistance method.

Adjusting Voltage For Temperature

The voltage reading should be corrected to allow for the ambient temperature around the regulator. See the machine Technical Manual.

A typical correction for a 12-volt regulator is 0.15 volts for every 10°F (5.5°C) over or under 125°F (52°C). Add to the reading if over, or subtract if under 125°F (52°C).

For a 6-volt regulator, the correction factor may be 0.075 volts. On 24-volt regulators, 0.3 volts is a typical correction.

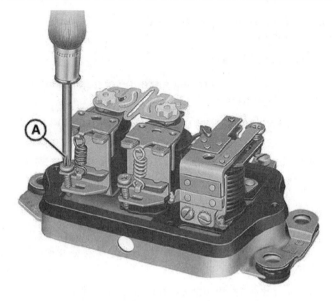

Fig. 54 — Voltage Setting Adjustment

A—Adjusting Screw (Turn to Adjust Setting)

On voltage regulators with an accelerator winding or series current windings, test at a specified amperage output because current flow in the windings affect the voltage of the test.

CUTOUT RELAY TESTS AND ADJUSTMENTS

There are three checks and adjustments on the cutout relay:

• Air Gap
• Point Opening
• Closing Voltage

The point opening and air gap tests must be made with the battery disconnected from the regulator.

OUO1082,0002C3E -19-16OCT12-14/20

Air Gap Check

Push the cutout armature down until the points are just touching. Measure the air gap between the armature and the center of the core using a feeler gauge (Fig. 55). Adjust the air gap as shown. Raise or lower the armature as needed and make sure the points are aligned. Tighten the screws after adjustment.

A—Armature   B—Core

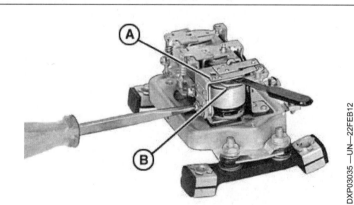

Fig. 55 — Air Gap Adjustment of Cutout Relay

Continued on next page   OUO1082,0002C3E -19-16OCT12-15/20

Point Opening Check

Check the point opening and adjust by bending the armature stop with a tool as shown in Fig. 56.

A—Armature Stop Bending   B—Armature Stop
    Tool

Fig. 56 — Point Opening Check

OUO1082,0002C3E -19-16OCT12-16/20

Closing Voltage Check

Connect a voltmeter between the generator terminal and ground (Fig. 57). Slowly increase the generator speed and note the relay closing voltage. Decrease the speed and make sure the points open before specified current flow is exceeded (with the battery connected).

A—Connect to Ground   D—Voltmeter
B—Variable Resistance   E—Regulator
C—Generator

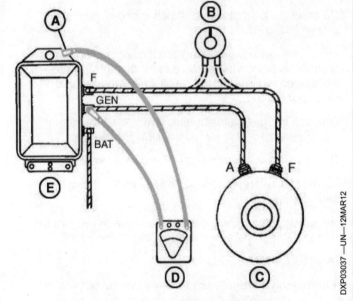

Fig. 57 — Check Closing Voltage of Cutout Relay

Continued on next page   OUO1082,0002C3E -19-16OCT12-17/20

Adjust the closing voltage as shown in Fig. 58. Turn the screw clockwise to increase the setting.

CURRENT REGULATOR TESTS

Two checks are required on the current regulator:

- Air Gap
- Current Setting

Air Gap Check

The air gap is tested and adjusted in the same manner as the voltage regulator air gap (see above).

A—Adjusting Screw (Turn to Adjust Closing Voltage)

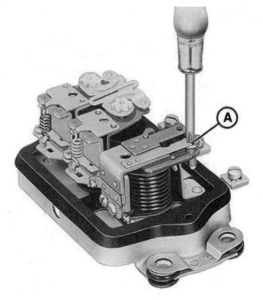

Fig. 58 — Adjusting Closing Voltage of Cutout Relay

OUO1082,0002C3E -19-16OCT12-18/20

Current Setting Check

Most current regulators have a temperature compensation. For these units, make the following test by the "load method."

1. Connect an ammeter into the charging circuit as shown in Fig. 59.

2. Turn on all accessories and connect an additional load across the battery (such as a bank of lights) to drop the system voltage about 1 volt below the voltage regulator setting.

3. Operate the generator at specified speed to warm it up. (See step 5 of "Preliminary Test Procedures.")

4. Cycle the generator and note the current setting.

5. Adjust the setting in the same way as for voltage setting (Fig. 53).

Before slowing down the generator, be sure to remove the extra load. This will prevent overloading of the wiring.

CLEANING CONTACT POINTS

A great majority of regulator problems can be eliminated by a simple cleaning of the regulator points.

On positive-grounded regulators, the contact points that require the most attention are located on the current regulator armature and on the stationary contact point of the voltage regulator.

On negative-grounded regulators, the other contact will require the most attention.

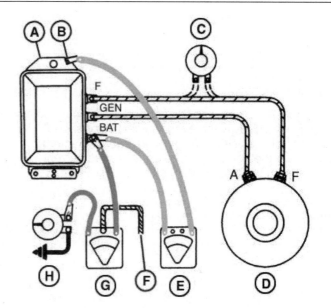

Fig. 59 — Checking Current Setting of Current Regulator

A—Regulator	E—Voltmeter
B—Connect to Ground	F—To Battery
C—Variable Resistance	G—Ammeter
D—Generator	H—Additional Load

It is not necessary to have a flat surface on the points. However, it is necessary to remove all the oxidation.

Continued on next page   OUO1082,0002C3E -19-16OCT12-19/20

Use a spoon or riffler file to remove the oxides until pure metal is exposed (Fig. 60).

Follow this with a thorough washing with trichlorethylene or a similar non-toxic solution. Wash by dampening a strip of lint-free cloth and drawing it between the points.

To clean the points it is necessary to remove the upper contact support as shown in Fig. 60.

Other smaller contact points of soft alloy do not oxidize, but they may be cleaned with a crocus cloth and then washed.

VOLTAGE REGULATOR SETTINGS FOR ABNORMAL OPERATION

The perfect voltage regulator setting will keep the battery at or near full charge with a minimum use of water. The specified voltage value is usually satisfactory for average conditions. However, the operating conditions may be above or below the average. Therefore, it is sometimes necessary to adjust for abnormal conditions.

Two conditions indicate that special adjustment of the voltage regulator is necessary:

1. If the battery uses too much water at normal setting, reduce the voltage regulator setting 0.2 or 0.3 volt. Check to see if this is an improvement over a reasonable length of time. Repeat this adjustment until the battery remains charged with a minimum use of water. Remember that any reduction of the voltage requires a reduced cutout relay setting.

2. If the battery stays undercharged (3/4 charge or less), increase the voltage regulator setting by 0.3 volt. Repeat until the battery is fully charged with a minimum use of water. When increasing the voltage setting,

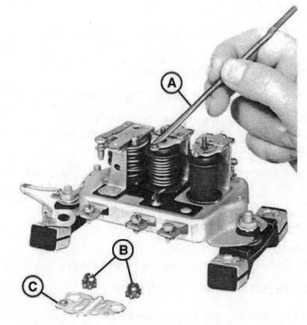

Fig. 60 — Cleaning the Regulator Contact Points

A—Spoon or Riffler File   **C—Upper Contact Support**
B—Nylon Support Nuts

avoid a high setting that could damage lights or other electrical equipment during cold-weather operation.

Always make sure that the battery is in top operating condition before making any of the above adjustments.

Now we must turn to the parts of the AC charging circuit.

OUO1082,0002C3E -19-16OCT12-20/20

ALTERNATORS

The alternator is the heart of the AC charging circuit.

Basically an alternator is like a generator. It converts mechanical energy into electrical energy.

We might say the alternator is an AC generator.

The difference is in the way the alternator rectifies its current to DC for the system. The alternator does this electrically using diodes.

Alternators are generally more compact than generators and can supply a higher current at low engine speeds.

In recent years, there has been more use of electrical accessories at low or idle engine speeds.

The alternator can best supply this output and for this reason AC charging circuits are used more today.

BASIC OPERATION OF ALTERNATOR

First let's compare the basic principles:

- Generators—moving conductor through stationary field = induced voltage
- Alternators—moving field across stationary conductor = induced voltage

Fig. 61 — Alternator (AC Generator) on a Modern Tractor

A—Alternator (AC Generator)

Now let's see how the alternator works.

Continued on next page   OUO1082,0002C3F -19-29OCT12-1/47

6-42

Fig. 62 shows a wire loop and a magnetic field, the same parts we saw earlier in the basic generator.

But now the wire loop is stationary, while the magnetic field is rotating.

The magnetic field is supplied by a bar magnet. (See N and S poles.)

The wire loop is connected to the charging circuit and its load (the light bulb.)

Let's start the operation. As the magnet rotates, its field cuts across the wire loop, inducing voltage. Since we have closed the loop circuit, current will flow. But in what direction?

This brings us back to another law of induction—magnetic lines of force leave the north pole of a magnet and enter its south pole.

In the upper diagram in Fig. 62, if the S pole is next to the upper part of the loop during that half-revolution, current will flow as shown by the arrows. The same direction is induced by the lower N pole on that side of the loop.

Since current flow is from positive to negative, the end of the upper loop is (+) while the lower end is (–) as shown.

Now let's go to the second half of the revolution as shown in the lower diagram in Fig. 62.

The bar magnet has reversed poles and so the direction of current flow has reversed. This action changes the polarity of the loop ends; the top one is now (–) while the bottom one is (+) as shown.

In summary: With each revolution, current flows from loop to load, first in one direction and then in the other. This is alternating current and the reason why the alternator is so named.

HOW VOLTAGE IS INDUCED

However, an alternator made with a bar magnet rotating inside a single loop of wire is not practical, since very little voltage and current are produced.

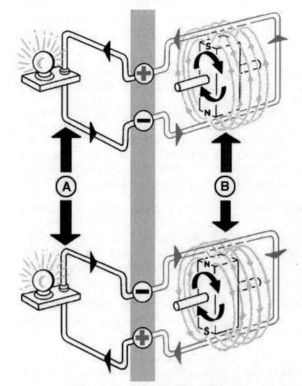

Fig. 62 — Basic Alternator Operation

A—Load Circuit   **B—Rotating Magnetic Field**

The performance is improved when both the loop of wire and the magnet are placed inside an iron frame. The iron frame not only provides a place onto which the loop of wire can be assembled, but also acts as a conducting path for the magnetic lines of force.

DXP03042 —UN—12MAR12

Continued on next page   OUO1082,0002C3F -19-29OCT12-2/47

6-43

Without the iron frame, magnetism leaving the N pole of the rotating bar magnet must travel through air to get to the S pole (Fig. 63).

Because air has a high reluctance to magnetism, only a few lines of force will come out of the N pole and enter the S pole.

Since iron conducts magnetism very easily, adding the iron frame greatly increases the number of lines of force between the N pole and the S pole. This means that more lines of force will be cutting across the conductor, which lies between the bar magnet and the frame.

It is important to note that a very large number of magnetic lines of force are at the center of the tip of the magnet, whereas there are only a few lines of force at the leading and trailing edges of the tips. Thus, there is a strong magnetic field at the center and a weak magnetic field at the leading and trailing edges.

This condition results when the distance, called the air gap, between the magnet and field frame is greater at the leading and trailing edges than at the center of the magnet.

The amount of the voltage induced in a conductor is proportional to the number of lines of force that cut across the conductor in a given length of time.

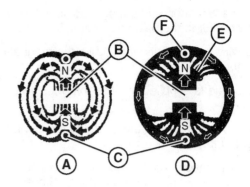

Fig. 63 — Magnetic Lines of Force

A—Air Path—High Reluctance
B—Rotor
C—Conductor
D—Iron Frame—Low Reluctance
E—Weak Field
F—Strong Field

OUO1082,0002C3F -19-29OCT12-3/47

Therefore, if the number of lines of force is doubled, the induced voltage will be doubled (Fig. 64).

The voltage will also increase if the bar magnet is made to turn faster, because the lines of force will be cutting across the wire in a shorter period of time.

Be sure to remember that either increasing the speed of rotation of the bar magnet, or increasing the number of lines of force cutting across the conductor, will result in increasing the voltage.

Similarly, decreasing the speed of rotation or decreasing the number of lines of force will cause the voltage to decrease.

As we saw earlier, the rotating magnet in an alternator is called the rotor, and the loop of wire and outside frame assembly is called the stator.

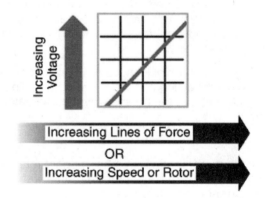

Fig. 64 — Increasing Voltage

Continued on next page OUO1082,0002C3F -19-29OCT12-4/47

Fig. 65 shows the different positions of the rotor as it rotates at constant speed. At the top is a curve showing the magnitude of the voltage that is generated in the loop of wire as the rotor revolves.

The voltage curve shows the generated voltage or electrical pressure that can be measured across the ends of the wire, just as voltage can be measured across the terminal posts of a battery.

With the rotor in the first position (1), there is no voltage being generated in the loop of wire because there are no magnetic lines of force cutting across the conductor.

As the rotor turns and approaches position (2), the rather weak magnetic field at the leading edge of the rotor starts to cut across the conductor, and the voltage increases.

When the rotor reaches position (2), the generated voltage has reached its maximum value, as shown above the horizontal line in the illustration.

The maximum voltage occurs when the rotor poles are directly under the conductor. It is in this position that the conductor is being cut by the heaviest concentration of magnetic lines of force.

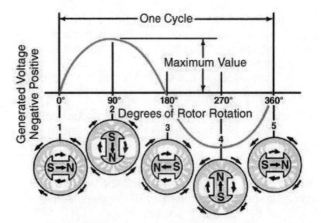

Fig. 65 — Pattern of Generated Voltage During Each Revolution

NOTE: *The magnitude of the voltage varies because the concentration of magnetic lines of force cutting across the loop of wire varies.*

The voltage curve shown is not the result of a change in rotor speed, because in the illustration the rotor is considered to be turning at a constant speed.

OUO1082,0002C3F -19-29OCT12-5/47

By applying the Right Hand Rule to position (2), the direction of current in the loop of wire will be out of the top end of the conductor, and into the bottom end (Fig. 66). Thus, the top end of the conductor will be positive, and the bottom end negative.

The voltage curve that is shown above the horizontal line in Fig. 66 represents the positive voltage at the top end of the wire loop, which is generated as the rotor turns from position (1) to position (3).

As the rotor turns from position (2) to position (3), the voltage decreases until at position (3) it again becomes zero.

As the rotor turns from position (3) to position (4), note that the N pole of the rotor is now passing under the top part of the wire loop, and the S pole under the bottom part. From the Right Hand Rule, the top end of the loop of wire is now negative, and the bottom end positive. The negative voltage at the top end of the loop is pictured in the illustration by the curve that is below the horizontal line.

The voltage again returns to zero when the rotor turns from position (4) to position (5).

DXP03046 —UN—22FEB12

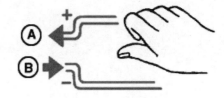

Fig. 66 — Right Hand Rule

A—OUT   **B—IN**

The voltage curve in the illustration represents one complete turn or cycle of the rotor.

With the rotor making 60 complete turns in one second, there will be 60 such curves, one coming right after the other, resulting in 60 cycles per second. The number of cycles per second is called the frequency. Since the generator speed often varies, the frequency also varies.

Continued on next page   OUO1082,0002C3F -19-29OCT12-6/47

In Fig. 67, the single loop of wire acting as a stator winding, and the bar magnet acting as the rotor, show how an A.C. voltage is produced in a basic alternator. When two more separate loops of wire, spaced 120 degrees apart, are added to our basic alternator, two more separate voltages will be produced.

With the S pole of the rotor directly under the A conductor, the voltage at A will be maximum in magnitude and positive in polarity.

After the rotor has turned through 120 degrees, the S pole will be directly under the B conductor and the voltage at B will be maximum positive. Similarly, 120 degrees later, the voltage at C will be maximum positive.

This means that the peak positive voltages at A, B, and C in each loop of wire occur 120 degrees apart. These loop voltage curves are shown in Fig. 67.

A—Rotor
B—Stator Winding

C—One Cycle

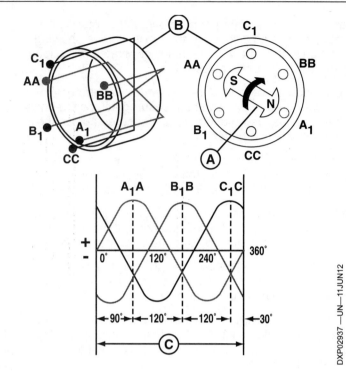

Fig. 67 — Loop Voltage

Continued on next page   OUO1082,0002C3F -19-29OCT12-7/47

PN=210

When the ends of the loops of wire marked A_1, B_1, and C_1 (Fig. 68) are connected to the ends marked B, C, and A respectively, a basic three-phase "delta"-connected stator is formed. The three AC voltages available from the delta-connected stator are identical to the three voltages previously discussed, and may now be denoted as the voltages from B to A, C to B, and A to C, or more simply BA, CB, and AC. Inspect the illustration to see the logic of this. Example: the voltage formerly called A_1A may now be called BA.

When the ends of the loops of wire marked A, B, and C are connected together, a basic three-phase "Y"-connected stator is formed (Fig. 69). The three voltages available from the "Y"-connected stator may be labeled BA, CB, and AC.

From the illustration you can see that each of these voltages consists of the voltages in two loops of wire added together. For example, the voltage measured from B to A consists of the voltages in loops B,B and A,A added together. This addition yields a voltage curve BA similar in shape and form to the individual loop voltages, except that the voltage curve BA will be approximately 1.7 times as large in magnitude as an individual loop voltage.

Remember that three AC voltages spaced 120 degrees apart are available from the "Y"-connected stator, as illustrated. These voltage curves will be considered in more detail in the following sections.

We have now developed the two basic types of stator windings, and have shown how three separate complete cycles of AC voltage spaced 120 degrees apart are developed for each complete revolution of the rotor.

Now we will look at the diode, and we will see how six diodes connected to the stator winding change the three AC voltages to a single DC voltage needed for the DC electrical system:

A—"Y" Stator   C—One Cycle
B—Stator Winding

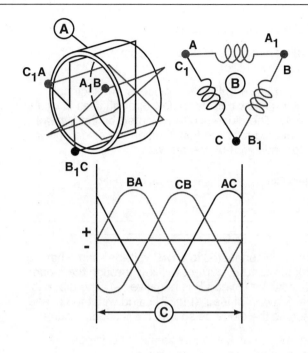

Fig. 68 — Phase Voltage (Delta Stator)

A—Delta Stator   C—One Cycle
B—Stator Winding

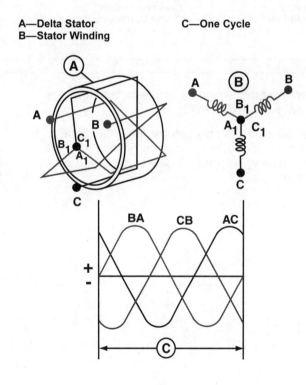

Fig. 69 — Phase Voltage, "Y" Stator

Continued on next page   OUO1082,0002C3F -19-29OCT12-8/47

HOW DIODES CHANGE AC TO DC

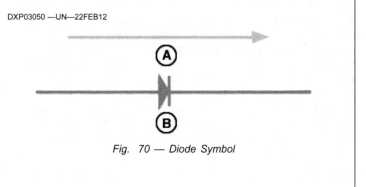

The operating principles of diodes are covered in Chapter "Electricity—How It Works."

Here we need know only that a diode is an electrical device that will allow current to flow through itself in one direction only. The diode is often pictured by the symbol in Fig. 70, and current can flow through the diode only in the direction indicated by the arrow.

A—Current Flow   B—Diode Symbol

Fig. 70 — Diode Symbol

OUO1082,0002C3F -19-29OCT12-9/47

When a diode is connected to an AC voltage source having ends marked A and B, current will flow through the diode when A is positive (+) and B is negative (−). The diode is said to be "forward-biased" (Fig. 71), and with the voltage polarity across the diode as shown, it will conduct current.

When the voltage at A is negative and at B is positive, the diode is said to be "reverse-biased" and it will not conduct current.

A—Forward Bias   C—Reverse Bias
B—Current Flow   D—No Current Flow

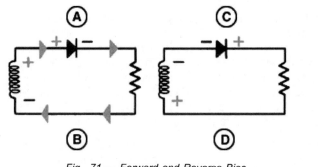

Fig. 71 — Forward and Reverse Bias

OUO1082,0002C3F -19-29OCT12-10/47

The current flow that would be obtained from this arrangement is illustrated in Fig. 72.

Since the current flows only half the time, the diode provides what is called "half-wave rectification" (Fig. 72). A generator having only one diode would provide very limited output.

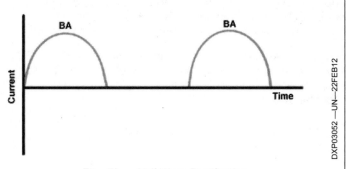

Fig. 72 — Half-Wave Rectification

Continued on next page   OUO1082,0002C3F -19-29OCT12-11/47

The output is increased when four diodes are used to provide "full-wave rectification" (Fig. 73). Note that the current is more continuous than with one diode, but that the current varies from a maximum value to a zero value.

It is particularly important to observe that the current flow through the external load resistor is in one direction only. The AC voltage and current have therefore been rectified to a unidirectional or DC voltage and current.

This circuit arrangement could be used to charge a DC battery, but it does not produce the most output that can be obtained in a generator.

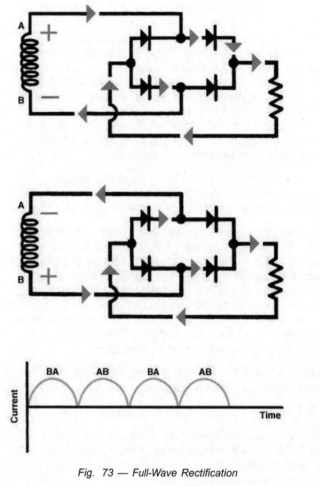

Fig. 73 — Full-Wave Rectification

OUO1082,0002C3F -19-29OCT12-12/47

In order to obtain a higher output and a smoother voltage and current, a three-phase stator is connected to six diodes which together form a "three-phase full-wave bridge rectifier" (Fig. 74).

The operation of the "Y"-connected stator will be illustrated first, then that of the delta-connected stator. A battery connected to the DC output terminal will have its energy restored as the alternator provides charging current. Note that the blocking action of the diodes prevents the battery from discharging directly through the rectifier.

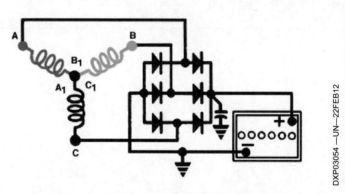

Fig. 74 — Three-Phase, Full-Wave Rectification

Continued on next page

OUO1082,0002C3F -19-29OCT12-13/47

To explain the direction of current flow in the stator-rectifier combination, we will review briefly our previous discussion concerning the three AC voltage curves produced in the "Y-connected stator winding (Fig. 75). Our first reference was to the voltages developed in each loop. These loop voltage curves A_1A, B_1B, and C_1C are reproduced here for reference. However, these individual loop voltages do not appear across the rectifier diodes, because the rectifier is connected only to the A, B, and C terminals of the stator. Therefore, the voltages that appear across the rectifier diodes are the phase voltages BA, CB, and AC.

The phase voltage curves BA, CB, and AC are also reproduced here, and are obtained as previously explained by adding together each pair of loop voltages (Fig. 75).

As an example, phase voltage BA is obtained by adding together the voltages in loops A_1A and B_1B. To obtain the phase curve BA, we add together the voltage from B to B_1, and the voltage from A_1 to A. Consider the instant when the voltage in curve BA is maximum in magnitude and positive in polarity. At this same instant the voltage B_1B is minus 8, or the voltage from B to B_1 is plus 8. This value added to the A_1A loop voltage of plus 8 volts yields a maximum positive voltage of 16 volts for curve BA.

By taking different instants of time, the entire curve BA and curves CB and AC can be obtained in this same manner.

VOLTAGE CURVES—"Y"-CONNECTED STATOR

For convenience, the three A.C. voltage curves provided by the "Y"-connected stator for each revolution of the rotor have been divided into six periods, 1 through 6. Each period represents one-sixth of a rotor revolution, or 60 degrees.

An inspection of the voltage curves during period 1 reveals that the maximum voltage being induced appears

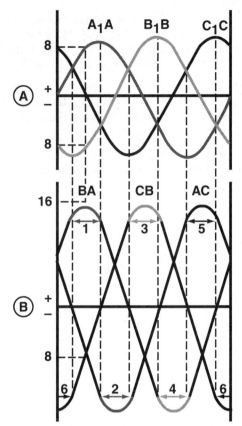

Fig. 75 — Loop and Phase Voltage Curves

A—Loop Voltage Curve   **B—Phase Voltage Curve**

across stator terminals BA. This means that the current flow will be from B to A in the stator winding during this period, and through the diodes as illustrated.

Continued on next page   OUO1082,0002C3F -19-29OCT12-14/47

To see more clearly why the current flows during period 1, assume that the peak phase voltage developed from B to A is 16 volts (Fig. 76). This means that the potential at B is zero volts, and the potential at A is 16 volts.

Similarly, from the curves the phase voltage from C to B at this instant is minus 8 volts. This means that the potential at C is 8 volts, since C to B, or 8 to zero, represents a minus 8 volts.

At this same instant the phase voltage from A to C is also minus 8 volts. This checks, since A to C, or 16 to 8, represents minus 8 volts.

Neglecting voltage drops in the wiring, and assuming a one volt drop in the conducting diodes, the voltage potentials are noted on the rectifier.

Only two of the diodes will conduct current, since these diodes are the only ones in which current can flow in the forward direction. The other diodes will not conduct current because they are reverse biased.

For example, the lower right-hand diode is reverse biased by 7 volts (15 − 8 = 7), and the right-hand middle diode is reverse biased by 15 volts (15 − 0 = 15). It is the biasing of the individual diodes, provided by the stator, that determines how current flows in the stator-rectifier combination.

Throughout period 1 the current flows as indicated, because the bias direction across the diodes does not

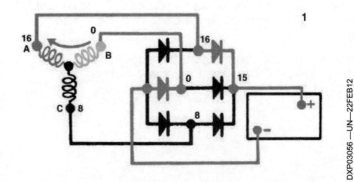

Fig. 76 — "Y" Stator, Period 1

change from that shown. Although the voltage potentials across the diodes will vary numerically, this variation is not sufficient during period 1 to change a diode from reverse bias to forward bias and from forward bias to reverse bias.

Inspect the phase voltage curves in Fig. 75 and you will see that between periods 1 and 2 the maximum voltage being impressed across the diodes changes or switches from phase BA to phase AC. This means that as the maximum voltage changes, the current flow will change from BA to CA.

OUO1082,0002C3F -19-29OCT12-15/47

It is important to note in Fig. 77 that the maximum voltage being produced in the stator windings during period 2 appears across phase AC and that this voltage is negative from A to C.

Taking the instant of time at which this voltage is 16 volts, the potential at A is 16, and at C is zero (A to C, or 16 to 0, is a negative or minus 16).

Similarly, at this same instant, the voltage across phase BA is 8 volts, and across phase CB is 8 volts. This means that the potential at B is 8 volts, as shown. The direction of current flow during period 2 is illustrated.

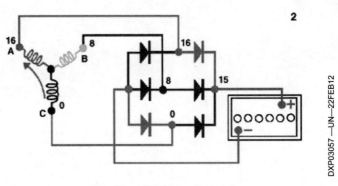

Fig. 77 — "Y" Stator, Period 2

Continued on next page

OUO1082,0002C3F -19-29OCT12-16/47

Following the same procedure for periods 3–6, the current flows can be determined, and are shown in Fig. 78 and Fig. 79.

These are the six major current flow conditions for a three-phase "Y"-connected stator and rectifier combination.

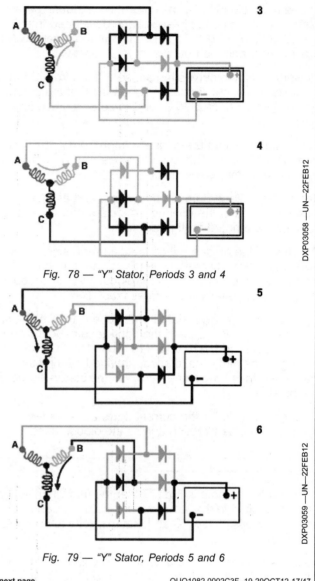

Fig. 78 — "Y" Stator, Periods 3 and 4

Fig. 79 — "Y" Stator, Periods 5 and 6

DXP03058 —UN—22FEB12

DXP03059 —UN—22FEB12

Continued on next page   OUO1082,0002C3F -19-29OCT12-17/47

110112
PN=216

The voltage obtained from the stator-rectifier combination when connected to a battery is not perfectly flat, but is so smooth (Fig. 80) that for all practical purposes the output may be considered to be a non-varying DC voltage. The voltage, of course, is obtained from the phase voltage curves, and can be pictured as shown.

An alternate method of establishing the direction of current flow through the rectifier for a "Y"-connected stator is to refer to the illustration showing the loop voltage curves (Fig. 75).

During period 1 the two loop windings having the largest voltages are A_1A and B_1B, with the voltage in loop C_1C always being less than the voltages in the other two loops. Since the voltage in A_1A is positive, and in B_1B is negative (positive from B to B_1), the current will flow from B to A during period 1. The phase voltage curve BA, of course, is simply a picture of the actual voltage that the two loop voltages A_1A and B_1B added together impress across the rectifier diodes.

Referring again to the loop voltage curves, the two loop windings having the largest voltages during period 2 are A_1A and C_1C. Since the voltage in A_1A is positive, and C_1C is negative (positive from C to C_1), the current will flow from C to A during period 2.

In the same manner, the current flow directions can be determined for the remaining four periods.

DXP03060 —UN—22FEB12

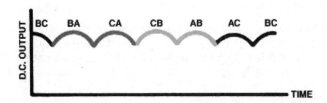

Fig. 80 — DC Current Output

Although this alternate method of using loop voltages can be used to determine the current flow directions, it cannot be used to explain why the current flows as it does through the stator-rectifier combination.

To explain why, it is necessary to determine the voltages that actually exist at the rectifier, because it is these voltages and the biasing of the diodes that determine the current flow directions. These voltages are represented by the phase voltage curves, which are the voltages that actually appear at the rectifier diodes.

Again, as we have already seen, the phase voltage curves are simply the loop voltage curves added together.

VOLTAGE CURVES—DELTA-WOUND STATOR

OUO1082,0002C3F -19-29OCT12-18/47

A delta-connected stator wound to provide the same output as a "Y"-connected stator also will provide a smooth voltage and current output when connected to a six-diode rectifier (Fig. 81).

For convenience, the three-phase AC voltage curves obtained from the basic delta connection for one rotor revolution are reproduced here and have been divided into six periods.

A—Delta Connection
B—Six Diode Rectifier
C—Battery
D—One Cycle

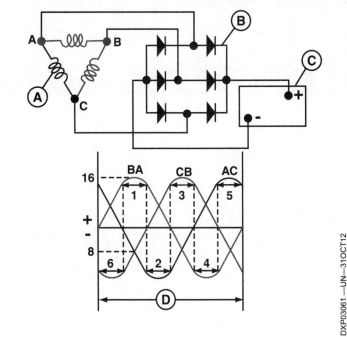

Fig. 81 — "Delta"-Wound Stator

DXP03061 —UN—31OCT12

Continued on next page   OUO1082,0002C3F -19-29OCT12-19/47

During period 1 (Fig. 82), the maximum voltage being developed in the stator is in phase BA.

To determine the direction of current flow, consider the instant at which the voltage during period 1 is a maximum, and assume this voltage to be 16 volts. The potential at B is zero, and at A is 16.

From the curve, it can be seen that the voltage of phase CB is a negative or minus 8 volts. Therefore, the potential at C is 8 (C to B or 8 to 0 is a minus 8 volts).

Similarly, the voltage of phase AC is minus 8 volts. This checks, since A to C, or 16 to 8, is a minus 8. These voltage potentials are shown in Fig. 82.

The current flow through the rectifier is exactly the same as for a "Y"-connected stator, since the voltage potentials on the diodes are identical.

An inspection of the delta stator, however, reveals a major difference from the "Y" stator. Whereas the "Y" stator conducts current through only two windings throughout

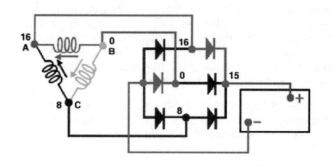

Fig. 82 — "Delta" Stator, Period 1

period 1, the delta stator conducts current through all three. The reason for this is apparent, since phase BA is in parallel with phase BC plus CA. Note that since the voltage from B to A is 16, the voltage from B to C to A also must be 16. This is true since 8 volts is developed in each of these two phases.

OUO1082,0002C3F -19-29OCT12-20/47

During period 2 (Fig. 83), the maximum voltage developed is in phase AC, and the voltage potentials are shown on the illustration at the instant the voltage is maximum.

Also shown are the other phase voltages, and again, the current flow through the rectifier is identical to that for a "Y" stator, since the voltages across the diodes are the same. However, as during period 1, all three delta phases conduct current as illustrated.

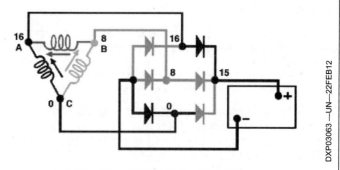

Fig. 83 — "Delta" Stator, Period 2

Continued on next page   OUO1082,0002C3F -19-29OCT12-21/47

Following the same procedure for periods 3–6 the current flow directions are shown in Fig. 84.

We have seen the six major current flow conditions for a delta stator.

This concludes our study of the fundamental principles by which a basic alternator develops and rectifies three AC voltages into a single DC voltage and current flow.

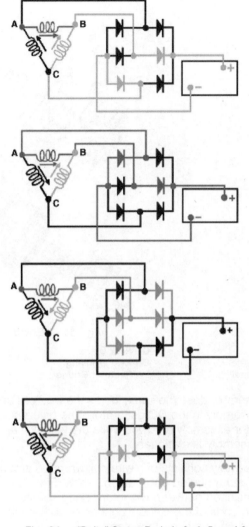

Fig. 84 — "Delta" Stator, Periods 3, 4, 5, and 6

OUO1082,0002C3F -19-29OCT12-22/47

ALTERNATOR CONSTRUCTION

Now let's look at the actual parts of a typical alternator (Fig. 85).

Alternators have three main units:

- Rotor Assembly—magnetic field, which rotates
- Stator Assembly—conductors, which are stationary
- Rectifier Assembly—diodes, which change AC to DC current

A—Field Terminal
B—Brush and Holder Cover
C—Pulley
D—Grounded Terminal
E—Output Terminal
F—Regulator (Auxiliary) Terminal

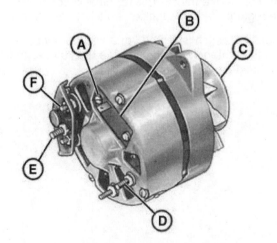

Fig. 85 — Complete Alternator

Continued on next page   OUO1082,0002C3F -19-29OCT12-23/47

ROTOR ASSEMBLY

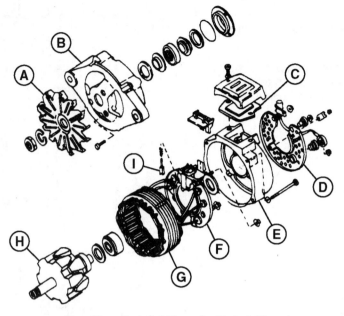

Fig. 86 — Exploded View of a Typical Alternator

A—Fan
B—Front Housing
C—Field Terminal
D—Rear Cover
E—Rear Housing
F—Rectifier Bridge
G—Stator
H—Rotor
I— Brush

The rotor assembly does the same job as the field coil and pole shoe assembly in the DC generator. The difference is that the rotor assembly revolves while the field coil and pole shoe assembly is stationary.

The rotor assembly consists of a wire coil wrapped around an iron core and mounted on a rotating shaft (Fig. 86). The coil is enclosed between two interlocking soft iron sections. The ends of the coil are connected to two slip rings mounted on one end of the shaft.

Small brushes ride on the slip rings. One of the brushes is connected to ground. The other is insulated and connected to the alternator field terminal. This terminal is connected through the regulator and the ignition switch to the battery.

When the ignition switch is turned on, a small amount of current from the battery flows through the regulator to the insulated brush, through one of the slip rings, into the coil, out through the other slip ring and the other brush to ground.

The current through the coil creates a magnetic field, which makes the rotor a rotating multi-pole magnetic field. Each finger on the iron section becomes a magnetic pole.

The rotor poles do not retain magnetism—unlike the generator's pole shoes. Direct current from the battery must flow through the rotor coil to magnetize the poles before the alternator will start to charge. The rotor or alternator field is, therefore, externally excited.

Continued on next page   OUO1082,0002C3F -19-29OCT12-24/47

STATOR ASSEMBLY

The stator assembly does the same job as the armature in a DC generator. However, the stator is fixed while the armature rotates. An actual stator assembly is shown in Fig. 87.

The stator assembly is a laminated soft iron ring with three groups of coils or windings in the slots.

Each group is made up of from 8 to 16 coils, depending on the design.

One end of each stator winding is connected to a positive and negative diode. (We will cover the diode installation later.)

A—End Frame   C—Stator
B—Windings

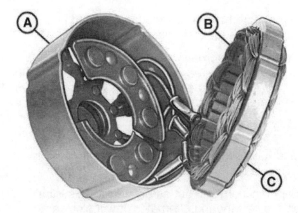

Fig. 87 — Stator Assembly

OUO1082,0002C3F -19-29OCT12-25/47

As we saw earlier, the other ends of the stator windings can be connected by either one of two ways (Fig. 88):

• "Y"-Connected Stator Windings
• Delta-Connected Stator Windings

The delta-connected alternator may be used for heavy-duty operations where lower voltage, but higher amperage, is needed.

The "Y"-connected alternator usually provides a higher voltage and a moderate amperage.

A—Y-Connected Stator B—Delta-Connected Stator

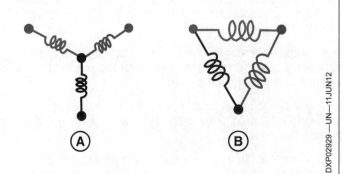

Fig. 88 — Two Connections of Three-Phase Stator Windings

OUO1082,0002C3F -19-29OCT12-26/47

RECTIFIER ASSEMBLY (DIODES)

To convert the AC to DC current, the rectifiers or diodes are used.

In a three-phase alternator, six diodes are mounted at the slip ring end of the alternator housing (Fig. 89). Three negative diodes are mounted in the end frame or in a heat sink bolted to the end frame. Three positive diodes are mounted in the heat sink that is insulated from the end frame.

A—Negative Diode Assembly C—Diode
B—Positive Diode Assembly

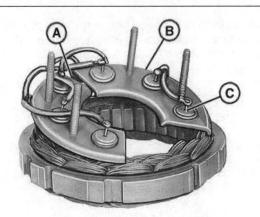

Fig. 89 — Diode Assemblies in Alternator

Continued on next page OUO1082,0002C3F -19-29OCT12-27/47

Some alternators have all six diodes mounted in one assembly, called a rectifier bridge (Fig. 90).

NOTE: On negative-grounded alternators, the positive diodes are mounted in the insulated heat sink. On positive-grounded alternators, the negative diodes are mounted in the insulated heat sink.

ISOLATION DIODE

Some alternators use an extra diode assembly in the circuit. This diode is called the isolation diode.

Its primary function is to act as an automatic switch between the battery and alternator. It will block any current flow from the battery back to the alternator and regulator when the alternator is not operating.

The isolation diode is mounted in a heat sink metal frame. (See Fig. 86.) Two diodes in parallel are used on some high-amperage alternators.

Because all output passes through this diode, high temperatures can be expected. For this reason, the diode and frame are mounted on the slip ring end frame to allow free circulation of air around it.

The charge indicator light is placed in parallel with the isolation diode and connected between the regulator terminal and the ignition switch.

The light supplies the initial current to the regulator to excite the rotor field. This is shown when it lights up while starting the engine.

Most alternators have a resistor in parallel with the light so that when the bulb burns out, the alternator will still be energized and charge the batteries.

The isolation diode and the charge indicator lamp operate as follows:

1. With the ignition switch off, there is no voltage at either end of the indicator lamp. The light is out and the isolation diode blocks current from the battery to the alternator.

Fig. 90 — Rectifier Bridge

A—Negative Heat Sink   C—Diodes
B—Positive Heat Sink   D—Insulation

2. When the ignition switch is turned on, voltage is applied to the one side of the indicator light. This will cause a small amount of current to flow through the regulator to the rotor field and this causes the indicator light to glow.

3. Once the rotor field is excited and the engine starts rotating, voltage is generated in the stator windings and the output through the rectifiers steadily increases.

4. Soon the generated voltage exceeds the voltage potential of the battery. At this time the indicator light goes out and the voltage regulator takes control of field voltage and current.

ALTERNATOR TYPES AND DESIGNS

The alternator's function in the electrical system is to supply current to charge the battery and operate electrical accessories.

Because each application makes its own special requirements on the alternator, there are many different types and designs.

Continued on next page   OUO1082,0002C3F -19-29OCT12-28/47

Some of the factors that determine alternator design are the type of mounting, vibration, belt loading, rotor speeds, current output, service life required, and environmental factors such as dust and dirt.

A—Test Hole
B—"BAT" Terminal

C—No. 1 Terminal
D—No. 2 Terminal

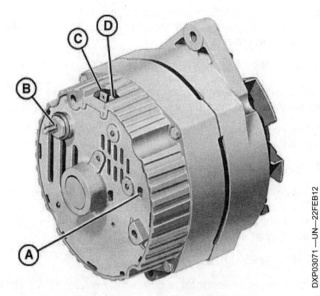

Fig. 91 — Typical Alternator ("A" Circuit Type Shown)

Continued on next page

OUO1082,0002C3F -19-29OCT12-29/47

PN=223

Fig. 91 illustrates one type of alternator that is used in many applications in the off-the-road and automotive field. It is shown in cutaway in Fig. 92.

VARIATIONS ON ALTERNATOR DESIGN

While basically every alternator is the same, there are variations for different uses:

- Housing: Open or closed
- Field Circuit: A or B type

OPEN-TYPE ALTERNATORS

The open-type alternator has openings in its housing for better air circulation. A fan mounted on the pulley end of the rotor shaft helps circulate air to cool the inner parts of the alternator.

CLOSED-TYPE ALTERNATORS

The closed-type alternator is completely encased, except for the pulley and fan assembly and its terminals.

It is designed for use in extremely dusty conditions or in areas where a spark might ignite combustible material. However, it is still necessary to cool these units by either of two methods:

- Air Cooling
- Oil Cooling

Air-Cooled Alternators

The first method of cooling is by circulating air. The fan is driven by the drive pulley and forces air around the sealed housing. Some alternators use two fans for cooling. The housing itself is made of lightweight aluminum that helps to dissipate the heat. The housing may also be ribbed or finned for better circulation of air.

Oil-Cooled Alternators

The other method of cooling is by circulating oil through the interior of the alternator.

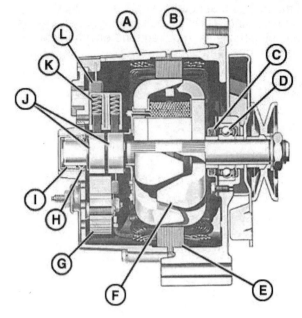

Fig. 92 — Typical Alternator ("A" Circuit Type)

A—Slip Ring End Frame	G—Rectifier Bridge
B—Drive End Frame	H—Seal
C—Seal	I— Bearing
D—Bearing	J— Slip Rings
E—Stator Assembly	K—Brush Assembly
F—Rotor Assembly	L—Regulator

The oil-cooled type is usually confined to use in stationary electrical systems. This design also eliminates the brush and slip ring assemblies.

ALTERNATOR FIELD CIRCUIT VARIATIONS

Two basic field circuit connections exist for an alternator: "A" circuit and "B" circuit.

Continued on next page   OUO1082,0002C3F -19-29OCT12-30/47

"B" Circuit Field

In a "B" circuit alternator (Fig. 93) the regulator is located before the field. The current flow is usually from the regulator terminal of the alternator (the output diode assembly, usually the positive diodes) to the regulator. After the regulator the current flows to the field coil in the rotor, then to ground, and finally to the negative or return diode assembly. Full alternator output is obtained by connecting the field terminal to the regulator terminal or output terminal.

A—Alternator
B—Field Terminal
C—Regulator Terminal
D—Output Terminal

E—Ignition Switch
F—Isolation Diode
G—Transistorized Regulator

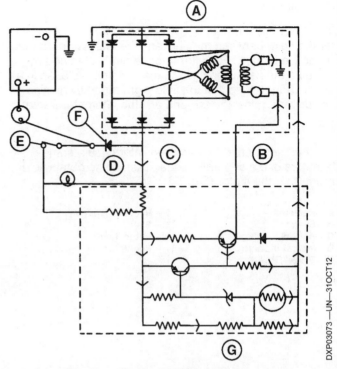

Fig. 93 — "B" Circuit Field for Alternator

DXP03073 —UN—31OCT12

Continued on next page

OUO1082,0002C3F -19-29OCT12-31/47

"A" Circuit Field

In an "A" circuit alternator (Fig. 94) the regulator is located after the field, between the field and the alternator ground or negative diodes. Full alternator output is obtained by grounding the field windings. One alternator has a tab in a test hole (Fig. 91) so that the field is grounded by placing a screwdriver against the tab end and the alternator frame.

Diode Trio

To further isolate the field and regulator circuit, some alternators use a separate diode assembly to obtain field current from the stator (Fig. 94).

A—Resistor
B—Switch
C—Battery
D—Indicator Lamp
E—Diode Trio
F—Rectifier Bridge
G—Stator
H—Rotor (field)
I— Regulator

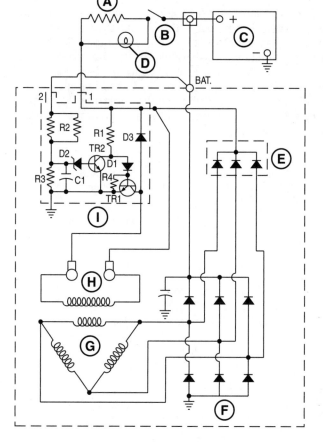

Fig. 94 — "A" Circuit Field for Alternator

Continued on next page   OUO1082,0002C3F -19-29OCT12-32/47

This diode assembly has three diodes and is called a diode trio (Fig. 95).

SUMMARY: OPERATION OF ALTERNATORS

- An alternator is an AC generator.
- It rectifies current to DC using diodes.
- Voltage is generated by moving a magnetic field across a stationary conductor.
- This is reverse of generator principle.
- Alternator = rotor (moving) + stator (fixed) + rectifier (diodes).

ALTERNATOR TESTING

NOTE: The following discussion refers to the two particular types of alternators shown on the following pages. For information on other types, refer to the Technical Manual covering that model.

GENERAL TESTING

Many of the general testing procedures and precautions that applied to the DC generator also apply to the alternator.

1. Make sure that all components, especially the alternator, are the exact models specified for the machine.

2. Make a complete visual check of all leads, wires, connections, etc., to find possible loose connections, broken wires, worn brushes, and dirty slip rings.

3. Use a recommended testing procedure to make a complete circuit check of all the circuit components. This will isolate the problem.

4. In testing or repairing the alternator, follow the recommended testing and service procedures and specifications. These will be found in the alternator Service Manual or the machine Technical Manual.

5. Disassemble the alternator only as far as necessary to make adjustments or repairs.

6. The following tools and test equipment are generally used:

    a. Machine or alternator Technical Manual for reference use

    b. Normal and special tools as noted by the Technical Manual

    c. Ammeter

    d. Voltmeter

    e. Ohmmeter (1-1/2 volt)

    f. Variable carbon pile resistor

    g. Test lamp in series with 12-volt battery

NOTE: A 110-volt test lamp can be used, but not to test diodes or any components while they are connected to the diodes. Use the lamp with extreme care.

Fig. 95 — Diode Trio

PRECAUTIONS FOR ALTERNATOR TESTING

Below is a list of general precautions that must be taken prior to and during alternator tests:

1. Before disconnecting the battery or alternator from the circuit, be sure that the proper polarity is observed.

2. Before installing the battery or alternator, be sure that proper polarity is observed. Turn off all switches and accessories. Then, before connecting the battery ground strap, momentarily touch it to the battery post. No sparks should occur.

3. Disconnect the battery ground strap when using or connecting a battery charger if you are not sure the charger is safe for an alternator charging circuit.

4. Never operate the alternator on open circuit. All three components of the circuit must be connected.

5. Never short or ground the alternator terminals unless instructed.

6. When making alternator tests in the circuit, be sure battery is in good condition and fully charged for control of alternator output with an external load.

IMPORTANT: Never attempt to polarize an alternator. To do so will damage the rectifying parts of the unit.

Failure to take the above precautions can result in damage to the regulator, the rectifier diodes, or other parts of the alternator.

GENERAL DIAGNOSIS OF ALTERNATORS

The following chart can help you to locate malfunctions within the alternator charging circuit.

At the end of this chapter we will relate these alternator problems to the whole charging circuit.

Below each problem are listed the most likely causes.

Alternator Fails To Charge

- Alternator belt loose/slipping
- Open or high resistance in charging circuit
- Worn or defective brushes

- Malfunctioning regulator
- Open isolation diode
- Open rotor field coil

Low Or Unsteady Charging Rate

- Alternator belt loose/slipping
- Open or high resistance in the charging circuit
- Open, worn, or defective brushes
- Faulty regulator
- Shorted or open rectifier diode
- Grounded or shorted rotor field coil
- Open, grounded, or shorted stator windings

Excessive Charging Rate

- Loose alternator or regulator connections
- Malfunctioning regulator

Noisy Alternator

- Defective or worn alternator belt
- Misaligned belt or pulley
- Loose pulley
- Worn bearings
- Shorted rectifier diodes

From this list, make the easy checks first. A good visual check of the charging components may help you to catch the more obvious causes of failures.

ALTERNATOR BENCH TESTING

As you can see, most of the problems listed in the chart can be caused by any one of the charging circuit components. This means that a complete circuit check must be made to isolate the faulty component.

Once you have located the problem in the alternator itself, service the alternator on the bench.

DISASSEMBLY OF ALTERNATOR

First disconnect the battery ground cable. Then disconnect the wires and drive belt from the alternator and remove the alternator from the machine. Select a clean, well-lighted work area for alternator service.

Prior to disassembly, take all the pre-test precautions. Also, remember that the alternator should be disassembled only as far as necessary to correct the problem.

For detailed procedures, refer to the alternator or machine Technical Manual. Here we will dismantle a standard alternator to give you only the general procedures.

OUO1082,0002C3F -19-29OCT12-34/47

Removing Main Parts

1. On alternators equipped with an isolation diode, remove this assembly (Fig. 96).

2. On some alternators, the regulator is mounted directly on the alternator housing. In this case, remove the mounting screws and wiring leads and lift off the regulator.

A—Isolation Diode Assembly

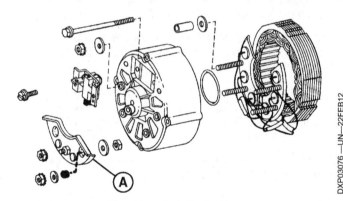

Fig. 96 — Isolation Diode

Continued on next page   OUO1082,0002C3F -19-29OCT12-35/47

3. The brush assembly may be either a separate unit or part of the slip ring end frame. If it is a separate unit, remove the mounting screws and any wire leads. Then tilt it slightly at the top and slip it out of its cavity (Fig. 97).

A—**Brush Assembly**   B—**Insulator**

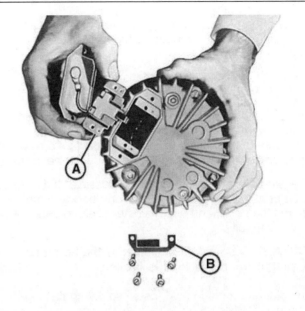

Fig. 97 — Removing the Brush Assembly

OUO1082,0002C3F -19-29OCT12-36/47

4. Separate the slip ring end frame, rectifier diode assembly, and stator from the drive end frame and rotor. Do this by removing the long thru bolts. Slip screwdrivers in the slots between the drive end frame and stator (not more than 1/16 inch because any deeper may damage the stator windings). Then gently pry the stator loose (Fig. 98).

5. To remove the slip ring end frame from the diode and stator assemblies, remove the lock nuts, insulators, and insulating washers from the diode terminal posts.

IMPORTANT: Notice the position of the insulators before removing them. They must be replaced in the same order.

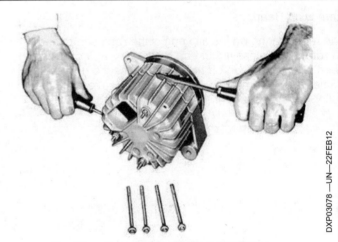

Fig. 98 — Removing the Slip Ring End Frame

OUO1082,0002C3F -19-29OCT12-37/47

6. On closed-type alternators, separate the diode assembly from the stator by removing the stator leads from the screw terminals (Fig. 99).

Fig. 99 — Removing Diode Assemblies, Closed Type

Continued on next page   OUO1082,0002C3F -19-29OCT12-38/47

On some open-type alternators, the stator leads must be unsoldered from the diodes to separate the two assemblies (Fig. 100).

Soldering And Unsoldering Diode Leads (Some Open-Type Alternators)

When soldering or unsoldering diodes, be sure to grip the diode lead with a pair of needle-nosed pliers between the connection and the diode. The pliers will act as a heat sink and prevent heat damage to the diode hermetic seal.

Also, avoid bending the diode lead, if possible. If the lead must be bent, use two pliers. Place one between the diode and the bend, and use the other pliers to bend the lead very carefully.

IMPORTANT: Diodes will be ruined if the hermetic seal at the diode lead is broken.

When soldering a diode lead, use a solder containing 60% tin and 40% lead.

IMPORTANT: Never use an acid-core solder. Use only a rosin-core solder.

Removing Bearings

The rear bearing on the slip ring of the rotor shaft need not be removed unless it must be replaced. The front bearing need not be pressed off the shaft unless the drive end frame is to be removed. Be sure to use the recommended pullers and presses for these jobs.

Fig. 100 — Removing Diode Assemblies, Open Type

A—Terminal Nuts C—Diode
B—Stator

Continued on next page   OUO1082,0002C3F -19-29OCT12-39/47

Replacing Diodes

On some closed-type alternators, individual diodes may be replaced by pressing the faulty diode out of the plate and pressing a new one in Fig. 101. On other alternators, replace the whole positive or negative diode plate assembly.

IMPORTANT: Be sure to replace a diode with one of the same type. Positive diodes are marked in red, while negative ones are marked in black.

TESTING THE INDIVIDUAL COMPONENTS

The tests given here are only general outlines to give you an idea of what tests should be performed on actual electrical components. The alternator Service Manual or machine Technical Manual will give you the detailed tests and specifications.

TESTING THE BRUSHES

First make a visual check of the brushes and leads. If the brushes are worn down to an exposed length of 1/4 inch (6 mm) or less or are otherwise defective, replace the entire brush assembly.

A—Special Driver
B—Drift Punch

C—Support Tools

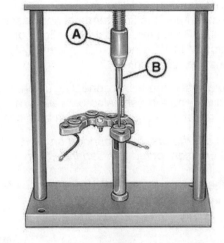

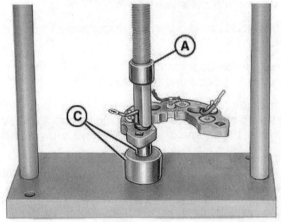

Fig. 101 — Replacing Individual Diodes (Closed-Type Alternators Only)

Continued on next page

OUO1082,0002C3F -19-29OCT12-40/47

An insulation test can be made by connecting an ohmmeter or test lamp to the field terminal and assembly bracket (Fig. 102). Resistance should be infinite or the test lamp should not light. If not, brush assembly is shorted and must be replaced.

A brush continuity test is made by connecting an ohmmeter to the field terminal and a brush. Also between bracket and brush. The resistance should be zero in both cases.

NOTE: In some alternators, the grounded brush is also insulated and connected to a separate terminal.

While making the tests, wiggle the brushes and leads to locate poor connections or intermittent grounds.

TESTING THE DIODES

Test the diodes in two steps:

1. Test the diodes before they are disconnected from the stator.

2. If a malfunction appears during this test, disconnect the suspected diode and retest the others.

The first indication of a faulty diode may be a humming or growling sound heard while the alternator is operating. At the same time, the alternator will usually have a low output.

Use a commercial diode tester, a 1-1/2-volt ohmmeter, or a test lamp connected in series to a 12-volt battery to test the diodes. Never use a 110-volt test lamp to test the diodes.

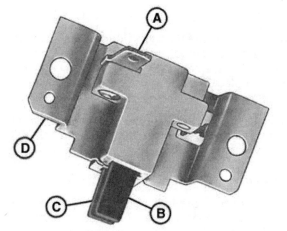

Fig. 102 — Visual Check of Brush Assembly on 12-Volt Alternator

A—Field Terminal   C—Grounded Brush
B—Insulated Brush   D—Bracket

Some commercial diode testers will check the diodes in one step.

OUO1082,0002C3F -19-29OCT12-41/47

Testing Individual Diodes With Ohmmeter

Connect one ohmmeter lead to the diode case and the other lead to the diode lead (Fig. 103). Note the ohmmeter reading.

Now reverse the ohmmeter leads and note the reading. A good diode has a high and a low reading.

After testing each group of diodes, compare the ohmmeter readings. If the high and low readings on all the diodes are the same, the diodes are good. If even a slightly different reading is obtained for one diode, it is probably defective. Disconnect it and recheck the diodes.

A—Diode Lead   C—Diode Case
B—Ohmmeter

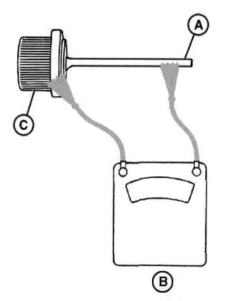

Fig. 103 — Testing Diode with an Ohmmeter

Continued on next page   OUO1082,0002C3F -19-29OCT12-42/47

Testing Diodes In The Rectifier Bridge

Reverse the ohmmeter probes and make the same checks. Note the ohmmeter readings.

Repeat this same procedure on the diodes on the opposite side of the rectifier bridge.

An ohmmeter is needed to determine if a diode is good or defective. A good reading indicates a diode has continuity in only one direction. A shorted diode has continuity in both directions; an open diode lacks continuity in either direction.

Fig. 104 — Testing Diodes in the Rectifier Bridge

OUO1082,0002C3F -19-29OCT12-43/47

Testing Diodes With Test Lamp

If a test lamp in series with a 12-volt battery is used, place one test probe on the base of the diode and the other probe on the diode lead. Then reverse the probes (Fig. 105).

The lamp should light in one direction but not the other. If the lamp lights in both directions, one or more of the diodes in the group are shorted. If the lamp does not light in either direction, all of the diodes are open.

Disconnect the diodes from the stator and test them one at a time to locate the shorted diode.

Testing Diodes With Alternator Diode Tester

A commercial diode tester usually has its own directions. Follow that testing procedure when checking out diodes.

When replacing diodes, remember their polarity. Positive diodes are marked in red, negative diodes in black.

TESTING THE STATOR ASSEMBLY

A visual inspection may uncover some defects in the stator windings. Shorted windings are usually discolored.

Test stator as follows:

1. If a 110-volt test lamp or an armature tester is used, disconnect the diodes from the stator to prevent damage to the diodes.

2. Disconnect the stator leads from the diode assemblies.

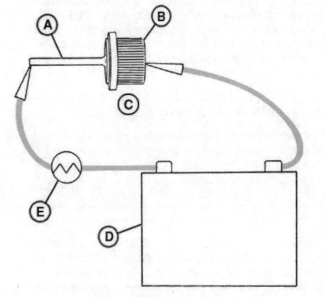

Fig. 105 — Testing Diode with Test Lamp

A—Lead
B—Case
C—Diode

D—12-Volt Battery
E—Test Lamp

3. Check for a grounded winding by connecting an ohmmeter to one stator lead and to the stator frame. The ohmmeter reading should be infinite.

Continued on next page   OUO1082,0002C3F -19-29OCT12-44/47

4. Check a "Y"-connected stator for an open circuit by connecting an ohmmeter from point A to B and B to C (Fig. 106).

5. Some delta-connected stator leads must be welded to the terminals and cannot be checked for an open circuit except by a sensitive ohmmeter.

6. If a very sensitive ohmmeter is available, use the following procedure. However, it will not detect a short or open circuit that occurs only when the stator is hot.

7. To check for a short-circuited winding or, on a delta winding, an open circuit, carefully zero the ohmmeter and connect the leads to A and B (Fig. 106). A typical reading would be 0.1 ohm for a delta stator or 0.2 ohm for a "Y" stator. If on a delta connected stator, the reading was approximately 0.2 ohm and then a 0.1 ohm reading was obtained in step 3, the phase winding is probably open-circuited. A high reading indicates two delta phase windings are open-circuited. Now touch the A and B leads together several times. The meter pointer should deflect to zero. If there is no pointer movement, the windings are shorted.

8. Repeat the open circuit and short circuit tests between A and C and between B and C in Fig. 106.

NOTE: *A single short-circuited winding of a delta-wound stator is very difficult to distinguish. Therefore, the accuracy of this test depends upon meter sensitivity to resistances of 0 to 1 ohm.*

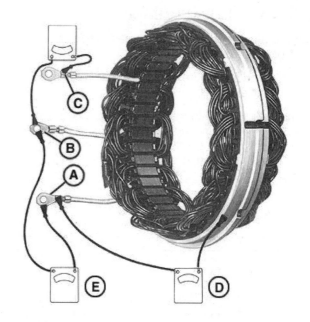

Fig. 106 — Checking "Y"-Connected Stator with an Ohmmeter

A—Lead A
B—Lead B
C—Lead C

D—Ohmmeter (Check for Grounds)
E—Ohmmeter (Check for Opens)

OUO1082,0002C3F -19-29OCT12-45/47

9. If a sensitive ohmmeter is not available for the above, and the leads are not welded together, carefully disconnect the stator leads (Fig. 107). Stator leads may be brittle if they have been overheated or if they are old.

10. Each phase winding may now be checked for shorts to an adjacent phase winding (A to B, B to C, and A to C). A delta-connected stator may be also checked for an open-circuited phase winding by connecting A to AA, B to BB, and C to CC.

11. After testing, connect stator leads again.

12. This completes the testing of the stator assembly.

Remember that a shorted stator is usually discolored and will smell. Replace the stator only after other components have proved to be satisfactory.

TESTING THE ROTOR ASSEMBLY

The rotor should be tested for grounds with an armature tester, a 12-volt test lamp, or a 110-volt test lamp. However, use caution when using an armature tester or a 110-volt lamp. When using a test lamp, place one of the

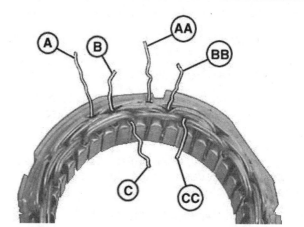

Fig. 107 — Testing the Delta Stator Assembly

A—Winding A
B—Winding B
C—Winding C

AA—Winding AA
BB—Winding BB
CC—Winding CC

probes on the slip ring and the other probe on the rotor coil. If the lamp lights, the rotor is grounded.

Continued on next page OUO1082,0002C3F -19-29OCT12-46/47

To check the rotor for shorted or open windings, connect a voltmeter to the slip rings (Fig. 108). Then connect an ammeter in series with a variable resistor to the slip ring and 12-volt battery as shown. Set the variable resistor to maximum resistance. Connect the other slip rings to the battery and adjust the resistor to obtain full battery voltage.

IMPORTANT: Removing the wire from the slip ring, will cause an arc and may damage the slip ring surface, requiring cleanup.

Rotor field current draw should equal the amount specified for the applied voltage. For example, it should be between 2.0 and 2.5 amperes at 12.4 volts.

Shorted windings are indicated by excessive current draw; open windings by no current draw at all.

If the slip rings are scored, turn them in a lathe until they just clean up. If desired, polish them sparingly with No. 00 sandpaper or No. 400 grit silicon carbide paper.

ASSEMBLY OF ALTERNATOR

Reassembly of the alternator is generally just the reverse of disassembly. However, observe the pre-test precautions again and use the specific directions for assembly given in the machine Technical Manual. Always test the alternator after assembly to be sure it is operating properly.

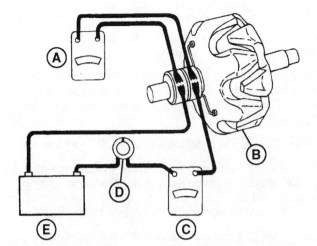

Fig. 108 — Testing the Rotor Assembly

A—Voltmeter
B—Rotor Assembly
C—Ammeter
D—Variable Resistor
E—Battery

OUO1082,0002C3F -19-29OCT12-47/47

ALTERNATOR REGULATORS

The AC regulator is the control for the alternator. Otherwise, the alternator would produce too much voltage.

The regulator does this by placing a resistance in the field circuit, which reduces current flow to the alternator rotor. This is much the same principle as used by the regulator in DC charging circuits.

How is the AC regulator different from the DC regulator?

- No current regulator is needed, since the alternator limits its output by setting its own opposing field during operation.
- The AC regulator is often only a voltage regulator.

There are special cases where combination regulator or field relay units are used for AC circuits, but these are not basic to our present story. (See "Other Types of Alternator Regulators.")

TRANSISTORIZED VOLTAGE REGULATOR

The most popular AC voltage regulator is transistorized (solid state). It is composed of resistors, diodes, Zener diode, transistors, and thermistor. These components (Fig. 109) are usually in a sealed case. This eliminates the need for adjustments or the chance of failure due to dirt or moisture. A basic description of each component is given below:

- Resistors—Devices made of wire or carbon that present a resistance to current flow.
- Zener Diode—A diode that is connected in a reverse bias and below a certain voltage works like the typical

Fig. 109 — Transistorized Voltage Regulator (For Circuit, see Fig. 112)

diode. However, beyond a predetermined voltage, the Zener diode will conduct reverse current.
- Transistor—Semiconductors that control the current flow in the circuit by allowing current flow or stopping it.
- Thermistor—The amount of its resistance varies with the temperature. A positive temperature coefficient (PTC) thermistor's resistance increases as the temperature increases. A negative temperature coefficient (NTC) thermistor's resistance decreases as the temperature increases. A thermistor controls the Zener diode so that a higher system voltage is produced in cold weather when needed.

OPERATION OF THE TRANSISTORIZED REGULATOR

Basically, the AC regulator has two jobs:

- Allow battery current to excite the alternator field coils.
- Control charging voltage at safe values during operation.

Continued on next page   OUO1082,0002C40 -19-12JUN12-1/7

Fig. 110 and Fig. 111 show the circuits for two typical alternators.

Since all regulators are similar in operation, let's take the regulator in Fig. 111 and see how it operates.

A—Field Discharge Diode   TR—Transistor
B—Zener Diode   RT—Thermistor
R—Resistor

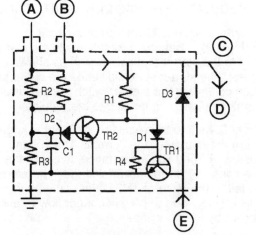

Fig. 110 — Circuit of One Transistorized Regulator (With NPN Transistors)

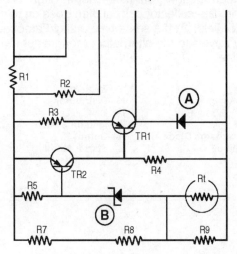

Fig. 111 — Circuit of Another Transistorized Regulator

Continued on next page   OUO1082,0002C40 -19-12JUN12-2/7

HOW THE REGULATOR WORKS DURING STARTING

When the starter switch is turned on, the circuit is completed (Fig. 112). Battery current flows to the starter solenoid and to the starter (ignition) switch as shown by the black lines. The starter solenoid sends the current on to the ignition coil, while the starter switch sends current to the alternator indicator lamps and to the regulator.

As the current flows into the regulator, different voltage values govern the course of the current. The voltage across resistors R7 and R8, for instance, is below the Zener diode critical or "break down" voltage. Therefore, the voltage felt at the base of TR2 is the same as the voltage at its emitter. So the current cannot flow through TR2 (as shown by the gray lines).

Thus the voltage difference in the emitter-base circuit of TR1 allows current flow from its emitter through its base and collector. The collector current then goes on to excite the alternator field. At the same time a slight amount of current flow travels to the alternator ground as shown by the dotted line.

A—Battery
B—Alternator
C—Field
D—Ground
E—Field Discharge Diode
F—Zener Diode
G—Regulator
H—Distributor
I—Coil
J—Ignition Switch
K—Output
L—Starter Motor

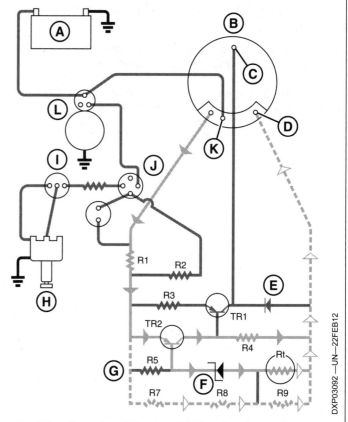

Fig. 112 — Operation of Transistorized Regulator During Starting

Continued on next page   OUO1082,0002C40 -19-12JUN12-3/7

HOW THE REGULATOR WORKS DURING ENGINE OPERATION

The early part of engine operation (Fig. 113) is similar to the starting period above, except that as the engine speeds up the alternator field around the rotor generates voltage that flows out to supply loads.

However, the voltage values are still the same and transistor TR1 still conducts the current to the alternator field as shown by the vertical line.

A—Battery
B—Alternator
C—Field
D—Ground
E—Field Discharge Diode
F—Zener Diode
G—Regulator
H—Distributor
I— Coil
J—Ignition Switch
K—Output
L—Starter Motor

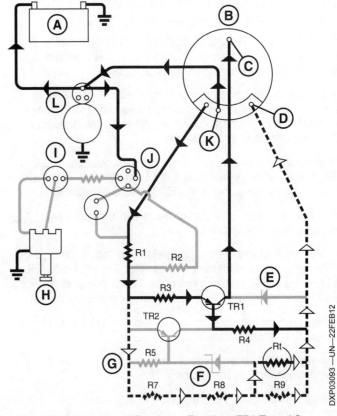

Fig. 113 — Operation of Regulator—Transistor TR1 Turned On

Continued on next page

OUO1082,0002C40 -19-12JUN12-4/7

As the engine operates and load requirements begin to decrease, the alternator voltage builds up (Fig. 114).

This causes the voltage across the resistors to also increase. Then the voltage across R7 and R8 becomes greater than the Zener diode critical voltage.

The Zener diode immediately breaks down" allowing current to flow through in a reverse direction. This turns on transistor TR2 and so current is able to flow through TR2's emitter-base and collector.

When current flows through TR2, the voltage at the base of TR1 is equal to or greater than at its emitter. This prevents current from flowing through TR1 to the alternator field.

This collapses the field and reduces the output of the alternator, protecting the circuit.

The system voltage then drops below the critical voltage of the Zener diode and it stops conducting. This turns off TR2 and turns on TR1 and current again flows to the alternator field. This operation is repeated many times a second.

In effect, the two transistors act as switches controlling the voltage and alternator output.

Note the field discharge diode in Fig. 114. This diode prevents damage to transistor TR1.

When TR1 turns off, the alternator field current cannot drop immediately to zero, because the rotor windings cause the current to continue to flow.

Before the current flow reaches zero, the system voltage and regulator start current flow again. However, the decreasing field current flow induces a high voltage and this can damage the transistor.

The purpose of the field discharge diode is to divert the high voltage away from the transistor.

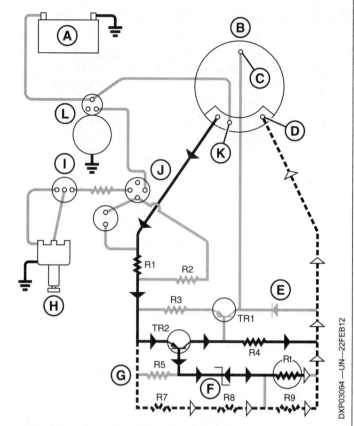

Fig. 114 — Operation of Regulator—Transistor TR2 Turned On

A—Battery
B—Alternator
C—Field
D—Ground
E—Field Discharge Diode
F—Zener Diode
G—Regulator
H—Distributor
I— Coil
J—Ignition Switch
K—Output
L—Starter Motor

Continued on next page

OUO1082,0002C40 -19-12JUN12-5/7

OPERATION OF REGULATOR WITH NPN TRANSISTORS

The second typical regulator we saw in Fig. 110 works as follows:

The alternator is generating current and supplying its own field current from the diode trio (Fig. 115). When voltage rises to the critical voltage of the Zener diode (D2), the diode conducts and a positive voltage is applied at the base terminal of driver transistor "TR2" and turns it on. (The positive voltage at the base terminal turns an NPN transistor on.) This reduces the voltage at the base terminal of the power transistor (TR1), which turns the power transistor off.

TESTING AND REPAIRING THE TRANSISTORIZED REGULATOR

First, make a complete circuit check to isolate the faulty component. Take all the normal precautions for safety.

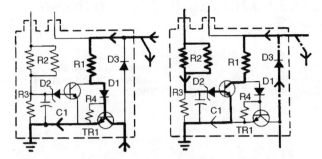

Fig. 115 — Operation of Regulator with NPN Transistors

For a general diagnosis, use the checks given earlier in the alternator testing section. Then make the more specific tests that follow.

For a particular test procedure, always follow the machine Technical Manual. The following test is an example of the type usually made on a transistorized regulator. Since the regulator is only used to control voltage, the voltage test is all that is required.

OUO1082,0002C40 -19-12JUN12-6/7

Voltage Test

1. This test can be performed either on or off the machine. Use an alternator that is known to be in good repair. Set up the test circuit shown in Fig. 116.

2. Connect a voltmeter to the alternator ground and output terminals as shown. Be sure to use a voltmeter with an accuracy within 0.1 volt.

3. Start the engine, momentarily connect jumper wire to excite the field, and apply a load of about 10 amperes (use lights, motors, carbon pile resistors, etc.).

4. Operate the circuit for about 15 minutes to stabilize the temperature of the regulators. Measure and record the temperature about one inch from the regulator case.

5. Compare the voltmeter reading with the voltage specifications listed in the machine Technical Manual. Do not forget to adjust the reading for the temperature recorded above.

Adjustment And Repair

Some transistorized regulators have an adjusting screw for changing the operating voltage for different conditions.

Since most transistorized regulators are sealed units, they offer no means of repair. Therefore, they must be replaced if they are faulty. But at the same time, this type of regulator is usually more reliable than other kinds.

OTHER TYPES OF ALTERNATOR REGULATORS

As popular as the fully transistorized regulator is, it is not the only regulator used. Vibrating contact regulators,

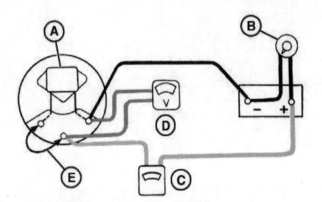

Fig. 116 — Voltage Test for Transistorized Regulator

A—Regulator
B—Variable Resistor
C—Ammeter
D—Voltmeter
E—Jumper Wire

similar to the units used in DC charging circuits, are still in use today.

TRANSISTOR VIBRATING CONTACT REGULATOR

This combination of old and new, so to speak, has been effectively used in some AC charging circuits.

A typical model has a circuit breaker to protect the alternator in case of shorts, grounds, or reverse polarity. A voltage regulator controls a transistor, which in turn energizes the alternator field. Diodes are used as safety devices to protect the regulator, while resistors also aid in controlling the circuit.

OUO1082,0002C40 -19-12JUN12-7/7

DIAGNOSIS AND TESTING OF CHARGING CIRCUITS

A—Used on 24-Volt System Only
B—Regulator
C—Generator
D—Indicator Lamp
E—Starter Switch (with resistor—24-volt system)
F—Battery

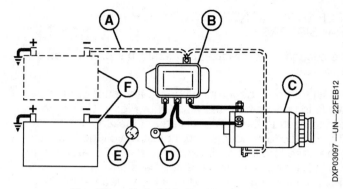

Fig. 117 — Typical DC Charging Circuit

Continued on next page   OUO1082,0002C41 -19-16OCT12-1/14

In this chapter we have strongly suggested that you begin by testing the complete charging circuit (Fig. 117 and Fig. 118). The checks given here should be done before any of the component tests given earlier in this chapter. A complete circuit check will isolate the failing component.

TROUBLESHOOTING OF CHARGING CIRCUITS

When using this chart, assume that the battery is in good operating condition. (Battery problems are covered in Chapter 5.)

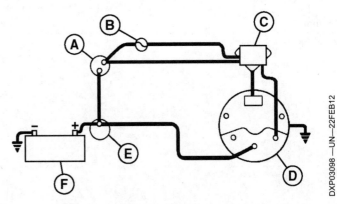

Fig. 118 — Typical AC Charging Circuit

A—Starter Switch
B—Indicator Lamp
C—Regulator
D—Alternator
E—Starter Solenoid
F—Battery

Table 1 — Troubleshooting of Charging Circuits	
Problem	**Possible Cause**
1. Low Battery Output	a. Faulty Regulator—AC or DC
	b. Faulty Generating Unit AC or DC
	c. Slipping Drive Belt—AC or DC
2. Low Generating Output	a. Slipping Drive Belt—AC or DC
	b. Poor Lead Connections— AC or DC
	c. High Circuit Resistance— AC or DC
	d. Cutout Relay Malfunction—DC
	e. Faulty Regulator Circuit Breaker—AC
	f. Regulator Diode Malfunction— AC
	g. Regulator Transistor Malfunction—AC
	h. Oxidized Regulator Points — AC or DC
	i. Open Isolation Diode—AC
	j. Shorted Field Circuit Windings—AC or DC
	k. Open Diodes—AC
3. Excessive Output	a. Faulty Regulator—AC or DC
	b. Grounded Field Terminal—DC
	c. High Voltage Regulator Setting—AC or DC
	d. High Temperature—AC or DC
	e. Shorted Regulator Transistor— AC
4. Noisy Generating Unit	a. Defective Bearings—AC or DC
	b. Loose Mounting—AC or DC
	c. Shorted Diode—AC
	d. Open Diode—AC
	e. Brush Chatter—DC
5. Battery Uses Too Much Water	a. Regulator Setting Too High— AC or DC
	b. Faulty Regulator—AC or DC
Table 1 — Troubleshooting of Charging Circuits Continued	

Continued on next page

OUO1082,0002C41 -19-16OCT12-2/14

Table 1 — Troubleshooting of Charging Circuits	
Problem	**Possible Cause**
6. No Generating Output	a. Sticking Brushes—AC or DC
	b. Loose or Open Connections— AC or DC
	c. Grounded, Shorted, or Open Armature—DC
	d. Grounded, Shorted, or Open Field Circuit—DC
	e. Grounded Terminals—DC
	f. Dirty or Corroded Commutator—DC
	g. Open Diodes—AC
	h. Open Stator Windings—AC
	i. Open Rotor Windings—AC
	j. Faulty Regulator Circuit Breaker—AC
	k. Faulty Cutout Relay—DC
	l. Faulty Current Regulator—DC
	m. Faulty Voltage Regulator—DC
	n. Open Transistor—AC
	o. Open Isolation Diode—AC

SAFETY RULES

Before we start the circuit tests, let's quickly review some of the precautions that have been mentioned in the previous sections of this chapter.

DC CIRCUITS

- Polarize the circuit after each test or adjustment.
- Be sure the battery is in good operating condition before making any tests or adjustments. Review the battery safety messages in Chapters 1 and 5.
- Disconnect the battery ground cable when removing the generator or battery.
- Never immerse the circuit components in a cleaning solution.

AC CIRCUITS

- Never attempt to polarize the circuit.
- Be sure the battery is in good operating condition before making any tests or adjustments.
- Never operate the alternator in an open circuit, except when instructed in the Technical Manual.
- Never short or ground the alternator terminals.
- Do not disconnect the voltage regulator while the alternator is running.
- Disconnect the negative battery cable first when removing the alternator or battery.

- Do not use acid-core solder on the alternator terminals. Use only a rosin-core solder.
- Never immerse the circuit components in cleaning solution.

TESTING THE DC CHARGING CIRCUIT

Remember that these are general tests performed on a circuit which has a standard shunt-type generator and a three-unit regulator. The battery should be considered in good operating condition for these tests.

GENERATOR OUTPUT TEST

The test equipment you should have for this test includes: an ammeter, a voltmeter, a tachometer, a variable resistor, and a jumper wire.

You will notice that we have shown this equipment in its basic form. An electrical testing unit as in Chapter 2 may combine them all into one unit. If this is the case, follow the tester's instructions in making test connections.

Test Procedure

1. Make a visual check of all wire leads, connections, and brushes.

Continued on next page   OUO1082,0002C41 -19-16OCT12-3/14

2. Disconnect the leads to the generator armature and field terminals.

3. Connect the ammeter and variable resistance in series with the generator armature terminal and ground (Fig. 119). Connect the voltmeter across the generator armature terminal and ground as shown.

4. Connect the jumper wire to the generator field terminal and to ground.

5. Adjust the variable resistor for the least resistance.

6. Operate the engine at the specified speed.

7. Adjust the variable resistor to obtain the specified voltage. For example, 14 volts for a 12-volt circuit, or 28.5 volts for a 24-volt circuit.

   The generator output should be as specified. For example, 20 amps for a 12-volt circuit, or 10 amps for a 24-volt circuit.

   If the results are not what is specified, the generator is faulty. Remove the generator from the circuit and make further tests.

   If the test shows a good generator, reconnect the leads to the terminals and polarize the generator.

RESISTANCE TESTS

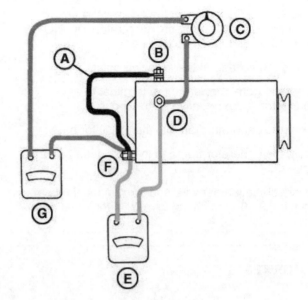

Fig. 119 — Generator Output Test (12-Volt Circuit)

A—Jumper Wire
B—Field Terminal
C—Variable Resistor
D—Armature Terminal
E—Voltmeter
F—Ground
G—Ammeter

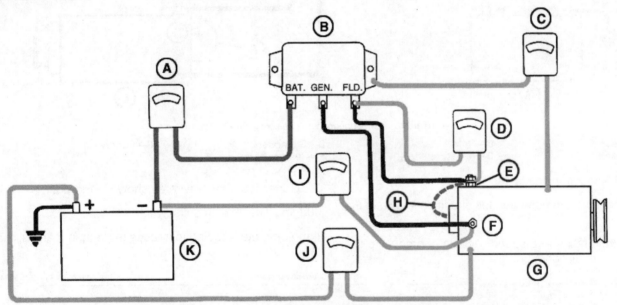

Fig. 120 — Wiring Resistance Tests (12-Volt Circuit)

A—Ammeter
B—Regulator
C—Voltmeter D
D—Voltmeter B
E—Field
F—Armature
G—Generator
H—Jumper Wire
I—Voltmeter A
J—Voltmeter C
K—Battery

As is shown in Fig. 120, we are again performing this on a 12-volt circuit. Because these tests are given as examples of the types of tests used, you will need to consult the machine Technical Manual for particular testing connections, procedures, and specifications.

Testing Procedure

1. Connect the ammeter to the regulator battery terminal and to the wire disconnected from this terminal.

2. Connect a jumper wire to the generator field terminal and to ground.

Continued on next page   OUO1082,0002C41 -19-16OCT12-4/14

3. With all accessories off, run the engine at a speed that will produce a 10-amp charging rate. (DO NOT exceed 10 amps in a 24-volt circuit.)

4. Measure the voltage at the following points:

   a. From the generator armature terminal to a pin connector in the negative battery post.

   b. From the generator frame to the regulator base.

   c. From the generator frame to the grounded battery post.

5. Disconnect the jumper wire and turn on the lights. Continue the 10-amp charging rate. If you must lower

the battery voltage to get the 10-amp charging rate, use a heavy-duty carbon pile resistor connected to the battery.

6. Check the voltage from the generator field to the regulator field terminal.

Judging The Test Results

If the voltage readings are too high, check out each circuit component individually.

If the readings are normal, reconnect the regulator lead and polarize the generator.

OUO1082,0002C41 -19-16OCT12-5/14

REGULATOR TESTS

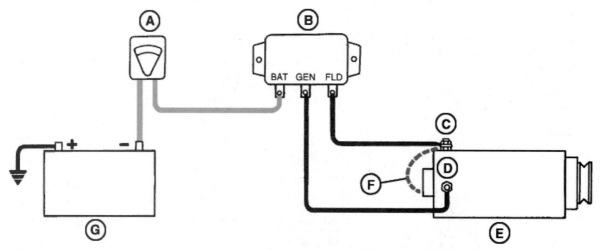

Fig. 121 — Regulator Test Connections—Checking for Oxidized Points

| A—Ammeter | C—Field | E—Generator | G—Battery |
| B—Regulator | D—Armature | F—Jumper Wire | |

Oxidized Regulator Points Test

1. Connect the ammeter into the circuit as shown in Fig. 121.

2. Run the engine at a speed capable of producing 8 amps with all lights on.

3. Connect a jumper wire as shown in Fig. 121.

Judging The Test Results

If the ammeter reading increases more than 2 amps, the regulator points are oxidized.

Continued on next page
OUO1082,0002C41 -19-16OCT12-6/14

Regulator Voltage Tests

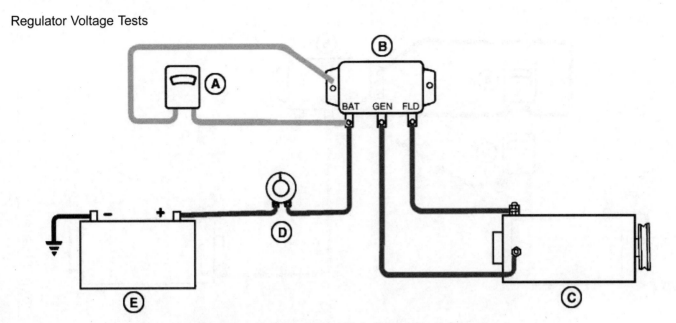

Fig. 122 — Regulator Voltage Tests (12-Volt Circuit Connections)

A—Voltmeter
B—Regulator

C—Generator
D—1/4 Ohm Resistor

E—Battery

1. Disconnect the battery wire from the regulator battery terminal.

2. Connect the voltmeter and a 1/4-ohm resistor as shown in Fig. 122. (On regulators with accelerator windings, use the specified resistor only.)

3. Run the engine for 15 minutes to reach the regulator operating temperature.

4. Stop and restart engine to cycle the generator.

5. Run the engine at the specified speed (for example, 1900 rpm).

6. Check the voltmeter reading and the operating temperature of the regulator. Compare these readings

with the specifications, such as the examples listed below:

Table 2 — Regulator Voltage Test	
Temperature	**Correct Voltage (12-Volt Circuit)**
85°F (29°C)	14.2–15.0 volts
105°F (41°C)	14.0–14.7 volts
125°F (52°C)	13.8–14.5 volts
145°F (63°C)	13.5–14.1 volts

Judging The Test Results

If the specifications are not met, check the voltage regulator unit of the regulator more closely.

Continued on next page   OUO1082,0002C41 -19-16OCT12-7/14

110112
PN=247

Regulator Current Test

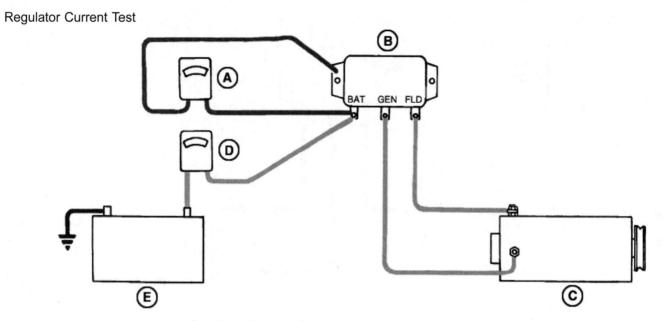

Fig. 123 — Regulator Current Test (12-Volt Circuit Connections)

A—Voltmeter   C—Generator   E—Battery
B—Regulator   D—Ammeter

Test instrument connections for this test are given in Fig. 122.

1. Disconnect the battery wire from the regulator battery terminal.

2. Connect the voltmeter and ammeter as shown in Fig. 123.

3. Start the engine several times to lower the battery voltage.

4. Turn on all lights and run the engine at the specified speed.

5. The voltmeter reading should be 1 volt below the voltage regulator setting.

6. The ammeter reading should be as specified. For example, 18.5 to 21.5 amps on a 12-volt circuit.

Judging The Test Results

Make further tests on the current regulator portion of the regulator if this test is unsatisfactory.

TESTING THE AC CHARGING CIRCUIT

In the following test examples, an open-type alternator and a transistorized regulator are used.

We remind you again to follow the precautions that we have given. To ignore them will only increase the chance of damaging the electrical components or injuring yourself.

The test equipment must be accurate and in good condition.

The instruments needed for these tests are these:

- Voltmeter
- Ammeter
- Variable Resistor
- Jumper Wire

Before making any electrical tests, be sure that all leads are firmly connected and in good repair. Also check the alternator drive belt tension.

Continued on next page   OUO1082,0002C41 -19-16OCT12-8/14

TEST NO. 1

1. Connect the voltmeter as shown in Fig. 124.

2. With the engine, ignition key switch, and accessories off, the voltmeter should read less than 0.1 volt.

Judging The Test Results

A high reading indicates a shorted isolation diode or ignition key switch.

TEST NO. 2

1. Under the same conditions as Test No. 1, turn the ignition key switch on.

2. The voltmeter reading should be between 2 and 3 volts.

Judging The Test Results

A high reading could be caused by a high resistance in the alternator field, defective brushes, or a defective regulator.

A low reading might indicate a shorted alternator field, a defective regulator, or an open circuit.

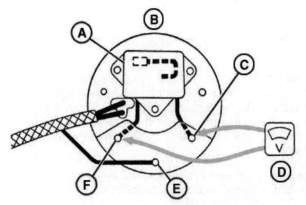

Fig. 124 — Voltmeter Test Connections

A—Regulator
B—Alternator
C—Ground Terminal

D—Voltmeter
E—Output Terminal
F—Regulator Terminal

OUO1082,0002C41 -19-16OCT12-9/14

TEST NO. 3

1. First, leave the voltmeter connected to the ground terminal and regulator terminal of the alternator (Fig. 125).

2. With the engine running and the key switch on but all accessories off, the voltmeter should read more than 15 volts.

3. Move the voltmeter lead from the regulator terminal to the output terminal. The voltmeter should read 1 volt less.

Judging The Test Results

If the regulator terminal voltage is correct and the output terminal is the same as battery voltage, then the isolation diode is open.

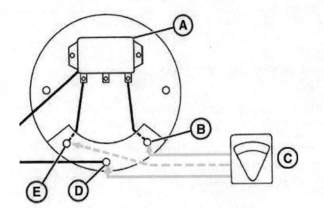

Fig. 125 — Voltmeter Connections

A—Regulator
B—Ground Terminal
C—Voltmeter

D—Output Terminal
E—Regulator Terminal

Continued on next page   OUO1082,0002C41 -19-16OCT12-10/14

TEST NO. 4

This test is usually performed if Test No. 2 indicated a malfunction.

1. With the engine and switch off, disconnect the regulator-to-alternator field terminal wire and the screws that hold the regulator to the alternator (Fig. 126). Let the regulator hang from the wires connected to it. Do not allow the regulator to touch the output terminal.

2. Connect the ammeter in series with a variable resistor to the field terminal and output terminal.

3. With all resistance eliminated, the ammeter should read 2.0 to 2.5 amps with the alternator cold.

Judging The Test Results

A high reading indicates a shorted field winding or brushes.

A low reading means a high resistance in the brushes or slip ring, or an open circuit in the field windings.

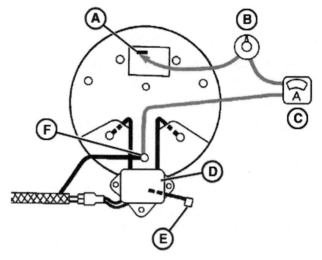

Fig. 126 — Ammeter Connections

A—Field Terminal
B—Resistor
C—Ammeter

D—Do Not Allow Regulator to Ground Output Terminal or Isolation Diode
E—Disconnect Green Wire
F—Output Terminal

OUO1082,0002C41 -19-16OCT12-11/14

TEST NO.5

1. Connect the voltmeter and jumper wire as shown in Fig. 127.

2. Run the engine at a specified speed, for example, 800 rpm.

3. This should give a voltmeter reading of 15 volts. Do not allow voltage to go above 16.5 volts.

OVERALL TEST EVALUATION

If test No. 5 proved to be satisfactory, but test No. 3 voltage was below specifications, the regulator is probably at fault.

If test No. 5 voltage was low, but tests No. 2 and No. 4 were satisfactory, the alternator is probably faulty.

WIRING RESISTANCE TEST

If the alternator and regulator operate properly, then check the wiring.

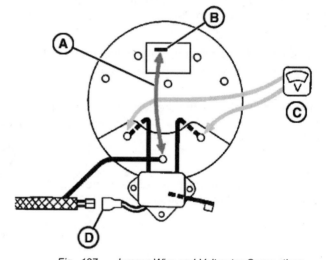

Fig. 127 — Jumper Wire and Voltmeter Connections

A—Jumper Wire
B—Field Terminal

C—Voltmeter
D—Regulator Disconnected

Continued on next page   OUO1082,0002C41 -19-16OCT12-12/14

Test Procedure

1. Make a quick visual check of the lead connections and wires.

2. Disconnect battery ground cable. Then disconnect alternator output wire and connect ammeter as shown in Fig. 128.

3. Connect ground cable and run engine to obtain a 10-amp charging rate.

4. With a voltmeter, check the voltage at different points as illustrated in Fig. 127.

5. The voltage between these points should be as listed in the chart below.

Table 3 — Test Point Voltage	
Test Points	**Maximum Voltage**
A–C	0.3 volt
B–D	0.3 volt
B–E	1.3 volts

6. Always disconnect battery ground cable to prevent accidental grounding while connecting the alternator output terminal wire. Then reconnect battery ground cable.

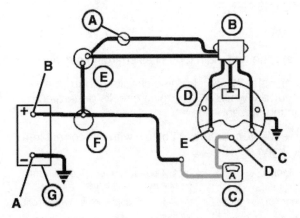

Fig. 128 — Wiring Test Points

A—Indicator Lamp
B—Regulator
C—Ammeter
D—Alternator
E—Starter Switch
F—Starter Solenoid
G—12-Volt Battery

Judging The Test Results

A high reading indicates a high resistance in the wiring or components.

OUO1082,0002C41 -19-16OCT12-13/14

REGULATOR TESTING PROCEDURE

1. Connect the voltmeter as shown in Fig. 129. Use an accurate voltmeter, one that will measure to within plus or minus 0.1 volt.

2. Run the engine to obtain a 10-amp charging rate for about 15 minutes to stabilize the regulator temperature.

3. Measure the regulator temperature about one inch from the regulator and check the voltmeter reading.

4. Compare the reading with the chart below.

Table 4 — Regulator Voltage Test	
Temperature	Correct Voltage (12-Volt Circuit)
40°F (4°C)	14.4–14.9 volts
60°F (16°C)	14.3–14.7 volts
80°F (27°C)	14.2–14.6 volts
100°F (38°C)	14.0–14.4 volts
120°F (49°C)	13.8–14.3 volts
140°F (60°C)	13.6–14.1 volts

Judging The Test Results

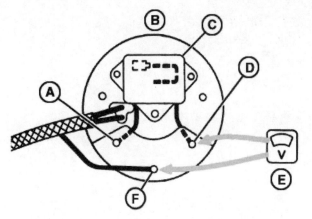

Fig. 129 — Regulator Test Connections

A—Regulator Terminal
B—Alternator
C—Regulator
D—Ground Terminal
E—Voltmeter
F—Output Terminal

If the voltage is not within limits, the regulator is faulty.

OUO1082,0002C41 -19-16OCT12-14/14

TEST YOURSELF

QUESTIONS

1. What are the two main jobs of all charging circuits?

2. (True or False?) DC charging circuits generate a direct current while AC charging circuits generate an alternating current.

3. Match each item on the left below with the correct item on the right.

a. During starting

b. During normal operation

c. During peak operation

1. Generator supplies all current and recharges battery

2. Battery supplies all load current

3. Battery helps generator supply current

4. What are the two main parts of a basic generator?

5. How is the current generated by these two parts?

6. A moving field in a fixed conductor describes a(n) _____ . A moving conductor in a fixed field describes a(n) _____ .

7. Name the three main units of an alternator.

8. Which of these units contains diodes?

9. What is the purpose of the diodes?

10. (True or False?) Never polarize an alternator.

11. What is the most popular type of alternator regulator?

12. In an "A" circuit alternator, the regulator is located _____ the field.

13. To further isolate the field and regulator circuit, some alternators use a _____ to obtain field current from the stator.

(Answers are in back of textbook.))

OUO1082,0002C42 -19-10JAN12-1/1

Starting Circuits

INTRODUCTION

DXP02707 —UN—23FEB11

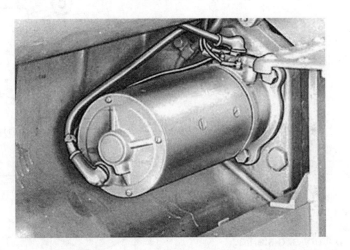

BB87125,000415C -19-07MAR12-1/1

HOW THE STARTING CIRCUIT WORKS

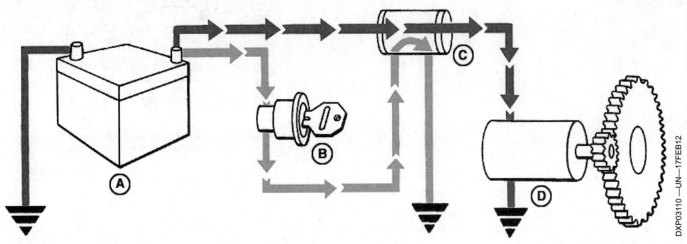

Fig. 1—Basic Starting Circuit

A—Battery   C—Solenoid
B—Key Switch   D—Starting Motor

The starting circuit converts electrical energy from the battery into mechanical energy at the starting motor to crank the engine (Fig. 1).

A basic starting circuit has four parts:

• The BATTERY supplies energy for the circuit.
• The STARTER SWITCH activates the circuit.

• The solenoid-operated MOTOR SWITCH engages the motor drive with the engine flywheel.
• The STARTING MOTOR drives the flywheel to crank the engine.

How do these parts work together as a team?

The starting circuit is shown in operation in Fig. 2, Fig 3, and Fig. 4.

Continued on next page OUO1082,0002C4B -19-10JAN12-1/4

When the starter switch is activated by the operator (Fig. 2), a small amount of electrical energy flows from the battery to the solenoid and back to the battery through the ground circuit.

A—Key Switch   **C—Solenoid**
B—Ground

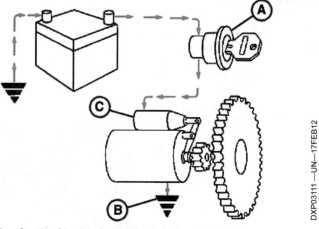

Fig. 2 — Starting Circuit in Operation: 1) As the Starter Switch Is Activated

OUO1082,0002C4B -19-10JAN12-2/4

As the solenoid gets this power from the battery, it moves the solenoid plunger and engages the pinion with the flywheel (Fig. 3). The plunger also closes the switch inside the solenoid between the battery and starting motor, completing the circuit and allowing a large amount of electrical energy to flow into the starting motor.

A—Key Switch   **C—Solenoid**
B—Starting Motor

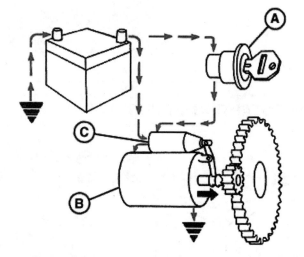

Fig. 3 — Starting Circuit in Operation: 2) Starting Motor Engages Flywheel

OUO1082,0002C4B -19-10JAN12-3/4

The starting motor takes the electrical energy from the battery and converts it into rotary mechanical energy to crank the engine (Fig. 4).

The battery is covered in Chapter 5 since it serves the whole electrical system. But remember that the battery is the source of power for starting the engine.

In our typical system, we have used a solenoid switch as an example. Motors can use other types of switches as we'll see later.

Now let's take a closer look at the starting motor itself.

A—Key Switch   **B—Starting Motor**

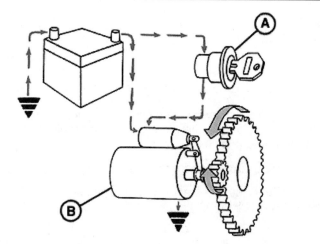

Fig. 4 — Starting Circuit in Operation: 3) Starting Motor Cranks Engine

OUO1082,0002C4B -19-10JAN12-4/4

HOW A STARTING MOTOR WORKS

The starting motor does the actual job of cranking the engine. It is a special type of electric motor:

- It is designed to operate for short intervals under great overload.
- It produces very high horsepower for its size.

The basic starting motor has a field frame assembly, an armature, and a drive mechanism.

Let's see how these parts work to convert electrical energy from the battery into mechanical energy to crank the engine.

First consider the pole pieces in the field frame assembly of the starting motor as the ends of a magnet (Fig. 5). The space between these poles is called the magnetic field.

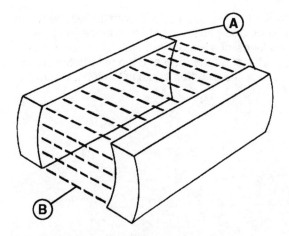

Fig. 5 — Pole Pieces and Their Magnetic Field

A—Pole Pieces   B—Magnetic Field

OUO1082,0002C4C -19-13MAR12-1/8

If a wire, called a field winding, is wrapped around these pole pieces and current is passed through it, the strength of the magnetic field between the pole pieces is increased (Fig. 6).

A—Field Winding

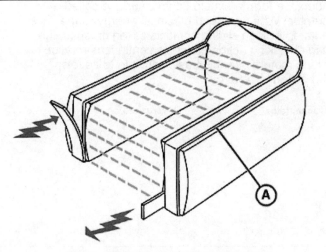

Fig. 6 — Field Winding Added to Pole Pieces

OUO1082,0002C4C -19-13MAR12-2/8

Now let's consider a loop of wire (Fig. 7). When we feed electrical energy from the battery into this loop, a magnetic field is also formed around the wire.

A—Battery Current   B—Magnetic Field

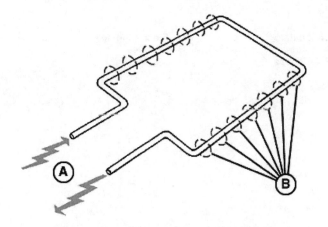

Fig. 7 — Loop of Live Wire and Its Magnetic Field

Continued on next page   OUO1082,0002C4C -19-13MAR12-3/8

If we place the loop of wire in the magnetic field between the pole pieces and pass current through the loop, we have the makings of a simple armature (Fig. 8). The magnetic field around the loop and the field between the pole pieces repel each other, causing the loop to turn.

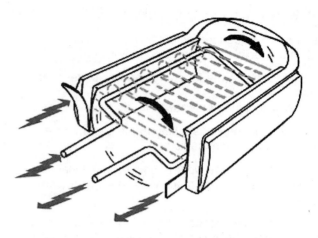

Fig. 8 — Loop of Wire Placed in Field between Poles

OUO1082,0002C4C -19-13MAR12-4/8

In an actual armature we use more loops (Fig. 9). By attaching separate metal segments to the ends of each loop, we form a simple contact surface called a commutator. When we feed electrical energy to the commutator through sliding contacts called brushes, the repelling or kicking action causes a continuous rotation. All starting motors use this basic principle to develop useful mechanical energy.

A—Commutator   **B—Brushes**

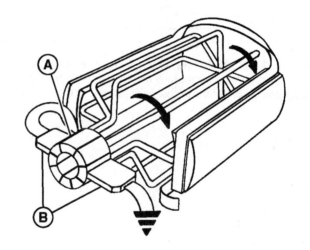

Fig. 9 — Armature for Starting Motor

OUO1082,0002C4C -19-13MAR12-5/8

Every starting motor has brushes, an armature, field windings, pole pieces, and a drive mechanism (Fig. 10 and Fig. 11.)

A—Commutator   **D—Field Windings**
B—Armature   **E—Brushes**
C—Pole Pieces

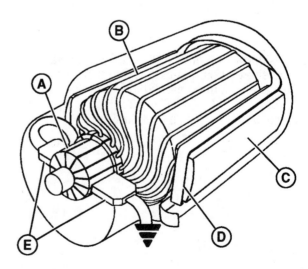

Fig. 10 — Armature and Brushes in Starting Motor

Continued on next page   OUO1082,0002C4C -19-13MAR12-6/8

Let's build on the basics of Chapter 2 and explain more about the repelling action of the brushes and the armature, which makes the starting motor operate.

A—Reduction Gear
B—Brush
C—Brush Spring
D—Field Coil
E—Armature

F—Solenoid
G—Overrunning Clutch
H—Idler Gear
I— Pinion Gear

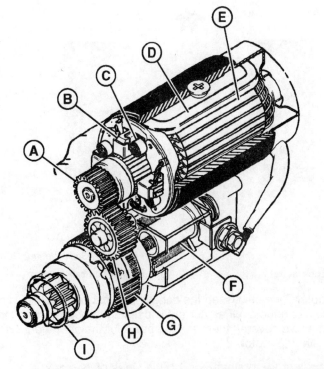

Fig. 11 — Cutaway View of a Gear Reduction Starting Motor

Continued on next page

OUO1082,0002C4C -19-13MAR12-7/8

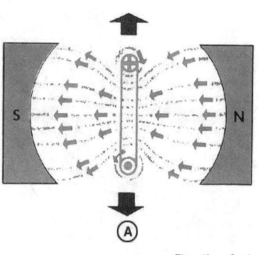
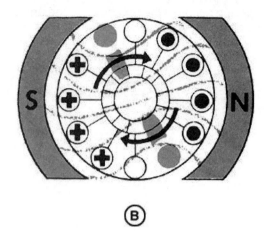

Fig. 12 — Static Neutral Point of Rotating Armature

A—Static Neutral   B—Operational Neutral

In Chapter 2 we discussed the behavior of magnetic fields around a conductor when current is passing through. The principles we covered there are the basis for the operation of the starting motor.

As the armature rotates (Fig. 12) the sides of its loops reach a point shown when they are as far out of the magnetic field as possible. This is the "static neutral point" and is always halfway between the pole pieces of the motor. Current must be changed at this point to keep the same turning force.

The reversal of current is done every half-turn by the commutator. It works as follows: When the armature moves, so does the commutator. By the time the left-hand side of the armature has swung around to the north pole, the commutator segments will have reversed their connections with the brushes. Current will then flow in the opposite direction in the armature windings. This change of current flow would cause the armature to reverse, but since the windings have made a half-turn while the commutator changed connections, the force exerted on the armature will continue its rotation.

So, to keep rotating the motor, the current flow must be reversed every half-turn of the armature. This keeps the magnetic lines of force acting in the same direction.

The static neutral point is always halfway between the pole shoes and is the point where the direction of current must be changed to maintain a turning force in the same direction. This is true whether the motor has two, four, or six poles. However, when current flows through the armature windings creating another magnetic field, the normal field between the pole shoes is distorted. Since

lines of force may be assumed not to cross each other, the neutral point is therefore shifted. The motor brushes are shifted back from the static neutral point to an operational neutral (against the direction of rotation) to prevent excessive arcing and to obtain more efficient operation.

The main point is that the magnetic field of the armature distorts the field of the pole shoes and shifts the neutral point to a new position. To match this, the motor brushes are mounted back at the new position.

SUMMARY: HOW A STARTING MOTOR WORKS

- A current-carrying conductor, formed in a loop and mounted on a shaft, will cause the shaft to rotate when placed inside a magnetic field. The result: a basic starting motor.
- If the direction of current flow in the loop is reversed as the loop passes the neutral position, the loop and shaft will keep on rotating. This is the way a starting motor is kept running.
- It follows that to increase the power of the motor, more loops of conductors connected in series with an equal number of commutator segments are needed.
- It also follows that increasing the strength of the magnetic field will affect the turning power of the motor, and will be directly related to the number of field poles and the number of ampere turns on each pole.
- Basically the starting motor is a series-wound, direct-current electric motor designed to provide high power for a short time using current from a storage battery. Most starting motors have two, four, or six field poles with windings, a wound armature with a commutator, and two, four, or six brushes.

OUO1082,0002C4C -19-13MAR12-8/8

TYPES OF STARTING MOTORS

Starting motors can be classified several ways:

• Motor Circuit
• Armature
• Switch Control
• Motor Drive

Let's compare the types of starting motors as given above.

OUO1082,0002C4D -19-10JAN12-1/1

STARTING MOTOR CIRCUITS

All starting motors have a stationary member (field) and a rotating member (armature). The field windings and the armature are usually connected so that all current entering the motor passes through both the field and the armature. This is the motor circuit.

The brushes are a means of carrying the current from the external to the internal circuit—in this case from the field windings to the armature windings.

The brushes are carried in brush holders. Normally, half the brushes are grounded to the end frame while the other half are insulated and are connected to the field windings.

Starting motors on most off-the-road machines are considered to be series wound; that is to say, the field windings and the armature windings are in series.

However, starting motors have four main types of field circuits:

• Series wound
• Parallel wound
• Series-parallel wound
• Compound wound

Let's look at the common series-wound circuit first. Then we will bring in the other three types.

SERIES-WOUND FIELD CIRCUITS

FOUR-POLE, TWO-COIL CIRCUITS

As shown in Fig. 13, some starting motors have four pole shoes and only two field windings.

Before looking at the circuit, we should understand the polarity of the pole shoes.

Using the Right-Hand Rule for coils (see Chapter 2) we can see that when the starting motor is in operation, the

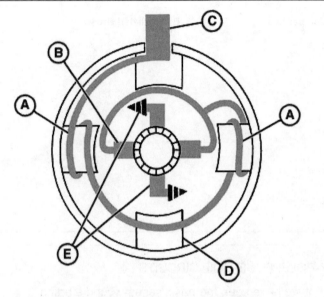

Fig. 13 — Four-Pole, Two-Coil, Series-Wound Motor

A—Field Winding
B—Brush
C—Current From Battery
D—Pole Shoe
E—Grounds

face of the pole shoe with the field winding has a north polarity. The magnetic lines of force pass from this pole to the pole without windings, through the frame, and back to the original pole to complete the magnetic circuit.

In all starting motors the adjacent pole shoes are of opposite polarity, providing a north, south, north, south sequence around the frame. These magnetic lines of force passing from pole to pole cause four magnetic paths through the armature windings.

The field circuit in Fig. 13 is the series-wound type. This provides a four-pole action with only two field windings.

Continued on next page   OUO1082,0002C4E -19-12JUN12-1/9

As a rule, all of the insulated brushes are connected together with jumper leads (Fig. 14) so that voltage in all the brushes is equalized. Without this, the result could be arcing and burning of commutator bars, insulating the brush contacts from the commutator surface. Once the brush contacts are insulated, the continuous current flow is interrupted and the motor stops.

A—Jumper Lead   B—Insulated Brush

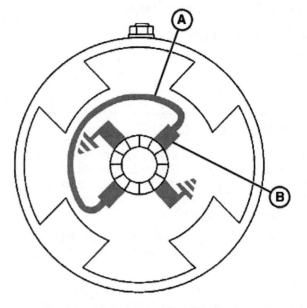

Fig. 14 — Motor Brushes Equalized by Jumper Leads

OUO1082,0002C4E -19-12JUN12-2/9

FOUR-POLE, FOUR-COIL CIRCUITS

Now that we have seen the basic series-wound starting motor, let's add field windings to the two bare poles. By doing so we create a four-pole, four-coil field circuit (Fig. 15).

By adding two field windings to the pole shoes we create more ampere turns of low resistance, resulting in a stronger magnetic field. Stronger fields produce greater torque, so we get more starting power from the four-coil motor than from the two-coil motor.

This field circuit has four field pole windings and four brushes. The field windings are in series so all current flow is through all of the windings before it flows through the two insulated brushes to the armature.

A—Brush   C—Field Coils
B—Commutator   D—Pole Shoe

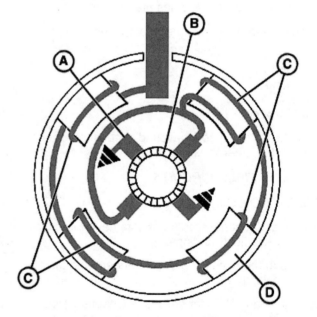

Fig. 15 — Four-Pole, Four-Coil, Series-Wound Motor

Continued on next page   OUO1082,0002C4E -19-12JUN12-3/9

SIX-POLE, SIX-COIL, SERIES-WOUND CIRCUITS

Fig. 16 illustrates a six-pole, six-coil series-wound motor. As in the four-pole type, the current flows through all the field coils before it flows to the armature. The addition of the two extra poles and windings adds to the torque of the motor.

A—Coil (6 Used)   B—Pole (6 Used)

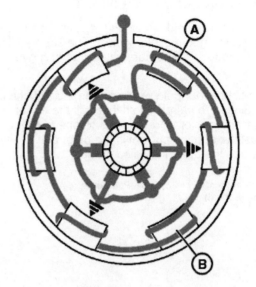

Fig. 16 — Six-Pole, Six-Coil, Series-Wound Motor

OUO1082,0002C4E -19-12JUN12-4/9

PARALLEL-WOUND FIELD CIRCUITS

Most field windings on larger engines are parallel-wound. That is, current flows through one field winding (Fig. 17) to the insulated brushes; also through the other field winding to the insulated brushes. Placing the field windings in parallel allows extra current flow to create greater torque or turning power.

A—Brush   D—Commutator
B—Field Winding   E—Pole Shoe
C—Field Winding   F—Grounds

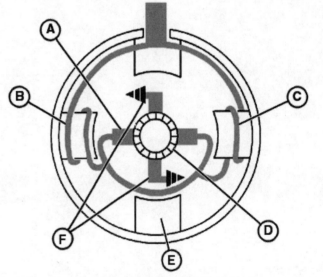

Fig. 17 — Parallel-Wound Field Circuit

Continued on next page   OUO1082,0002C4E -19-12JUN12-5/9

FOUR-POLE, FOUR-COIL FIELD CIRCUIT

The four-coil, four-pole field circuit (Fig. 18) is often used for smaller gasoline and diesel engines. The stronger four-coil fields produce the torque required to turn over these engines.

This field circuit has four pole windings and four brushes. The field windings are paired off so that half the current flows through one pair of field windings to one of the insulated brushes, and the current in the other pair of field windings flows to the other insulated brush.

A—Parallel Windings   **C—Pole Shoe**
B—Field Coil (4 Used)

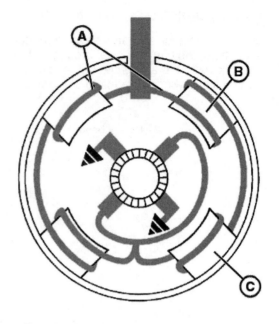

Fig. 18 — Four-Pole, Four-Coil, Parallel-Wound Motor

Continued on next page
OUO1082,0002C4E -19-12JUN12-6/9

The field circuit shown in Fig. 19 is a four-pole, four-coil circuit similar to those we have seen before. But this particular circuit has been developed recently for large diesel engines. In the past, large diesel engines required 24-volt starting motors for dependable starting. Because of 12-volt lighting and charging circuits, the 24-volt starting circuit required the installation of complicated wiring circuits to satisfy both needs. The new 12-volt high output starting motor is the answer. It simplifies installation and maintenance since it permits operation of the whole starting circuit on the conventional 12-volt system.

However, the high-output starting motor circuit needs extra power from the batteries to produce the output required by large engines. Reducing the motor voltage from 24 to 12 volts means that the circuit must carry about twice the current to provide the same output. This is usually done by retaining the same number of batteries that were used in series on the 24-volt starting system, but connecting them in parallel. This gives the increased current at 12 volts.

How does this high-output starting motor work? Let's start with the fact that the power (watts) produced by a starting motor is equal to the product of voltage and current flow:

Watts = Voltage x Current

The high-output starting motor, which operates at twelve volts, must be able to carry the increased current to produce the same amount of power or watts as a 24-volt starting motor.

For example, if a 24-volt starting motor will carry 500 amps of current, the watts produced would be 12,000. If the high-output starting motor is to operate at a lower voltage (twelve volts), the current flow must be almost doubled to develop the same output as the 24-volt motor. For example, 12 volts and 1000 amps of current will produce 12,000 watts, the same power output as the 24-volt motor.

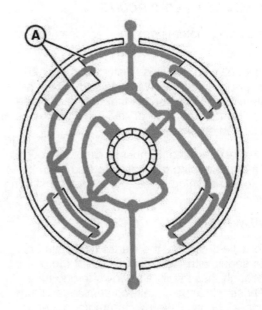

Fig. 19 — 12-Volt High-Output Starting Motor Circuit

A—Parallel Circuits

The increased current flow in the high-output motor requires a different type of field winding circuit than the normal 12-volt motor. The four-coil, four-pole starting motor circuit in Fig. 18 is the high output circuit. It differs from the previous circuits shown in that the field windings are in parallel instead of series wound. This parallel circuit in the field windings permits the increased current flow needed at a reduced battery voltage.

Continued on next page   OUO1082,0002C4E -19-12JUN12-7/9

SERIES-PARALLEL FIELD CIRCUITS

This type of starting motor is designed for heavy-duty service.

A six-pole, six-coil field circuit is illustrated in Fig. 20. Here the current is split three ways instead of two, as in a four-pole circuit. The result is that one-third of the current flows through each pair of field windings to one of the three insulated brushes.

In this way we increase the number of circuits through the starting motor, keeping resistance low so that higher current can flow to develop more horsepower for starting the engine.

COMPOUND-WOUND FIELD CIRCUITS

In the previous field circuits, the starter field coils are connected in series with the armature. All of the current that flows through these coils also flows through the armature. These windings usually contain several turns of heavy copper ribbon. Free-running motor speed is quite high.

As the armature speed increases, a counter-voltage (CEMF) in the armature windings also increases. The counter-voltage is induced into the armature windings when they pass through the magnetic field of the field coils. We can now see that the faster the armature turns, the greater will be the counter-voltage in the armature,

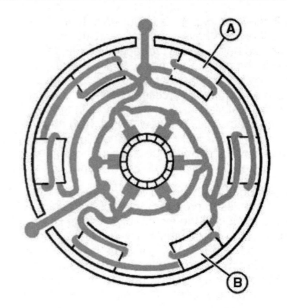

Fig. 20 — Six-Pole, Six-Coil, Series-Parallel-Wound Motor

A—Coil (6 Used)　　　　　B—Pole (6 Used)

until finally the armature counter-voltage reduces current flow to a point where maximum free speed is reached.

Continued on next page　　OUO1082,0002C4E -19-12JUN12-8/9

In some cases excessively high free speed could result in the armature windings being thrown from their slots. However, to prevent excessively high free running speed, one or more of the poles is wound as a shunt winding. A shunt winding has many turns of small wire. The field circuit with a shunt winding as shown in Fig. 21 is known as a compound-wound field circuit.

The compound-wound starter shunt winding prevents overspeeding because the shunt winding is connected directly to ground. The current flow is at a high constant value of magnetic flux, as determined by battery voltage, and is not affected by the armature counter-voltage. With a consistently high magnetic field from the shunt coil, the armature counter-voltage is higher at lower armature speeds, thus reducing the series field winding and armature current flow as well as the armature free speed.

For an example of magnetic flux values, consider a typical compound-wound starter drawing 220 amps when cranking (200 amps for the series coils and 20 amps for the shunt coil) and 70 amps when at free running speed.

When cranking, the series coils drawing 200 amps and containing 11 turns of copper strap will have 2200 ampere-turns of magnetic flux. The shunt winding containing 110 turns and drawing 20 amps will also have 2200 ampere-turns of magnetic flux. Compare this to when turning at free running speed, and the series coils will have about 550 ampere-turns each while the shunt will probably have more than 2200 ampere-turns (battery voltage rises).

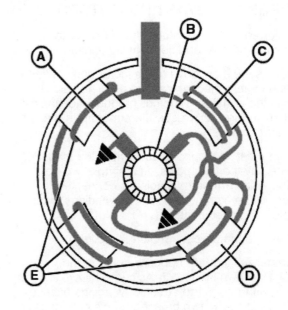

Fig. 21 — Compound-Wound Motor

A—Brush
B—Commutator
C—Shunt Coil
D—Pole Shoe
E—Series Coils

OUO1082,0002C4E -19-12JUN12-9/9

ARMATURES FOR STARTING MOTORS

We have referred to the armature often in order to understand the field pole and field winding circuit.

The armature is the main drive of the motor and converts electrical energy into mechanical energy. The field windings and the armature windings produce mechanical rotary motion. In Fig. 22 we see the armature in the starting motor circuit.

The armature must be wound to conform to the magnetic fields provided by the field poles. In a simple two-coil, two-pole unit, each armature winding is connected to one segment of the commutator, and all windings in the armature are connected in series.

Current flows into the typical armature as follows:

Two brushes are placed on opposite sides of the commutator as shown in Fig. 22. As current flows into the brushes, it flows through the armature windings except those shorted out by the two brushes. Since both ends of a winding contact a brush at the same time, the winding is shorted out in the commutating position. This provides two separate and parallel paths for the current to follow. Current flows in the same direction in all conductors passing before the pole pieces, but the direction of current flow changes at the neutral position as the armature turns up and out of the magnetic field between the pole pieces.

WAVE- AND LAP-WOUND ARMATURES

Wave-wound armatures have only two paths for current flow.

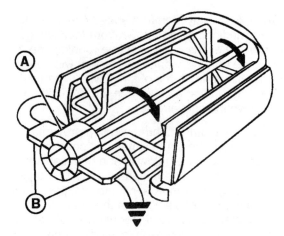

Fig. 22 — The Armature in the Starting Motor Circuit

A—Commutator   **B—Brushes**

Lap-wound armatures have as many paths as there are pole pieces.

The lap-wound armature is connected in series and divided into individual paths to permit large amounts of current to flow through it. This increased current capability is the reason the lap-wound armature is used in the high output starting motor we described earlier in this chapter.

OUO1082,0002C4F -19-12JUN12-1/1

SWITCHES FOR STARTING MOTORS

We learned earlier that starting motors convert electrical energy into mechanical energy. Now let's see how the switch performs a mechanical job electromagnetically, and completes the circuit from the battery to the starting motor.

Starting motors can use four types of switches:

- Manual Switch
- Magnetic Switch
- Solenoid Switch
- Series-Parallel Switch

Let's talk about each one.

MANUAL SWITCHES

A manual switch performs a mechanical operation by the simple closing of switch contacts. Operation of this type of switch closes a circuit or opens a circuit as in turning an electric light on and off. A simple manual switch is shown in Fig. 23.

The manually operated starting switch may be mounted where it is directly accessible to the operator, or it may be mounted on the starting motor and made accessible by various devices such as a hand lever.

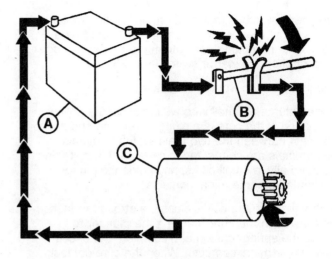

Fig. 23 — A Manual Switch

A—Battery   C—Starting Motor
B—Heavy Switch

OUO1082,0002C50 -19-12JUN12-1/11

MAGNETIC SWITCHES

To understand the magnetic switch and, later on, the solenoid switch, we must review the fundamentals of an electromagnet.

We learned in Chapter 2 that a magnetic field is made stronger by placing a soft iron core in a coil. We also learned that the polarity of the core is the same as for the coil. If the core has freedom to move, and is placed at one end of the coil in Fig. 24, it will also assume the polarity of the coil. Therefore, the adjacent poles are of opposite polarity, and the core is drawn into the center of the coil when current flows through the coil. As soon as current stops flowing, the field collapses and the core is free to move away from the coil. This is the principle of magnetic and solenoid switches.

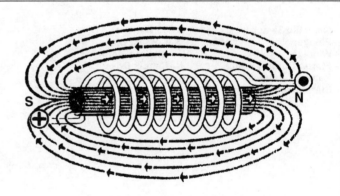

Fig. 24 — Polarity of an Electromagnet

Continued on next page

OUO1082,0002C50 -19-12JUN12-2/11

The magnetic switch is mounted on the starting motor frame like some manual switches. It is operated by a magnetic coil energized directly from the battery through a start control on the starter switch (Fig. 25).

The magnetic switch works as follows:

It has many turns of small wire wound around a hollow core. Floating in the core is a plunger with one end acting as a contact between the two main switch terminals. These terminals are connected in series with the starting motor. Normally, a small coil spring holds the plunger away from the main terminal contacts.

When the circuit to the coil is closed, a strong magnetic field is created in the core, causing the plunger to overcome the spring tension and complete the circuit between the terminal contacts. When the core contacts the terminals, the main circuit to the starting motor is completed and the engine is turned over.

When the control circuit is opened at the starter switch, the magnetic field collapses and the spring forces the plunger to its original position, opening the starting motor circuit. The motor then stops turning.

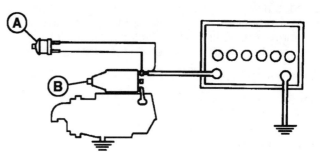

Fig. 25 — Magnetic Switch Circuit

A—Starter Switch   **B—Magnetic Switch**

Magnetic switches are normally used with Bendix drives since there is no mechanical shifting action provided with this switch.

OUO1082,0002C50 -19-12JUN12-3/11

A Bendix drive with a magnetic switch is shown in Fig. 26.

A—Magnetic Switch
B—Plunger
C—Winding
D—Starter Control Switch
E—Battery Terminal
F—Starter Motor Terminal
G—To Batteries
H—Contact Disk
I—Starting Motor
J—Bendix Drive
K—Return Spring

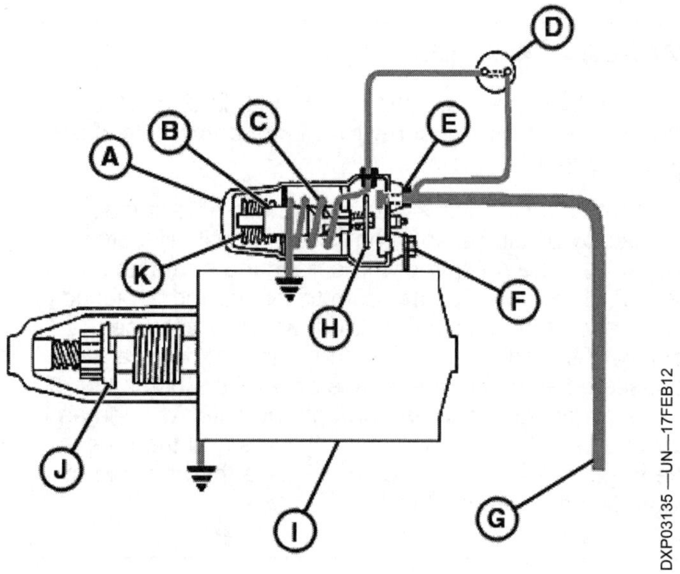

Fig. 26 — A Typical Magnetic Switch Circuit

Continued on next page   OUO1082,0002C50 -19-12JUN12-4/11

SOLENOID SWITCHES

The solenoid switch is very similar to a magnetic switch, but in addition to closing the circuit, the solenoid provides a mechanical means of shifting the starting motor pinion into mesh with the flywheel ring gear (Fig. 27).

A—Return Spring   C—Pinion
B—Solenoid Shift Lever

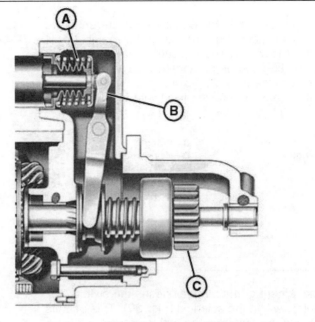

Fig. 27 — Solenoid Shift Lever

OUO1082,0002C50 -19-12JUN12-5/11

The solenoid circuit is shown in Fig. 28.

The solenoid switch has two coils of wire wound in the same direction.

The pull-in winding is made up of heavy wire connected to the motor terminal of the solenoid and through the motor to ground.

The hold-in winding has an equal number of turns of fine wire with one end connected to ground.

These coils are energized directly from the battery through the start position on the starter switch.

In Fig. 29, Fig. 30 and Fig. 31 we will show how the solenoid switch operates from the moment the operator turns the starter switch.

A—Hold-In Winding   G—Starting Motor
B—Pull-In Winding   H—Contact Disk
C—Battery Terminal   I— Overrunning Clutch
D—Starter Control Switch   J—Shift Lever
E—Starter Motor Terminal   K—Plunger
F—To Battery   L—Solenoid

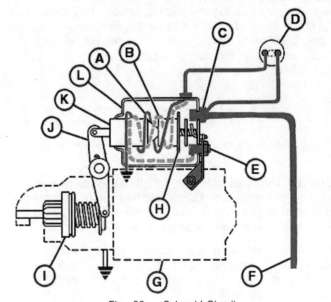

Fig. 28 — Solenoid Circuit

Continued on next page   OUO1082,0002C50 -19-12JUN12-6/11

When the operator turns the starter switch, current flows to the starter solenoid (Fig. 29). Since the solenoid coils are wound in the same direction, current flows in the same direction, creating a strong magnetic field which pulls the plunger into the field as shown. The initial plunger movement engages the drive pinion with the flywheel ring gear.

A—Magnetic Field C—Plunger
B—Windings   D—Key Switch On

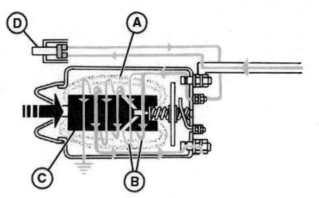

Fig. 29 — Solenoid Plunger Starting to Move as Starter Switch Is Turned On

OUO1082,0002C50 -19-12JUN12-7/11

Further movement of the plunger closes the switch contact points within the solenoid (Fig. 30). This permits a heavy flow of current from the battery into the starting motor to crank the engine.

Inside the solenoid the closing of the points shorts out the heavy pull-in winding, leaving only the fine hold-in winding energized during the starting period. The initial flow of current through the pull-in winding is of very short duration. The flow of current through the hold-in winding continues as long as the control circuit is closed.

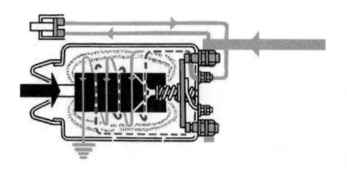

Fig. 30 — Motor Engaged and Cranking the Engine

OUO1082,0002C50 -19-12JUN12-8/11

When the engine begins to run and the starter switch is released, several things happen quickly (Fig. 31).

First, current through the starter switch to the solenoid is cut off. Then a strong return spring pushes out the solenoid plunger, breaking the circuit from the battery to the starting motor and simultaneously pulling the pinion out of mesh.

Inside the solenoid, what has happened is this: when the starter switch opened the circuit, the two solenoid windings became connected in series and were energized from the motor terminal.

The current then flowed in a reverse direction in the pull-in winding, but continued in the same direction as before through the hold-in winding, since it is grounded. Since the number of turns in the two windings is equal, the ampere flow is equal, and the direction of flow is opposite. The magnetic field of one coil opposes that of the other, causing an immediate collapse of the magnetic field. Therefore, spring tension quickly moves the plunger back to its original position.

SOLENOID SWITCH MOUNTINGS

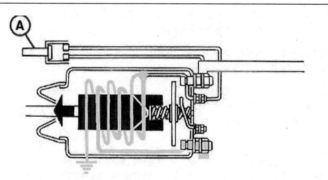

Fig. 31 — Motor Disengages as Key Switch Is Released

A—Key Switch Off

Solenoid switches are mounted in two ways:

• Coaxial Mounting—enclosed in the motor housing.
• External Mounting—piggyback on the motor housing.

The solenoids do the same basic job with either mounting.

Continued on next page OUO1082,0002C50 -19-12JUN12-9/11

In the coaxial mounting, the solenoid switch is completely enclosed and the windings are around the armature shaft. (These solenoids have no pull-in windings.) Coaxial mountings are primarily used for adverse conditions or where space is not available for the bulkier piggyback arrangement. A coaxial starter is shown in Fig. 32. In the external mounting, an open or enclosed shift lever is used to actuate the pinion. An external solenoid model is shown in Fig. 33.

SERIES-PARALLEL SWITCHES

A higher voltage in the starting circuit may be needed on some heavy-duty engines, especially diesel models.

Cold weather starting and other adverse conditions also draw more heavily on the starting circuit.

In some cases the high output starting motor can handle these conditions on a 12-volt circuit.

But in other cases, higher voltage starting motors must be used. By using a 24-volt battery supply, much higher starting speeds can be produced under heavy loads.

However, since lighting circuits have not yet been developed which meet highway regulations with 24-volt systems, special provisions for lighting must be made.

The series-parallel switch is one solution to this problem. This makes it possible to connect two 12-volt batteries in parallel for normal operation, but to connect the batteries in series through the switch during starting. This gives adequate power for starting the engine.

Fig. 32 — Coaxial Starting Motor with Enclosed Solenoid

Fig. 33 — Starting Motor with External Solenoid

Continued on next page   OUO1082,0002C50 -19-12JUN12-10/11

Fig. 34 shows a series-parallel switch for a 24-volt starting circuit. The series connection between the two batteries and the starting motor is shown in solid black lines. The starter solenoid circuit is shown in solid gray lines.

Operation during starting is as follows:

As the starting switch is closed, the solenoid coil within the series-parallel switch is energized (dashed gray lines) creating a magnetic force that attracts the series-parallel switch plunger. The plunger closes the two main switch terminals and connects the two batteries in series with the starting motor.

At the same time the solenoid circuit is completed by a set of points mechanically closed by the series-parallel switch plunger. This completes the battery-to-starting motor circuit and the starter turns over.

After the engine is started and the starting switch is released, the two batteries become connected in parallel when the series-parallel switch goes into a neutral position. (See Fig. 47.) This permits operation of the machine's electrical equipment at a normal system voltage of 12 volts.

A—12 V Generator
B—12V Regulator
C—To Lights and Accessories
D—Start Switch
E—Battery B
F—12 Volts
G—24 V Starter Motor
H—Solenoid
I— Ammeter (Battery B)
J—Fuse
K—Series-Parallel Switch
L—Battery A

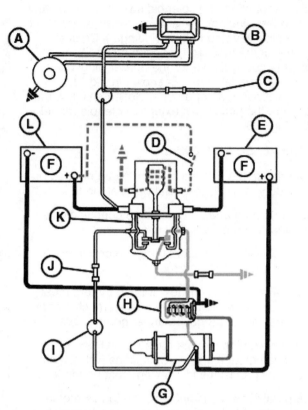

Fig. 34 — Series-Parallel Switch for 24-Volt Starting Motor Operation

DXP03143 —UN—17FEB12

OUO1082,0002C50 -19-12JUN12-11/11

STARTING MOTOR DRIVES

After electrical power is transmitted from the battery through a switch to the starting motor, some type of connection is needed to put this energy to work.

The last link in the starting circuit is the starting motor drive. The drive makes it possible to use the mechanical energy produced by the starting motor.

Let's learn more about these drive mechanisms and see what some of them look like.

INTRODUCTION

The starting motor armature revolves at a relatively high speed to produce turning power. Since the turning speed required to start an engine is comparatively slow, the starting motor is equipped with a small drive pinion which meshes with the teeth of the flywheel ring gear. The result is a gear reduction with the armature revolving as much as twenty times for every revolution of the flywheel. This permits the starting motor to develop high armature speeds and considerable power while turning the engine over at a lower speed.

But when the engine starts, it speeds up immediately and may soon reach as high as 2000 rpm. This is too fast for the starter and would result in damage to the armature.

To prevent this, starter drives are used. These are devices on the end of the armature shaft which mesh the drive pinion with the ring gear on the flywheel, and then prevent the starting motor from overspeeding after the engine has started.

TYPES OF DRIVES

There are two basic ways in which starter drives are engaged:

• Inertia Drives
• Electromagnetic Drives

On an inertia drive, the pinion gear is weighted on one side to aid in its initial rotating motion. The Bendix drive is a type of inertia drive.

Electromagnetic drives are shifted in or out of mesh by the magnetic field of the switch. The overrunning clutch, Dyer drive, and Sprag clutch drive are electromagnetic types.

BENDIX DRIVE

The Bendix drive depends upon inertia of the counterweight pinion and acceleration of the armature to move the pinion into mesh with the flywheel (Fig. 35).

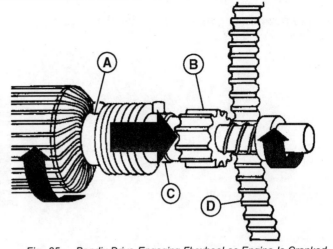

Fig. 35 — Bendix Drive Engaging Flywheel as Engine Is Cranked

A—Armature Shaft   C—Sleeve
B—Drive Pinion   D—Flywheel

The Bendix drive is normally out of mesh and separated from the flywheel ring gear.

When the starting switch is closed and the battery voltage is fed to the motor, the armature shaft accelerates rapidly. The pinion gear, due to inertia created by the counterweight, runs forward on the revolving screw sleeve until it meets or meshes with the flywheel gear (Fig. 35).

In other words, the Bendix drive uses inertia of the pinion and high starting speed of the armature shaft to move the pinion into mesh with the flywheel.

When the pinion becomes fully meshed, its forward motion stops, locking the pinion to the rotating armature shaft. The spring cushions the shock as the rotating armature starts to turn the flywheel.

This spring also acts as a cushion while cranking the engine against compression. In addition, it dampens the shock on the gear teeth during meshing or when there is a backfire of the engine.

Continued on next page OUO1082,0002C51 -19-12JUN12-1/9

All parts are now rotating as a unit, turning the engine over as shown in Fig. 36.

A—Pinion

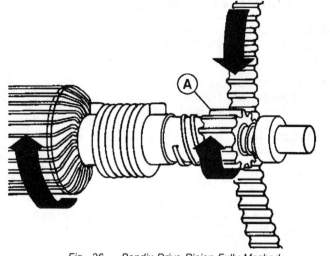

Fig. 36 — Bendix Drive Pinion Fully Meshed

OUO1082,0002C51 -19-12JUN12-2/9

When the engine starts, the flywheel rotates faster than the armature shaft, causing the pinion to turn in the opposite direction on the screw and spin itself out of mesh (Fig. 37). This prevents the engine from driving the starting motor at an excessive speed.

The centrifugal effect of the weight on one side of the pinion, when spun from the flywheel, holds the pinion to the sleeve in an intermediate position until the starting switch is opened and the motor armature comes to rest.

For as long as the operator keeps the motor energized with the engine running, the motor will free speed. This is why the starter switch should be released immediately after the engine has started.

Certain precautions must be observed in operating a Bendix-type starting motor. If the engine backfires with the pinion in mesh with the engine flywheel, and the starting motor operating, a terrific stress is placed on the parts. This is because the motor armature attempts to spin the drive pinion in one direction while the engine, having backfired, turns the drive pinion in the opposite direction. This clash of opposing forces sometimes breaks or "wraps up" the Bendix spring.

Engine ignition timing should be checked and corrected to overcome backfiring.

Damage may also occur when the engine starts, throwing the Bendix drive pinion out of mesh with the engine flywheel teeth. When the engine is coming to rest it often rocks back, or rotates in reverse, for part of a revolution. If the operator attempts to re-engage the drive pinion at the instant the engine is rocking back, serious damage will result. As in a backfire, it may break the drive housing or "wrap up" the Bendix spring.

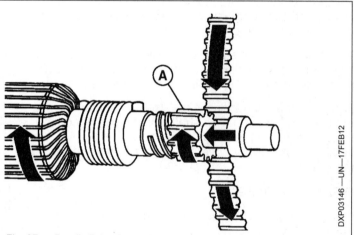

Fig. 37 — Bendix Drive Pinion Spinning Out of Mesh after Engine Starts

A—Pinion

To prevent this, the operator should always wait at least five seconds between attempts to crank so that the engine stops turning.

VARIATIONS ON BENDIX DRIVES

Another Bendix drive known as the Folo-thru has a detent pin which locks the drive in the cranking position to prevent disengagement on false starts. This pin is thrown out by centrifugal force when the engine runs, and the pinion then disengages.

Some heavy-duty cranking motors use a friction-clutch-type Bendix drive. This type of drive functions in much the same manner as other Bendix drives. However, it uses a series of spring-loaded clutch plates, instead of a drive spring, which slip momentarily during engagement to relieve shock.

Continued on next page

OUO1082,0002C51 -19-12JUN12-3/9

OVERRUNNING CLUTCH DRIVE

Now let's take a look at one of the most widely used drive mechanisms, the overrunning clutch (Fig. 38). It allows positive meshing and demeshing of the drive pinion with the flywheel.

The overrunning clutch uses a shift lever to actuate the drive pinion. The pinion, together with the overrunning clutch mechanism, is moved endwise along the armature shaft and into, or out of, mesh with the flywheel. The shift lever may be either manual or operated by a solenoid. Operation is given below.

As we learned earlier, the drive pinion is normally out of mesh and separated from the flywheel ring gear. When the starting switch is closed, current flows to the solenoid, closing the switch circuit. As the solenoid switch closes, the shift lever moves the pinion into mesh and completes the circuit to the starting motor. If the pinion and the flywheel teeth meet, instead of meshing, the spring-loaded pinion rotates the width of one-half tooth and drops into mesh as the armature starts to rotate.

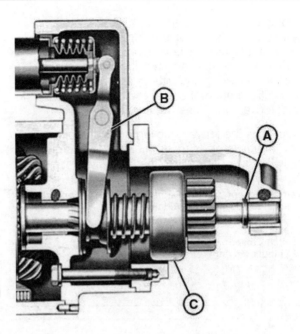

Fig. 38 — Overrunning Clutch Drive

A—Pinion Stop   C—Overrunning Clutch
B—Shift Lever

OUO1082,0002C51 -19-12JUN12-4/9

When the armature shaft rotates during cranking, small rollers become wedged against the clutch collar attached to the pinion. This wedging action locks the pinion gear to the armature shaft and causes the pinion to rotate with the shaft, as shown in Fig. 39.

When the engine starts, the flywheel spins the pinion gear faster than the armature, releasing the rollers and unlocking the pinion from the armature shaft. The pinion, still meshed with the flywheel, overruns safely and freely until the switch is opened and the shift lever pulls the pinion out of mesh. This feature prevents the armature from being driven at excessive speed by the engine.

DYER DRIVE

The Dyer drive is a special drive mechanism that provides positive meshing of the drive pinion with the flywheel, before the cranking motor switch is closed and the armature begins to rotate.

This action eliminates the clashing of pinion teeth with flywheel teeth, as well as the possibility of broken or burred teeth on either gear.

The Dyer drive is used on heavy-duty applications where it is important that the pinion be engaged before rotation begins. Engagement of the pinion while in motion is impossible because of the high horsepower developed and the acceleration of the armature when the starting circuit is completed.

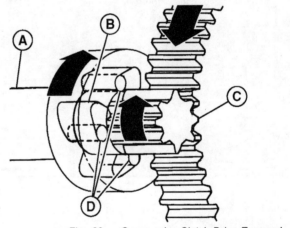

Fig. 39 — Overrunning Clutch Drive Engaged

A—Armature Shaft   C—Pinion Gear
B—Collar   D—Rollers

The Dyer drive works as follows:

Movement of the motor shift lever forces the shift sleeve and pinion endways along the armature shaft so that the pinion engages the flywheel.

Further movement of the shift lever then closes the starting motor switch and the engine is turned over.

Continued on next page   OUO1082,0002C51 -19-12JUN12-5/9

The pinion, fitting loosely on the armature shaft splines, rotates freely while the pinion guide is forced to rotate forward on the spiral splines. The rotation of the pinion guide is transmitted to the pinion by two lugs on the pinion guide. The pinion rotates freely, without any forward movement, until alignment of the gear teeth takes place. Then it is thrust forward into mesh as shown in Fig. 40.

The pinion stop limits the forward movement of the pinion. As the shift lever completes its travel, it closes the starting motor switch, linked mechanically to the shift lever.

A—Shift Lever Movement Forces Sleeve Endways, Engaging the Pinion with the Flywheel
B—Starter Switch Closed: Solenoid Plunger Moving Shift Lever
C—Pinion Stop Limits Forward Pinion Travel

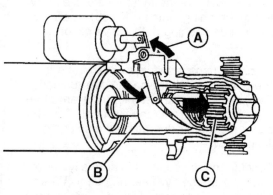

Fig. 40 — Dyer Drive in Operation: 1. Solenoid Plunger Moving Shift Lever

OUO1082,0002C51 -19-12JUN12-6/9

The motor armature then begins to rotate. This rotates the sleeve back, away from the pinion, to its original position as shown in Fig. 41.

A—Solenoid Contacts Closed: Armature Rotating
B—As Cranking Begins, Sleeve Rotates Away from the Pinion

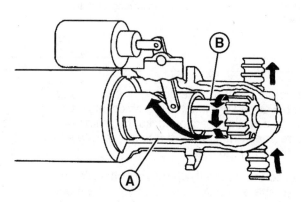

Fig. 41 — Dyer Drive in Operation: 2. Armature and Pinion Rotating Flywheel

Continued on next page   OUO1082,0002C51 -19-12JUN12-7/9

The instant that the engine starts, the flywheel attempts to drive the pinion faster than the armature is turning. Then both the pinion and the pinion guide are spun out of mesh with the ring gear (Fig. 42). The pinion guide drops into the milled section of the shaft splines, locking the pinion out of mesh.

It is impossible to start another cranking cycle without completely releasing the shift lever. The lever must drop all the way back to the "at rest" position.

On any automatic disengaging drive, it is always good policy to wait five seconds after a false start before attempting another start. In this period of time the engine will be at complete rest, and damage to the drive mechanism due to improper meshing is less likely to occur.

A—Engine Starts

B—Flywheel Speed Increases Forcing the Pinion to Unmesh

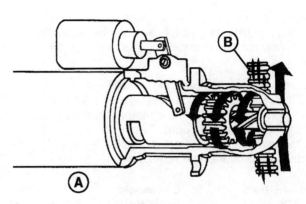

Fig. 42 — Dyer Drive in Operation: 3. Flywheel Spinning Pinion Out of Mesh

OUO1082,0002C51 -19-12JUN12-8/9

SPRAG CLUTCH DRIVE

The sprag clutch drive is constructed and operates like the overrunning clutch drive, except that a series of sprags replace the rollers between the shell and sleeve. The sprags are held against the shell and sleeve surfaces by a spring. This assembly is then splined to the armature shaft with a stop collar on the end of the sleeve (Fig. 43).

Movement of the shift lever against the collar causes the entire clutch assembly to move endways along the splined shaft and the pinion teeth to engage the ring gear. If a clash of teeth should occur, continued movement of the shell and spiral splined sleeve causes the pinion to rotate and clear the teeth. The compressed meshing spring then forces the pinion into mesh with the ring gear. If the pinion does not clear before the two retainer cups meet, shift lever movement is stopped by the retainer cups, and the operator must start the engagement cycle over again. This prevents closure of the switch contacts to the motor with the pinion not engaged, which would result in damage due to spinning meshes. On the second attempt, the pinion will engage in a normal manner.

With the pinion engaged and the switch closed, torque is transmitted to the pinion through the sprags. The sprags tilt slightly and are wedged between the shell and sleeve. When the engine starts, the ring gear drives the clutch faster than the armature, and the sprags tilt in the opposite direction to allow the pinion and sleeve to overrun the

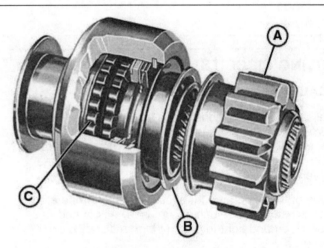

Fig. 43 — Sprag Clutch Drive

A—Pinion
B—Shift Collar

C—Sprags

shell and armature. To avoid prolonged overrunning, the starting switch should be opened as soon as the engine starts.

The sprag clutch drive is used primarily on larger starting motors to carry the high torque required to turn over high-compression engines.

OUO1082,0002C51 -19-12JUN12-9/9

GEAR REDUCTION DRIVE

A gear reduction drive (Fig. 44) consists of the motor, reduction gear, overrunning clutch, and a solenoid switch. The solenoid switch and overrunning clutch are on the same axis.

In a conventional starter motor, the armature and overrunning clutch pinion rotate at the same speed. In a reduction-type starting motor, the armature rotation speed is reduced by the reduction gears. Electrical current and armature torque requirements are reduced. The solenoid acts directly on the overrunning clutch.

A—Reduction Gears   C—Solenoid
B—Armature   D—Overrunning Clutch

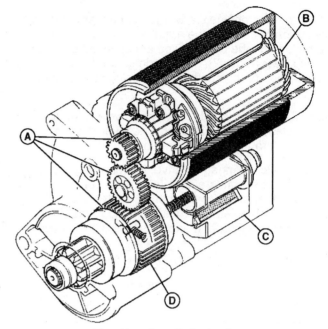

Fig. 44 — Gear Reduction Starter

OUO1082,0002C52 -19-10JAN12-1/1

STARTING CIRCUITS

TYPICAL STARTING CIRCUIT

Typical starting circuits consist of a low resistance cable connection from the storage battery, through a control switch, to a direct-current starting motor. The return circuit is to the battery, through the engine block and the frame of the vehicle.

Because of the large amount of current used to operate the starting motor, large cables are used. All connections must be clean and tight to prevent high resistance or voltage drop.

Closing the switch completes the starting circuit (Fig. 45).

Current will flow from the battery, through the cable, across the switch contacts, through the starting motor fields and armature, and back to the battery through ground.

DXP03154 —UN—17FEB12

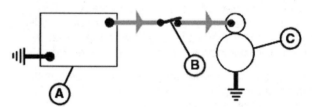

Fig. 45 — A Typical Starting Circuit (12 Volt)

A—Battery   C—Starting Motor
B—Starting Switch

Switches are often added to the starting circuit to protect operator safety. These switches prevent the machine from starting if a hazardous condition exists.

Continued on next page   OUO1082,0002C53 -19-12JUN12-1/5

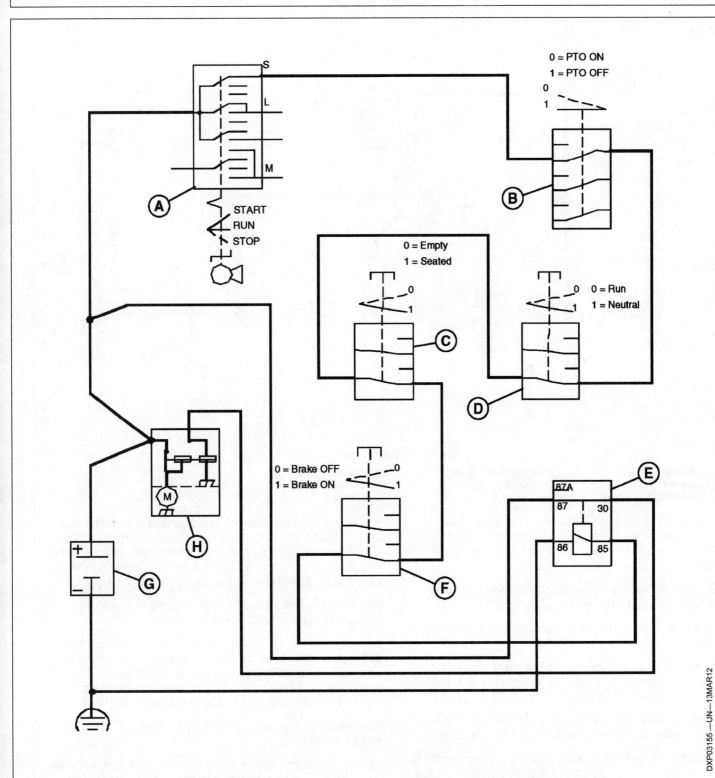

Fig. 46 — Typical Starting Circuit with Safety Switches (Key Switch in S Position)

A—Key Switch
B—PTO Switch
C—Seat Switch
D—Neutral Switch
E—Start Relay
F—Park Brake Switch
G—Battery
H—Starting Motor

Fig. 46 is an example of a starting circuit equipped with safety switches for PTO, transmission shift linkage, operator seat, and park brake. These switches are connected in series between the key switch and the starter solenoid. For the machine to start all of these, switches must be closed (ON). If any one of these conditions is open (OFF), the machine will not start.

Continued on next page   OUO1082,0002C53 -19-12JUN12-2/5

SPLIT-LOAD CIRCUIT

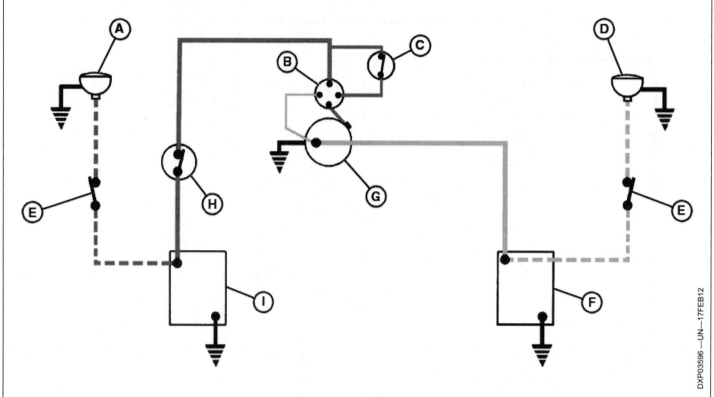

Fig. 47 — Split-Load Circuit (24 Volt)

A—Left-Side Lights	D—Right-Side Lights	G—Starting Motor
B—Solenoid	E—Light Switch	H—Ignition Switch
C—Neutral Safety Switch	F—Battery B	I— Battery A

We learned earlier that diesel engines and similar heavy-duty engines require high-output starting motors. We also learned that regulation lighting systems have not been developed for 24-volt systems.

Let's look at two methods used to provide this extra starting power, as well as adequate lighting.

The first method is the 24-volt split-load circuit illustrated in Fig. 47.

This circuit is called split load because the lights and accessories are split as equally as possible with each half connected to a 12-volt circuit.

The right-hand light circuit draws current from battery A and the left-hand circuit draws current from battery B.

The batteries and lights of each circuit are connected to a common ground, completing the circuit to the source. The vehicle frame and engine block are often used as the ground, and actually become part of the circuit.

When the switch in the starting circuit is closed, the vehicle frame becomes part of a series circuit between batteries A

and B so that enough voltage and current is supplied to the 24-volt starting motor. The starting motor and the starting circuit are insulated so that none of the components in the circuit are attached to a common ground, allowing the circuit to be completed at the terminal of B battery.

Although the batteries are in series, the left- and right-hand lighting circuits remain split.

If the light switches are closed as shown, each light circuit will draw current from the battery to which it is connected. The light switches are shown in the closed position for illustration purposes only. Of course, better starting performance is obtained by starting with the lights off.

For details on the batteries used with split-load circuits, see Chapter 5.

NOTE: *Some split-load circuits have four six-volt batteries instead of two 12-volt batteries. In this case, two batteries operate each 12-volt circuit.*

Continued on next page   OUO1082,0002C53 -19-12JUN12-3/5

SERIES-PARALLEL CIRCUIT

Another method of using two 12-volt batteries to provide 24-volt starting is the series-parallel switch shown in Fig. 48.

In Chapter 2 we learned about series and parallel circuits. We know that two 12-volt batteries connected in series will provide increased voltage while the current flow remains the same.

This applies directly to the series-parallel starting circuit. When the starting switch is closed, the series-parallel switch is actuated, connecting the terminals between A and B batteries as shown. We now have an insulated series circuit to the starting motor giving the 24 volts required.

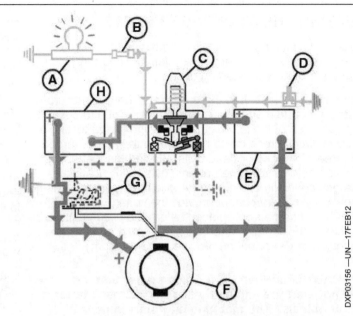

A—12 Volts   E—Battery B
B—Fuse   F—Starter Motor 24 V
C—Series-Parallel Switch   G—Solenoid 24 V
D—Start Switch   H—Battery A

Fig. 48 — Series-Parallel Circuit During Starting (24 Volt)

OUO1082,0002C53 -19-12JUN12-4/5

As soon as the engine starts and the starting switch is opened, the series-parallel switch also opens. This breaks the series connection between the batteries and provides a parallel circuit like the one shown in Fig. 49.

The starting switch operates as follows: The plunger moves up, opening the ground circuit for the 24-volt solenoid, which stops current flowing to the starting motor. As the plunger moves on up, it opens the series connection.

Until recently, a 12-volt starting motor could not produce the torque required to start diesel and other high-performance engines. But the 12-volt high-output starting motor provides the features common to 24-volt starting motors, and may be used to replace the 24-volt systems we have covered. (The 12-volt high-output motor circuit is shown in Fig. 19.)

TESTING AND DIAGNOSING THE STARTING CIRCUIT

We have seen how each part of the starting circuit works and how the parts operate as a whole. Now we will look at the main troubles and how to test, diagnose, and remedy them. Let's start with the complete starting circuit on the machine. We should locate the trouble first, before we start removing components.

Several checks, both visual and electrical, can be made to isolate the trouble before removing any part of the circuit. Many times a component is removed from the machine only to find that it is not defective after making reliable tests.

Therefore, be sure to make the following tests before removing a component from a defective starting circuit.

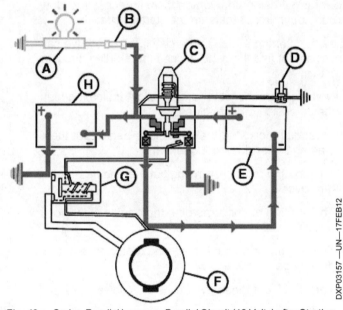

Fig. 49 — Series-Parallel becomes Parallel Circuit (12 Volts) after Starting

A—12 Volts   E—Battery B
B—Fuse   F—Starter Motor 24 V
C—Series-Parallel Switch   G—Solenoid 24 V
D—Start Switch   H—Battery A

OUO1082,0002C53 -19-12JUN12-5/5

TESTING THE STARTING CIRCUITS

Let's begin with the battery. The battery is the source of energy for all vehicle electrical systems. Therefore, it is also important to the starting circuit.

If the battery is less than three-quarters charged, accurate tests cannot be made in the starting circuit due to below par operation of the entire circuit. It is vital to the testing of starting circuit problems to have the battery fully charged and free of shorted or dead cells. Placing the test points of a voltmeter across the battery posts will indicate the charged condition of the battery while the engine is turning over. If the battery cannot provide the voltage required it must be recharged or replaced before the circuit can be checked. (For details, see Chapter 3. Also review the battery safety information provided in Chapter 1.)

⚠ CAUTION: When performing starter test, do not start the engine by shorting across starter terminals. The machine may start in gear if normal circuitry is bypassed.

If the battery is eliminated as a possible cause of starting circuit problems, inspect all clamps and connections in the circuit for corrosion and tighten them if necessary. Now we can continue our tests on the starting circuit.

When the starting switch in the circuit is closed, we can expect one of five things to occur if the starting circuit is defective:

1. Nothing happens—there is no "click" indicating that the solenoid contacts closed.

2. An audible "click" in the solenoid is heard, but the starting motor does not operate.

3. The starting motor is running but the engine does not turn over.

4. The starting motor turns over the engine slowly or erratically.

5. The engine starts but the starting motor drive does not disengage from the flywheel.

We can check out these five cases as follows:

Case No. 1: *We closed the starting switch and nothing happened.* This indicates that current is not reaching the solenoid and the switch contacts are not closing to complete the circuit. We can suspect then that the problem lies in the part of the circuit leading up to the solenoid, or in the solenoid.

To check this diagnosis, connect a jumper lead from the battery post to the switch terminal of the solenoid. (Be sure that the machine is not in gear.) If the engine starts, the circuit is open somewhere between the battery and the solenoid. However, if the solenoid switch does not close, the solenoid is defective. Perform tests on the solenoid as covered later in this chapter.

Case No. 2: *The solenoid contacts "clicked" but the starting motor did not operate.* This indicates that the circuit problems lie within the starting motor. If the solenoid switch contacts close, and the switch begins to "chatter," there is low voltage at the starter because of low battery charge or high resistance in the circuit, or an open circuit exists in the hold-in winding of the solenoid. If low voltage at the starter is not the cause, the starting motor should be removed and tested as covered later in this chapter. (On 24-volt motors, a defective solenoid return wire could also cause the above symptom.)

Case No. 3: *The starting motor ran but did not turn over the engine.* We know that the starting motor is getting enough current to operate. The problem, then, is either in the shifting of the drive assembly into mesh, a broken armature shaft, or a dirty or faulty drive assembly. These causes require disassembly of the starting motor and proper service or repair.

Case No. 4: *The starting motor turned the engine over slowly or erratically.* The problem may be in the starting motor or in the drive assembly. Before removing the motor, a voltage drop test should be made. A voltage drop test will locate any high-resistance connections or shorted or grounded windings which would affect starting motor efficiency. This test is made with a voltmeter while the engine is turning over. With test points on the insulated battery post and the starting motor terminal, the voltage drop generally should not exceed 0.3 volts. With test points on the battery ground post and the starter frame, the voltage drop in the ground circuit usually should not exceed 0.1 volt. (On 24-volt motors, the return circuit is insulated and the voltage drop should be less than 0.3 volt.)

If no high-resistance connections are detected, the pinion drive and the flywheel ring gear can be inspected by removing the starting motor. If either gear is damaged, it must be replaced. If they are not damaged, the starting motor must be disassembled and tested.

Case No. 5: *The engine starts but the motor drive does not disengage from the flywheel.* This indicates a defect in the drive mechanism, the solenoid pull-in windings, solenoid contacts, or solenoid control circuit which will not allow the drive to disengage. The starting motor or the circuit should be serviced.

Summary: In each of these cases the trouble can be located without extensive circuit testing. Once the trouble has been found, follow the test procedures for the component as outlined later in this chapter.

Below is a brief list of general diagnosis tips for tests on the complete starting circuit.

HOW TO DIAGNOSE STARTING CIRCUIT FAILURES

STARTING SWITCH IS ON BUT NO OPERATION.

Look for an open circuit, defective starting switch or starter safety switch, poor connections, open solenoid windings, stuck drive plunger, or pinion.

SOLENOID CONTACTS CLOSE BUT STARTING MOTOR DOES NOT OPERATE.

Continued on next page   OUO1082,0002C54 -19-10JAN12-1/2

110112
PN=282

Brushes are sticking, worn, or have weak spring tension. Commutator bars are dirty, burned, worn, pitted, or rough. Armature or field windings, armature bearings, or solenoid contacts are defective.

STARTING MOTOR OPERATES BUT ENGINE DOES NOT TURN OVER.

Drive assembly not meshing. Dirty or faulty drive assembly. Drive pinion or flywheel ring gear damaged. Broken armature shaft.

MOTOR DRIVE PINION DOES NOT MOVE OUT OF MESH.

Solenoid switch is defective. Drive assembly dirty or damaged. Armature shaft dirty or damaged.

SUMMARY: TESTING AND DIAGNOSING THE STARTING CIRCUIT

We have now covered testing and diagnosis of the complete starting circuit.

All of these checks should be made before removing any components for repair.

Next we will cover the testing and servicing of the various components of the starting circuit, once they are pinpointed as possibly defective.

Let's begin with the starting motor.

OUO1082,0002C54 -19-10JAN12-2/2

TESTING AND SERVICING STARTING MOTORS

Once you have tested the complete circuit and find that the starting motor may be defective, make the tests given here to confirm your diagnosis.

TESTING MOTOR BEFORE DISASSEMBLY

The tests below should be made before the starting motor is disassembled.

PRELIMINARY CHECKS

Even before you remove the starting motor, inspect it.

Listen for the grinding of clashing teeth when the starting motor drive is engaged, and for a squealing or rattling noise when the motor drive is released from the flywheel. These are indications of a dry or worn drive mechanism.

Look at the starting motor. Are there any loose mounting bolts? Remove the commutator end frame and check for burned commutator bars, high mica, worn brushes, or an oily commutator and brushes. These can all cause inadequate starting and must be corrected before further testing of the motor.

Also, be sure to check the motor for freedom of movement. Both the pinion gear and the armature must be free to move during the no-load test.

Check the pinion for freedom of operation by turning the shaft. If the pinion turns freely, turn the pinion and check the armature operation. If the armature drags, look for tight, dirty, or worn bearings, a bent armature shaft, or a loose pole shoe screw. In this case, disassemble the starting motor immediately. The no-load test may damage the starting motor if the armature does not turn freely.

NO-LOAD TEST

The no-load test is the basic check of the starting motor's internal condition.

To perform a no-load test, connect the starting motor to a fully charged battery (Fig. 50).

Insert an ammeter capable of measuring several hundred amperes between the battery and the starting motor. (If the technical manual specification is for basic motor only, connect the jumper wire between the S terminal and the battery post so the solenoid current draw is not measured.) Connect the voltmeter to the starting motor terminal and frame. Connect a carbon pile resistor across the battery as shown. Place a jumper lead between the battery terminal and the S terminal on the solenoid to complete the test circuit. Place a tachometer on the end of the armature to measure armature speed.

When the leads are connected to the battery terminals, current flows to the starting motor. The variable resistor is used to obtain the specified operating voltage of the starting motor. Do this by varying the resistor until the proper reading is on the voltmeter. When the specified voltage is attained, read the ammeter for the current

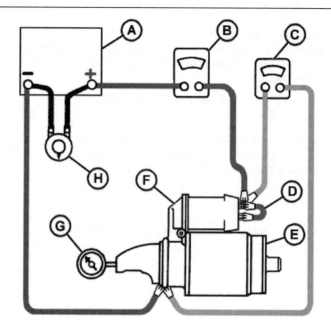

Fig. 50 — No-Load Test Circuit

A—Battery	E—Starter Motor
B—Ammeter	F—Solenoid
C—Voltmeter	G—Tachometer
D—Jumper Wire	H—Carbon Pile Resistor

drawn, and the tachometer for the armature speed. Compare these readings with the Technical Manual specifications for the starting motor being tested.

HOW TO INTERPRET THE NO-LOAD TEST RESULTS

Take the no-load test readings and judge them by the possible results and causes given below.

NOTE: Open-circuited field coils will not be detected with this test on starters with series field coils which are connected in parallel with each other.

1. Rated current draw and no-load speed indicates a normal starting motor condition.
2. Low free speed and high current draw indicates:
    a. Too much friction—Tight, dirty, or worn bearings, bent armature shaft or loose pole shoes allowing armature to drag.
    b. Shorted armature—This defect can be checked on a growler after disassembly.
    c. Grounded armature or fields—Check further after disassembly.
3. Failure to operate with high current draw indicates:
    a. A direct ground in the terminal or fields.
    b. "Frozen" bearings (this should have been determined when attempting to turn the armature by hand).
4. Failure to operate with no current draw indicates:
    a. Open field circuit. This can be checked after disassembly by inspecting internal connections and tracing circuit with a test lamp.

Continued on next page   OUO1082,0002C55 -19-12JUN12-1/20

   b. Open armature coils. Inspect the commutator for badly burned bars after disassembly.
   c. Broken brush springs, worn brushes, high insulation between the commutator bars, or other causes which would prevent good contact between the brushes and commutator.
5. Low speed and low current draw indicates:
   a. High internal resistance due to poor connections, defective leads, dirty commutator, or an open field circuit.
6. High free speed and high current draw indicate shorted fields. If shorted fields are suspected, replace the field winding assembly and check for improved performance.

NOTE: The lock-torque test, requiring special equipment, can be used to diagnose motor malfunctions. However, a thorough no-load test will usually reveal these faults without extra testing.

DISASSEMBLY OF THE MOTOR

GENERAL

Now that we have completed the no-load test and interpreted the results, let's assume the starting motor does not perform per the specifications. This requires disassembly and further testing of the motor.

Normally the starting motor should be disassembled only as far as necessary to repair or replace the defective parts. But to show the procedures, we will completely disassemble and assemble a typical starting motor with an externally-mounted solenoid switch. As a precaution, wear safety glasses while doing this job.

As the starting motor is disassembled, clean each part and inspect it for excessive wear or damage. An overall inspection should be made during disassembly. Things which are easy to do during disassembly are: 1) checking bearings for proper clearance, roughness, or galling, 2) removing oil and dirt from insulation, and 3) inspecting the condition of the insulation.

DISASSEMBLING THE MOTOR

The first step in disassembling the starting motor is to remove the commutator end frame. Mark the position of the end frame and the main frame with chalk before removal to aid in aligning the parts when reassembling. While removing the end frame, note the location of the brush assembly.

Brushes may be located in the end frame—be careful during removal of these—or they may be located in the main frame. While removing the end frame, check the brushes to see if they slide freely in their holders and make full contact on the commutator. Brushes worn to half their original length or less should be replaced.

The second step in disassembly is to disconnect the solenoid (externally-mounted). After removing the fasteners to the main frame and the drive housing, the solenoid can be removed along with the main frame assembly.

Removal of the main frame will expose the armature and commutator. The commutator should be checked for evidence of excessive arcing, discoloration, or excessive wear. If it is only slightly dirty, glazed or discolored, cleaning with No. 00 or 000 sandpaper will restore the commutator to a serviceable condition. never use emery cloth to clean a commutator.

If the commutator is worn or rough, however, it should be turned on a lathe and the mica under-cut if recommended, see the Technical Manual. At this point the armature can also be inspected for rough bearing surfaces, and rough or damaged splines.

The solenoid shift lever must be disconnected from the drive housing to separate the armature and drive housing. In doing so, the complete armature shaft is exposed along with the drive mechanism. When the drive housing is removed, inspect it for cracks, and check the bearing for excessive wear. Remove any rust, paint, or grease from the housing flange before reassembly.

Continued on next page   OUO1082,0002C55 -19-12JUN12-2/20

With the overrunning clutch drive and armature shaft exposed as in Fig. 51, make a visual inspection for damage due to overheating.

Overheating occurs if the starting switch is not released as soon as the engine begins to operate, causing the drive pinion to remain in mesh and overrun the armature. Clutch mechanisms can withstand this for only a brief time before the lubricant gives out and they seize, causing excessive armature speeds. Look for galling of clutch bearings under the drive pinion, and bluing or deposits of bearing material on the armature shaft. If this is evident, replace the armature.

CHECKING THE OVERRUNNING CLUTCH DRIVE

After inspecting the motor, check the drive mechanism. Simply turn the clutch by hand to find out whether the drive slides freely on the splines. Replace the drive if it does not move freely. The pinion should turn smoothly in one direction and lock when turned slowly in the other direction. Replace the pinion if it is excessively worn or damaged.

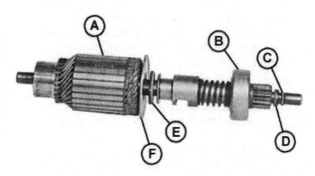

Fig. 51 — Armature and Drive Assembly

A—Armature
B—Motor Drive
C—Snap Ring
D—Pinion Retainer
E—Brake Washer
F—Center Bearing Assembly

OUO1082,0002C55 -19-12JUN12-3/20

Never clean the overrunning clutch by any high-temperature or grease-removing methods. This removes the lubricant originally packed in the clutch and causes rapid clutch failure. The overrunning clutch can be wiped or brushed clean with a solvent as shown in Fig. 52, but should never be submerged since it cannot be repacked with grease.

CHECKING THE BENDIX DRIVE

The spiral threads on the Bendix drive sleeve should be free of dirt and grease. If the pinion teeth are badly burred, chipped or otherwise damaged, replace the pinion and shaft assembly.

Fig. 52 — Cleaning an Overrunning Clutch

OUO1082,0002C55 -19-12JUN12-4/20

Distorted drive springs can cause breakage of the motor drive housing. When the drive spring is distorted, as shown in Fig. 53, replace it. When installing a new spring, always use new locks on the screws. Be sure to lock the screws securely and apply a thin coat of oil to the spiral threads.

CHECKING THE DYER AND SPRAG DRIVES

The Dyer and Sprag drives vary with the application. This means varied cleaning procedures, lubrication requirements, and adjustments. Consult the machine's Technical Manual before cleaning these drive mechanisms.

REMOVING THE DRIVES

A—GOOD   B—DISTORTED

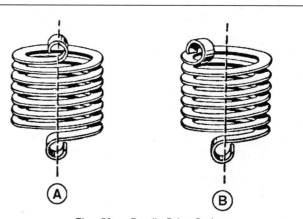

Fig. 53 — Bendix Drive Springs

Continued on next page   OUO1082,0002C55 -19-12JUN12-5/20

To separate the drive from the armature shaft, the pinion stop Fig. 54 must be removed. When removing the drive assembly, use a pipe coupling or suitable metal cylinder to drive the pinion stop toward the armature core and reveal the snap ring. After removing the snap ring, the drive assembly will slide off the armature shaft.

TESTING AND SERVICING THE MOTOR COMPONENTS

When the starting motor has been disassembled, inspect the motor parts in preparation for component testing.

General inspection helps to locate trouble spots which could cause later failures of the motor.

Mechanical failures, such as worn bushings, bent armature shafts, worn brushes, or worn motor drive, are common troubles. Except for these, starting motor failures are generally caused by one of the following:

Open-Circuited Winding—This occurs due to a broken wire, poorly soldered connection, or a disconnection at a terminal. The result is usually no operation or a decrease in starting ability.

Grounded Winding—This occurs when insulation becomes defective and a bare winding wire contacts the metal of the armature, frame, or field poles. This usually results in failure of the motor to operate.

Short-Circuited Winding—This occurs when insulation becomes defective and the winding coils contact adjacent coils, resulting in decreased motor cranking power.

Fig. 54 — Removing Pinion Stop

A—Pinion Stop

OUO1082,0002C55 -19-12JUN12-6/20

TESTING AND RECONDITIONING THE ARMATURE

When the no-load test shows a low armature speed and a high current draw, the armature should be tested for opens, grounds, and short circuits. If the armature is tested, perform all of the tests given below.

Before testing, check the armature shaft for straightness. A bent armature shaft will allow the armature to drag, resulting in reduced starting performance and increased current draw.

To check, put the shaft in a lathe or rest in V-blocks and check the shaft with a dial indicator as shown in Fig. 55. Replace a bent or damaged shaft.

Open-Circuit Test

If the armature shaft is straight, test it for open circuits in the commutator.

Open circuits are usually caused by too-long starting periods. The most likely place for an open circuit or loose

Fig. 55 — Checking Armature Shaft for Straightness

connection to occur is at the commutator riser bars. Poor connections cause arcing and burning of the commutator bars as the starting motor is operated.

If the commutator bars are not too badly burned, they can often be repaired by resoldering or welding the leads in the riser bars (using rosin flux) and turning down the commutator to remove the burned material. The insulation should usually be undercut. Refer to "Reconditioning Armature," later in this chapter.

Continued on next page OUO1082,0002C55 -19-12JUN12-7/20

A growler is shown in Fig. 56 with the armature mounted for testing open circuits. Use a two-pronged tester and span the adjacent commutator bars as illustrated. Slowly rotate the armature back and forth to get the maximum reading. If necessary, adjust the voltage control so that the meter hand rests about midway on the scale.

Voltage readings should read approximately the same as each commutator bar is tested with the adjacent bar. Wide deviations in readings will indicate an open circuit.

If an open circuit exists in the armature that cannot be located or repaired, the armature must be replaced.

Ground Test

A—Compare Readings

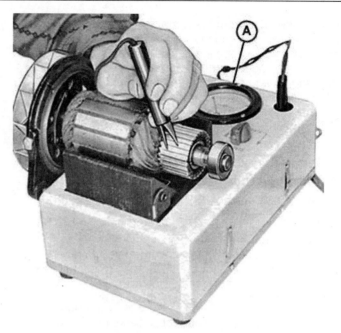

Fig. 56 — Testing Armature for Open Circuits

OUO1082,0002C55 -19-12JUN12-8/20

When testing for grounds, place one test point on the iron core of the armature and the other test point on the copper commutator (Fig. 57). We are checking for connections between the copper and iron core which would cause a grounded armature. The test lamp should not light while making this test. If it does light, a winding is grounded and the armature must be rewound or replaced.

Short-Circuit Test

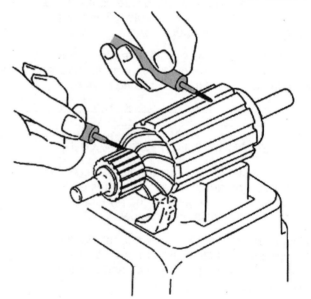

Fig. 57 — Testing Armature for Grounds

Continued on next page　　　　OUO1082,0002C55 -19-12JUN12-9/20

An indication of a shorted armature is a burned commutator bar. To verify this, place the armature on a growler as shown in Fig. 58 and test it. With the growler turned on, place a thin strip of steel or a hacksaw blade on the armature as it is slowly rotated. If the metal strip vibrates over a winding, that winding is short-circuited.

Short-circuited windings are sometimes caused by metal in the commutator bridging the gap from one commutator bar to the next. By removing the bridged metal, this condition can be corrected. However, if this does not correct the short, replace the armature.

Reconditioning The Armature

If tests indicate that the armature is suitable for service, turn the commutator down and undercut it before the starting motor is assembled.

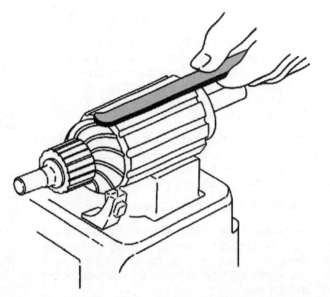

Fig. 58 — Testing Armature for Short Circuits

DXP03166 —UN—17FEB12

OUO1082,0002C55 -19-12JUN12-10/20

To turn down a commutator, use a suitable tool, such as the one illustrated in Fig. 59. If a tool specifically for turning commutators is not available, the commutator can be turned down on a lathe. In either case, remove only enough metal to true up the commutator.

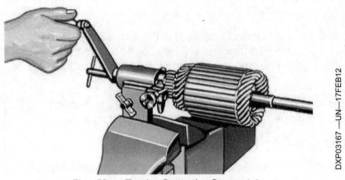

Fig. 59 — Turning Down the Commutator

DXP03167 —UN—17FEB12

Continued on next page

OUO1082,0002C55 -19-12JUN12-11/20

On some starters, after trueing the commutator, undercut the mica between the commutator bars. A tool used for this purpose is shown in Fig. 60. If a tool for undercutting is not available, use a hacksaw blade with the sides of its teeth ground to the same width as the distance between commutator bars. An undercutting tool is preferred, however, since it can provide more accurate and consistent reconditioning.

Always consult the starting motor specifications before reconditioning the armature. Most high-output starting motor armatures should not be undercut after the commutator is turned down.

TESTING AND SERVICING FIELD WINDINGS

Field windings should be checked for grounded wiring and open circuits while the armature is removed. Grounded wiring is caused by the copper wiring touching the steel case due to worn insulation or trapped metal between a winding and the case.

Before testing the field windings in a compound-wound starting motor, separate the shunt field winding lead from

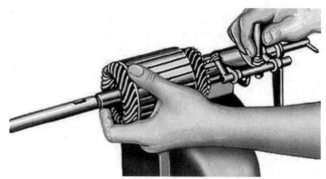

Fig. 60 — Undercutting Mica on Commutator

the series field winding lead. By doing this step, the shunt is eliminated from the circuit during the tests for grounds and open circuits.

Grounded-Circuit Test

OUO1082,0002C55 -19-12JUN12-12/20

To test for a grounded circuit, first disconnect the field winding ground connections. Then connect one test point to the field frame and the other to the field connector (Fig. 61).

If the test lamp lights, the field windings are grounded. Field windings may be repaired or replaced if faulty.

Open-Circuit Test

An open-circuit test can also be made with a test lamp. If the test lamp does not light with the test points applied at the ends of the windings, the field winding circuit is open and current cannot flow through them.

When testing 24-volt starting motors, two sets of terminals are tested when checking for open circuits. Place one test point on the input terminal of the starting motor and the other test point on the winding as we did before. Test the second set of field windings by moving the test point from the winding to the insulated terminal.

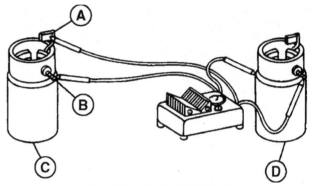

Fig. 61 — Testing Field Windings

A—Brush
B—Field Connector Terminal
C—Open Circuit
D—Grounded Windings

Continued on next page   OUO1082,0002C55 -19-12JUN12-13/20

To check parallel-wound field windings for an open circuit, make connections shown in Fig. 62. Adjust carbon pile resistor to obtain 60 to 75 amperes. Place a steel bar against the pole shoe. No magnetism at pole shoe indicates an open-circuited field winding. Connect to other brush lead and check the other field windings.

Short-Circuit Test

Because of the low resistance in the field windings there is no satisfactory test for short-circuited field windings. If the starting motor does not perform after all other tests have been made and no defects were found, a short circuit can be suspected. It usually shows up in the no-load test as high ampere draw and high free speed.

Replacing Field Windings

If the field windings must be removed for repair or replacement, use a pole shoe spreader and pole shoe screwdriver. Be careful in replacing the field windings to prevent grounding or shorting them.

When the pole shoe has a long tip on one side, assemble it in the direction of armature rotation.

TESTING AND SERVICING BRUSHES

Before assembling the starting motor, the brushes should be inspected and tested. To test the insulated brush holders, connect one test point to the brush holder and connect the other test point to the motor frame. The

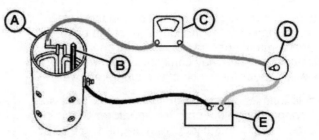

Fig. 62 — Open Circuit Test in Parallel-Wound Field Winding

A—Brush Lead
B—Steel Bar
C—Ammeter
D—Carbon Pile Resistor
E—12-Volt Battery

test lamp should not light. If all of the brush holders are insulated, the test lamp should light when connected to opposite brush holders, but should not light when connected to adjacent brush holders or from any brush holder to the frame. Repair or replace the brush holder if tests indicate faulty brush holders. Always use matched sets when replacing the brushes.

On some motors, the brushes are soldered to the field coils instead of using mechanical fasteners. To replace these brushes, cut off the brush leads at the points where they are attached to the field coils. The ends of the coils must then be prepared for soldering on the new brush lead assemblies.

Continued on next page
OUO1082,0002C55 -19-12JUN12-14/20

Assemble all brushes to the brush arms in the proper direction. In many cases, the long side of the brush is toward the commutator end frame as shown in Fig. 63. Otherwise the brushes may come in contact with the riser bars. Always check the brush offset during removal.

When soldering leads, solder the backs of the coils so that the connection will not rub the armature. Clean the ends of the coils thoroughly by filing or grinding off the old brush lead connections. Remove varnish only as far back as necessary to make the solder connections. Using rosin flux, the leads may then be soldered to the field coils, making sure that they are in the same position as the original brush holders. If the leads are overheated, solder will run on them and they will no longer be flexible.

To replace grounded brush assemblies, remove the old brush holders, the same as insulated brushes, and then attach the new assemblies to the frame. If the brush holder assemblies have retainers, peen the screws with a hammer so that the nuts cannot vibrate loose during engine operation.

When the field coil and brush assembly is reassembled in the frame, check the frame and field assembly with a test lamp to make sure that the soldered connection is not touching the frame and grounding the fields.

Spring Tension

The brushes should make good, clean contact with the commutator and should have the proper spring tension. They must also have freedom of movement so they can follow the commutator.

Never allow brush spring tension to fall below the specified limits. Starting motor brushes carry a high current, so good contact between the brush and the commutator will cut resistance. Most brush springs test above the specified tension but since the starting motor is used intermittently, this is not objectionable. Weak or distorted springs, or springs that show evidence of overheating, rust, or excessive wear should be replaced. Check the spring tension of most brushes during assembly of the starting motor. (See later in this chapter.)

SERVICING BUSHINGS

Commutator End Frame Bushing

The bushing in the commutator end frame should be inspected for wear or damage. An excessively worn bushing will allow the armature to drag on the pole shoes.

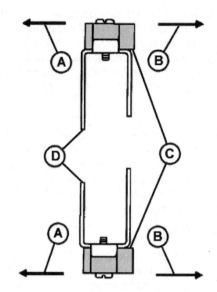

Fig. 63 — Assembling Brushes to Brush Arm

A—Riser Bars
B—End Frame

C—Long Side of Brushes toward End Frame (In Most Models). Check During Removal.
D—Brush Arms

The bronze bushings in the starting motor are oil-impregnated and should need no added lubrication. They should be lubricated when the motor is disassembled; at this time a few drops of light engine oil may be placed on each bushing before reassembly. Be careful so that no oil reaches the commutator.

In some cases, the bushing is lubricated by a felt wick. To replace a lubricated bushing, do the following.

Replacing Lubricated Bushings

Remove the oil plug so that the oil wick can be removed. Then drive the expansion plug out of the housing. Note the depth of the old bushing; drive it out, and press the new bushing in to the same depth as the original.

Continued on next page   OUO1082,0002C55 -19-12JUN12-15/20

After the new bushing is in place, use a drill the same size as the oil wick hole to drill the bushing (Fig. 64). Remove the burrs and clean out the oil wick hole before testing the bushing with the respective bearing surface of the armature. If the armature does not turn freely, ream the bushing.

The bushing can collapse when installing a prelubricated or absorbent bronze type. To prevent this, use the proper bushing arbor to obtain a correct bearing fit. The arbor is usually several ten-thousandths larger than the armature shaft. If the prelubricated bushing is undersized after installation, burnish it to size (polish by friction or rubbing). avoid reaming (cutting excess metal away) if possible.

Drive Housing And Center Bearing Bushings

If the drive housing bushing or the center bearing bushing is worn, replace it. Loose-fitting center bearings are normal. The loose fit allows easier bushing alignment. When replacing the bushing, follow the same steps used to replace the commutator end frame bushing.

Before assembling the armature shaft with the drive mechanism, lubricate the armature shaft with a light coat of SAE 10 engine oil. Using a heavier oil may cause failure of the drive to mesh at low temperatures.

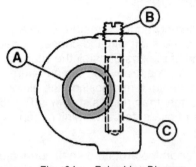

Fig. 64 — Rebushing Diagram

A—Bushing   C—Wick
B—Plug

When assembling motors having a center bearing, lubricate the center bearing in the same way and slide the bearing and washers onto the armature shaft ahead of the drive assembly. (Use a graphite-type starting motor lubricant as recommended.)

Continued on next page

OUO1082,0002C55 -19-12JUN12-16/20

ASSEMBLY OF MOTOR

Place the drive assembly on the armature shaft and slide the pinion stop onto the shaft with the cupped surface facing the open end of the shaft. Install the snap ring and squeeze it so it fits into the groove on the armature. Slide the thrust ring onto the shaft and position the pinion stop and washer next to the snap ring as shown in Fig. 65. By using two pairs of pliers, force the pinion stop over the snap ring.

With the thrust collar on the armature shaft, lubricate the bushing surface in the drive housing with the starting motor lubricant. Then guide the armature and solenoid shift lever into the drive housing. Secure the lever with the pivot screw and move the lever back and forth. The shift lever and drive assembly should move freely in both directions.

If the starting motor has a center bearing, secure it to the drive housing after checking the shift lever.

Refer to the machine Technical Manual for drive assembly tests on coaxial or heavy-duty starting motors.

Next, install the solenoid gasket, the return spring, and the solenoid. Before attaching the solenoid to the drive housing, use a recommended sealing compound between the solenoid flange and the starting motor main frame.

Install the main frame and guide the brushes onto the commutator, being careful not to damage the brushes or the brush holders. After the main frame is installed, hold down the brush holders to align the brushes with the commutator and tighten the brushes.

SEATING THE BRUSHES

If new brushes were installed while servicing the starting motor, they may require seating before completing assembly.

To seat the brushes, wrap a piece of No. 00 or 000 sandpaper around the commutator so that the exposed end is trailing when the armature is turned in the running

Fig. 65 — Forcing Pinion Stop over Pinion Ring

A—Thrust Collar   C—Pinion Stop
B—Snap Ring

direction. The sandpaper should be one-eighth inch wider than the commutator and one inch longer than needed to reach around the commutator. Turn the armature clockwise as viewed from the drive end of the starting motor. Do not turn the armature for too long. A few turns will seat the brushes without too much brush wear. Be sure to remove all dust and abrasive particles.

CHECKING BRUSHES

We have learned that improper contact of the brushes with the commutator can cause faulty motor performance. Therefore, on most motors it is good practice to make one final check before completing assembly. That test is for spring tension on the brushes. (On some heavy-duty motors, this test is not recommended.)

Continued on next page
OUO1082,0002C55 -19-12JUN12-17/20

Measure brush spring tension using a spring scale (Fig. 66). By pulling the spring scale on a line parallel to the brush, we can obtain a reading at the point where the spring just leaves the brush holder. Consult the motor specifications in the technical manual, since spring tension ratings vary with different starting motors. To adjust the tension of the brushes, bend the springs or holders.

COMPLETING ASSEMBLY OF MOTOR

To complete assembly, lubricate the bushing in the commutator end frame with a starting motor lubricant and slide it onto the armature shaft. Arrange the brush leads so that the thru bolts will clear them and align the register marks on the main frame and the commutator end frame. Install the thru bolts and tighten the commutator end frame. Lubricate the oil reservoirs with a light SAE 10 engine oil.

CHECKING PINION CLEARANCE

The pinion clearance test is made to check for proper assembly of the starting motor and excessive wear in the shift linkage. Many starting motors have no provision for pinion adjustment. As a result, always refer to the machine technical manual for details on pinion adjustments. If the pinion is not adjustable, the drive shift assembly must be replaced when it becomes worn or faulty.

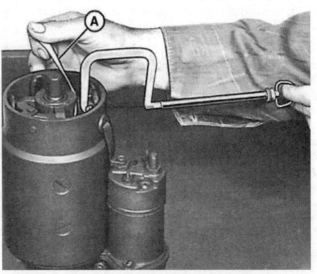

Fig. 66 — Testing Brush Spring Tension

A—Piece of Paper

OUO1082,0002C55 -19-12JUN12-18/20

To check pinion clearance, disconnect the field coil connector from the solenoid motor terminal (Fig. 67). Then connect a battery, of the same voltage as the solenoid, from the solenoid switch terminal to the solenoid frame or ground terminal. Momentarily connect a jumper lead from the solenoid motor terminal to the solenoid frame or ground terminal to shift the drive into starting position. It will remain there until the battery is disconnected. Now the pinion clearance can be checked as given below.

A—Jumper Cable   C—Starting Motor
B—Battery   D—Solenoid

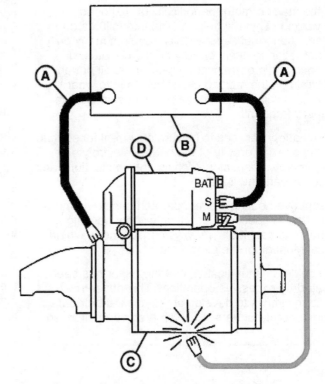

Fig. 67 — Circuit for Testing the Pinion Clearance

Continued on next page

OUO1082,0002C55 -19-12JUN12-19/20

Check the pinion clearance by pressing the pinion or drive towards the commutator to take up slack movement and measuring the clearance between the pinion and pinion stop as shown in Fig. 68.

The correct pinion clearance will vary for different motors. Consult the machine Technical Manual for specific readings and procedures.

FINAL ASSEMBLY CHECK

It is good practice to give an overhauled starting motor a no-load test. If current draw is too high, two or three raps with a rawhide hammer will often help align the bearings and free up the armature.

A—Press on Clutch as Shown   D—Pinion Clearance
    to Take Up Movement   E—Feeler Gauge
B—Pinion
C—Pinion Stop

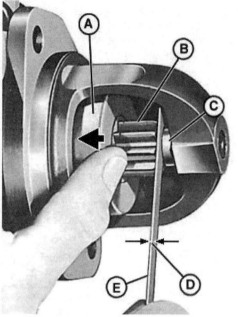

Fig. 68 — Checking Pinion Clearance (Intermediate-Duty Clutch Motor Shown)

OUO1082,0002C55 -19-12JUN12-20/20

PERIODIC MAINTENANCE OF STARTING MOTORS

Check the starting motor periodically during operation on the vehicle. This will help to eliminate failures due to neglect. Abnormal service which requires many daily starts, operation in dusty or very humid climates, or operation in arctic or tropical temperatures, all put an added strain on the starting circuit and tend to wear the parts more rapidly. Under these conditions, inspect the motor more frequently.

Keep the battery serviced to be sure of current for starting. Check the specific gravity of the battery electrolyte at regular intervals. Inspect the cables and connections and keep them clean and tight.

To prevent overheating, never operate the starting motor for more than 30 seconds at a time without pausing a few minutes to cool it off. (Always consult the machine Technical Manual for the exact safe period.)

Thrown solder is an indication that the motor has been overheated by excessive operation. This abuse may cause open circuits to develop at the commutator bars, resulting in burnt-out bars. Each time an open-circuited

bar passes under a brush, severe arcing occurs and the bar soon becomes badly burned. If the bars are not severely burned when the starting motor is serviced, the commutator may be repaired by resoldering the leads and turning down the commutator.

Always keep the starting motor mounting tight and be sure the drive is in good condition. The condition of the drive can be checked by operating the starting motor two or three times while noting the action of the drive. The motor may have to be removed to actually examine the drive.

On clutch-type motors, operating the motor also serves as a check on the freedom of shift lever operation.

The high-output starting circuit, especially, must be kept in good condition to get maximum performance from the high-output motor. Refer to the machine Technical Manual for circuit maintenance and specifications when servicing these circuits.

As a final step in periodic maintenance, lubricate the starting motor by adding a few drops of light engine oil to the visible hinge cap oilers. The bearings in many starting motors are of the oilless type, but they require oiling when the motor is reassembled.

OUO1082,0002C56 -19-10JAN12-1/1

TESTING OF SWITCHES

No starting motor service is complete unless the switch is checked out.

The allowable resistance (or voltage drop) of the switch contacts will vary with the machine. See the Technical Manual.

TESTING MANUAL SWITCHES

A general inspection will indicate whether the manual switch is serviceable or faulty (Fig. 69).

If the switch has a bypass ignition terminal, check it to be sure that contact is made as the switch button is pushed in. The ignition terminal should be in good condition, and if there is doubt, it should be replaced. If the terminal stud is burned or bent, it should also be replaced. However, if it is not, remove any burrs with a file, and polish the contacts with No. 00 sandpaper. Install new insulators when the switch is replaced on the starting motor.

TESTING SOLENOID SWITCHES (STARTER REMOVED)

To prevent damage, the solenoid must be on the starter when testing the windings. Remove terminal cover and field coil connector. If equipped, disconnect shunt field winding lead from terminal on field frame.

Replace the solenoid if it fails any of the following tests:

• No-load test
• Return test
• Pull-in winding test

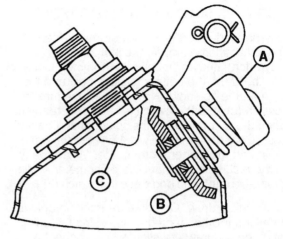

Fig. 69 — Manual Switch

A—Plunger
B—Contact
C—Terminal

NOTE: Refer to your machine Technical Manual for the correct solenoid test procedure. Some solenoids are tested using the alternate procedure given on page 5-32 rather than the following typical procedures. If the machine manual recommends testing of both windings at once, use the procedures recommended in the machine manual. Note the ammeter reading at the end of its swing upward.

Continued on next page

OUO1082,0002C57 -19-13JUL12-1/4

TESTING STARTER SOLENOID (NO-LOAD TEST)

To make the no-load test requires an ammeter (can measure several hundred amps), two jumper wires (one of them with a switch), and an inductive tachometer. Connect the ammeter between the battery positive post and the BAT terminal on the solenoid. Now connect the jumper wire with switch (ensure the switch is open until ready to test) between the M terminal on the solenoid and battery positive post. Connect a jumper wire between the battery negative post and the starter motor frame. When ready to perform the test, hold the inductive tachometer at the starter motor drive shaft end and close the switch (Fig. 70).

Measure the current draw. Compare the reading against the specifications for the starting motor being tested. If speed and current draw are slightly low, connect a voltmeter between the starter motor terminal and frame. Observe voltage during test. Voltage may be reduced because of high current draw on battery.

Evaluating No-Load Test

Fails to Operate—Low Current Draw

• Open series field circuit.
• Open armature coils.
• Defective brush contact with commutator.

Fails to Operate—High Current Draw

• Grounded terminal or fields.
• Seized bearings.

Low Speed—Low Current Draw

• High internal resistance.
• Defective brush contact with commutator.

Low Speed—High Current Draw

• Excessive friction.
• Shorted armature.
• Grounded armature or fields.

High Speed—Low Current Draw

• Open shunt field circuit.

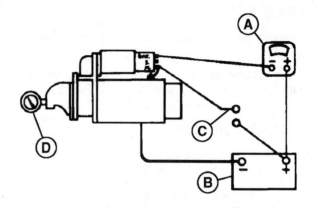

Fig. 70 — Solenoid No-Load Test

A—Ammeter   C—Switch
B—Battery   D—Tachometer

High Speed—High Current Draw

• Shorted series field coils.

TESTING MAGNETIC SWITCHES

A magnetic switch can be checked by connecting the test leads to the main switch terminals.

If the switch is in good condition, the plunger will close the main switch contacts.

If the action is slow or the plunger does not operate, take an ammeter reading of the current drawn by the coils.

1. Ammeter readings higher than specified mean a shorted or grounded wire.

2. A low reading means excessive resistance.

3. No reading means that there is an open circuit in the coils.

Most magnetic switches are sealed, so any of the above conditions mean that the switch must be replaced.

Continued on next page   OUO1082,0002C57 -19-13JUL12-2/4

TESTING STARTER SOLENOID (ALTERNATE METHOD)

Some machine Technical Manuals use the following solenoid tests. Make these tests with the solenoid on the starter and the leads disconnected.

Pull-In Winding

Make connections as illustrated in Fig. 71.

Adjust the carbon pile to obtain 8 volts.

When the jumper wire is connected, the solenoid should move the pinion out to the stop.

When the jumper wire is disconnected, the pinion should remain out at the pinion stop.

A—12-Volt Battery   D—Jumper Wire
B—Carbon Pile   E—Ground to Frame
C—Voltmeter

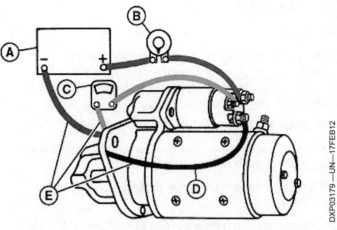

Fig. 71 — Solenoid Pull-In Winding Test

OUO1082,0002C57 -19-13JUL12-3/4

Testing Solenoid Return

Make connections as illustrated in Fig. 72. Close the switch and pull drive out until pinion contacts the pinion stop. When released, the drive should return without hesitation.

Evaluating Alternate Test

Fails to Pull In (at 8 Volts)

• Defective pull-in winding

Fails to Remain Out

• Defective hold-in winding

Fails to Return

• Defective pull-in winding

A—12-Volt Battery   B—Switch

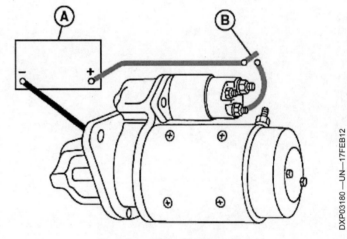

Fig. 72 — Solenoid Return Test

OUO1082,0002C57 -19-13JUL12-4/4

TEST YOURSELF

QUESTIONS

1. (Fill in the blanks.) In a basic starting circuit, the _____ supplies the energy to the _____ which drives the engine flywheel. The circuit is activated by a _____.

2. What are the four main types of starting motor circuits?

3. (True or False?) The coaxial-mounted solenoid switch is on the outside of the motor housing.

4. What is the basic test of the starting motor's internal condition?

5. Replace motor brushes worn to (3/4—1/2—1/4—1/3) their original length.

6. When cleaning the commutator, which material should be used?

   a. Emery cloth.

   b. No. 00 sandpaper.

   c. A smooth mill file.

7. (Fill in the blanks.) To prevent _____, never operate the starting motor for more than _____ at a time without pausing for a few minutes.

(Answers are in the back of the textbook.)

OUO1082,0002C58 -19-10JAN12-1/1

Ignition Circuits

DXP02708 —UN—23FEB11

8

Continued on next page

DXP03203 —UN—07MAR12

OUO1082,0002C79 -19-29OCT12-1/2

The ignition circuit creates the spark that ignites fuel and powers the gasoline or LP-gas engine.

To do this, the ignition circuit must:

1. Step up low voltage to high-voltage surges

2. Time these surges to the engine

The coil transforms the low voltage from the battery to a high voltage for producing a spark.

Opening the distributor points collapses the magnetic field in the coil to produce a high voltage. The condenser protects the distributor points against arcing.

The DISTRIBUTOR does three things:

1. Opens and closes the primary circuit, causing the coil to produce high-voltage surges.

2. Times these surges to engine rotation.

3. Directs each high-voltage surge to the proper spark plug.

The spark plugs ignite the fuel-air mixture within each cylinder of the engine.

The battery of the charging circuit is the initial power source for the voltage in the ignition circuit, while the ignition switch turns on the circuit when it cranks the engine.

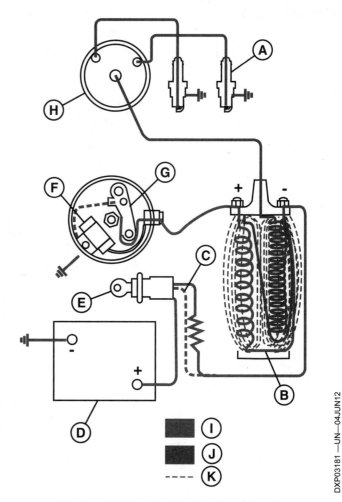

A—Spark Plugs
B—Ignition Coil
C—Bypass
D—Battery
E—Ignition Switch
F—Condenser
G—Points
H—Distributor
I— Primary Circuit
J—Secondary Circuit
K—Magnetic Field

Fig. 1 — Ignition Circuit (Bypass-Type Shown)

OUO1082,0002C79 -19-29OCT12-2/2

HOW THE IGNITION CIRCUIT WORKS

The ignition circuit must take low voltage from the battery and create high voltage to fire the engine. It must do this very accurately and very rapidly—100 or more times per second.

Let's see how the circuit does this complex job.

The ignition circuit has two separate circuits:

• Primary Side: low-voltage circuit
• Secondary Side: high-voltage circuit

The primary circuit is the path for low-voltage current from the power source. Fig. 1 shows this circuit in light gray. It includes these parts:

• Battery
• Ignition Switch
• Resistor
• Coil Primary Winding

• Distributor Contact Points
• Condenser

The secondary circuit is the high-voltage path for current stepped up by the coil. Fig. 1 shows this circuit in dark gray. It includes these parts:

• Coil Secondary Winding
• Coil Wire
• Distributor Cap
• Distributor Rotor
• Spark Plug Wires
• Spark Plugs

Now let's take these circuits and see how they work.

To simplify, let's divide the operation into two parts—before the distributor points open and after they open.

OPERATION BEFORE THE DISTRIBUTOR POINTS OPEN

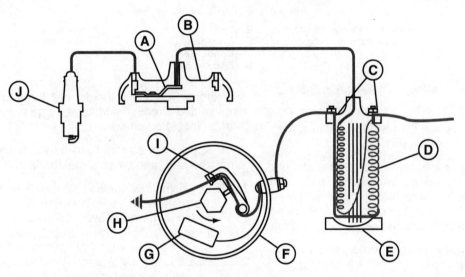

Fig. 2 — Operation Before the Distributor Points Open

A—Rotor
B—Distributor Cap
C—Primary Terminals
D—Primary Winding
E—Coil
F—Distributor
G—Condenser
H—Breaker Cam
I—Contact Points (Closed)
J—Spark Plugs

Before the engine is started, the distributor points are closed (Fig. 2).

But when the ignition switch is turned on, current flows from the battery into the primary windings of the coil.

This current creates a magnetic field around the winding.

From the primary winding, the current—at low voltage—simply travels through the closed distributor points and back to ground.

Continued on next page OUO1082,0002C7A -19-16OCT12-1/2

OPERATION AFTER THE DISTRIBUTOR POINTS OPEN

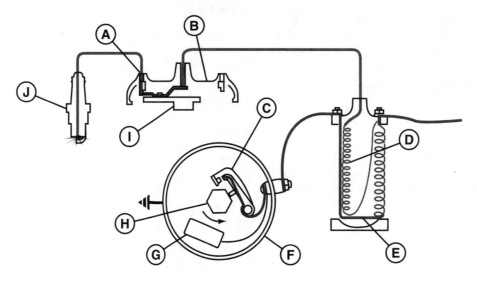

Fig. 3 — Operation After the Distributor Points Open

A—Spark Plug Terminal
B—Distributor Cap

C—Contact Points (Open)
D—Secondary Winding

E—Coil
F—Distributor
G—Condenser
H—Breaker Cam

I— Rotor
J—Spark Plug

As the engine rotates in starting, it drives the distributor shaft and the breaker cam.

When the breaker cam opens the distributor points, the second phase of ignition begins (Fig. 3).

As the points open, the flow of primary current is stopped instantly. Stopping this flow of current allows the magnetic field built up around the windings to collapse instantly. This field collapse creates an induced voltage that causes current to flow in both the primary and secondary windings.

The surge of induced voltage in the primary winding is absorbed by the condenser.

The magnetic field collapsing around the secondary winding induces voltage that causes current to flow. Because the secondary winding is composed of many more turns of much finer wire than the primary winding, a much higher voltage is induced—from 4000 to 20,000 volts.

This surge of high voltage "pushes" current through the secondary winding and the high-tension terminal into the distributor cap.

The rotor inside the distributor cap turns to a spark plug terminal and directs the voltage surge to the correct plug through insulated cables.

At the spark plug, current flows down the center electrode, jumps the gap, and creates the spark.

NOTE: *In a "bypass" ignition system (Fig. 1), there are two primary leads from switch to coil. When the switch is turned to start, full battery voltage flows through the light gray dotted "bypass" line, resulting in a hotter spark for first ignition. When the ignition switch is released, primary current flows through the solid line and resistor to the coil. In a 12-volt system, the resistor reduces voltage by half and allows use of a 6-volt coil. The reduced primary voltage gives longer life to the distributor points, condenser, and coil because of less heat.*

Now that we know the basic operation of the ignition circuit, let's see how each component works.

OUO1082,0002C7A -19-16OCT12-2/2

IGNITION COIL

You have already seen the three main parts of the ignition coil, the primary and secondary windings, and the high-tension terminal. Now let's see how these parts of the coil induce the high voltage surge.

The center of the coil is a soft iron core (Fig. 4). The secondary winding of fine wire is wrapped around this core. One end of the secondary winding is connected to the high-tension terminal, the other end to the primary winding.

The primary winding of heavy wire is wrapped around the secondary winding. The two ends of the primary winding are attached to the primary terminals in the coil cap. One of these terminals is connected to the power source; the other is connected to the distributor points.

A shell of laminated material is placed around the windings and core as shown. The core, windings, and shell are then encased in a metal container. The container is filled with either oil or insulating material and hermetically sealed with the coil cap.

The cap is made of a molded insulating material with the two primary terminals and one high-tension terminal molded into it.

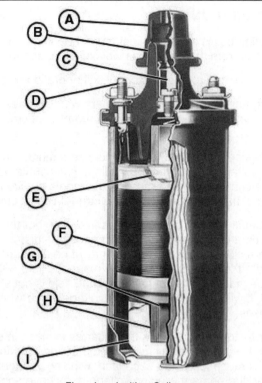

Fig. 4 — Ignition Coil

DXP03184 —UN—07MAR12

A—Sealing Nipple
B—Coil Cap
C—High-Tension Terminal
D—Primary Terminal
E—Secondary Winding
F—Primary Winding
G—Iron Core
H—Lamination
I— Porcelain Insulator

Continued on next page   OUO1082,0002C7B -19-10JAN12-1/5

COIL OPERATION

The ignition coil is a pulse transformer that steps up the low voltage from the battery, as we explained above.

Let's discuss some other factors of coil operation (Fig. 5).

The magnetic field around the primary winding does not reach its full potential at once. A moment of time is needed to build up the field strength.

This is because the field buildup induces a momentary counter voltage in the primary winding. The countervailed opposes current flow and must be overcome by circuit voltage so that current flow and field strength can increase.

Only a small fraction of a second is involved, but this buildup time is important. At high speeds, the distributor points are closed for a very short time. If no allowances are made, the current flow and the magnetic field will never reach their full potential. Since the field is not strong enough, it will never induce a high voltage surge when it collapses.

Another factor to consider is the voltages induced in the winding. We have already mentioned that primary winding voltage is much less than secondary winding voltage. However, the primary winding voltage does have some effect. It is absorbed by the condenser, and thus collapses the magnetic field faster.

Voltage in the secondary winding may go as high as 20,000 volts. However, it will go only as high as needed to cause the current to jump the spark plug gap.

Jumping the gap creates another reaction that helps in ignition operation. By jumping the gap, the secondary circuit is completed. Then a magnetic field is created around the secondary winding. This field partly stops the field collapse around the primary winding. The voltage induced by the primary winding field in the secondary winding helps sustain the spark for a short period of time.

TESTING THE COIL

Many electrical system problems can be caused by more than one failing component. In the ignition circuit, it is even harder to find a failure because faulty parts are not the only causes that must be considered.

If the ignition coil is faulty, expect some of the following problems:

- The engine will not start.

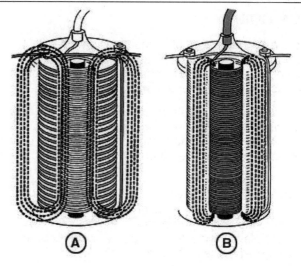

Fig. 5 — Coil Operation

A—Primary Winding Operation   B—Secondary Winding Operation

- The engine is hard to start.
- The engine misfires on a warm, humid day.
- The engine suddenly stops.

Of course, some of these problems can be caused by other failures in places other than the coil.

COIL TESTS

1. Make a visual check of the ignition circuit to find broken leads, broken or loose connections, or possible cracks or broken components.

2. Make a complete electrical check of the circuit to isolate the faulty component.

COIL POLARITY

Wrong polarity of the coil is not a serious problem, but it can cause damage over a long period of time. A coil that is wrongly connected to the power source and the distributor will require an extra 4000 to 8000 volts to create the spark.

The wrong coil polarity makes the center electrode of the spark plugs have the wrong polarity. This can cause misfiring as the voltage required to jump the spark gap increases.

Continued on next page   OUO1082,0002C7B -19-10JAN12-2/5

Fig. 6 illustrates the proper coil connections.

On negative-ground systems, the negative primary terminal is connected to the distributor.

On positive-ground systems, the positive primary terminal is connected to the distributor.

Most coils have the polarity signs imprinted in the cap by each terminal.

ELECTRICAL TESTS ON THE COIL

Most well-equipped shops have an electrical service tester that can be used to test many of the ignition circuit components. When testing the coil with one of these testers, follow the recommended test procedures.

Basically, the ignition coil is tested for its voltage strength. Two methods are generally used:

• The Spark Gap Tester Method
• The Meter Tester Method

Testing Coil With Spark Gap Tester

The spark gap tester is connected into the ignition circuit, usually off the high-tension terminal of the coil. When the distributor points open, a spark jumps a gap in the tester. This gap is adjustable. In this way, the distance the spark is able to jump determines the strength of the coil voltage.

When using this tester, you must have a good coil for a comparison. Both the good coil and the coil being tested must be of the same temperature and use identical test leads.

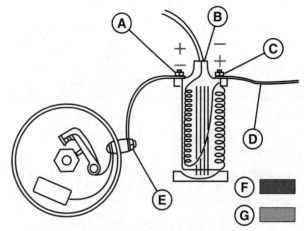

Fig. 6 — Correct Coil Polarity

A—Coil Primary Terminal
B—High-Tension Terminal
C—Primary Terminal
D—To Ignition Switch
E—Distributor Primary
   Terminal
F—Negative-Ground System
G—Positive-Ground System

With the spark gap tester, many variables enter into the test results. These include altitude, temperature, and atmospheric conditions.

Because the test procedures differ between the different models of this tester, follow the manufacturer's recommendations.

OUO1082,0002C7B -19-10JAN12-3/5

Testing Coil With Meter-Type Coil Tester

This type of tester may be part of an electrical service or just a single unit (Fig. 7). It may also be capable of testing the condenser for shorted, open, or grounded coil windings.

The tester uses a graded meter to show the condition of the coil. The meter may have two scales—one scale marked "Bad, Fair, Good"; the other scale marked in numbers from 1 to 10. The "10" side of one scale usually corresponds with the "Good" range in the other scale.

For each model of meter tester, follow the tester's instructions.

NOTE: *Of the two types of testers, the meter-type coil tester is more accurate because it is not affected by other variables.*

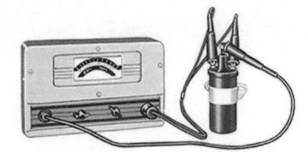

Fig. 7 — Meter-Type Coil Tester

Continued on next page OUO1082,0002C7B -19-10JAN12-4/5

TESTING COIL FOR GROUNDED WINDINGS

To test the windings, a test lamp and probes are used (Fig. 8).

To find a grounded primary or secondary winding, place one of the probes on a clean part of the coil case. Place the other probe on the primary terminal or the high-tension terminal as shown in Fig. 8.

If the lamp lights or a spark appears on contact, the windings are grounded.

On some insulated or two-wire systems, this test doesn't apply to the secondary winding. However, the test can always be used on the primary windings.

TESTING COIL FOR OPEN WINDINGS

To test for an open primary winding, place the test lamp probes on the two primary terminals (Fig. 8).

If the lamp does not light, the winding is open.

To test for an open secondary winding, place one probe on the high-tension terminal and the other probe on the primary terminal. Rub the probes over the terminals.

No sparking indicates an open winding. If the windings are okay, a light sparking should occur but the lamp will not light.

SERVICING THE COIL

The only service required on the coil is to keep the terminals and connections clean and tight. The coil itself should also be kept reasonably clean.

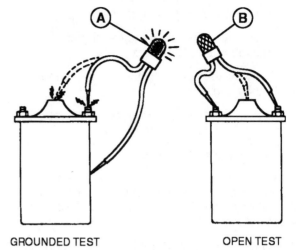

GROUNDED TEST   OPEN TEST

Fig. 8 — Testing Coil for Grounded or Open Windings

A—Lamp Lights Up =
Grounded Winding

B—Lamp Not Lit = Open
Winding

A rubber boot on the high-voltage terminal helps in preventing "tracing" or leakage of current across the exposed surfaces.

A coil cannot be repaired. If it is cracked or has bad wiring, replace the coil. A crack in the coil tower breaks the hermetic seal and allows moisture to enter the coil.

OUO1082,0002C7B -19-10JAN12-5/5

IGNITION CONDENSER

The condenser prevents arcing at the distributor points when they begin to open.

Excess current flows into the condenser as the points separate.

The coil is controlled by the opening and closing of the distributor points. However, the points cannot do this job alone because:

- The points open and close mechanically, a fairly slow action.
- The points open only a short distance.
- Voltage within the coil can become very high.

Without a condenser, what happens is this:

- Induced voltage in the coil primary gets too high and pushes current across the gap—burning the points.
- Current flow does not stop quick enough, and the field collapses too slowly. So the secondary voltage is too low and no high-voltage surge is produced to fire the spark plug.

The condenser helps eliminate both of these problems by absorbing the arc current, thus helping to induce a higher voltage for the spark plugs.

CONDENSER CONSTRUCTION

The condenser (Fig. 9) is mounted in the distributor and is connected across the points.

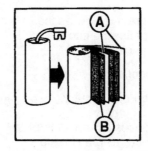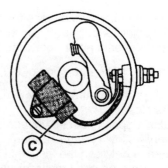

Fig. 9 — Condenser Installed in Distributor

A—Foil   C—Condenser
B—Insulation

The condenser is made up of two foil plates that are insulated from each other with a special paper. The plates and the paper are wrapped around an arbor to form a winding. Each plate has a wiring lead—one connected to the condenser case and the other connected to the main wiring lead. The whole assembly may be encased in metal or epoxy.

Continued on next page OUO1082,0002C7C -19-10JAN12-1/2

CONDENSER OPERATION

The condenser provides a place for current to flow as the distributor points separate. This current flowing into the condenser prevents an arc between the points.

Fig. 10 explains the operation of the condenser.

1. Steady, straight current flow through coil primary, points closed.
2. As points open, induced voltage causes current in the primary to flow into the condenser, creating a voltage difference between the insulated foil sheets.
3. High charge on condenser foil sheet forces current back through coil primary, collapsing magnetic field faster and creating a hotter spark.
4. Drained condenser foil sheets now have lower voltage charge than adjacent grounded sheets, so current flow again reverses as shown until all coil energy is used up.

The condenser holds only a limited amount of current. It fills up or is "charged" very quickly. This stops the current flow in the primary winding. Then the field around the winding collapses, inducing voltage in both the primary and secondary windings. The greatest voltage, of course, is induced in the secondary winding.

The voltage induced in the primary winding causes a current to flow in the primary winding. This current also helps to charge the condenser, which creates still more opposition to current flow, producing a further collapse of the field and high voltage.

The voltage keeps on rising to try to force the current to flow. But by this time the points are far enough apart so that the voltage never "pushes" current across the gap.

All arcing is not eliminated, however. In spite of the condenser, arcing does occur during the first millionth of a second that the points separate. But it is a small spark much like the one produced when a wiring connector is pulled apart.

TROUBLESHOOTING THE CONDENSER

Listed below are the problems that can be caused by a faulty condenser.

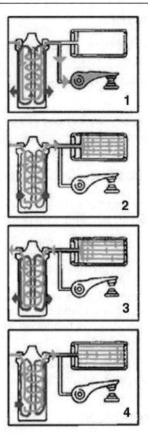

Fig. 10 — Operation of the Condenser

Table 1 — Troubleshooting the Condenser	
Problem	**Cause**
Engine cranks, but won't start	Faulty condenser
Engine runs, but misses on all cylinders	Faulty condenser
Pitted distributor points	Wrong-capacity condenser
Burned distributor points	High resistance in the condenser

Remember that some of these problems may be caused by other faulty components. Only a complete circuit check will finally pinpoint the cause of the problem.

REPAIRING THE CONDENSER

The condenser is not repairable. If it fails, replace it.

OUO1082,0002C7C -19-10JAN12-2/2

DXP03190 —UN—07MAR12

IGNITION DISTRIBUTOR

The distributor (Fig. 11) does three jobs:

• Opens and closes the primary circuit
• Times the high-voltage surges
• Delivers current to the spark plugs

A—Coil   B—Reference Mark

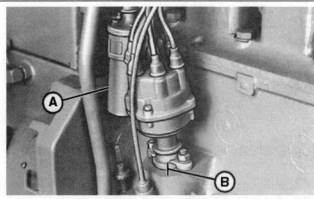

Fig. 11 — Ignition Distributor

Continued on next page   OUO1082,0002C7D -19-13JUL12-1/15

Fig. 12 shows the parts of the distributor. We can put all the distributor parts into three groups:

Primary Circuit Operation	Timing	Delivery
• Drive Shaft	• Drive Shaft	• Drive Shaft
• Breaker Cam	• Breaker Cam	• Rotor
• Breaker Plate	• Centrifugal Advance	• Cap
• Contact Points	• Contact Points	

Let's see what each of these distributor parts does and then we'll see how they all operate.

DRIVE SHAFT—The engine camshaft drives the distributor drive shaft—at one-half engine speed—which drives the centrifugal advance mechanism, the breaker cam, and the rotor.

BREAKER CAM—Slip-mounted on the drive shaft and pinned to the centrifugal advance. As you can see in Fig. 12, the cam has lobes or corners—one for each engine cylinder. As the cam rotates, each lobe pushes against the contact point breaker lever, opening the contact points.

BREAKER PLATE—A mounting for the contact points and condenser. It also has a terminal that connects the points and condenser into the primary circuit.

CONTACT POINTS ASSEMBLY—Two contact points, a breaker lever, and a breaker lever spring. All three are mounted on a base that is attached to the breaker plate. The two points are usually made of tungsten. One is fixed to the base. The other is attached to the breaker lever and aligned with the first. The breaker lever is mounted on a pivot pin to the assembly base. The lever is made of metal with a nylon or bakelite rubbing block that contacts the breaker cam lobes. The breaker lever spring is attached to the breaker lever. The spring holds the lever to the cam after each cam lobe passes the rubbing block.

ROTOR—Mounted on the upper part of the breaker cam. A flat side of the rotor hub fits on a flat side of the cam. In this way the rotor will fit in only one position. On the top of the rotor, a spring metal piece is in contact with the center terminal of the distributor cap. A rigid piece completes the circuit to each spark plug terminal in the cap as the

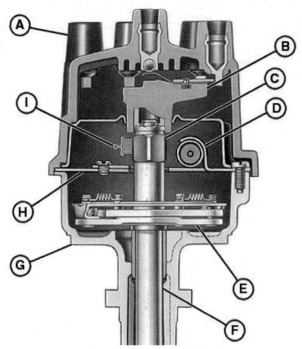

Fig. 12 — Cutaway of Distributor

A—Cap	F—Drive Shaft
B—Rotor	G—Housing
C—Cam	H—Breaker Plate
D—Condenser	I— Breaker Lever
E—Advance Mechanism	

rotor turns. The rotor itself is molded of a plastic material, which makes it a good insulator.

DISTRIBUTOR CAP—Molded of a plastic material. Metal inserts are embedded in the cap. These contacts are equally spaced around the cap and lead to the spark plug terminals in the top of the cap. A carbon button in the center of the cap contacts the rotor and leads to the center high-voltage terminal in the top of the cap. The cap is notched into the housing to prevent a wrong installation.

Later we will cover another feature of the distributor—the advance mechanism.

Continued on next page OUO1082,0002C7D -19-13JUL12-2/15

DISTRIBUTOR OPERATION

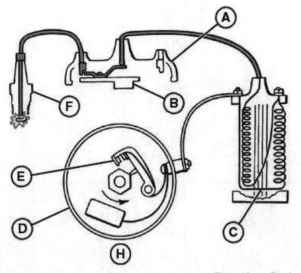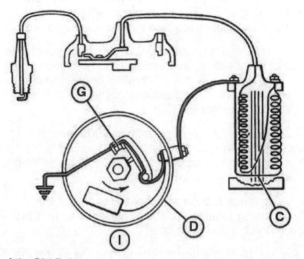

Fig. 13 — Basic Operation of the Distributor

A—Cap
B—Rotor
C—Coil
D—Distributor

E—Points-Open
F—Spark Plug
G—Points-Closed

H—Points Open
I— Points Closed

As the drive shaft turns, the breaker cam lobe pushes the breaker lever rubbing block. This action opens the contact points, stopping the current flow in the coil primary circuit. See at left in Fig. 13.

The collapsing field and the resulting high-voltage surge in the coil's secondary winding forces current into the center terminal of the distributor cap. The distributor rotor picks up this current and delivers it to the proper spark plug to fire the engine.

Meanwhile, the distributor cam lobe has moved away from the rubbing block and spring tension brings the points back into contact (see at right in Fig. 13). The primary circuit is again complete and current flows until the next lobe opens the points. The cycle then repeats itself.

In this way a spark is created as each lobe of the cam opens the contact points. The entire cycle for each spark takes place at a very high speed.

OUO1082,0002C7D -19-13JUL12-3/15

CENTRIFUGAL ADVANCE MECHANISM

Basically, an advance mechanism (Fig. 14) is a device that advances the spark timing in relation to engine speed or load. Why is a spark advance necessary?

The distributor must deliver the spark to the engine when it is most effective. This is determined by the position of the piston and the time required to ignite the fuel-air mixture in the cylinder.

A—Cam
B—Advance Weight

C—Primary Lead
D—Weight Spring

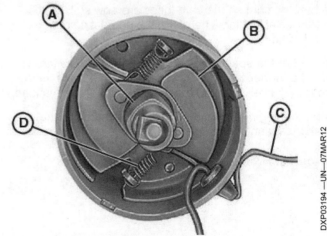

Fig. 14 — Centrifugal Advance Mechanisms

Continued on next page   OUO1082,0002C7D -19-13JUL12-4/15

Let's assume that the engine piston must be at 12 degrees after top dead center (ATDC) to get the full force from combustion (Fig. 15). The 12 degrees after top dead center stays the same regardless of the engine speed.

Let's also assume that it takes 0.002 second to reach the full force of combustion, and that at 1000 revolutions per minute (rpm) the piston would travel 16 degrees during this time. Therefore, the spark must come at 4 degrees before top dead center (BTDC).

Now if we double the engine speed to 2000 rpm, the distance the piston would travel is also doubled to 32 degrees. The spark must then occur at 20 degrees before top dead center to get maximum power.

What the advance mechanism does is to adjust the distributor timing to allow for speed changes so that the spark will occur at the right time.

The most popular advance mechanism is the centrifugal advance. This device has two weights, a weight base, and two springs.

The weight base is part of the distributor drive shaft. The springs are connected to the base, while the weights are placed on the base. The distributor breaker cam has two pins that connect it to the springs and weights. The pins also sit in slots in the base.

At idle speeds the breaker cam is "pinned" to the base and rotates with the drive shaft. The cam lobes then open the points at a preset time—such as 4 degrees before top dead center (BTDC).

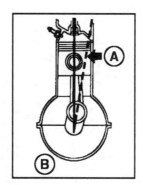

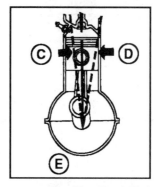
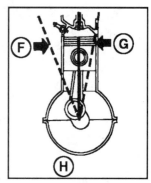

Fig. 15 — Spark Timing of the Engine Combustion

A—12° ATDC
B—Idle
C—Spark @ 4° BTDC
D—12° ATDC

E—1000 RPM
F—Spark @ 20° BTDC
G—12° ATDC
H—2000 RPM

OUO1082,0002C7D -19-13JUL12-5/15

As the engine speeds up, centrifugal force throws the weights out against spring tension (Fig. 16). This turns the breaker cam so the cam lobes are now striking the breaker lever earlier. Therefore, the contact points open ahead of time.

The higher the speed, the farther the weights are thrown out. The farther the weights are thrown, the more they turn the breaker cam and the more the spark is advanced.

When the engine slows down, the springs return the breaker cam and weights to their original position.

A—No Advance   B—Full Advance

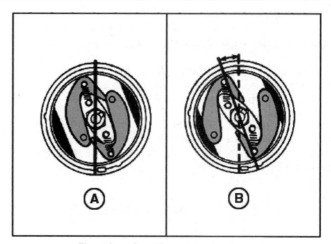

Fig. 16 — Centrifugal Advance Operation

Continued on next page   OUO1082,0002C7D -19-13JUL12-6/15

VACUUM ADVANCE MECHANISM

For greater fuel economy, an extra advance mechanism is used on some distributors. This is the vacuum advance (Fig. 17).

A vacuum develops in the engine intake manifold, allowing less fuel into the cylinder. Because a lean fuel mixture will burn slower, ignition must take place sooner in the cycle than the centrifugal advance can provide. So a vacuum advance is used to advance the spark still further.

The vacuum advance uses an airtight diaphragm connected to a manifold vacuum port (Fig. 17). The diaphragm is connected by linkage to the distributor housing or the breaker plate.

When a vacuum at the intake manifold draws air from the diaphragm chamber, it causes the diaphragm to rotate the distributor breaker plate in the opposite direction of drive shaft rotation. This moves the breaker lever to contact the breaker cam lobes sooner and thus advances the spark.

EXTRA-DUTY FEATURES OF DISTRIBUTORS

There are extra design features that can be added to a distributor. They may provide a needed service or can increase the reliability. The following is a list of these features:

- Screw-type distributor cap terminals
- Distributor caps and rotors made of mica
- Built-in distributor shaft lubrication

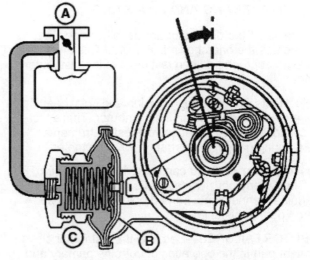

Fig. 17 — Vacuum Advance Mechanism

A—Carburetor   C—Vacuum Advance
B—Diaphragm

- Flexible shock-absorbing drive gears
- Breaker cam lubricator
- Tungsten-tipped rotor
- Heavy-duty contact points
- Dust sealing cover on breaker compartment
- Elastic terminal nipples

Continued on next page   OUO1082,0002C7D -19-13JUL12-7/15

DISTRIBUTOR TESTING AND ADJUSTING

Electrical tests on the distributor are usually made with a tester such as the one shown in Fig. 18. This unit is called a synchrograph and can test most of the distributor operations.

Mechanical tests such as spring tension and point opening distance are also performed on the distributor. These tests usually call for the use of mechanical test instruments such as a spring gauge, feeler gauge, or micrometer.

The most important test you can make is a good visual check. Often many physical failures such as cracks, loose terminal connections, burned points, etc., will be discovered during this check.

DISTRIBUTOR FAILURES—Because the distributor plays an important part in the operation of both the primary and secondary circuits, any distributor failure will directly affect the ignition circuit and engine operation.

CHECKING DISTRIBUTOR CAPS—A visual check is usually the only test performed on the cap.

First, wipe the distributor cap clean. Never clean the cap with a degreasing solution.

Check the cap for the following:

• Carbon Paths
• Cracks and Chips
• Eroded Spark Plug Contacts

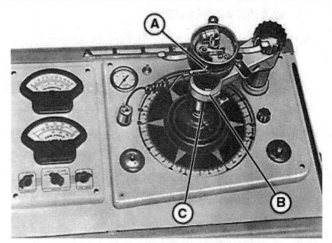

Fig. 18 — Distributor Tester

A—Primary Insulated Terminal   C—Flexible Drive Coupling
B—Split Bushing

• Worn Center Terminal Carbon Button

Let's discuss these failures of the cap.

CARBON PATHS—Carbon paths are burnt areas on the distributor cap. Since carbon is a conductor, these burnt areas provide an easy path for current leakage between terminals or between the terminals and ground.

Continued on next page   OUO1082,0002C7D -19-13JUL12-8/15

Carbon paths can be formed on the outside of the cap by an accumulation of dirt (Fig. 19). Dirt will retain moisture and thus conduct a current. Current leakage, usually from the center terminal to a retaining clip, will create a carbon path. Once the path is formed, it will continue to conduct current.

Carbon paths inside the cap are usually found between the spark plug terminals or between the terminals and a grounded surface. They are caused by moisture and arcing in the cap.

A distributor cap with a carbon path must be replaced. This is because the path will continue to conduct current, especially in damp weather. Eventually, it will burn through the cap.

Cracks And Chips

Cracks and chips allow moisture and dirt into the cap and breaker lever area. Carbon paths as well as burnt points, breaker cam lobe wear, and arcing can be caused by this. Caps with cracks or chips must also be discarded.

Terminal Erosion

Spark plug insert terminals that are eroded will widen the gap between the rotor and the inserts. As the gap increases, secondary voltage requirements also increase, resulting in poor engine performance, overloading, and ultimate failure of the coil. These gaps also promote arcing and resulting carbon paths. A cap with eroded inserts must also be replaced.

SERVICING THE DISTRIBUTOR CAP—The distributor cap should be kept clean. The wiring leads should fit tight in the terminals. The use of elastic nipples over the center terminal and spark plug terminals can reduce some of the problems of dirt and moisture.

DISTRIBUTOR ROTOR CHECKS—The rotor should be checked for cracks or chips and for erosion on the tip of the rigid contact.

Check the rotor spring contact for proper tension against the distributor cap carbon button. Too little tension can create a gap between the contact and button. Too much tension can cause excessive wear. Be careful when bending the spring to adjust the pressure.

Always replace a chipped or cracked rotor.

DISTRIBUTOR BREAKER CAM CHECK—Check the cam lobes periodically for excessive wear and lack of lubrication. Worn lobes will not open the points enough to create a strong spark.

The lobes can be checked visually. However, the syncrograph is the best way to check for cam wear.

The point openings as caused by the breaker cam should be evenly spaced within plus or minus one degree. For example, a four-lobe cam should open the points every 90 degrees, a six-lobe cam every 60 degrees, etc.

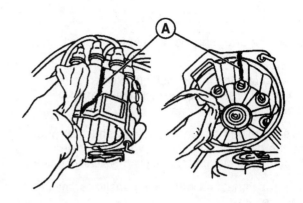

Fig. 19 — Carbon Paths on Distributor Caps

A—Carbon Paths

Wear on the cam is usually caused by abrasive material such as dirt in the breaker plate area. Replace an excessively worn cam.

CENTRIFUGAL ADVANCE CHECKS—The centrifugal advance should turn freely. Check this by turning the breaker cam in the direction of rotation and then releasing it. The advance springs should return the cam to its original position without sticking.

Use a distributor tester to check the centrifugal advance operation.

1. Set the distributor into the tester and drive it at various specified speeds.

2. At each test speed, note the amount of advance. It should be within plus or minus one degree of specifications.

3. When the highest specified speed is reached, speed up for a moment, then return to zero.

4. While returning the speed to zero, check each test speed again. The centrifugal advance should be the same.

5. If the advance is excessive during both acceleration and deceleration, either the advance springs are too weak or the wrong springs are installed.

6. If the advance is too little during both acceleration and deceleration, the springs are too tight.

7. If the advance is slow during acceleration but fast during deceleration, the advance weights are sticking.

8. In any case, new springs may be needed or the weights may need cleaning and a light oiling to free them. On some distributors, spring tension can be adjusted by bending the outer spring support.

Continued on next page   OUO1082,0002C7D -19-13JUL12-9/15

DISTRIBUTOR DRIVE SHAFT CHECKS

If you suspect the drive shaft is worn or misaligned, check for:

- A worn carbon button in the distributor cap
- One side of the breaker cam excessively worn
- Engine misfiring

Check the shaft alignment on a syncrograph tester (Fig. 20). While the distributor is driven by the tester at a specified speed, the distributor case is physically shaken.

If the test shows variations in the firing positions, the shaft or bushings are worn.

TESTING AND ADJUSTMENT OF DISTRIBUTOR CONTACT POINTS

The contact points are the key to good timing.

Check the contact points assembly for these things:

- Pitted Contact Points
- Burned Points
- Worn Rubbing Block
- Alignment of Points
- Worn Breaker Plate Pivot Post
- Tension of Breaker Lever Spring
- Gap of Contact Points
- Cam Angle (Dwell)

PITTED CONTACT POINTS—A visual inspection will usually reveal pitted or rough contact points. However, points in this condition are not necessarily worn.

During normal operation, material may transfer from one point to another. The transferred material will appear rough and gray in color. However, the points will have a greater contact area than when they were new. For this reason, don't replace the points until the buildup is over 0.020 inch (0.5 mm).

Sometimes pitted points can be reconditioned by removing them and honing each surface smooth and flat. You need not remove all the pits. To clean the points, use a few drops of lighter fluid on a strip of lint-free cloth. Then pull a dry strip through the points to remove the residue. BE CAREFUL when using lighter fluid. Do not use emery cloth or sandpaper to clean the points.

During a tune-up, however, replace pitted points to ensure good operation.

BURNED CONTACT POINTS—Burned points are usually caused by either high voltage, oil deposits, foreign material, a defective condenser, or improper point adjustment.

High voltage causes a high current flow through the points. This heats up the points and rapidly burns them.

Fig. 20 — Checking the Distributor Drive Shaft

Oil or crankcase vapors can seep up through the distributor and deposit on the points, causing them to burn. Look for a smudgy oil line beneath the points.

If the point opening gap is too small, the points will be closed for too long. Then even an average current flow through the points will be too high, burning the points.

WORN RUBBING BLOCK—Rubbing block wear is not a usual cause of trouble. Normally the contact points will wear out before the rubbing block wears enough to affect operation.

In some extreme cases, abrasive foreign material has caused rubbing block wear.

ALIGNMENT OF POINTS—To see if the contact points are aligned, use a distributor tester. With the distributor operating at 1000 rpm, you should be able to see a slight arc between the points.

If the points are aligned, the arc will appear in the *center* of the points when seen from above and from the side.

WORN BREAKER PLATE PIVOT POST—If this pivot post is loose or worn, replace the breaker plate. A worn or loose post will cause the rubbing block and breaker lever to ride erratically on the breaker cam. (On some distributors, the pivot post is part of the contact point assembly. Replace this assembly if the post is loose or worn).

Continued on next page   OUO1082,0002C7D -19-13JUL12-10/15

TENSION OF BREAKER LEVER SPRING—

Spring tension can be tested with the distributor on or off the distributor tester.

Use a tension tester placed on the movable point and pull it at right angles to the breaker lever (Fig. 21). The instant the points separate, note the reading on the tester.

Since the distributor tester can "show" the instant the points separate, using it will aid in this test.

Proper breaker spring tension is important. Excessive tension can cause the rubbing block, breaker cam, and contact point to wear. Too little tension can allow the points to bounce at high speeds, causing arcing, burned points, and engine misfire.

A—Spring Attaching Screw

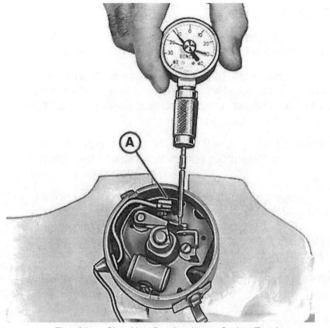

Fig. 21 — Checking Breaker Lever Spring Tension

OUO1082,0002C7D -19-13JUL12-11/15

Adjust the breaker spring by bending it toward the breaker lever (to decrease tension) or away from the lever (to increase tension) (Fig. 22). Some springs can also be adjusted by sliding the spring in or out under the attaching screw.

Fig. 22 — Adjusting Tension of Breaker Lever Spring

Continued on next page

OUO1082,0002C7D -19-13JUL12-12/15

CONTACT POINT GAP—

The distance the points open and the length of time that they stay open are important in distributor operation.

Too wide a point gap will cause the points to open sooner and stay open longer. This situation will limit buildup time in the coil, and the coil will not produce enough voltage for a spark at high speed.

Too narrow a point gap will allow the points to be closed longer, causing the rubbing block to wear and the points to burn.

A feeler gauge can be used to set the gap on new points. However, old points that are serviceable but are also pitted should not be set with a feeler gauge. The gauge will only measure the high spots on the points and so will not give a true picture of the gap.

Therefore, to check old contact points, use a dial indicator (Fig. 23).

Fig. 23 — Checking Contact Point Gap

Continued on next page

OUO1082,0002C7D -19-13JUL12-13/15

CAM ANGLE (Dwell)—

The cam angle is the number of degrees that the breaker cam rotates from the time the points close until they open again (Fig. 24). As the cam angle increases, the point gap decreases, and vice versa.

Too little cam angle can cause engine to misfire at high speed.

Too much cam angle allows the points to close for too long, causing burned points.

Use the dwell meter on the distributor tester to check the cam angle. Then adjust the points to the specified dwell angle.

If the cam angle reading on the meter varies more than two degrees, look for a bent distributor drive shaft or worn distributor bushings.

If the cam angle and point gap cannot both be set to specifications at the same time, check for these problems:

• Improper spring tension
• Wrong contact point assembly
• Worn breaker cam
• Points not following cam at high speeds
• Bent drive shaft

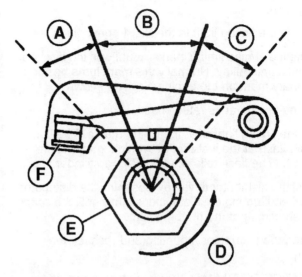

Fig. 24 — Cam Angle (Dwell)

A—Points Open
B—Points Closed (Cam Angle)
C—Points Open
D—Direction of Rotation
E—Cam
F—Points

SERVICING THE DISTRIBUTOR

This section will give you a general idea of the services that the distributor may require.

In all disassembly, repair, testing, and servicing, follow the machine technical manual or the manufacturer's recommendations.

1. Disassemble the distributor only as far as necessary to make repairs or tests.

2. When removing the distributor from the engine, set the No. 1 cylinder at top dead center (TDC) at the end of the compression stroke. Mark the rotor position on the distributor housing and drive gear. This step will allow you to turn the crankshaft while the distributor is off the engine.

3. If necessary, clean or hone the contact points. (See earlier under "Pitted Contact Points") Do not use emery cloth or sandpaper to clean the points. Abrasive material will embed in the points, causing them to arc and burn.

4. Some breaker cams are self-lubricated. Others require a light coating of cam lubricant on the hubs.

5. Some distributors require a few drops of light engine oil on the pivot post at certain intervals.

6. Avoid too much lubrication of the distributor. Excess oil may get on the contact points, causing them to burn.

TIMING THE DISTRIBUTOR

After service, the distributor must be timed or "geared" to the engine.

Good timing ensures that a spark will occur when it will do the most good during the compression stroke of the piston.

The centrifugal advance has already been set to ensure a spark at various speeds. Now we must time the basic spark without the advance mechanism.

There is no hard and fast rule on when this spark should occur. It depends upon the engine design and specifications. It might have to occur before top dead center, at top dead center, or even after top dead center.

Continued on next page OUO1082,0002C7D -19-13JUL12-14/15

The best method of timing the distributor is with a timing light (Fig. 25).

1. Connect the timing light to the No. 1 spark plug wire.

2. Locate the engine timing marks, usually on the flywheel or crankshaft pulley. Normally this mark turns beside a stationary mark on the engine block as shown.

3. Run the engine at its rated speed.

4. Hold the timing light over the timing marks. The light should flash at the instant the two timing marks are aligned. (The flash tells when the No. 1 cylinder fires.)

5. Adjust the distributor timing by loosening the distributor mount and turning the distributor slightly until the spark or flash occurs at the right moment.

6. Tighten the distributor mounting and recheck the timing.

IMPORTANCE OF TIMING—Improper timing can affect engine performance in several ways.

For example, if the spark occurs a little late, a distinct loss of power will result. In this case, the piston has traveled partway on its downward power stroke without the aid of the combustion force. Part of the combustion power is then lost and the engine may also overheat.

However, a late spark is not as bad as an advance spark. When the spark occurs too soon, it ignites the fuel-air mixture, resulting in a combustion force. But the combustion power then opposes the upward travel of the piston, causing a knocking or "pinging" sound. This sound means that great force is being placed on the piston, pins, rings, and connecting rods as it tries to overcome the power of combustion.

If you have an advance spark while using a low-octane fuel, another problem occurs. Normally, the spark ignites

Fig. 25 — Timing the Distributor with a Timing Light

A—"S" Mark
B—Timing Mark

C—Distributor Clamp
   Loosened

the fuel around the spark plug and the resulting flame travels across the combustion chamber. With low-octane fuel, part of the fuel is ignited by the advance spark and part of it is ignited by compression heat on the other side of the chamber. The two resulting combustion forces meet head-on and a sharp "ping" is heard. This force can be strong enough to punch a hole through the piston head. With low-octane fuels, the timing should be retarded to prevent "knocking" and pinging".

IMPORTANT: Improper timing can cause loss of power and damage to engine parts.

OUO1082,0002C7D -19-13JUL12-15/15

SPARK PLUGS

The spark plug ignites the fuel-air mixture in the engine cylinder.

We have learned that there is no current flow in an open circuit. In most cases this is true. However, if the opening in the circuit is small and a strong voltage is present, the circuit can still be completed. In this case, the strong voltage is able to force the current to jump the opening or gap, thus completing the circuit. This is the principle of the spark plug.

SPARK PLUG OPERATION

The plug has two conductors, or electrodes. One is connected by wire to the distributor cap and the other is connected to ground. The other end of each electrode is separated by a small opening or gap from the other.

The high-voltage surge induced in the coil causes a current to flow from the coil to the distributor cap and through a cable to one of the spark plug electrodes. This current then jumps the gap to the other electrode and on to ground. By jumping the gap, the current has completed the circuit and continues to flow.

Completing the circuit is of secondary importance, however. The important fact is that when the current jumps the gap, a spark is created. This is the final goal of the ignition circuit.

After all the ignition action, the current jumping the gap to create the spark seems rather simple. However, creating a controlled spark is a different story, and this story is told in the construction of the spark plug.

SPARK PLUG CONSTRUCTION

Although the spark plug has no moving parts, each of its parts is designed for a specific purpose. For this reason, many types of spark plugs are available.

Fig. 26 shows the parts of a typical spark plug. Basically, all spark plugs have the same parts and only the design is different. Let's look at the parts of the spark plug.

OUTER SHELL—Each spark plug has a steel outer shell. The top of the shell is hex-shaped for tightening the plug when installing it. The lower part of the shell is threaded and screws into the cylinder head. The grounded electrode extends out from the lower part of the shell.

A gasket slips over the threaded portion of the plug and rests against the flange at the bottom of the upper part of the shell. The gasket serves two purposes—it seals the plug against compression loss and provides a path for the transfer of heat to the cooling system.

A gasket is not always used. Some spark plugs use a tapered seat instead of a flat flange with gasket.

The distance from the flange to the end of the plug threads is called the reach (Fig. 26). The reach of a spark plug is very important in plug selection. A spark plug with

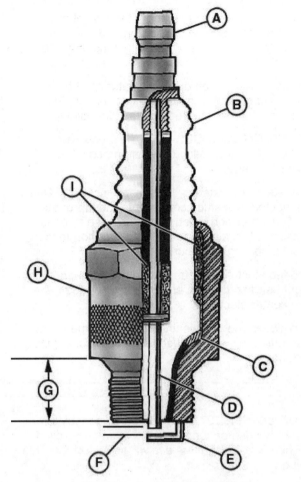

Fig. 26 — Spark Plug Construction

A—Terminal	F—Spark Gap
B—Insulator	G—"Reach"
C—Gasket	H—Steel Outer Shell
D—Center Electrode	I— Sealing Material
E—Ground Electrode	

a reach longer than specified will extend too far into the combustion area. Not only will the plug run hotter, but it also can be damaged when hit by a piston or valve. A plug with a reach shorter than specified will run cold and cause misfiring due to fouled electrodes.

The thread diameter may vary according to the size of the spark plug hole in the cylinder head.

The engine Technical Manual can give you the exact spark plug specifications for each engine.

SPARK PLUG INSULATOR—The insulated core, or insulator, is mounted in the outer shell. The outer end carries the spark plug terminal. The core is usually made of such insulating materials as white ceramic or porcelain.

The insulator is held in position and shielded from the outer shell by an inside gasket and sealing compound (Fig. 26).

Continued on next page

OUO1082,0002C7E -19-12JUL12-1/16

110112
PN=323

Besides holding the center electrode, the insulator is a shield for the electrode so that current will flow only through the electrode. It must also withstand extreme heat and cooling and vibrations.

The exposed upper portion of the insulator must be kept clean to prevent current from leaking out. Many plugs have ribbed insulators to discourage this dirt buildup.

SPARK PLUG ELECTRODES—The electrodes are usually made of a metal alloy to withstand constant burning and erosion.

The center electrode extends through the insulator. One end is connected to a stud screwed into the top of the insulator. The other end extends out the nose or cone of the insulator. The electrode is held in position in the insulator by a sealing compound.

The grounded electrode is attached to the outer shell. It has a slight bend so that the end is directly beneath the end of the center electrode.

The gap between the two electrodes is the prime factor in plug operation. This gap must be set to exact engine specifications.

If the gap is too narrow, the spark will be weak and fouling and misfiring is the result.

Too wide a gap may work okay at low speeds, but at high speeds or loads it will strain the coil, resulting in misfire.

The surfaces of the two electrodes at the sparking point or gap should be parallel and have squared corners. This gives the current a better "jump" across the gap.

SPARK PLUG HEAT RANGE

The heat range of a spark plug is as important as the gap setting. In fact, the various heat ranges of different spark plugs are used to classify them.

The term "heat range" refers to the plug's ability to transfer the heat at the firing tip to the cooling systems of the engine. This is determined by the distance the heat must travel.

OUO1082,0002C7E -19-12JUL12-2/16

As you can see in Fig. 27, the end of a plug insulator that has a long nose or cone is further from the cooling system. Therefore, heat at the end will travel further. This type of plug will then run hot.

The end of a short insulator cone is closer to the cooling system and heat will transfer faster. A plug with a short insulator cone will then operate cooler.

A—Cold Plug
B—Short insulator seat quickly carries heat from core and makes a Cold Plug
C—Hot Plug
D—Long insulator seat allows core to retain maximum heat and makes a Hot Plug

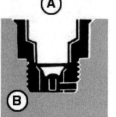

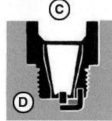

Fig. 27 — Spark Plug Heat Range

Continued on next page   OUO1082,0002C7E -19-12JUL12-3/16

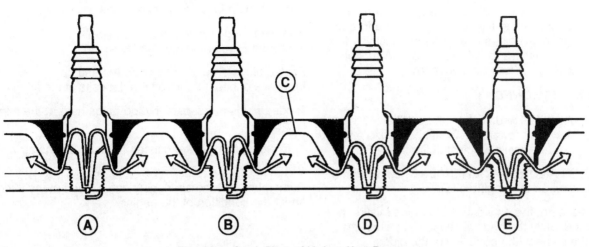

Fig. 28 — Spark Plugs of Various Heat Ranges

A—Hot   C—Engine Water System   D—Medium Cold
B—Medium Hot   E—Cold

Engine design and operating conditions will decide which type of spark plug—hot or cold—should be used. Generally, an engine that operates at fast speeds or heavy loads, and thus hotter, will require a cold plug so that the heat will transfer faster. On the other hand, a hot plug will be used in an engine that operates at low or idle speeds most of the time. Hot plugs will burn off the deposits that occur in this type of operation. For normal engine operations, a plug that falls somewhere between hot and cold is used (Fig. 28).

SPECIAL TYPES OF SPARK PLUGS

As we have said, there are many variations on the standard spark plug. In addition, there are several kinds of spark plugs which are unique in design and which suit a special application. We will briefly describe some of these plugs for you.

RESISTOR-TYPE PLUGS—Resistor-type plugs have a resistor between the terminal and center electrodes. These plugs are used to avoid radio and television static generated via the ignition circuit.

AUXILIARY-GAP PLUGS—This plug gives extra protection against fouling in cooler operations. They are useful when deposits can short out the current, preventing a spark. The gap is placed within the center electrode and holds in the voltage that could be drained off by the shorting deposits.

SURFACE-GAP PLUGS—This plug eliminates the grounded electrode. The spark fires across the insulator tip between the center electrode and the shell. This also gives fouling protection. However, it is used only in special high-voltage systems.

INSULATOR-TIP PLUGS—These plugs have the insulator tip extended farther into the combustion area. By doing this, the tip is said to be cooled by the incoming fuel-air mixture and cleaned of deposits by the hot exhaust gases.

REMOVING AND INSTALLING SPARK PLUGS

Observe these practices when removing and installing plugs:

1. Pull the wire from the plug by grasping the terminal, not by pulling on the wire.

2. After loosening the plug but before removing it, always clean the area around the spark plug by blowing, wiping, or brushing. (Be sure to protect your eyes.) This will prevent dirt from falling into the cylinder after removal.

3. Use a deep-well socket to remove the spark plugs. Also remove the gaskets with the plugs (if used).

4. If the plugs are to be reused, be sure to note which cylinder each came from. The condition of the spark plug can tell you a lot about the operation of a particular cylinder.

5. When replacing spark plugs, it is best to replace all of them at the same time.

6. When installing spark plugs with gaskets, be sure the gaskets are in place. The gaskets act as a seal to prevent loss of compression around the plug. Without a gasket, the reach of the plug would also change, affecting plug operation.

7. Remember another point on gaskets: Most manufacturers recommend installing new gaskets with both new and reconditioned spark plugs. This is due to the crush of a used gasket, which might prevent adequate sealing. However, always remove the old gasket from the spark plug. Never use both the old and the new gaskets. Here again, spark plug reach is affected.

Continued on next page   OUO1082,0002C7E -19-12JUL12-4/16

8. Tighten the spark plugs as specified and connect the spark plug wires to the proper plugs. If a torque wrench is not available, tighten the plug until you feel it seat, then turn it 1/2 to 3/4 turn more. (With steel gaskets, tighten 1/4 turn after seating).

SPARK PLUG FAILURES

A visual inspection will usually tell the condition of the spark plugs. However, for an electrical check, use a spark plug analyzer and follow its test instructions.

SPARK PLUG FAILURES—GENERAL—The first sign of failing plugs is when the engine misfires.

Faulty plugs are not the only cause of engine misfire, nor are the plugs usually the original cause. But when the engine misfires, check the condition of the plugs.

The two main failures of spark plugs are these:

- Fouled Plugs (dirty deposits on tips)
- Eroded Plugs (badly burned tips)

Fouled plugs around the electrodes and tip can result from lack of heat to burn off the deposits at the firing point.

Eroded plugs are caused by too much heat at the firing point.

These plug failures are caused by many things as we'll see now.

Remember that the spark plug can tell you many things about the condition of the engine.

OUO1082,0002C7E -19-12JUL12-5/16

SPARK PLUG FAILURES—FOULED PLUGS—Pictures of fouled plugs are shown in Fig. 29 through Fig. 35.

For comparison, a plug in normal operation is shown in Fig. 29). A normal plug will have brown to grayish-tan deposits and a slight wear on the electrodes. This indicates good adjustments of the engine.

A spark plug having this appearance can be cleaned, regapped, and reinstalled.

DXP03209 —UN—07MAR12

Fig. 29 — Spark Plug Failure—Normal Plug

OUO1082,0002C7E -19-12JUL12-6/16

An oil-fouled plug is shown in Fig. 30. Wet, oily deposits with a slight electrode wear can mean that oil is getting into the combustion area. It can be caused by overfilling the engine crankcase, excessive clearance on the valve stem guides, or broken or poorly seated piston rings. Plugs in this condition can usually be degreased, cleaned, and reinstalled. If the oily deposits are more than shown, the plug should be replaced.

DXP03210 —UN—07MAR12

Fig. 30 — Spark Plug Failure—Oil-Fouled Plug

Continued on next page

OUO1082,0002C7E -19-12JUL12-7/16

A carbon-fouled plug is shown in Fig. 31. This plug has dry, fluffy, black deposits. These can be caused by too "rich" a fuel-air mixture or a clogged air cleaner, or by reduced voltage from faulty components in the ignition circuit. After the cause has been corrected, this type of plug can usually be cleaned, regapped, and reinstalled.

Fig. 31 — Spark Plug Failure—Carbon-Fouled Plug

OUO1082,0002C7E -19-12JUL12-8/16

A deposit-fouled plug is pictured in Fig. 32. Red, brown, yellow, and white powdery deposits are usually the by-products of combustion and come from fuel and lubricating oil additives. These powdery deposits are usually not harmful. However, they can cause intermittent misfire at high speeds or heavy loads. If the insulator is heavily coated, replace the plug.

Hard, sandy deposits (not shown) can be caused by a faulty air cleaner or an engine operating in extremely dusty conditions. Replace these plugs.

Plug fouling can be caused by a "cold" plug being used in an engine that operates at low or idle speeds most of the time. Heat is dissipated so quickly that it does not have time to burn the excessive deposits from the firing point. So the deposits build up and the engine misfires.

Fig. 32 — Spark Plug Failure—Deposit-Fouled Plug

OUO1082,0002C7E -19-12JUL12-9/16

SPARK PLUG FAILURE—EROSION AND BREAKAGE

Erosion can be caused by the use of a "hot" spark plug in an engine operating at fast speeds or heavy loads. The extreme heat is not dissipated to the cooling system fast enough, resulting in burned or blistered insulator tips and badly eroded electrodes.

Preignition is the firing of the fuel-air mixture by a hot spot before the spark occurs. Hot spots in the combustion chamber, including hot carbon deposits, hot running engine, hot spots in the piston head or cylinder walls, extreme hot valve edges, or hot electrodes, can cause preignition. Preignition, which can cause blistered insulators and eroded electrodes as shown in Fig. 33, is another cause of electrode erosion.

A lean fuel-air mixture can also cause erosion.

Fig. 33 — Spark Plug Failure—Erosion Because of Preignition

Continued on next page

OUO1082,0002C7E -19-12JUL12-10/16

Wrong coil polarity can cause the grounded electrode to erode or "dish out" as shown in Fig. 34.

**A—Grounded Electrode
"Dished"—Wrong Coil
Polarity**

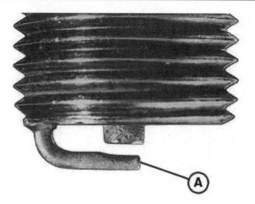

Fig. 34 — Spark Plug Failure-Wrong Coil Polarity

OUO1082,0002C7E -19-12JUL12-11/16

Broken insulator tips and broken electrodes can be caused by three things:

• Broken insulator tips might be caused by heat shock (Fig. 35). This is when there is a rapid increase in tip temperature under severe operating conditions. It can usually be prevented by allowing an adequate warm-up period at low speeds and by having the correct timing and the proper octane fuel.
• The tip can be broken by mishandling during gap adjustment, particularly if an attempt is made to bend the center electrode.
• The tip and the electrodes can be broken if they are hit by the piston or valves. Using a spark plug with the correct reach will solve this problem.

Replace spark plugs with electrode and tip erosion or breakage.

Fig. 35 — Spark Plug Failure—Heat Shock Failure

Continued on next page   OUO1082,0002C7E -19-12JUL12-12/16

SPARK PLUG FAILURE CAUSES—

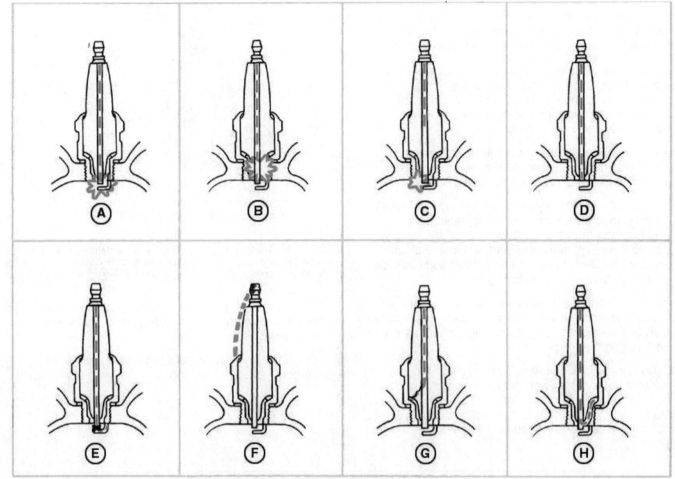

Fig. 36 — Cause of Spark Plug Misfires

A—Normal Ignition
B—Tracking Ignition
C—Pre-Ignition
D—Erosion at Gap
E—Gap Deposits
F—Flashover
G—Cracked Insulator
H—Deposits on Insulator

In nearly every case of spark plug failure, the cause must be corrected before new or reconditioned spark plugs are installed. Otherwise, servicing will be needed again in a short time.

Fig. 36 illustrates what takes place in a faulty spark plug during ignition. The following numbered statements tell what causes the misfire.

1. Normal ignition occurs when a spark of adequate energy is delivered at the correct instant across the electrode gap as shown.

2. Tracking ignition occurs when the spark, jumping from one deposit "island" to another, ignites the fuel charge at some point along the insulator nose. The effect is to retard ignition timing.

3. Pre-ignition occurs when some surface in the combustion chamber becomes hot enough to fire the fuel-air mixture before the spark occurs.

4. Gap erosion of the plug electrodes may prevent voltage from jumping the gap.

5. Deposits may have bridged the gap so that the coil voltage is drained away without a spark occurring.

6. Flashover is caused by moisture or dirt or by a worn-out terminal boot. This allows voltage to short across the outside of the insulator.

7. Cracks in the plug insulator may allow high voltage to short-circuit to the ground.

8. Deposits formed on the insulator surface may drain away voltage.

SPARK PLUG SERVICING

Spark plug service has three steps:

• Inspection
• Cleaning
• Gap Adjustment

Most engine technical manuals recommend a specific time interval for ignition services. Follow this timetable very closely.

Continued on next page   OUO1082,0002C7E -19-12JUL12-13/16

SPARK PLUG INSPECTION—

When inspecting the plugs, look for the normal or abnormal wear we have just described in Fig. 37. Then decide whether to recondition or replace the plugs.

Remember, if one plug is replaced, all the plugs should be replaced to get the full advantage of new plug performance and economy. This is not applicable, of course, if unusual conditions cause premature failure to just one in a fairly new set of plugs.

Normally, replace the whole set of plugs after long intervals of use. Normal wear can double the voltage requirements of a spark plug even in a short period of time.

SPARK PLUG CLEANING—There are two types of spark plug cleaning machines that do an acceptable job of removing deposits from the insulator and electrodes. One unit uses an abrasive compound and air blast to clean the insulator and electrodes. The other machine uses a strong liquid cleaner to do the same job.

Make a careful inspection, however, after using an abrasive blast machine to ensure that all abrasive particles have also been removed. Engine damage could result if they were left on the plugs.

NOTE: *Do not use a power wire brush to clean the plugs. Most makers of plugs do not recommend this.*

Badly fouled plugs should be replaced. It is doubtful sand blasting or liquid cleaning will remove all the deposits from such plugs.

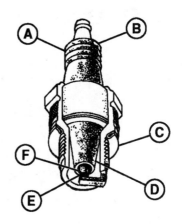

Fig. 37 — Maintenance of Spark Plugs

A—Check for Cracks
B—Wipe Clean
C—Replace Gasket
D—Clean Insulation Until White
E—File and Re-Gap
F—Clean Electrodes

Clean the threads with a wire hand brush or a powered soft wire brush wheel.

Wet, oily plugs may require cleaning with a petroleum solvent before abrasive cleaning.

OUO1082,0002C7E -19-12JUL12-14/16

Before gapping the electrodes, file them with a small point file to flatten their surface at the firing point and square up the edges (Fig. 38). Squaring the surface edges can reduce voltage requirements, even more than if the plugs are only cleaned.

A—Electrode
B—File

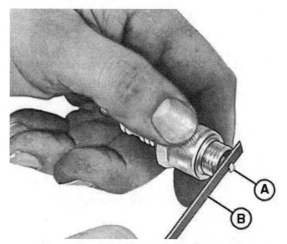

Fig. 38 — Filing the Spark Plug Electrodes

Continued on next page

OUO1082,0002C7E -19-12JUL12-15/16

110112
PN=330

ADJUSTING SPARK PLUG GAPS—

Whether the plug is new or used, always check the gap before you install the plug.

Use a wire spark plug gauge to check the gap (Fig. 39).

The wire gauge will give a true gap reading even if the electrode surface is not flat.

If the gap is far too wide, the plug may need replacing.

Use a bending tool to adjust the gap to specifications (Fig. 40). Often the bending tool is part of the wire gauge as shown.

After adjusting, check to be sure the electrode surfaces are parallel.

Never bend the center electrode. Doing so may crack or break the insulator tip.

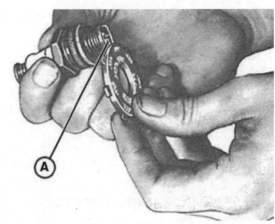

Fig. 39 — Checking the Spark Plug Gap

A—Wire-Type Gauge

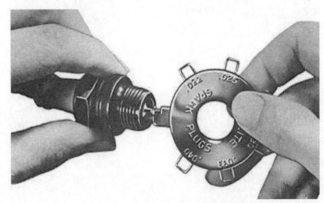

Fig. 40 — Adjusting the Spark Plug Gap

OUO1082,0002C7E -19-12JUL12-16/16

IGNITION WIRING

The type of wiring used in the ignition circuit is important as well as its condition.

Light wiring is used in the primary circuit because of the relatively low voltage.

Heavy wire or cables are used in the secondary circuit (coil to distributor cap, distributor cap to spark plugs) because they are subject to high voltage. High-voltage wires usually have metal terminal ends: female and male on the spark plug cables, male on the coil to distributor cap cable.

Some ignition circuits have an ignition resistor in the form of a special resistance wire. When the engine is running, the resistor wire is in series with the coil and reduces the voltage at the coil to normal operating voltage. To provide a better spark when starting, however, the resistor wire is bypassed and a stronger battery voltage is applied at the cable.

SERVICING WIRES AND CABLES

Connections should always be kept clean and tight.

The wires themselves should be kept clean and free of oil, which could rot the insulation.

Periodically, check the wiring for cracked or broken insulation and loose connections.

When installing high-voltage wires, do not let them touch a ground or each other.

OUO1082,0002C7F -19-10JAN12-1/1

TESTING AND DIAGNOSING THE IGNITION CIRCUIT

Ignition tests are usually made with an ignition analyzer—either the oscilloscope or meter types (see Chapter 2).

Many of these tests can also be made with all components in place on the machine.

Follow the test procedures given with the analyzer, and consult the engine technical manual for the expected readings.

TROUBLESHOOTING CHART FOR IGNITION PROBLEMS

Engine operating problems can be caused by many things, both mechanical and electrical. The chart below lists some of the engine problems and how they can be caused by a faulty ignition circuit.

Table 2 — Ignition Problems	
PROBLEM	CAUSE
Lack of power	a. Incorrect timing
	b. Pitted distributor points
Hard starting	a. Weak spark
Engine overheats	a. Advance mechanism sticking
Engine knocks	a. Incorrect timing
Engine backfires	a. Advance mechanism sticking
Engine preignition	a. Faulty spark plugs
Engine misfires	a. Dirty spark plugs
	b. Faulty cables
	c. Incorrect distributor point gap
Engine uses too much fuel	a. Fouled spark plugs
	b. Incorrect timing
Engine runs irregular	a. Faulty ignition
Slow acceleration	a. Advance mechanism sticking
	b. Defective coil or condenser
	c. Faulty distributor points
Engine will not start	a. Faulty coil
	b. Faulty condenser
	c. Faulty distributor points
	d. Coil high tension wire out of socket
	e. Cracked distributor rotor
	f. Faulty spark plugs
	g. Incorrect timing
	h. Spark plug cables installed incorrectly
Engine starts but will not continue to run	a. Faulty coil
	b. Faulty condenser
	c. Faulty distributor points
	d. Faulty bypass resistor
Poor ignition of fuel	a. Incorrect spark plug gap
	b. Dirty spark plugs
	c. Faulty cables or wiring
	d. Incorrect timing
	e. Faulty distributor points
	f. Faulty condenser
	g. Defective coil
	h. Cracked distributor cap or rotor

CHECKING OUT IGNITION PROBLEMS

Once the cause of the problem has been isolated to the ignition circuit, check each component to find the faulty one.

We have already described the tests that are made on the components. Usually, they can be made with the unit on or off the machine. To refresh your memory, we will now give you a brief list of items to check.

VISUAL INSPECTION

Check for:

1. Loose or broken connections and cables.

Continued on next page   OUO1082,0002C80 -19-02APR12-1/3

2. Cracked coil cap.

3. Cracked or broken distributor cap and rotor.

4. Carbon paths on and in distributor cap.

5. Burned, pitted, or worn distributor points.

6. Worn distributor breaker cam and breaker lever rubbing block wear.

ELECTRICAL TESTS

Check these items:

1. Coil for grounded, shorted, or open windings and coil polarity.

2. Condenser for leakage, series resistance, and capacity.

3. Cam angle (dwell) of distributor.

4. Timing of distributor.

5. High voltage strength. Check this by removing the coil high-tension cable from the distributor cap and holding it (with insulated pliers) 1/4 inch (6 mm) from the engine while cranking. If a good spark appears, the trouble is probably in the distributor cap, rotor, spark plug wires, or spark plugs.

6. Ignition circuit for high resistance, open circuits, and grounds (Fig. 41). and the following instructions for details on this test.

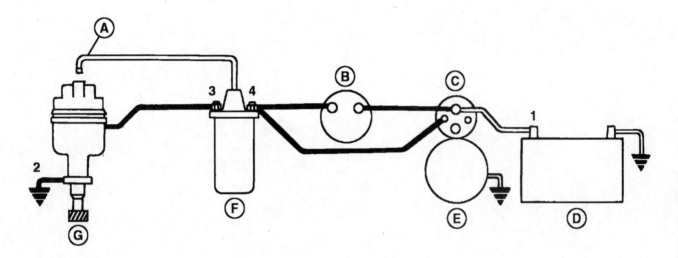

Fig. 41 — Ignition Circuit Test Points (Typical 12-Volt Negative-Ground Circuit)

A—Disconnect and Ground the Coil Wire
B—Ignition Switch
C—Solenoid
D—Battery
E—Starting Motor
F—Ignition Coil
G—Distributor

General Test Of Ignition Circuit

1. Use a voltmeter with a range of 0.1 to 20 volts.

2. Make all tests with lights and accessories off.

3. An example of the test results on a typical 12-volt negative-ground electrical system is given in the chart in table 3 below.

Table 3 — Ignition Circuit Test Results			
Voltmeter Connected to Points (Fig. 41)	Ignition Switch Position	Distributor Breaker Points Position	Voltmeter Reading if Circuit in Good Condition
1 & 4	Cranking	....	1 volt (max.)
2 & 4	Cranking	....	10 volts (approx.)
2 & 4	On	Open	Battery voltage
2 & 4	On	Closed	4.8 volts (approx.)
2 & 3	On	Closed	0.2 volt (max.)

SUMMARY: SERVICING THE IGNITION CIRCUIT

By performing periodic servicing of the ignition circuit, making all adjustments, and operating the engine within the specified limits, the ignition circuit should give long, dependable service.

Continued on next page OUO1082,0002C80 -19-02APR12-2/3

TEST YOURSELF

QUESTIONS

1. What is the final goal of the ignition circuit?

2. Name the four basic parts of an ignition circuit.

3. Match the items below:

   a. Primary circuit   1. High voltage

   b. Secondary circuit   2. Low voltage

4. What does an advance mechanism do for a distributor?

5. (True or False?) Use emery cloth or fine sandpaper to clean the distributor points.

6. What is the difference between fouled and eroded spark plugs? Which is caused by too much heat? Which by too little heat?

(Answers are in back of textbook).

OUO1082,0002C81 -19-10JAN12-1/1

INTRODUCTION

DXP02709 —UN—23FEB11

9

Many modern agriculture and industrial machines have two major electronic systems:

• Electronic Ignition

• Electronic Fuel Injection

Let's discuss both of these systems in detail.

OUO1082,0002C82 -19-12JUN12-1/2

ELECTRONIC IGNITION

An electronic ignition system does not use breaker points and condenser, which are the main elements of a conventional ignition system distributor (see Chapter 8). Instead of breaker points and condenser, electronic ignition systems (Fig. 1) contain a reluctor and sensor in the distributor and an ignition control unit (ICU). The control unit causes the flow of primary current to stop, thus inducing high voltage through the secondary winding.

All other ignition circuit components are common to both electronic and conventional systems.

IMPORTANT: Electronic and conventional ignition coils are similar in construction, but must not be interchanged. Electronic ignition coils generally deliver much higher voltage. Use of a coil not designed for a particular ignition system may damage other components of the system. See Chapter 8 for coil construction and operation.

A—Distributor
B—Rotor
C—Spark Plugs
D—Coil
E—Ignition Control Unit (ICU)
F—Bypass
G—Battery
H—Ignition Switch
I— Sensor Coil
J— Reluctor
K—Primary Circuit
L—Secondary Circuit

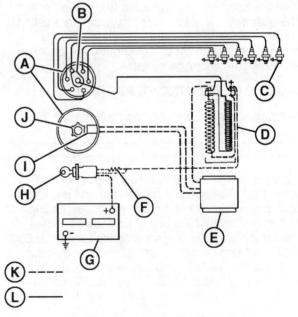

Fig. 1 — Electronic Ignition System

OUO1082,0002C82 -19-12JUN12-2/2

TYPES OF ELECTRONIC IGNITION SYSTEMS

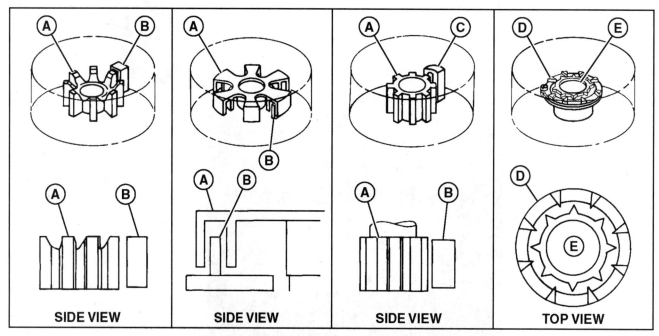

Fig. 2 — Various Styles of Reluctor-Sensor Assemblies

A—Reluctor
B—Sensor

C—Sensor or Pickup Coil

D—Coil
E—Magnetic Pickup

Most electronic ignition systems are constructed and operate like the one just described. There are a few variations in the electronic ignition systems. One difference is the style of the reluctor-sensor assembly (Fig. 2). Some types of electronic ignition systems have all of the components (including the ignition coil) inside the distributor. These types of systems are called self-integrated electronic ignitions. Ignition systems that fire the spark plug without a distributor are another variation in electronic ignition systems.

ADVANTAGES OF ELECTRONIC IGNITION

The advantages of electronic ignition systems are these:

- No problems caused by malfunctioning distributor points and condenser (there are no points and condenser).
- Quicker starts in all kinds of weather. This places less drain on the battery.
- Electronic ignition produces a hotter spark of longer duration, which will ignite marginal air-fuel mixtures under adverse weather conditions. A conventional ignition system in good condition delivers about 25,000 volts. An electronic ignition system in good condition delivers 35,000 or more volts.
- The hotter spark of longer duration provides more complete combustion of the fuel mixture, which improves fuel efficiency and lessens exhaust emissions.

OUO1082,0002C83 -19-12JUN12-1/2

- The hotter spark of longer duration helps increase spark plug life. The spark plugs can burn off detrimental deposits that settle on electrodes and cause fouling. Electronic ignition and the use of unleaded gasoline have combined to extend spark plug life to over 20,000 miles (32,187 km). Vehicles without electronic ignition and not using unleaded gasoline have an expectant spark plug life of about 10,000 miles (16,093 km) (Fig. 3).

A—Conventional Ignition And Leaded Gasoline

B—Electronic Ignition And Unleaded Gasoline

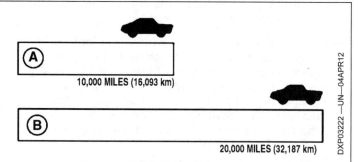

Fig. 3 — Spark Plug Life Comparison

OUO1082,0002C83 -19-12JUN12-2/2

HOW ELECTRONIC IGNITION WORKS

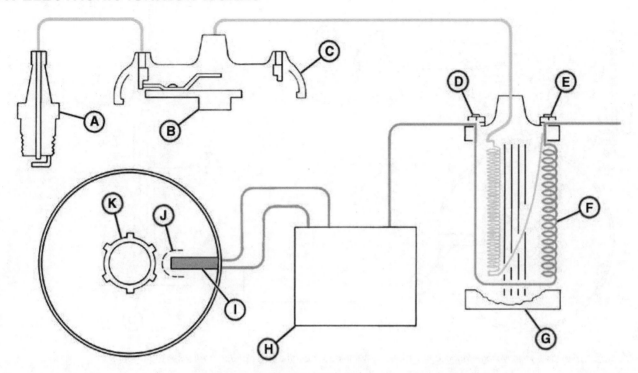

Fig. 4 — Operation Before Reluctor Passes Through Electromagnetic Field

A—Spark Plugs
B—Rotor
C—Distributor Cap
D—Primary Terminal

E—Primary Terminal
F—Primary Winding
G—Coil

H—Ignition Control Unit (ICU)
I— Sensor
J— Magnetic Field

K—Reluctor

The Ignition Control Unit (ICU) contains solid-state components, permanently sealed in a material that resists vibration and environmental conditions. The unit has built-in reverse polarity and transient voltage protection.

The ICU cannot be repaired. If a malfunction occurs, the unit must be replaced.

When the ignition key is turned on, an oscillator in the ignition control unit excites the sensor in the distributor. The sensor (a small coil of fine wire) develops an electromagnetic field that is sensitive to the presence of metal (Fig. 4).

As the engine camshaft rotates, it drives the distributor shaft, which causes the reluctor to rotate. As the leading edge of a metal tooth of the rotating reluctor enters the electromagnetic field of the sensor, the strength of the oscillator in the sensor is reduced. This acts as a signal to a demodulator in the ignition control unit. The demodulator controls a power switch transistor, which is in series with the ignition coil primary circuit.

Continued on next page

OUO1082,0002C84 -19-12JUN12-1/2

110112
PN=337

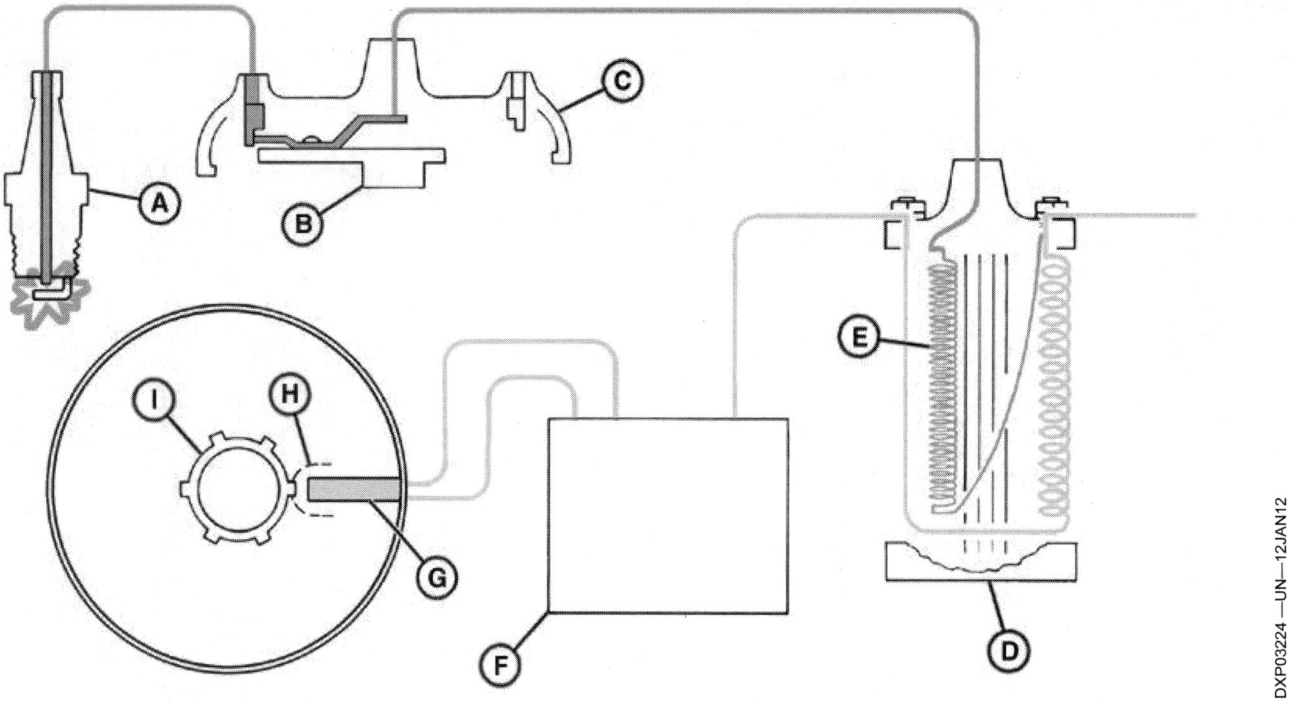

Fig. 5 — High Voltage Induced in Secondary Winding When the Reluctor Tooth Aligns with the Sensor

A—Spark Plug	D—Coil	G—Sensor
B—Rotor	E—Secondary Winding	H—Magnetic Field
C—Distributor Cap	F—Ignition Control Unit (ICU)	I— Reluctor

The demodulator causes the power switch transistor to switch off the coil primary circuit, inducing high voltage in the ignition coil's secondary winding (Fig. 5). This high voltage is distributed to the spark plugs through the distributor cap, rotor, and spark plug cables.

This distributor does not require periodic maintenance other than to clean the distributor cap and check the cap and rotor terminals for damage. The reluctor and sensor cannot be repaired. If testing reveals a malfunction, they must be replaced. The electronically timed dwell of the circuit, which is the period of time that the circuit is closed, cannot be adjusted on most electronic ignition systems.

OUO1082,0002C84 -19-12JUN12-2/2

TROUBLESHOOTING ELECTRONIC IGNITION MALFUNCTIONS

The following describes tests of a typical electronic ignition system. Refer to the machine Technical Manual for machine specific tests.

Test the ignition system when the engine fails to start or when there is no spark at the spark plugs. An ignition malfunction may also cause the engine to not start on the first attempt and stall when running. In these situations, the engine will eventually start or restart if it stalls.

NOTE: Ignition-related problems, such as backfiring and poor starting, can occur if the distributor cap and rotor are damaged, and if the spark plug cables and distributor-to-ignition coil cable are defective. These problems are common to all ignition systems and are discussed in Chapter 8.

IDENTIFY GENERAL LOCATION OF TROUBLE

When an ignition problem is suspected, first test the battery. Be certain to check the battery terminals and make sure the cables are attached securely and not corroded.

To avoid shock, turn the ignition switch OFF.

1. Remove the high-voltage cable from the center tower of the distributor.

2. Using insulated pliers, hold the end of the cable approximately 1/4 inch (6.4 mm) from ground and crank the engine (Fig. 6). If a spark arcs the gap, a problem exists in the distributor cap, rotor, spark

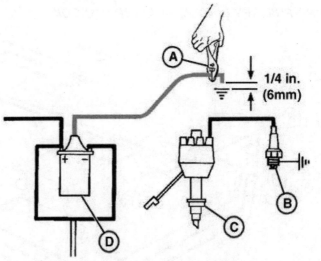

Fig. 6 — Use Insulated Pliers

A—Insulated Pliers　　　C—Distributor
B—Spark Plug　　　　　　D—Coil

plug wires, or spark plugs. If a spark does not arc, the problem exists in the ignition control unit, coil, ignition switch, sensor, or a wire.

Troubleshooting electronic ignition systems requires using a test light, voltmeter, ohmmeter, jumper wire, and possibly a tester switch if recommended by the manufacturer.

Continued on next page　　　　　　OUO1082,0002C85 -19-12JUN12-1/18

TESTING PRIMARY CIRCUIT—BATTERY TO COIL

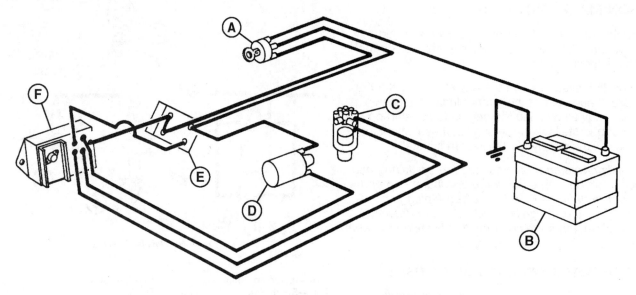

Fig. 7 — System with External Dual Ballast Resistor

A—Ignition Switch
B—Battery

C—Distributor
D—Coil
E—Dual Ballast Resistor

F—Ignition Control Unit (ICU)

One type of electronic ignition system uses a dual ballast resistor that is contained in a unit outside the ignition control unit (ICU) (Fig. 7). To test the primary circuit wires:

OUO1082,0002C85 -19-12JUN12-2/18

1. Unplug the wiring harness connector from the ICU to reveal five cavities or pins (Fig. 8).

2. Turn the ignition switch to ON and connect the negative lead of the voltmeter to ground.

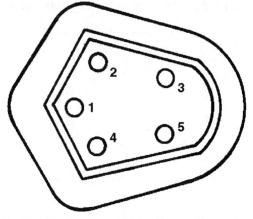

Fig. 8 — Five Cavities of Wiring Harness Connector

Continued on next page

OUO1082,0002C85 -19-12JUN12-3/18

IMPORTANT: All accessories must be off.

3. Connect the positive lead of the voltmeter to the wiring harness connector of the No. 1 cavity (Fig. 9). The voltage reading should be within one volt of battery voltage.

4. Check No. 2 and No. 3 cavities in the same way. If there is more than a one volt difference in any reading, inspect the circuit for that particular wiring harness cavity to be sure all connections are clean and tight.

A—Wiring Harness Connector   B—Voltmeter

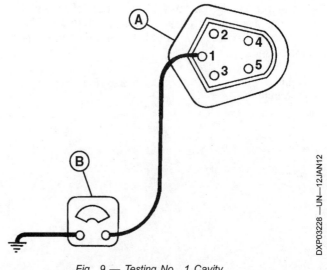

Fig. 9 — Testing No. 1 Cavity

OUO1082,0002C85 -19-12JUN12-4/18

For ignition systems without the external dual ballast resistor, connect the voltmeter to ground and to the ignition coil positive terminal (Fig. 10). Turn the ignition switch to ON. If the voltmeter does not record battery voltage, check for high resistance between the battery and ignition coil or a defective ignition switch.

TESTING THE IGNITION CONTROL UNIT, COIL, AND SENSOR

There are three methods of testing the ICU, depending on the type of electronic ignition system being tested. If malfunctions occur in any system, make sure wires are not broken and connections are tight and free of corrosion.

TESTING WITH A TEST LIGHT

When testing the ICU of the system with a reluctor-sensor configuration as in B, (Fig. 2):

1. Disconnect the distributor lead connector.

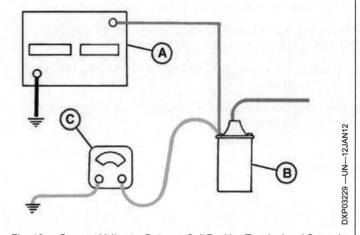

Fig. 10 — Connect Voltmeter Between Coil Positive Terminal and Ground

A—Battery   C—Voltmeter
B—Coil

Continued on next page
OUO1082,0002C85 -19-12JUN12-5/18

2. Connect a test light across the terminals of the ignition coil (Fig. 11) and turn the ignition switch to the ON position. If the bulb does not light, replace the ignition control unit.

A—Light
B—Distributor

C—Unplug Here
D—Coil

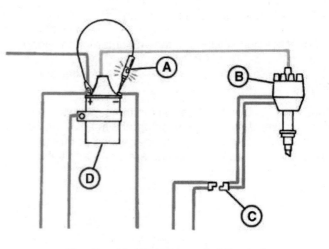

Fig. 11 — Test Light Across Coil Terminals

OUO1082,0002C85 -19-12JUN12-6/18

If the bulb lights with the ignition switch in the ON position, place a jumper wire across the ICU lead terminals (Fig. 12). If the bulb remains lit, replace the ignition control unit.

If the bulb goes out when you place the jumper across the ICU's lead terminals, do the following:

1. Disconnect one end of the jumper wire at one of the lead terminals.

2. Remove the high-voltage cable from the center tower of the distributor.

A—Light
B—Jumper Wire

C—Ignition Control Unit (ICU)
D—Coil

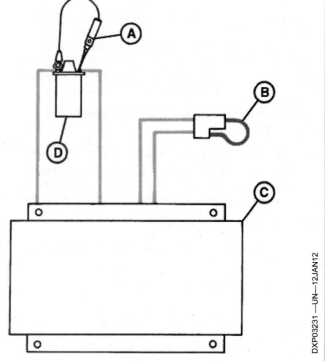

Fig. 12 — Place Jumper Wire Across Ignition Control Unit Lead Terminals

Continued on next page

OUO1082,0002C85 -19-12JUN12-7/18

3. Using insulated pliers, hold the end of the cable 1/4 inch (6.4 mm) from ground (Fig. 13).

4. Have someone crank the engine while you again short out the ICU's lead terminals by reconnecting the jumper wire.

If a spark jumps the gap between the end of the high-voltage cable and ground, the sensor in the distributor is defective and must be replaced (see next page). If no spark occurs, replace the ignition coil.

TESTING WITH AN OHMMETER

A—Insulated Pliers   D—Ignition Control Unit (ICU)
B—Distributor   E—Coil
C—Jumper Wire

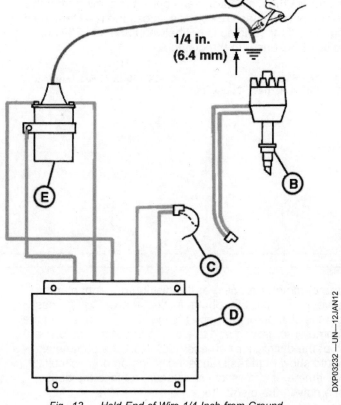

Fig. 13 — Hold End of Wire 1/4 Inch from Ground

OUO1082,0002C85 -19-12JUN12-8/18

For the electronic ignition system with an external dual ballast resistor, unplug the wiring harness connector from the ICU and turn OFF the ignition. Connect an ohmmeter to wiring harness connector cavities No. 4 and No. 5 (Fig. 14). The ohmmeter resistance reading should be between 350 and 550 ohms.

A—Wiring Harness Connector   B—Ohmmeter

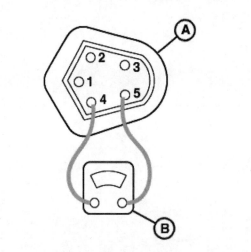

Fig. 14 — Ohmmeter Between Cavities No. 4 and 5

Continued on next page   OUO1082,0002C85 -19-12JUN12-9/18

If the reading is less than 350 or more than 550 ohms, disconnect the distributor lead connector coming from the distributor and check resistance across the lead terminals (Fig. 15). If the reading is not between 350 and 550 ohms, replace the sensor in the distributor.

A—Ohmmeter   C—Distributor Lead Terminal
B—Wiring Harness Connector

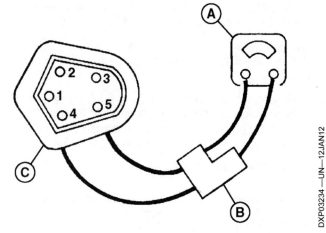

Fig. 15 — Connect Ohmmeter Across Distributor Lead Terminal

OUO1082,0002C85 -19-12JUN12-10/18

If the ohmmeter reading at the distributor connector is between 350 and 550 ohms, inspect the wiring harness from the distributor connector to the ICU by connecting the ohmmeter to ground and to either distributor lead terminal pin of the distributor harness (Fig. 16). The ohmmeter should show high resistance indicating an open circuit. If the ohmmeter shows low resistance, replace the sensor assembly in the distributor.

A—Ohmmeter   C—Distributor Harness
B—Wiring Harness Connector

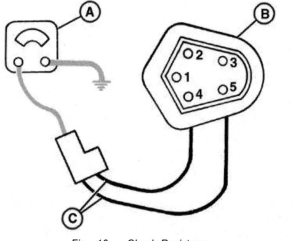

Fig. 16 — Check Resistance

Continued on next page   OUO1082,0002C85 -19-12JUN12-11/18

Connect the ohmmeter to ground and to the wiring harness connector of the No. 5 cavity (Fig. 17). The ohmmeter should show continuity. If not, tighten the bolts holding the ICU to the firewall.

Retest. If continuity does not exist, replace the Ignition Control Unit (ICU).

TESTING WITH A VOLTMETER

The electronic ignition system with the reluctor-sensor assembly shown in A, Fig. 2, can be tested by using a voltmeter at the distributor lead connection. To perform this test:

A—Wiring Harness Connector   **B—Ohmmeter**

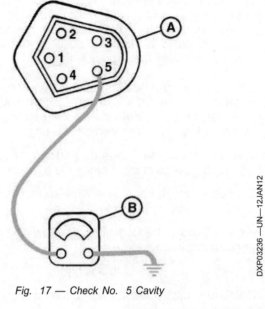

Fig. 17 — Check No. 5 Cavity

OUO1082,0002C85 -19-12JUN12-12/18

---

1. Disconnect the distributor lead connector.

2. Connect a voltmeter between the two parallel blades (Fig. 18).

3. Set the voltmeter scale at 2.5 volts and crank the engine. The voltmeter reading should fluctuate.

If the voltmeter reading does not fluctuate:

1. Inspect the distributor for a defective cap or rotor, loose reluctor, broken reluctor tooth, or misaligned keeper pin.

2. See that the reluctor rotates when the engine is cranked.

3. If it doesn't rotate, replace the sleeve and advance plate assembly.

A—Distributor Connector   **B—Voltmeter**

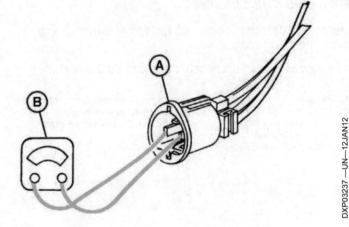

Fig. 18 — Voltmeter Between Parallel Blades

Continued on next page
OUO1082,0002C85 -19-12JUN12-13/18

NOTE: *When disassembling the distributor, make reference marks on the reluctor and some adjacent part of the distributor. The reluctor must be assembled in the same position as it was removed to ensure proper timing.*

4. If this examination does not reveal the reason for the voltmeter needle not fluctuating, install a new sensor assembly in the distributor. Use the exploded view shown in Fig. 19 to reassemble the unit.

If the voltmeter reading fluctuates, perform the spark test with the high-voltage cable. During the test:

1. If a spark arcs the gap, check the spark plug wires, distributor cap, and rotor for damage.

2. If spark does not appear, install a new ICU and perform another spark test.

3. If spark occurs, the old ICU is bad.

4. If still no spark appears, replace the coil.

5. If the problem still exists, test each wiring circuit as outlined in the manufacturer's Service Manual.

REPLACING THE SENSOR

To remove a defective sensor of the type shown in B, Fig. 2, from the distributor:

1. Remove the distributor cap, rotor, and dust shield.

A—Sensor
B—Reluctor
C—Reluctor Stop Ring
D—System Ground
E—Vacuum Advance Link

F—Wiring Harness Connector
G—Base Plate Assembly
H—Sleeve and Advance Plate
    Assembly
I— Base Casting

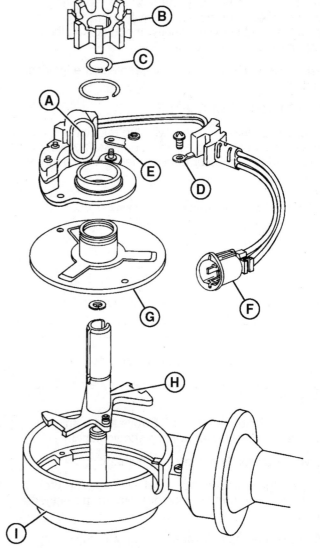

Fig. 19 — Exploded View of Distributor

Continued on next page

OUO1082,0002C85 -19-12JUN12-14/18

IMPORTANT: Do not press directly on the shaft. Make sure the jaws of the puller grip the inner shoulder of the reluctor.

2. Using a small gear puller, remove the reluctor by placing a spacer (thick flat washer or nut) between the turn-down of the gear puller and the distributor's center shaft (Fig. 20).

A—Spacer   B—Puller Jaws

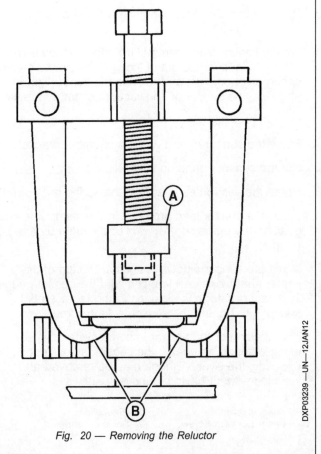

Fig. 20 — Removing the Reluctor

DXP03239 —UN—12JAN12

Continued on next page   OUO1082,0002C85 -19-12JUN12-15/18

3. Remove the sensor locking screw that holds the sensor (Fig. 21).

4. Lift the sensor lead grommet from the distributor, and pull the sensor leads out of the slot around the sensor spring pivot pin. Lift and release the sensor spring, and slide the sensor off the vacuum chamber bracket.

To install a new sensor:

1. Place the sensor on the vacuum chamber bracket.

2. Put the sensor spring on the sensor.

3. Route the sensor leads around the spring pivot pin.

4. Install the sensor lead grommet in the distributor, and position the leads so they won't be caught by the reluctor.

5. Move the sensor sideways against the flat of the center shaft yoke until you can seat the sensor gauge. The sensor gauge is included in the replacement sensor kit. Tighten the sensor locking screw.

6. The position of the sensor in some systems is set using a sensor gauge. If the sensor is positioned correctly, the sensor gauge may be removed and installed without having to move it sideways.

A—Sensor Assembly
B—Sensor Locking Screw
C—Pivot Pin
D—Sensor Spring

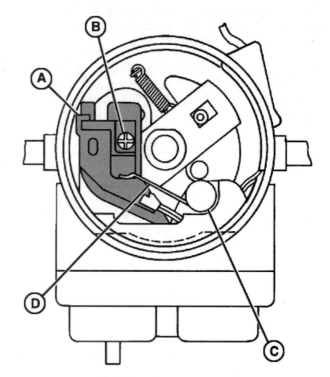

Fig. 21 — Sensor Locking Screw

DXP03240 —UN—12JAN12

OUO1082,0002C85 -19-12JUN12-16/18

IMPORTANT: The reluctor legs should not touch the sensor core. If so, the legs may break or wear and result in hard starting.

7. With the sensor in correct position, place the reluctor on the yoke of the distributor shaft, so the sensor core is in the center of the reluctor legs (Fig. 22).

8. Press the reluctor down on the shaft. Measure clearance below the reluctor as specified by the manufacturer.

9. Apply two drops of light motor oil to the felt pad on top of the distributor shaft yoke. Install dust shield, rotor, and distributor cap.

10. Set ignition timing to specification.

In the ignition system with the external dual ballast resistor, it is necessary to remove the upper and lower plates to remove the sensor. In these distributors:

1. Remove the distributor cap and rotor.

2. Remove the screws and lock washers holding the vacuum control to the distributor housing. Disconnect

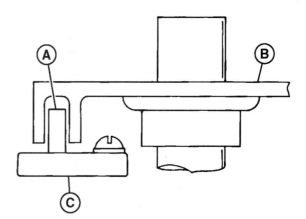

Fig. 22 — Correct Position of Reluctor

DXP03241 —UN—12JAN12

A—Sensor Core
B—Reluctor
C—Sensor Base

the vacuum control arm and remove the vacuum control.

Continued on next page

OUO1082,0002C85 -19-12JUN12-17/18

3. Remove the reluctor keeper pin. Place two screwdrivers under the reluctor on opposite sides of the distributor shaft. Pry evenly with the screwdrivers until the reluctor comes off the shaft (Fig. 23). Be careful to not damage reluctor teeth.

4. Remove the screws and lock washers holding the lower plate to the distributor housing. Lift off the lower plate, upper plate, and sensor assembly.

5. Install a new sensor assembly with the upper and lower plates

6. Install the reluctor and keeper pin. Press the reluctor down firmly.

7. Lubricate the felt pad on top of the reluctor sleeve with a drop of light engine oil.

8. Set the air gap between the sensor and reluctor by loosening the sensor locking screw. Use a

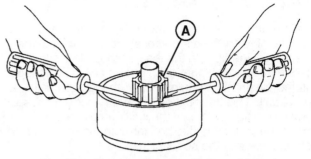

Fig. 23 — Removing Reluctor with Screwdrivers

A—Reluctor

nonmagnetic gauge to adjust the sensor until the specified gap is obtained. Tighten the screw.

OUO1082,0002C85 -19-12JUN12-18/18

SELF-INTEGRATED ELECTRONIC IGNITION

The self-integrated ignition system is unique because all components (including the ignition coil) are inside the distributor (Fig. 24). The distributor is larger than a conventional unit and contains terminal studs on the distributor cap where spark plug cables are connected.

The ignition coil of a self-integrated system is smaller than a conventional ignition coil. It has more primary and secondary windings than a conventional coil and is constructed like a true transformer; that is, the windings are surrounded by a laminated iron core. In a conventional ignition coil, the iron core is surrounded by the windings.

Other parts of this distributor are a rotor, a magnetic pickup assembly (containing a permanent magnet, a pole piece with internal teeth, and a pickup coil), and an electronic module.

There is also a capacitor inside the distributor that is used for noise suppression. It has no bearing on ignition.

A—Cover	E—Vacuum Unit
B—Seal	F—Connector
C—Spring	G—Cap
D—Rotor	H—Coil

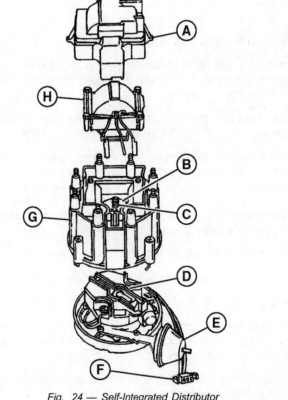

Fig. 24 — Self-Integrated Distributor

Continued on next page
OUO1082,0002C86 -19-12JUN12-1/9

HOW THE SELF-INTEGRATED SYSTEM WORKS

The teeth of the timer core of the movable magnetic pickup assembly on the distributor shaft rotate inside the pole piece and line up with the teeth of the pole piece (Fig. 25). This induces a voltage in the pickup coil. The voltage signals the electronic module to open the ignition coil primary circuit. This interruption of primary current causes high voltage to be induced in the ignition coil secondary winding. High voltage is directed through the rotor and spark plug cables to the spark plugs.

TROUBLESHOOTING THE SELF-INTEGRATED SYSTEM

Test this system using a voltmeter and an ohmmeter. Other test equipment may be recommended by the manufacturer.

IMPORTANT: **Before proceeding, make sure the connector on the side of the distributor is secure and all spark plug cables are securely connected.**

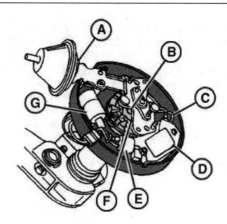

Fig. 25 — Distributor Components

A—Vacuum Control Plate
B—Magnetic Pickup Assembly
C—Pickup Coil Leads
D—Electronic Module
E—Module Connector
F—Pole Piece with Internal Teeth
G—Capacitor

OUO1082,0002C86 -19-12JUN12-2/9

IF THE ENGINE WILL NOT START:

1. Connect a voltmeter between ground and the BAT (battery) terminal lead of the distributor (Fig. 26). Turn ON the ignition switch.

2. If the voltage reading is zero, look for an open circuit between the BAT (battery) terminal and the battery.

3. If the voltmeter records battery voltage, use insulated pliers to remove a spark plug cable and hold it one-quarter inch from ground. Crank the engine. If spark occurs, look for worn spark plugs or a fuel system problem. If there is no spark, test distributor components (see below).

IF THE ENGINE RUNS ROUGH:

1. Check to see that fuel is reaching the carburetor.

2. Check vacuum hoses and connections for leaks.

3. With the engine running, check all spark plug cables by looking and listening. If a cable is weak, sparks will be heard or can be seen jumping to ground.

4. Check the ignition timing and centrifugal advance settings with a stroboscopic timing light.

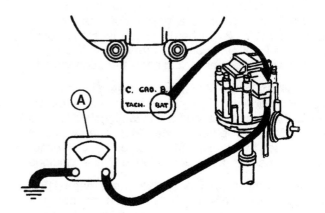

Fig. 26 — Voltmeter Connected to BAT Terminal

A—Voltmeter

5. Check all spark plugs for correct gap and fouling.

If the problem isn't solved, test distributor components.

Continued on next page   OUO1082,0002C86 -19-12JUN12-3/9

TO TEST DISTRIBUTOR COMPONENTS:

1. Depress each fastener holding the distributor cap and turn 180° to remove the cap (Fig. 27).

2. Replace any distributor cap, ignition coil, or rotor when it is burned or corroded.

A—Screwdriver   **C—Distributor**
B—Fastener

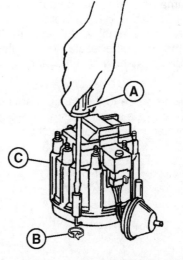

Fig. 27 — Removing Distributor Cap

OUO1082,0002C86 -19-12JUN12-4/9

3. Connect an ohmmeter between terminals 1 and 2 in the distributor cap (Fig. 28). The meter should show little or no resistance. If it does not, replace the ignition coil (see next page).

A—Distributor Cap   **D—Terminal 1**
B—Terminal 3   **E—Ohmmeter**
C—Terminal 2   **F—Coil Button**

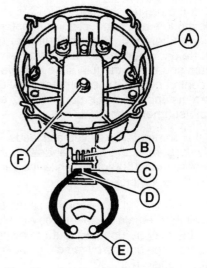

Fig. 28 — Inside of Distributor Cap

Continued on next page   OUO1082,0002C86 -19-12JUN12-5/9

4. Connect an ohmmeter lead to the ignition coil button inside the distributor cap (Fig. 29). Connect the other lead first to the No. 2 terminal, and then to the No. 3 terminal. Set the ohmmeter scale on its highest setting. If both readings show high resistance, replace the ignition coil.

5. Connect a vacuum source to the vacuum advance. The vacuum control plate should move as vacuum is applied. If not, replace the vacuum advance.

A—Distributor Cap   D—Terminal 2
B—Coil Button   E—Terminal 1
C—Terminal 3   F—Ohmmeter

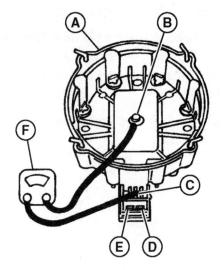

Fig. 29 — Testing Distributor with Ohmmeter

OUO1082,0002C86 -19-12JUN12-6/9

6. Disconnect the pickup coil leads (Fig. 30) from the electronic module and connect an ohmmeter between lead No. 1 and ground. Set the ohmmeter on the middle scale and operate the vacuum advance, using the vacuum source, to the full range of travel of the vacuum control plate. The ohmmeter should show very little resistance as this is done. If not, replace the pickup coil (see next page).

7. Connect the ohmmeter to pickup coil leads 1 and 2, and apply vacuum. If the meter reads less than 500 ohms or more than 1500 ohms while the vacuum is applied, replace the pickup coil.

8. If tests to this point fail to reveal the cause of the problem, all that remains is to replace the electronic module. This may be done without removing the distributor from the engine by removing the two screws holding the module (Fig. 30).

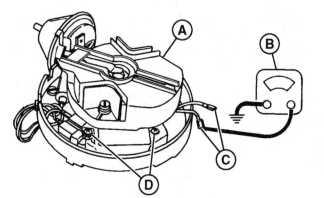

Fig. 30 — Pickup Coil Leads and Module Screws

A—Rotor   C—Pickup Coil Leads
B—Ohmmeter   D—Electronic Module Screws

Continued on next page   OUO1082,0002C86 -19-12JUN12-7/9

REPLACING THE IGNITION COIL

Remove the three screws holding the coil to the distributor cap (Fig. 31). Remove the ground wires from the coil, push the coil leads from the underside of the connectors, and remove the coil.

IMPORTANT: **A number of different ignition coils are made for this self-integrated system. They work the same way, but the correct one for the particular setup must be used.**

A—Screw (3 used)

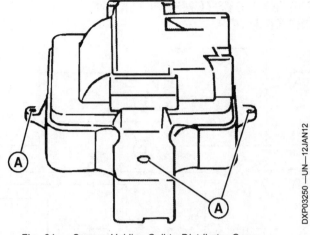

Fig. 31 — Screws Holding Coil to Distributor Cap

OUO1082,0002C86 -19-12JUN12-8/9

REPLACING THE PICKUP COIL

Remove the distributor and mount it in a workbench vise. Drive the pin from the distributor shaft gear (Fig. 32). Remove the rotor shaft assembly from the housing and take off the thin C-clip. This releases the pickup coil.

Install a new pickup coil. Replace the C-clip and rotor shaft assembly. Place the keeper pin back in the distributor shaft gear and reinstall the distributor.

A—Distributor Shaft   B—Drift

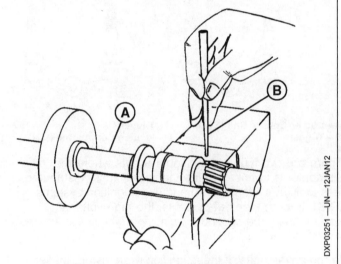

Fig. 32 — Distributor Shaft Gear Pin

OUO1082,0002C86 -19-12JUN12-9/9

IGNITION SYSTEMS WITHOUT DISTRIBUTORS

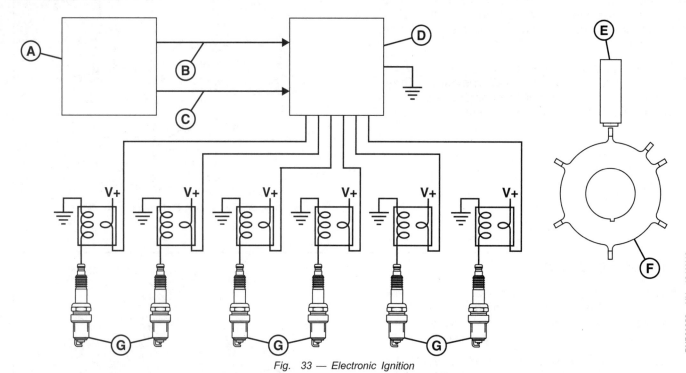

Fig. 33 — Electronic Ignition

A—Engine Control Unit (ECU) C—Trigger E—Camshaft Position Sensor G—Spark Plugs
B—Trigger D—Ignition Control Unit (ICU) F—Camshaft Trigger Wheel

There are two types of ignition systems where the distributor is not used to fire the spark plugs: distributor less ignition systems (DLI) and direct ignition systems (DIS). In both types of systems, the high voltage generated by the secondary winding of the coil is applied directly to the spark plug.

Some advantages of these ignition systems are these:

• Improved reliability
• Greater ignition spark control
• Electrical interference from the distributor is eliminated
• Ignition timing can be controlled over a wider range

There are two basic methods for generating sparks in these ignition systems.

• Independent ignition (non-waste spark)
• Simultaneous ignition (waste spark)

Independent ignition uses one coil per cylinder. Simultaneous ignition systems use one coil and two cylinders, which are paired according to piston position.

A typical direct ignition system is shown in Fig. 33. It is a non-waste spark, camshaft-referenced, inductive ignition system. For a detailed description of the operation of the ignition system of a particular machine, refer to the Technical Manual for the appropriate machine.

The overall operation of the ignition system is controlled by the Engine Control Unit (ECU). The spark timing is controlled by the ECU based on engine speed, manifold absolute pressure, and engine coolant temperature.

The manifold absolute pressure sensor sends a signal to the ECU to indicate the manifold (boost) pressure. The ECU interprets this signal as an indication of the load on the engine.

The ECU monitors signals from the camshaft position sensor to determine engine speed and piston position. The ECU determines the desired timing advance and then outputs a trigger signal to the Ignition Control Unit (ICU) when a coil should be fired. A synchronized pulse is also sent by the ECU to the ICU so the ICU fires the correct coil.

SUMMARY: ELECTRONIC IGNITION

Electronic ignition systems operate similar to conventional ignition systems except that the spark is electronically timed. Electronic ignition systems do not have points or a condenser so they require little maintenance. They also produce a hotter spark of longer duration for:

• Quicker starts under adverse weather conditions
• More complete combustion
• Longer spark plug life

OUO1082,0002C87 -19-12JUN12-1/1

ELECTRONIC DIESEL FUEL INJECTION

INTRODUCTION

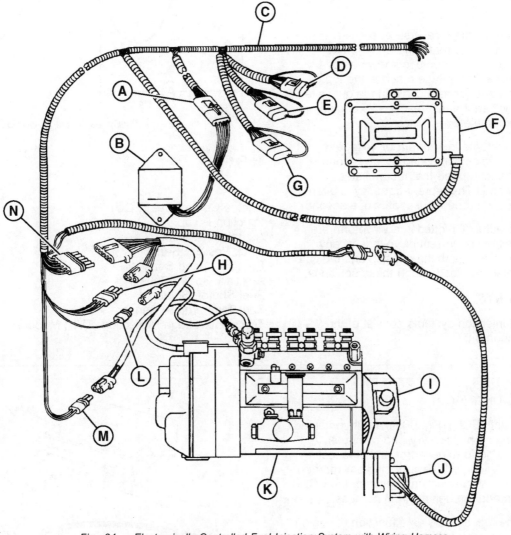

Fig. 34 — Electronically Controlled Fuel Injection System with Wiring Harness

A—TVP Connector
B—TVP Module
C—Application Wiring Harness
D—Diagnostic Voltage Connector

E—Diagnostic Reader Connector
F—Engine Control Unit (ECU)
G—Service Connector
H—Actuator Connector

I— Injection Pump Rear Cover
J— Auxillary Speed Sender
K—Fuel Injection Pump
L—Fuel Shutoff Connector

M—Fuel Temperature Connector
N—Speed Sensor/Rack Sensor
   Connector

Conventional fuel injection systems include an in-line multiple plunger injection pump equipped with a mechanical fly weight governor and aneroid control. An engine-driven gear on the pump camshaft drives the pump at one-half engine speed.

Some of these pumps are distributor-type pumps. In these pumps, a fuel metering valve is controlled by the governor.

A governor-operated control rack is connected to the control sleeves and plungers to regulate the quantity of fuel delivered to the engine.

The hydraulically actuated aneroid controls rack track travel and, therefore, fuel delivery. The aneroid control

is in effect until the manifold pressure is high enough to overcome the aneroid diaphragm spring pressure.

Newer machines utilize electronic fuel injection systems (Fig. 34). These systems usually do not use an aneroid. They rely on electronic governing to control fuel quantity. These systems consist of an Engine Control Unit (ECU), an auxiliary speed sensor, a Transient Voltage Protection (TVP) module, and an injection pump/actuator assembly.

The injection pump/actuator assembly includes the injection pump, actuator solenoid, rack position sensor, primary speed sensor, fuel shutoff solenoid, and fuel temperature sensor.

Continued on next page   OUO1082,0002C88 -19-12JUN12-1/14

HOW ELECTRONIC DIESEL FUEL INJECTION WORKS

In order to understand how electronic fuel injection works, it is first necessary to comprehend frequency, cycles, and waveforms.

Alternating current and voltage reverse at regular intervals. This forms a curve that can be plotted or graphically represented. This curve is known as a waveform. When current or voltage reaches the top of this curve, it reverses and forms a curve in the opposite direction (Fig. 35). When it again reaches its original starting point, it has completed a cycle.

The frequency of an alternating current or voltage is the number of these cycles completed every second. Electricity travels at such speed that it completes many cycles per second. Therefore, frequency is often measured in milliseconds (one thousandths of a second).

In summary, what is actually plotted in a waveform are the instantaneous values of current or voltage at any time. Waveforms represent both the position and the time elapsed while electricity rotates through these positions.

MAJOR COMPONENTS

Most electronic fuel injection systems consist of the following major components:

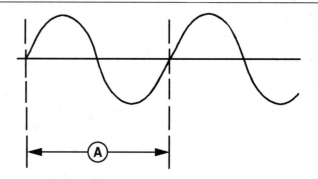

Fig. 35 — Frequency Cycles Create a Waveform

A—Cycle

• Engine Control Unit (ECU)
• Injection Pump
• Actuator Assembly
• Rack Position Sensor
• Primary Speed Sensor
• Auxiliary Speed Sensor
• Fuel Shutoff Solenoid
• Fuel Temperature Sensor
• Transient Voltage Protection (TVP) Module

OUO1082,0002C88 -19-12JUN12-2/14

ENGINE CONTROL UNIT (ECU)

The Engine Control Unit (ECU) (Fig. 36) is a self-contained module containing electronic circuitry and computer software. It is used to perform governor and diagnostic functions. The ECU is mounted in a protected environment away from the engine. All connections between the ECU and the engine are made through a wiring harness.

The ECU controls the fuel delivery as a function of engine speeds and throttle command. It also controls the fuel limiting for torque curves and the governing speed control.

Additionally, the ECU performs self-diagnosis on the control system. In most cases, a trouble code will be stored in memory if a problem occurs. The diagnostic capabilities of the system are covered in more detail later in this chapter.

A—Engine Control Unit   C—Wiring Harness
B—Connector

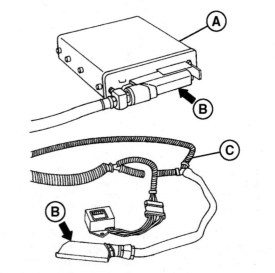

Fig. 36 — Engine Control Unit with Wiring Harness and Connector

Continued on next page   OUO1082,0002C88 -19-12JUN12-3/14

INJECTION PUMP

The electronically controlled in-line injection system uses the same basic hydraulic pumping mechanism used in mechanically governed in-line pumps.

The mechanical governor mechanism is replaced with the actuator assembly, which includes the actuator solenoid to move the control rack, rack position sensor, primary speed sensor, and a toothed speed wheel (Fig. 37).

The throttle lever mechanism used on the mechanical pumps is removed and its function is implemented by a throttle position sensor input to the Engine Control Unit (ECU). Fuel is transferred from fuel tanks with a fuel supply pump. The injection pump fuel inlet connection is located at the rear of the pump on the fuel inlet assembly, which includes the fuel shutoff solenoid and the fuel temperature sensor.

Fig. 37 — The Fuel Injection Pump and Actuator Assembly

Continued on next page   OUO1082,0002C88 -19-12JUN12-4/14

ACTUATOR SOLENOID

The actuator solenoid is contained within the actuator housing, mounted on the rear of the injection pump (Fig. 38). The actuator solenoid responds to signals received from the Engine Control Unit (ECU) to control the position of the fuel pump rack.

The injection pump control rack is spring-loaded to the fuel shutoff position or "zero rack." When the engine key switch is turned to the START position, the ECU powers the actuator solenoid, causing the rack to move to the starting fuel position.

Once the engine has started, the ECU determines the optimum fuel delivery based on various inputs (primarily throttle position and engine speed). The ECU adjusts the current level to the actuator solenoid, causing a corresponding movement of the rack to provide the correct fuel delivery.

The ECU has the ability to control the current to the solenoid in order to position the control rack anywhere between zero rack (fuel shutoff) and full rack (maximum fuel delivery).

The actuator solenoid can be serviced only by an authorized shop. The injection pump will also require recalibration after the actuator housing is removed.

RACK POSITION SENSOR

The rack position sensor is within the actuator housing. The sensor supplies rack position information to the Engine Control Unit (ECU) so that a specific rack position can be controlled.

The sensor includes an electronic module mounted in the actuator housing, which provides an input signal to the ECU, indicating the position of the rack. The ECU constantly monitors the input signal in order to determine the rack position. The ECU then controls the rack position by adjusting the current level to the actuating solenoid until the rack position signal matches the commanded signal.

The rack position signal is used to control the rack position for all operating conditions. If this critical sensor were to fail, the controller would be forced to shut down the engine due to loss of control of the fuel delivery.

The rack position sensor produces an output voltage that is available for diagnostic purposes and is not used by the governor system. This voltage signal is proportional to the pump rack position, and therefore can be used to determine if the governor control system is actually

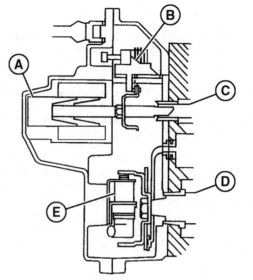

Fig. 38 — Actuator Assembly

A—Actuator Solenoid
B—Rack Position Sensor
C—Rack
D—Pump Camshaft
E—Speed Sensor

moving the rack to the proper range for a given operating condition. As the rack moves from low fuel delivery to maximum fuel delivery, the voltage signal should vary from a low voltage to a higher voltage.

The relationship between the rack position voltage and the rack position may vary depending on the system application. Consult the engine Technical Manual for complete instructions and specifications.

PRIMARY SPEED SENSOR

The primary speed sensor is located in the actuator assembly. The sensor is a magnetic pickup that generates electrical pulses as the teeth on the speed wheel move past a sensor. The Engine Control Unit (ECU) monitors the electrical pulses to determine the speed of the engine. The ECU continually adjusts current to the actuator solenoid to maintain the desired engine speed.

If this sensor were to fail completely, the ECU would use the signal from the auxiliary speed sensor to govern the engine speed.

Because the primary speed sensor is located inside the actuator housing, it can be serviced only by an authorized repair shop.

Continued on next page   OUO1082,0002C88 -19-12JUN12-5/14

AUXILIARY SPEED SENSOR

The auxiliary speed sensor (Fig. 39) is typically located on the front of the engine. It is also a magnetic pickup that generates voltage pulses to the Engine Control Unit (ECU) as the teeth on the timing gear pass by the tip of the sensor. The frequency of the voltage pulses is proportional to the engine speed.

The ECU receives the input signal from the auxiliary speed sensor, and then transmits the auxiliary speed output signal for use by other electronic modules such as the tachometer. The auxiliary speed sensor serves as a back-up speed sensor in the event of a complete failure of the primary speed sensor.

The auxiliary speed sensor is a serviceable part. No recalibration is required when this sensor is replaced.

Fig. 39 — Auxiliary Speed Sensor

A—Auxiliary Speed Sensor

OUO1082,0002C88 -19-12JUN12-6/14

FUEL SHUTOFF SOLENOID

The fuel shutoff solenoid (Fig. 40) is energized (opening the valve) when the engine key switch is turned to the ON position. The shutoff solenoid will shut off the fuel supply to the injection pump when the key switch is turned to the OFF position.

If a problem occurs where the Engine Control Unit (ECU) cannot control the rack position, the fuel shutoff solenoid is turned off in addition to the actuator solenoid being de-energized.

FUEL TEMPERATURE SENSOR

The fuel temperature sensor (Fig. 40) is located at the fuel inlet to the pump. This sensor monitors the temperature of the fuel entering the injection pump.

The sensor is a temperature-sensitive variable resistor. As the temperature goes up, resistance goes down. Even small changes in temperature can be determined by monitoring the resistance of the sensor. The Engine Control Unit (ECU) continually sends a voltage signal to the sensor, monitors the voltage drop across the resistor, then compares the sensor voltage to preprogrammed values to determine the fuel temperature.

The ECU uses fuel temperature to determine the optimum fuel delivery for starting and, depending on the application, to maintain constant power over a predetermined temperature range.

The ECU uses engine speed and initial fuel temperature to control the rack position during starting. This permits

Fig. 40 — Fuel Shutoff Solenoid and Fuel Temperature Sensor

A—Fuel Temperature Sensor   B—Fuel Shutoff Solenoid

the use of excess fuel and retarding the timing for cold temperatures, but less fuel and no retard for hot starts. Thus cold starting is improved, and black smoke can be greatly reduced on hot starts.

The ECU provides nearly constant fuel delivery to the engine by compensating for changes in the fuel density over any desired temperature range. The fuel temperature compensation characteristic is dependent on engine application and is programmed at the factory.

If the fuel temperature sensor were to fail, a low temperature would be assumed by the ECU. In warm weather this might result in a slight drop in maximum torque and increased smoke on hot starts.

Continued on next page   OUO1082,0002C88 -19-12JUN12-7/14

TRANSIENT VOLTAGE PROTECTION (TVP) MODULE

The main function of the Transient Voltage Protection (TVP) module is to limit high-energy voltage transients (from the charging system) to a maximum of 40 volts to protect the electronic circuitry in the Engine Control Unit (ECU) (Fig. 41).

HOW THE ELECTRONICALLY CONTROLLED FUEL INJECTION SYSTEM WORKS

When the key switch is turned to the ON position, power is supplied to the Engine Control Unit (ECU) and the fuel shutoff solenoid. When energized, the shutoff solenoid opens the fuel shutoff valve. The fuel shutoff valve closes when the current flow to the shutoff solenoid is stopped.

When the key switch is turned to the START position, the ECU commands the actuator solenoid to move the injection pump rack to the starting fuel position. Starting fuel quantity is not affected by throttle position.

In the starting mode, the ECU monitors fuel temperature and engine speed. Based on this information, the ECU will regulate the position of the pump rack to deliver the correct amount of fuel for starting. This permits the use of excess fuel and retarding of the timing for cold temperature, but less fuel and no retard for hot starts. Thus, cold weather starting is improved, and black smoke can be greatly reduced on hot starts.

Once the engine has started, fuel delivery is controlled by the ECU based on various inputs (primarily throttle and engine speed). The ECU controls the pump rack position by adjusting the current level to the actuator solenoid.

The electronic actuator responds to the signals received from the ECU to control the positioning of the fuel pump rack. The actuator also provides feedback to the ECU on engine speed and rack position. The ECU adjusts the current level to the actuator solenoid until the rack position signal from the actuator matches the commanded signal.

When no fuel is desired, the ECU turns off current to the actuator solenoid. If a problem occurs where the ECU

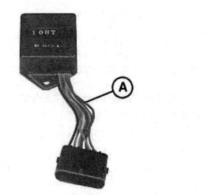

Fig. 41 — Transient Voltage Protection (TVP) Module

A—Transient Voltage
  Protection (TVP) Module

cannot control rack position, it will shut off current to the fuel shutoff solenoid in addition to the actuator solenoid.

GOVERNOR MODES

The governor mode is preset at the factory. Based on application, the engine controller can provide either all-speed governing or minimum-maximum (min-max) governing. When using all-speed governing, the controller regulates the engine speed based on the throttle command and selected speed regulation (droop).

When using the min-max governor, the controller provides the same minimum (slow idle) and maximum (fast idle) speed governing as with the all-speed governor. However, in between the minimum and maximum speeds, the throttle and engine speed inputs are used by the controller to select a fuel quantity. Thus, the throttle commands fuel quantity rather than engine speed in the min-max governor mode.

The percent of droop can be programmed at the factory to provide three switch-selectable combinations of droop, rated speed, and fast idle, including zero percent (isochronous).

Continued on next page   OUO1082,0002C88 -19-12JUN12-8/14

Look at Fig. 42, it shows these combinations of engine speed: LI is low (slow) idle, Nr is normal rated, and FI is fast idle.

The engine application determines which droops will be programmed into the controller and whether or not they will be switch-selectable. If no input signal is present, the normal droop/fast idle combination is selected. The engine controller provides isochronous governing at the slow idle speed regardless of the speed regulation selected for governing over the rest of the operating range.

The slow idle, fast idle, and breakaway speeds are programmed at the factory and are values that are precisely repeatable, eliminating system-to-system variations.

A—Power   B—Engine Speed

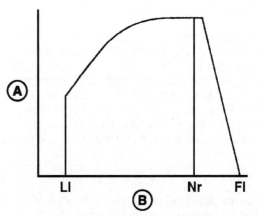

Fig. 42 — Combinations of Engine Speed

OUO1082,0002C88 -19-12JUN12-9/14

MAXIMUM FUEL QUANTITY CONTROL

The Engine Control Unit (ECU) limits the maximum fuel delivery as a function of engine speed. This function is set at the factory to obtain the proper fuel limit curve (power curve).

Some electronic governors provide an optional feature that allows the power curve to be switched to any one of three factory-programmed power curves (Fig. 43). Switching between the power curves can be accomplished by the ECU while the engine is running.

The normal power curve is selected if no input signal is present.

A derated power curve is usually selected by shorting the input signal to ground. A temperature switch is one method used to select the derated power curve.

The third curve is typically used for a Power Boost mode. Since operation using this curve can be limited by timers within the ECU, this power curve is selected by connecting the input to ground through a 2 k-ohm resistor. The ECU will limit Power Boost operation to the amount of time programmed in the ON timer. If the ON time limit is reached, the ECU will automatically switch back to the normal power curve. The OFF time must then be reached before the ECU will allow reselection of the Power Boost curve.

THROTTLE OPTIONS

There are three throttle options available for use with the electronically controlled fuel injection system. The

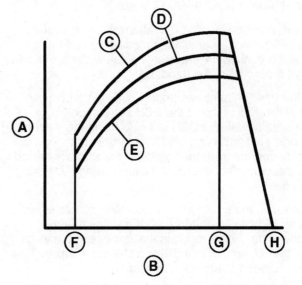

Fig. 43 — Fuel Delivery as a Function of Engine Speed

A—Power   E—Derated Power Curve
B—Engine Speed   F—Low Idle
C—Power Boost   G—Rated Speed
D—Normal Power Curve   H—Fast Idle

selection of a throttle option is dependent on the application and is programmed into the ECU. These options are:

• Analog Throttle
• Three-State Throttle
• Pulse-Width-Modulated (PWM) Throttle

Continued on next page   OUO1082,0002C88 -19-12JUN12-10/14

Analog Throttle

The analog throttle is commonly used with either all-speed or min-max governing. The analog throttle provides a continuously variable voltage input to the Engine Control Unit (ECU). The voltage input normally passes through a potentiometer (variable resistor) (Fig. 44); then the ECU converts this voltage into a percentage of full throttle command. The signal is sent to the injection pump actuator solenoid to control fuel delivery and engine speed accordingly.

Three-State Throttle

The three-state throttle uses a simple switching arrangement to select one of three fixed speeds. Typical applications are generator sets where one or two fixed speeds are desired, and combines, which use three fixed speeds.

Fig. 44 — Speed Control Potentiometer

A—Speed Control
   Potentiometer

OUO1082,0002C88 -19-12JUN12-11/14

Pulse-Width-Modulated (PWM) Throttle.

The Pulse-width-modulated (PWM) throttle is a signal received from another electronic module (usually a transmission controller) that uses a pulse width to indicate the desired percent of full throttle.

The PWM throttle input has priority over the analog throttle. This means that if the ECU starts receiving a PWM throttle signal, the ECU will stop using the analog throttle and will start using the PWM throttle to determine the throttle command. If the PWM throttle signal is turned off or is disconnected, the ECU will start using the analog throttle again.

The illustration in Fig. 45 shows the PWM throttle signal waveform. "Pulse-Width-Modulated" means that the frequency of the signal remains the same, and the width of the pulse is changed to indicate a change in value. This signal is repeated every 10 milliseconds.

SMOKE CONTROL

Smoke control is based on mathematical equations that use known engine characteristics. The engine controller implements smoke control based on the instantaneous values and the rates of change of throttle, load, and speed. This "math model" smoke control is used for most applications since it provides good smoke control without requiring intake manifold sensors.

FUEL TEMPERATURE COMPENSATION

The engine controller monitors the injection pump inlet fuel temperature with the fuel temperature sensor located

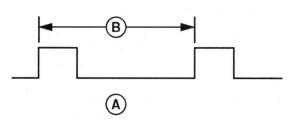

Fig. 45 — Pulse-Width-Modulated Throttle Data Signal

A—PWM Throttle Input Signal   B—10 msec
   Waveform

at the fuel shutoff valve manifold. The controller can provide nearly constant fuel delivery (horsepower) by compensating for changes in fuel density over any desired temperature range. The fuel temperature compensation characteristic is dependent on engine application and is programmed at the factory.

FUEL FLOW/THROTTLE OUTPUT SIGNAL

The ECU sends a pulse-width-modulated signal that indicates the percentage of full load/rated speed fuel delivery and percentage of full throttle. This signal is primarily intended for use by a transmission controller, but is also useful for monitoring performance if the engine application has compatible electronics.

Continued on next page

OUO1082,0002C88 -19-12JUN12-12/14

110112
PN=362

The illustration in Fig. 46 shows the waveform of the signal. "Pulse-Width-Modulated" means that the frequency of the signal remains the same, and the width of the pulse is changed to indicate a change in value. The width of the synchronizing pulse remains constant and indicates the beginning of the signal. This signal is repeated every 20 milliseconds.

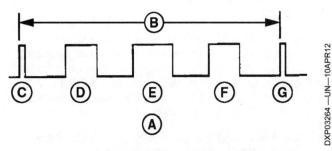

A—Fuel Flow/Throttle Output
    Signal Waveform
B—20 msec
C—Sync
D—Percent Fuel

E—Percent Throttle
F—Percent Fuel
G—Sync

Fig. 46 — Pulse-Width-Modulated Signal Waveform

OUO1082,0002C88 -19-12JUN12-13/14

AUXILIARY SPEED OUTPUT SIGNAL

The engine controller receives the auxiliary speed input from the sensor and then transmits the auxiliary speed output signal for use by other electronic modules such as the tachometer and other controllers. Only the ECU receives the signal from the auxiliary speed sensor at the front of the engine.

The illustration in Fig. 47 shows the waveform of the auxiliary speed output signal. The signal is the same frequency as the auxiliary speed sensor. This may be 10 or 23 pulses per engine revolution, depending on the application.

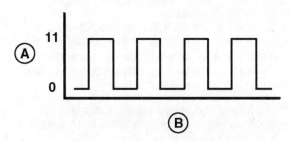

Fig. 47 — Auxiliary Speed Output Data Signal

A—Volts

B—Time

OUO1082,0002C88 -19-12JUN12-14/14

TROUBLESHOOTING ELECTRONIC FUEL INJECTION

The Engine Control Unit (ECU) contains electronic circuitry and a computer program that performs diagnostic functions when the ECU is in the governor mode (normal engine operating mode). In most cases, the ECU will display a diagnostic code to indicate a specific problem (Fig. 48). The ECU can also flash a fault lamp.

When troubleshooting the fuel injection system, check if there are diagnostic codes being displayed. If no diagnostic codes are present, verify that a problem does not exist in the basic electrical system or in the fuel supply system before continuing troubleshooting of the fuel injection system. Some areas that should be checked include:

- Charging system—alternator output, condition of the batteries and battery cables.
- Power distribution system—fuses or circuit breakers, key switch and any relays between the battery and fuel injection system, starter solenoid wiring connections.
- Fuel source—fuel in the tank, quality of fuel, condition of fuel filters and fuel lines.

If the fault is in one of the above areas, fuel injection system diagnostic procedures will probably not locate the problem.

CHECKING WIRING AND CONNECTORS

When diagnosing electrical system problems, note the condition of the wiring and connectors since a high percentage of problems originate here.

Check for loose, dirty, damaged, or disconnected connectors. Inspect for wires that may have been pulled out of their connector terminal. Look for poorly positioned terminals and inspect for corroded wires and terminals.

Inspect wiring for possible shorts caused by wires rubbing against metal edges or other external parts.

RUNNING ENGINE AT DIFFERENT SPEEDS

If the engine will start, operate the throttle control(s) at slow-to-medium rate between the slow idle and the fast idle stops with the engine running. If the engine speed "catches" or "drops," this may indicate a problem with the throttle adjustment, throttle sensor operation, or the wiring between the Engine Control Unit (ECU) and the throttle sensor(s). Using this method of changing engine speed, you may be able to identify problems that occur only at certain speeds or throttle settings.

SELF-DIAGNOSIS AND BACK-UP FEATURES

NOTE: *If the operator is able to keep the engine running during a fault condition, no damage to the engine should result. However, the problem should be fixed at the earliest convenience.*

The Engine Control Unit (ECU) self-diagnoses as many system faults as practical. This includes determining if

Fig. 48 — Tachometer Display of Diagnostic Codes

any of the sensor input voltages are too high or too low, if the engine speed signals are valid, and if the pump control rack is responding properly.

The ECU also monitors its own operation for problems. In most cases, it will output a diagnostic code to indicate the specific problem that has been detected. If the ECU indicates a fault condition, it will also store the diagnostic code within its own memory. The diagnostic code messages will help isolate the problem and allow quicker repair.

A diagnostic reader is used to interpret and display diagnostic codes to the operator. A diagnostic code is typically displayed as a number or a series of numbers.

A diagnostic reader can be as simple as a digital tachometer located in the vehicle's instrument panel or as sophisticated as a portable electronic governor testing device. The ECU can also flash a fault lamp that indicates the diagnostic status of the system.

Each diagnostic code represents a specific fault condition that may be caused by one or more conditions. If only one diagnostic condition is present, the code for that condition is transmitted every second and displayed continuously by the reader. If multiple conditions are present, the codes are transmitted one after another, once per second, until all conditions have been transmitted. The order in which the codes are transmitted has no meaning, and the display sequence is repeated continuously.

A diagnostic code is transmitted as long as the fault condition exists. If an intermittent condition is present, the code may be present for only a short time.

The ECU has the capability to save the diagnostic codes that have occurred. The codes are saved even when the engine key switch is turned off. This allows a service person to check to see if a diagnostic code has occurred in the past even though it is not presently occurring. This is helpful for intermittent failure conditions.

Continued on next page   OUO1082,0002C89 -19-12JUN12-1/2

NOTE: *Record stored codes before disconnecting the battery. Once the battery is disconnected, stored codes will be erased.*

If the ECU detects a problem that can be diagnosed, it will switch to a safe mode of operation as a back-up whenever possible, or it will shut down the engine if control of the engine cannot be maintained.

In some fault conditions, little or no degradation in performance will be noticed. For example, the engine will continue to operate normally using the auxiliary speed sensor in the event of a primary speed sensor fault.

Consult the Technical Manual specific to your engine for the specifications and diagnostic procedures for that engine.

DIAGNOSTIC CODES

Following is a sample listing of diagnostic codes that can occur in an electronic governor system. Not all of these codes will be present in all engine applications. Refer to the engine Technical Manual for detailed information on diagnostic codes.

28—Engine Control Unit (ECU) Failure

29—Sensor Excitation Voltage Too High or Too Low

32—Actuator Circuit Fault

33—Actuator Solenoid Output Shorted High

34—Rack Position Error

35—Rack Position Voltage Too Low

36—Rack Position Voltage Too High

37—Fuel Temperature Input Voltage Too High

38—Fuel Temperature Input Voltage Too Low

39—Primary Speed Input Error

41—Start Signal Missing

42—Engine Over-Speed

43—PWM Throttle Input Erratic

44—Auxiliary Speed Input Error

47—Derated Torque Curve Selected

51—Electrical Noise on Analog Throttle Input

54—Electrical Noise on Rack Position Voltage Input

55—Electrical Noise on Fuel Temperature Input

56—Electrical Noise on Fuel Limit Select Input

57—Electrical Noise on Speed Regulation Select Input

58—Electrical Noise on Three-State Throttle Input

59—Electrical Noise on +5 V Sensor Excitation

OUO1082,0002C89 -19-12JUN12-2/2

USING ELECTRONIC GOVERNOR TESTER

The Electronic Governor Tester (Fig. 49) is a portable diagnostic reader that provides a display of diagnostic codes, throttle position, or commanded fuel quantity. The Electronic Governor Tester is used by connecting it to the Diagnostic Reader Connector of the governor system wiring harness. The reader is powered through this connector so the engine key switch must be ON to obtain a display. Refer to the engine Technical Manual for detailed information on the Diagnostic Reader Connector.

Diagnostic codes are obtained by pressing the DISPLAY CODES switch. Stored diagnostic codes can be recalled by pressing the DISPLAY CODES and then holding the RECALL CODES switch to display the codes. Stored diagnostic codes can be cleared by simultaneously pressing both the RECALL CODES and CLEAR CODES switches for at least one second.

Throttle position is obtained by pressing the % THROTTLE switch. The throttle position is given as a percentage of full throttle. The range for the percent throttle is 0%–100%.

Commanded fuel quantity is obtained by pressing the % FUEL switch. Fuel quantity is given as a percentage of rated fuel delivery. The range for the percent fuel is 0%–159%.

Fig. 49 — Electronic Governor Tester

A—Electronic Governor Tester

For detailed test procedures and specifications of a particular engine, consult the appropriate Technical Manual for that engine.

Continued on next page   OUO1082,0002C8A -19-12JUN12-1/3

DIAGNOSTIC VOLTAGES CONNECTOR

The Diagnostic Voltages Connector, a part of the electronic governor system wiring harness, provides access to important governor system voltages that can be read using a digital multimeter (Fig. 50). The following voltages should be present at the connector:

• Analog Throttle +5 V
• Throttle Input Voltage
• Rack Position Voltage
• Sensor Common

The ANALOG THROTTLE +5 V is the source voltage from the engine control unit (ECU) for the analog throttle. This voltage signal can be used to check on the condition of the ECU internal power supply system. The nominal voltage should be 4.8–5.2 volts. If the voltage is outside this range, the ECU may be faulty or there may be a short within the wiring harness. The absence of the +5 V indicates a failure within the ECU or a problem in the wiring harness or throttle sensor.

The THROTTLE INPUT VOLTAGE is the input to the ECU from the throttle sensor. It is proportional to the throttle position and the analog +5 V supply. This signal can be used to check throttle sensor adjustment and performance of the throttle sensor.

As the throttle is moved from slow idle to high idle, the throttle input voltage should vary from low voltage to a high voltage. The voltage should change smoothly as the throttle is moved slowly through its range. If voltage readings do not change or change erratically rather than smoothly, the throttle sensor may be defective.

The RACK POSITION VOLTAGE signal is proportional to the injection pump rack position. The voltage reading can be used to determine if the governor control system is actually moving the rack to the proper range for a given operating condition. Consult the engine Technical Manual for the rack position voltages specific to the engine.

The SENSOR COMMON is the system "common" or "ground" reference point for the throttle and rack position voltages. The "ground" input should be connected to the common socket of the sensor when measuring these voltages.

Refer to the engine Technical Manual for detailed information on diagnostic voltage testing.

SUMMARY: ELECTRONIC FUEL INJECTION

The electronic fuel injection system consists of an engine controller, injection pump/actuator assembly, auxiliary speed sensor, and transient voltage protection module.

The central component of the electronic fuel injection system is the Engine Control Unit (ECU), which contains electronic circuitry and a computer program that performs governor and diagnostic functions. It controls fuel delivery as a function of engine speed and throttle command. It also controls the fuel limiting for torque curves and the governing speed control. Aneroids are eliminated, and for

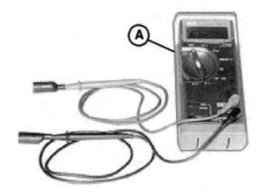

Fig. 50 — Digital Multimeter

A—Digital Multimeter

most applications the controller can control fuel delivery to limit smoke without using additional sensors.

The electronically controlled in-line injection system uses the same basic hydraulic pumping mechanism used in mechanically governed in-line pumps except that the mechanical governor mechanism is replaced with the actuator assembly. This assembly includes an actuator solenoid to move the control rack, a rack position sensor, a primary speed sensor, and a toothed speed wheel.

The auxiliary speed sensor serves as a back-up speed sensor in the event of complete failure of the primary speed sensor. The transient voltage protection module limits high energy voltage transients from the charging system to protect the electronic circuitry in the ECU.

Some advantages of an electronic fuel injection system include:

• Decreased smoke.
• Maximum fuel quantity control.
• Fuel temperature compensation which delivers nearly constant fuel delivery.
• Self-diagnostic and back-up features.

SUMMARY OF ELECTRONIC GOVERNOR BENEFITS

Some benefits of the electronic governor system are:

• Fewer mechanical parts in governor to encounter wear.
• Different governor modes are possible for specific operating conditions.
• Precise fuel control based upon engine speed and fuel temperature.
• Quick start-up with less smoke and faster warm-up.
• Improved fuel economy and reduced exhaust smoke.
• Consistent power and performance.
• Engine performance is fine-tuned to meet a specific load requirement.
• Engine Control Unit (ECU) is programmable to provide precise torque curve characteristics designed for each application.
• Capable of communicating with other machine equipment such as transmission controllers.

Continued on next page   OUO1082,0002C8A -19-12JUN12-2/3

- Built-in self-diagnostics allow for quick and accurate repairs.

OUO1082,0002C8A -19-12JUN12-3/3

TEST YOURSELF

QUESTIONS

1. What three of the following parts are found in electronic ignition systems and not in conventional ignition systems?

    a. Ignition coil

    b. Sensor

    c. Distributor

    d. Spark plug wires

    e. Reluctor

    f. Ignition Control Unit (ICU)

2. What are three advantages of electronic ignition?

3. (True or False?) The reluctor and sensor may be repaired if they malfunction.

4. Why must the reluctor and sensor not contact each other?

5. How is a self-integrated electronic ignition system different from other types of electronic ignition systems?

6. The number of cycles electricity completes in one second is known as _____.

7. Engine control units rely on _____ governing to regulate fuel.

8. When the controller regulates the engine speed based on the throttle command and selected speed regulation, this is called _____ governing.

9. Electronic fuel injection systems use a "math model" to control _____.

(Answers on page B-3 in back of text.))

OUO1082,0002C8B -19-10JAN12-1/1

INTRODUCTION

DXP02710 —UN—23FEB11

10

DXP03269 —UN—08NOV11

This chapter covers all the extra equipment which completes the electrical system on modern machines.

We have covered the basic system in the preceding chapters on batteries and charging, starting, and ignition circuits.

Now let's fill in the remainder of the system with the lighting and accessory circuits.

This chapter will cover the following accessories in the order shown:

• Lighting Circuits

• Wiring Harnesses
• Electromagnetic Clutches
• Gauges
• Meters
• Horns and Buzzers
• Electric Motors
• Cigarette Lighters
• Convenience Outlets
• Flame Rods
• Glow Plugs (for Diesel Engines)

We will describe each accessory and give a brief story on testing and maintaining it in its circuit.

OUO1082,0002C96 -19-12JUN12-1/1

LIGHTING CIRCUITS

Lights are used on most all farm and industrial machines. They are required by the local government for night driving or towing in most areas. To avoid trouble, know your local regulations.

On modern tractors, the required lights are often two or four headlights (Fig. 1) and one taillight.

In addition, a flashing warning lamp is required in some states. This lamp warns other traffic that a slow-moving vehicle is on the road.

Most motorists on public roads are not farmers. In fact, the percentage of people who have farming backgrounds or those who even know farmers is becoming smaller each year. So, only a small percentage of the motoring public is likely to give much thought to the unique nature of a farm machine when they see it on the highway.

A motorist topping a hill at 55 mph and seeing a tractor 400 feet ahead of him travelling at 15 mph will have a closing speed of 40 mph. The motorist has less than seven seconds to recognize the speed of the tractor, react, and slow down.

Fig. 1 — Lighting on a Modern Tractor

Situations similar to the one above lead to thousands of slow-moving vehicle accidents each year. The motorists aren't able to stop in time. Many accidents are fatal.

OUO1082,0002C97 -19-26JUN12-1/6

Every vehicle intended to travel 25 mph or less is considered a slow-moving vehicle and should be identified with a slow moving vehicle (SMV) emblem visible from the rear (Fig. 2).

The triangular SMV emblem is the universal symbol to tell everyone the vehicle travels 25 mph or less. The emblem surface should be kept clean and in good repair for both day and night identification. When the reflective red border or fluorescent orange center lose their brilliance, the emblem should be replaced. The emblem should always be mounted securely with a point upward to clearly identify it is a universal symbol as intended.

In addition, lights and reflectors should be kept in good working order for farm machines traveling on public roads. Operate flashing lights both day and night so you can be recognized as an SMV.

On many farm implements, special lighting is used for night work in the field. On a self-propelled combine, for example, a special floodlight is used to light up the area where the grain is being cut and fed into the combine. Another floodlight shows the operator when the grain tank is full of grain.

Fig. 2 — An SMV Emblem Combined with Proper Machine Lighting Help Prevent Slow-Moving Vehicle Accidents

Continued on next page   OUO1082,0002C97 -19-26JUN12-2/6

LAYOUT OF THE LIGHTING CIRCUIT

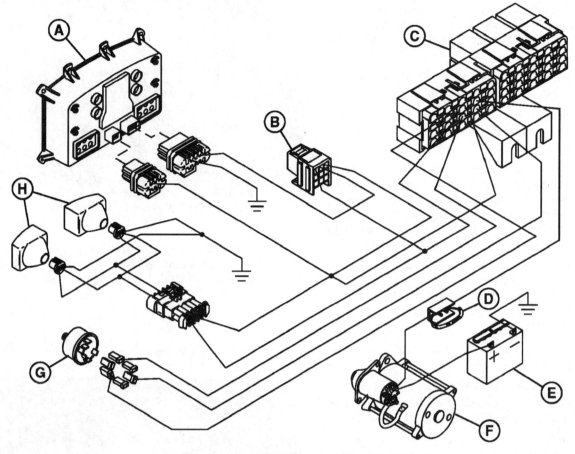

Fig. 3 — Layout of a Typical Lighting Circuit

A—Instrument Module	C—Circuit Breakers, Fuses, and	E—Battery	H—Headlight (2 used)
B—Lighting Relay	Relays	F—Starter	
	D—Fused Link	G—Light Switch	

The lighting circuit is normally a part of the complete electrical system. It operates on power from the battery with help from the charging circuit.

The parts of a typical lighting circuit are shown in Fig. 3. They are the various lamps which are operated by a light switch connected by the wiring harness. Other accessories shown are an electrical outlet socket and indicator lamps. The circuit is protected from a current overload by the circuit breakers and a fuse.

On most machines, the ignition switch must be turned on before the lights can be operated by the light switch. Also, some machines have indicator lamps which light up when the ignition switch is turned on and then go out when the engine is running, showing that the generator, oil pressure, etc., are normal.

On machines with two or four batteries, a split-load lighting circuit is sometimes used. This divides the load equally between both batteries when the lights are turned on. (For details on balancing batteries in split-load systems, see Chapter 5.)

LAMPS

Lamps used for lighting of modern machines are:

• Sealed-beam units (for headlights and flood lamps)
• Light bulbs (for other lights)

SEALED-BEAM UNITS

Headlights and flood lamps are normally sealed-beam units.

The headlights throw out a high-intensity beam and should always be dimmed when approaching a vehicle at night.

Caution should be exercised when replacing halogen bulbs. Halogen bulbs contain gas under pressure which could cause them to shatter. Turn off the light switch and allow the bulb to cool. Wear eye protection. Handle the bulb by its base. Do not drop or scratch the bulb.

Continued on next page   OUO1082,0002C97 -19-26JUN12-3/6

ADJUSTING HEADLIGHTS

When headlights are used on public roads, be sure they are adjusted so that the glare of the lights will not shine into the eyes of approaching drivers.

Looking at Fig. 4 it shows how to adjust the headlights on a typical tractor.

Position the tractor as shown on level ground and directly facing a wall 25 feet (7.6 m) away.

Turn the headlights on "bright" and check the height of the beams on the wall. The centers of the light beams should be 1–4 feet (0.3–1.22 m) high, depending upon the height of the tractor headlights. Keep the intense part of the beams at least 5 inches (127 mm) below the center of the light from which it comes.

The headlights should also be parallel to the tractor centerline. Look down the center of the tractor hood and see if the centers of the beams are at equal distances from the centerline (about 4 feet [1.22 m] apart or 2 feet [0.61 m] off center on most tractors).

On tractors with dual headlights, also check the outer flood lamps on "dim" to see that they shine downward and outward to illuminate the desired area as shown in Fig. 4.

To adjust the lights, loosen the lamp mounting bracket and rotate them as desired. Then retighten the mounting bracket. Remember: Only the lamp mounting bracket is adjustable—not the sealed-beam unit itself.

On other machines with headlights mounted higher than those on a tractor, always adjust the lamps downward far enough to avoid glare to oncoming traffic.

LIGHT BULBS

Miscellaneous lights such as taillights, dash lamps, and indicator lamps are normally equipped with single- or double-contact bulbs.

When replacing bulbs, make sure the replacement is of the same style and part number as the old one. Otherwise, the system can be damaged or the bulb may burn out rapidly.

Special light bulbs for special lighting effects may be required for some taillights, flasher lamps, or indicator lamps.

Indicator lamps are often used in place of gauges for generator, oil pressure, and temperature checks.

If the indicator lamp lights up or glows while the engine is running, this shows a failure in the system being monitored. For example, an oil pressure light may glow when the engine is low on oil.

When an indicator lamp comes on, be sure to stop the engine at once and check out the possible causes. But also remember that a burnt-out indicator lamp never lights up, even while the engine is being damaged.

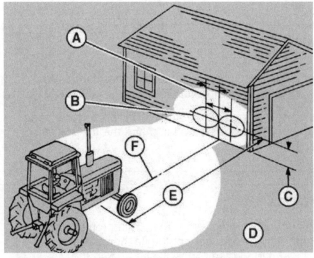

Fig. 4 — Adjusting Headlights

A—Width of Beam
B—High Intensity Beam
C—Height of Beam
D—Floodlit Area
E—25 ft. (7.6 m)
F—Centerline of Tractor

LED'S

LED's are now becoming a big part of illumination, due to the low power consumption and high efficiency, versus traditional light bulbs.

LED's can be used for the interior as well as the exterior, especially in the automotive interior lighting, LED has become so sophisticated, it is found in the instrument panel, backlight switch, auto reading lamp, and display systems, On the exterior LED headlamps (high beam, and low beam), LED tail lamps, Daytime running lamps, turn indicators, and fog lights.

Advantages of LED's

- Longer Life—LED's can last thousands of hours over conventional light bulbs
- Size—The smaller size diversity allowing to change lighting patterns
- Lower Voltages—LED's require less power to operate.

LASERS

Technology is still advancing and laser lighting will soon be part of vehicles. Lasers lights will have a greater intensity with a beam 1000 times more intense than conventional LEDs, and consuming less than half the energy. Another advantage is that these laser light diodes will be even smaller than LED's allowing even more possibilities in terms of illumination.

FAILURES OF LAMPS

Failure of lamps may be caused by a defective unit, a broken wire, a disconnected wire, a corroded connection, a switch failure or an open circuit breaker.

Continued on next page OUO1082,0002C97 -19-26JUN12-4/6

To check a light bulb, visual inspection is best. A good bulb will be clear while a burnt-out bulb may be dark. Where the bulb glass is not dark, the filament wire will be visible. If it is broken, the bulb is defective.

To check a lighting circuit, test the faulty part for voltage drop. For details on making voltmeter tests, see Chapter 2.

If the voltage is correct but the lamp is dim, look for a poor wiring connection between the lamp and the main wiring harness.

If there is no voltage across the lamp, look for a broken wire, poor contact in the light switch, or a disconnected wiring connector. Replace or repair any defective parts.

If the lights all go out suddenly, check for a tripped circuit breaker or a blown fuse. For details, see "Circuit Breakers" and "Fuses," which follow in this chapter.

OUO1082,0002C97 -19-26JUN12-5/6

FLASHING LAMPS

When a flashing warning lamp (Fig. 5) is prohibited by local regulations, disconnect the flasher unit and the short wire connected to the flasher. (See the Operator's Manual.) If you want to burn the warning lamp continuously, connect the wire from the lamp directly into the lighting circuit wiring harness.

A—Flashing Lamp   B—Wiring Lead

Fig. 5 — Flashing Lamp

OUO1082,0002C97 -19-26JUN12-6/6

LIGHTING CIRCUIT WIRING HARNESS

A wiring harness is the trunk and branches which feed the electrical circuit. Wiring leads from one part of the circuit enter the trunk or sheath, joining other wires, and then emerge at another point in the circuit (Fig. 6). The harness sheath is normally made of rubber, cloth, electrical tape, or plastic tubing.

Be careful when installing a wire harness. Disconnect the battery, negative cable first. The harness must not interfere with moving parts of the machine. Also make certain the clips which hold the harness do not pinch through the harness and cut the wires. This can cause a short in the circuit. Make sure the harness is routed away from hot parts of the equipment and away from sharp objects.

Individual wires in a harness may be replaced by cutting off the defective wire at each end of the harness. Discard the removed ends of the wire. Run the new wire around the harness; do not try to thread the wire through the harness. Place the new wire in clips with the harness or attach to the harness with electrical tape. Avoid any sharp bends when installing the harness.

The proper gauge or size of an electrical wire depends on:

1. Total length of the wire in the circuit.

2. Total amperage that the wire will carry.

When replacing a defective wire in a circuit always use the same gauge of wire for replacement. Never use an undersized wire as it will not carry the required load and will overheat.

TESTING AND DIAGNOSIS OF WIRING

In Chapter 2, we said that a wiring circuit may fail in three ways:

1. Open or break

2. Ground

3. Short

The following chart tells how to test for each of these three failures.

The column on the right give the test results you can expect if the wiring has failed.

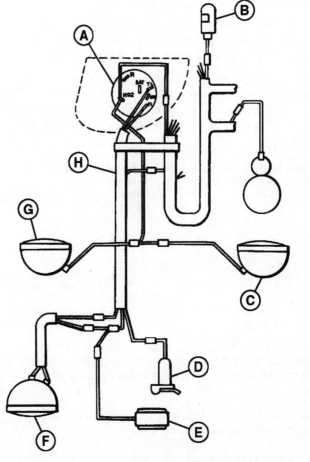

Fig. 6 — Wiring Harness

A—Light Switch	E—Warning Lamp
B—Dash Lamp	F—Rear Lamp
C—Right Headlight	G—Left Headlight
D—Outlet Socket	H—Wiring Harness

Wiring Test Chart	
Type of Failure	**Test Unit and Expected Results if Wiring Fails**
Open (Broken Wire)	Ohmmeter—infinite resistance at other end of wire. Infinite resistance to adjacent wire. Infinite resistance to ground. Voltmeter—Zero volts at the other end of the wire.
Ground (Bare Wire Touching Frame)	Ohmmeter—Zero resistance to ground. Infinite resistance to adjacent wire. May or may not be infinite resistance to the other end of the wire. Voltmeter—Instead of testing, look for blown fuse or tripped circuit breaker.
Short (Rubbing of Two Bare Wires)	Ohmmeter—Zero resistance to adjacent wire. Infinite resistance to ground. Voltmeter—Voltage will be read at both wires.

OUO1082,0002C98 -19-12JUN12-1/1

ELECTROMAGNETIC CLUTCHES

An electromagnetic clutch is an electric magnet device which stops the operation of one part of a machine while the other part of the unit keeps on operating.

A typical use of an electromagnetic clutch is on an air conditioning compressor (Fig. 7). When a current is applied to the clutch coil, a magnetic field pulls the drive plate in contact with the pulley, which causes the pump shaft to turn.

A—Pump Shaft
B—Pulley Bearing
C—Dust Cover
D—Hub and Drive Plate Assembly
E—Pulley
F—Clutch Coil

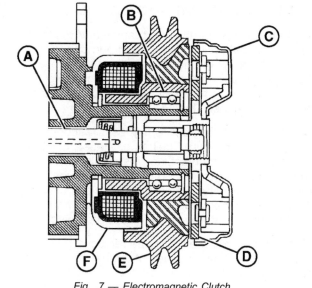

Fig. 7 — Electromagnetic Clutch

OUO1082,0002C99 -19-12JUN12-1/5

Another use of an electromagnetic clutch is on a grain combine where it is desirable to stop the cutting operation and yet continue the separation and cleaning operations (Fig. 8).

The clutch consists of a field coil assembly, rotor unit, face plate, condenser, and operating switch.

A—Rotor Unit and Condenser
B—Electromagnetic Clutch
C—Drive Sheave

Fig. 8 — Electromagnetic Clutch on a Grain Combine

Continued on next page

OUO1082,0002C99 -19-12JUN12-2/5

The basic theory of electromagnetism is covered in Chapter 2. The clutch works as follows (Fig. 9):

When the switch is actuated, current through the field coil inside the rotor assembly sets up a magnetic field which draws the face plate against the clutch facing on the rotor assembly. (The face plate is free to slide on the drive studs of the mechanism.) Power is then transmitted from the drive pulley through the face plate, rotor, and hub to the drive mechanism.

When the switch is operated again, the magnetic field is collapsed. The face plate is freed from the rotor and the transmission of power to the mechanism is instantly stopped.

A—Clutch Facing
B—Rotor Assembly
C—Field Assembly
D—Connecting Strap
E—Drive Sheave
F—Drive Studs

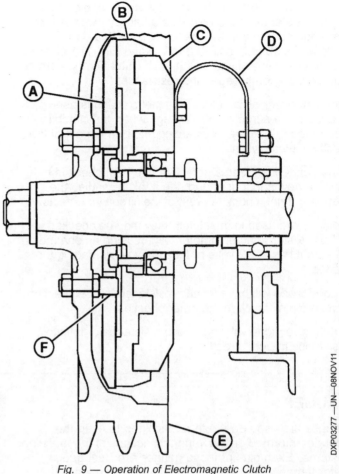

Fig. 9 — Operation of Electromagnetic Clutch

OUO1082,0002C99 -19-12JUN12-3/5

TESTING AND DIAGNOSIS

If the clutch suddenly loses power and fails to function, it is probably due to a failure in the electrical circuit.

First check all electrical connections, wires, switch, and circuit breaker in the switch. If these components are okay, then check the voltage to the field and the amperage of the field.

A—Clutch Assembly
B—Battery Eliminator

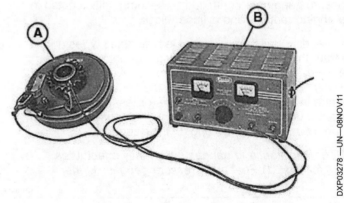

Fig. 10 — Checking Field Coil with Battery Eliminator

Continued on next page   OUO1082,0002C99 -19-12JUN12-4/5

To check the voltage to the field, the amperage of the field or the resistance of the field, use a battery eliminator or a storage battery and a volt-ohmmeter with a 0 to 15 volt scale and a 10 amp scale. (Fig. 10 and Fig. 11.) Check the individual specifications on each clutch for the correct voltage input, amperage, and resistance.

The condenser on an electromagnetic clutch is used to absorb the surge of high voltage when the clutch is disengaged. This prevents arcing and burning out of the electric clutch switch.

If the condenser seems defective, the best check is to install a new condenser and see if this remedies the problem. If not, check the rest of the circuit for defects.

If diodes are used in the clutch, they may be checked with a diode tester or an ohmmeter. When using an ohmmeter, be sure it has 1-1/2 volts or less to avoid damaging the diodes.

A good diode will have infinite resistance in one direction and zero resistance in the other direction.

A defective diode will show zero resistance or infinite resistance in both directions.

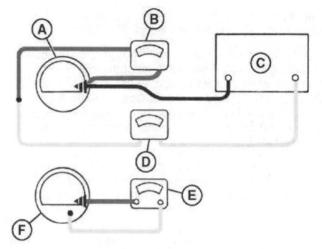

Fig. 11 — Checking Field Coil

A—Clutch Assembly
B—Voltmeter
C—Battery
D—Ammeter
E—Ohmmeter
F—Clutch Assembly

OUO1082,0002C99 -19-12JUN12-5/5

GAUGES

Gauges are used on modern machines to keep the operator informed on the various functions of the machine systems. Examples of these gauges are: fuel gauge, water temperature gauge, and oil pressure gauge. (Fig. 12.)

The fuel gauge is controlled by a sending unit located in the fuel tank, and the water temperature gauge and oil pressure gauge are controlled by sending units located in the engine radiator and cylinder block.

The sending units are all variable resistance types and operate the gauges in the following manner: The higher the water temperature, oil pressure, or level of fuel, the lower (or higher) the resistance in the sending unit. This change in resistance causes more (or less) current to pass through the connecting wire to the gauge coil, which in turn causes a new reading on the gauge.

NOTE: Resistance in gauges is normally affected as follows: 1) Fuel and pressure gauges: higher

Fig. 12 — Gauges on the Dash of a Modern Machine

level = higher resistance in gauge coils. 2) Temperature gauges: higher temperature = lower resistance in gauge coil.

Continued on next page   OUO1082,0002C9A -19-12JUN12-1/2

TESTING AND DIAGNOSIS OF GAUGES

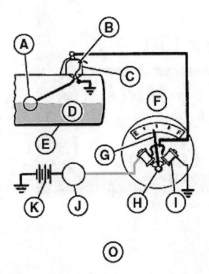 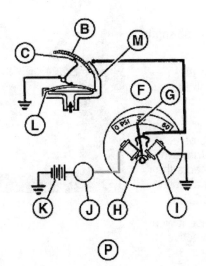 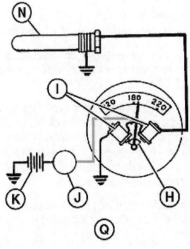

Fig. 13 — Three Gauges and Their Circuits

A—Float
B—Resistance
C—Sliding Contact
D—Fuel
E—Fuel Tank
F—Dash Unit
G—Pointer

H—Armature
I— Coil(s)
J— Ignition Switch
K—Battery
L—Oil Pressure Moves Diaphragm

M—Engine Unit
N—Sending Unit Is Immersed in Engine Coolant. Resistance of Unit Decreases with Heat.

O—Fuel Gauge
P—Oil Pressure Gauge
Q—Oil Temperature Gauge

Look at Fig. 13, it shows the circuits for three common gauges.

Diagnose the failures of gauges as given below.

If a gauge does not register, the cause could be:

1. Lack of current to the gauge.

2. Poor ground connection.

3. Connecting wire grounded to implement.

4. A defective sending unit or gauge.

If a gauge consistently registers too high, the cause could be:

1. Poor connection between gauge and connecting wire.

2. Broken connecting wire.

3. Poor ground at sending unit.

4. Failure of gauge or sender, usually the sender.

To test a gauge, use a commercial gauge tester. Follow the manufacturer's instructions closely.

If a commercial gauge tester is not available, substitute a new gauge and make sure it is satisfactory. A new sending unit may also be installed to check or to replace a defective unit.

Indicator lamps often use small light bulbs which glow to tell of a failure.

If these lamps do not glow when starting the engine, first check for a defective bulb. Then, if necessary, check out the other causes listed.

OUO1082,0002C9A -19-12JUN12-2/2

METERS

AMMETERS

The ammeter is an instrument for measuring the strength of an electric current in terms of amperes.

Normally, the ammeter is connected directly to the regulator to measure the flow of current through the electrical system.

A typical low-cost ammeter consists of a moving magnet with attached needle placed close to a conductor between the ammeter terminals. Current flow through the conductor creates a magnetic field that deflects the moving magnet and causes the needle to deflect away from zero on the meter scale.

If an ammeter does not register correctly, replace it with a new ammeter. Do not attempt to repair a defective ammeter.

VOLTMETER

Voltmeters are used to indicate the voltage of the electrical input in a circuit.

A typical low-cost voltmeter consists of a needle attached to a moving iron vane placed inside two stationary coils. The coil winding is parallel with the needle pivot and one winding tends to keep the needle at zero while the other tends to move the needle to the full-scale deflection.

Voltmeters are connected in parallel with the voltage to be measured. Since the voltmeter has a high resistance, adding this component to the circuit will change the total circuit current very little, and the voltage reading obtained shows the true voltage present without the meter in the circuit.

If a voltmeter does not function properly, a new voltmeter must be installed. A defective voltmeter cannot be repaired.

ELECTRIC HOUR METER

Electric hour meters (Fig. 14) are used to show the operating time of a machine while the engine is operating at its rated speed.

The hour meter records the time in hours and operates only when the engine is running.

Do not attempt to repair a defective hour meter or its sending unit. When they fail, new components must be installed.

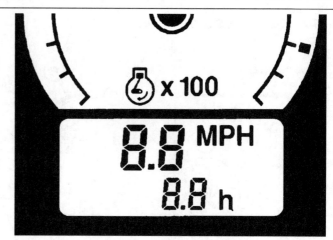

Fig. 14 — Electric Hour Meter

Continued on next page   OUO1082,0002C9B -19-12JUN12-1/2

MOISTURE METER

The moisture meter is a portable electronic device used to measure the moisture content of grain (Fig. 15). In grain drying, the moisture content is the percentage (by weight) of water in the grain.

Moisture in the grain is measured by penetrating the sample with high frequency radio waves. The effect the grain has on the radio waves varies with the amount of moisture. This is measured electronically by observing the change required to rebalance the meter when the grain is added. Because the waves penetrate the grain, the surface condition of the grain or mixed wet and dry grain will not affect the accuracy of the meter.

The moisture meter is accurately calibrated at the factory and should provide accurate measurements for years of normal use. To ensure accuracy and long life, avoid exposing the meter to rain and excessive dampness. When out of the carrying case, keep the meter covered with the plastic cover except when in use.

The electronic circuit cannot be repaired by a local electronic repair shop without destroying the factory

Fig. 15 — Moisture Meter

calibration. Never remove the case from the meter. If the moisture meter fails, return it to the factory where it can be repaired and accurately calibrated.

Some parts of the meter can be replaced in the field. In case of breakage or loss, the plastic index hand, knobs, scales, grain cup, small weight, and drawer can be replaced.

OUO1082,0002C9B -19-12JUN12-2/2

HORNS AND BUZZERS

Horns and buzzers are used on machines as signaling and warning devices (Fig. 16).

For example, on some grain combines, two different horns are used. One horn is used as a "call" horn to call the truck to the combine for unloading the grain tank when it is full of grain. The other horn is a signal device located inside the combine separator to warn the operator when the separator is overloading.

On farm and industrial tractors, horns are used to warn other vehicles and pedestrians that a moving machine is in the area. Horns are also used to warn the operator of some equipment when the engine is heating up.

Horns and buzzers are the same in design and operation. The only difference is in the sound. This is achieved by the use of different air columns. In a horn, the air column

Fig. 16 — Horn

is formed into a compact seashell form. This shape produces the maximum volume from the sound generated by the diaphragm.

Continued on next page   OUO1082,0002C9C -19-12JUN12-1/2

Two types of horns or buzzers may be used:

- The type S air-tone horn is shown in Fig. 17.
- The type C air-tone horn is similar to a type S horn except that it is smaller in size and does not have a resistor.

The horn or buzzer has a vibrating power unit to actuate a diaphragm which produces the sound as a warning signal.

When energized, current flows through the field coil to the contact points, then to the ground. The field coil magnetic field pulls the armature into the field coils, moving the diaphragm and opening the contact points. Opening the points de-energizes the field coil and the spring force of the diaphragm pulls the armature from the field coils, closing the points. This cycle is repeated 360 times per second on a high-note horn. Some horns are capable of sounding three notes.

The adjusting screw (Fig. 17) controls the time of point opening, which in turn controls current draw and frequency.

On a type S horn, the resistor connected across the contact points reduces the arcing of the points.

TESTS AND ADJUSTMENTS

IMPORTANT: Do not turn the horn adjusting screw more than 1/4-turn. To do so may damage the horn.

Before adjusting the horn, check the available voltage when the current draw is 10 amps. Adjusting the horn to compensate for excessive voltage drop will shorten the service life of the horn.

If the horn fails to operate with normal voltage, energize the horn and tap it lightly. If the horn now operates, the horn contacts were probably held open by a foreign particle. The horn should continue its normal operation when it is re-energized.

If the contacts are open as a result of wear, it will be necessary to tap the horn again after it is re-energized. A rough current adjustment can be made by turning the adjusting screw 1/4-turn counterclockwise.

To make further tests, connect an ammeter and a voltmeter to the horn.

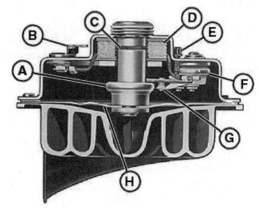

Fig. 17 — Cutaway View of Horn

A—Armature	E—Adjusting Screw
B—Terminal	F—Resistor
C—Air Gap	G—Contact Points
D—Field Coil	H—Diaphragm

Apply voltage to the horn and check the readings as follows:

1. No current indicates a broken lead or open circuit due to overheating. Overheated horns have the usual odor of burned insulation and should be replaced. On type C horns, no current flow also indicates open contacts. Turn the adjusting screw counterclockwise and recheck the horn.

2. On type S horns, a reading of approximately 2.5 amps indicates open contact points and that current is flowing through the horn resistor only. Turn the adjusting screw counterclockwise and recheck the horn.

3. A reading of approximately 20 to 25 amps indicates that the contact points are not opening. Turn the adjusting screw clockwise. One-quarter turn clockwise is usually enough unless the horn has been tampered.

4. When the horn is operating, adjust the current draw to the horn specifications in the machine Technical Manual. Turn the adjusting screw clockwise to decrease current. Turn the adjusting screw only 1/10-turn at a time.

OUO1082,0002C9C -19-12JUN12-2/2

ELECTRIC MOTORS

Small DC electrical motors are used to perform auxiliary functions on some machines. For example, motors are used to operate air conditioner blower, ventilating and heating fans, and windshield wipers. (Fig. 18.)

Small electric motors operate on the same principle as a starting motor. Refer to Chapter 5 for complete theory and operation.

If the proper equipment is not available, take defective motors to a good electrical shop for servicing.

A—Electric Motor

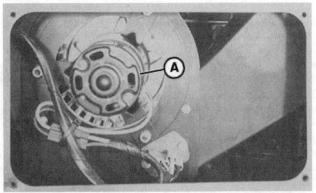

Fig. 18 — Electrical Motor Used to Operate Air Conditioner Blower Fan

OUO1082,0002C9D -19-12JUN12-1/1

CIGARETTE LIGHTERS

The cigarette lighter contains a heating element which contacts the electrical circuit when the lighter is pushed in. This causes the element to heat up and glow. The element will remain heated long enough to permit lighting a cigarette or cigar.

The lighter employs a circuit breaker to cut off the electrical current to the lighter element when it has heated to its peak.

Failure of the cigarette lighter may be caused by a broken wire, disconnected wire, burned-out element, defective lighter shell, or a tripped circuit breaker.

Some circuit breakers on lighters are equipped with a reset opening (Fig. 19). If the lighter fails to operate, the circuit breaker may be open and must be reset.

To do this, insert a small wire in the small hole in the end of the lighter as shown and push in against the spring tension.

Fig. 19 — Resetting Circuit Breaker on Cigarette Lighter

If a lighter has a burned-out element or a defective shell, these parts must be replaced.

OUO1082,0002C9E -19-12JUN12-1/1

CONVENIENCE OUTLETS

Some machines are equipped with electrical outlets for use with trailers or implements (Fig. 20). Always use auxiliary light on a towed implement when the tractor rear signals and other lights are obscured.

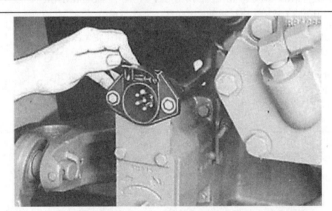

Fig. 20 — A Seven-Terminal Auxiliary Electrical Outlet

Continued on next page
OUO1082,0002C9F -19-12JUN12-1/2

In addition, some machines have a 12-volt electrical outlet used for connecting auxiliary electrical equipment, such as seed monitors or implement control boxes (Fig. 21). If the outlet is already used, you may use two unused terminals of the load center for an auxiliary power source: the IGN and ACC terminals. These terminals are controlled by the IGN and ACC key switch positions respectively.

Fig. 21 — Accessory Electrical Outlet

OUO1082,0002C9F -19-12JUN12-2/2

FLAME RODS

A flame rod is a device used in a gas-fired crop dryer to sense the presence of flame in the dryer. The flame rod is located in the firing port (Fig. 22) and works as follows:

AC electrical current is fed from the protector relay to a flame rod which is in direct contact with the normal burner flame. The flame completes the electrical circuit between the rod and the ground (the flame plate and firing port). However, because of the relatively small size of the flame rod compared with the ground, the current is rectified, or converted to DC. This small current flow indicates "flame" and signals the protector relay to hold the solenoid valves open. But if the flame loses contact with the rod, the circuit is broken and the solenoid valves are de-energized within 2 to 4 seconds. Thus the supply of gas to the burner is stopped as soon as the flame goes out.

Short circuits or high-resistance grounds cannot simulate the presence of a flame. A component failure within the system has the same effect as a loss of flame.

These are truly safety shutdowns, as there is no attempt at automatic restarting.

The burner must be restarted manually after the cause of the shutdown is corrected.

For service of flame rods, see the crop dryer Operator's Manual. Also see the proper manuals for operation of the complete dryer and its LP-Gas and electrical systems.

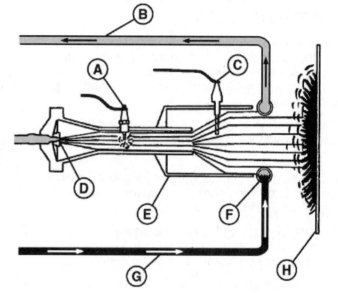

Fig. 22 — Flame Rod in Operation

A—Spark Plug
B—Vapor LP-Gas
C—Flame Rod
D—Gas Vapor Orifice
E—Firing Port
F—Vaporizer
G—Liquid LP-Gas
H—Flame Plate

OUO1082,0002CA0 -19-12JUN12-1/1

GLOW PLUGS

Some diesel engines have electrical pre-heating devices called glow plugs (Fig. 23). They are used as a starting aid when starting a cold engine and are mounted in the precombustion chamber of each cylinder.

TESTING GLOW PLUGS

Glow plugs are tested most accurately with the use of an ammeter.

1. Remove the wiring leads from all the glow plugs.

2. Connect the ammeter in series between the glow plug terminal and the lead wire.

3. A glow plug should be replaced if the amperage is either too low or too high. (See the machine specifications.)

Check each glow plug by this method. If all glow plugs check out to be too low, but the readings on them are equal, the starter switch or wiring harness is probably at fault.

A—Washer
B—Terminal
C—Body
D—Heating Element

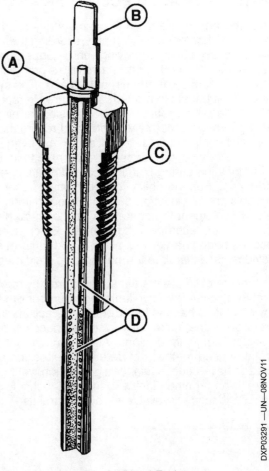

Fig. 23 — Glow Plug for Diesel Engine

OUO1082,0002CA1 -19-12JUN12-1/1

DXP03291 —UN—08NOV11

SATELLITE-BASED POSITIONING SYSTEMS

A **positioning system**, as the name suggests, is a general method of identifying and recording the location of a stationary object or moving vehicle or person. Such a system may be used to chart a vehicle's progress along the earth's surface, in the air, or in space. The systems are of great benefit in modern agriculture. In fact, it may be considered the foundation of precision farming by helping farmers accurately identify and record the location of a machine in the field. Yes, it's true that even without precision farming, the farmer must be able to identify his or her location during planting, cultivating, harvesting, and so on. But, the ability to electronically record the vehicle's precise location during field operations has helped implement the concept of precision farming. For example, recording a combine's position every few seconds during harvesting, along with data from sensors, provides essential data for making crop yield maps.

Systems to estimate the acreage covered by tractors and combines have been available for a number of years. However, the chances for error and the accumulation of errors over time make such systems unacceptable for precision farming operations. All we can say is that simple formula-based methods of determining position and acreage have been in use for a generation, yet the interest in precision farming didn't expand until technologies like GPS became available for agricultural use. Today,

Fig. 24 — Satellite-Based Positioning Systems

satellite-based positioning systems are the only method used to help navigate and record positions of agricultural vehicles during field operations.

A **Global Positioning System** (GPS). **GPS** is the most common and the most significant positioning system for precision farming and many other civilian applications. Since position accuracy is the main issue with any system, we discuss the accuracy users demand from a positioning system, especially for various farming activities. Users employ certain methods to make positioning systems as accurate as possible. We describe common ways of doing so, including a method to reduce position errors using a process known as **differential correction**. This procedure results in what is called a **Differential Global Positioning System (DGPS)**.

MM61211,00012C6 -19-12JUL12-1/1

WHAT IS GPS

GPS is a satellite-based navigation and radio-positioning system created and operated by the United States **Department of Defense** (DoD). Initial development started in the early 1960s. By the early 1990s, the system was being used by the military in the Persian Gulf War, and operations in Somalia and Haiti. However, the GPS system was not declared "fully operational" until April 27, 1995. Fully operational meant that the system consisted of its full constellation of satellites and successfully completed testing for military functionality. The system was originally designed to serve as a worldwide navigational aid for the U.S. military, but now GPS serves industrial, commercial, and civilian interests as well. This service is available free of charge, 24 hours a day in all weather conditions. In fact, U.S. industry, commerce, and transportation rely more and more on its uninterrupted availability. GPS makes land, sea, and air travel safer and more efficient. Not surprisingly, then, its reliability and accuracy greatly benefits precision farming. To better describe GPS, we can divide the entire system into three segments:

- **Space Segment**
- **Control Segment**
- **User Segment**

Space Segment

The United States Space satellite constellation is called NAVSTAR (Navigation by Satellite Timing and Ranging). The complete constellation consists of over twenty-four satellites, which are consistently repaired and replaced. As satellites approach their end-of-life they serve as

GPS SATELLITE CONSTELLATION

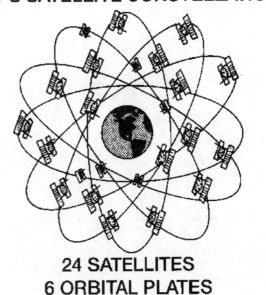

24 SATELLITES
6 ORBITAL PLATES

Fig. 25 — GPS constellation of 24 satellites (minimum) commonly described as the SPACE SEGMENT

functional spares. Orbiting at 10,900 nautical miles (20,200 km) above the earth's surface, each satellite circles the globe twice a day, or once every 12 hours. They follow six orbital paths, with four or more satellites in each path. This particular constellation (arrangement of satellites) guarantees that at least four satellites will be "in view" of your GPS receiver anywhere in the world, 24 hours a day.

Continued on next page
MM61211,00012C7 -19-12JUL12-1/5

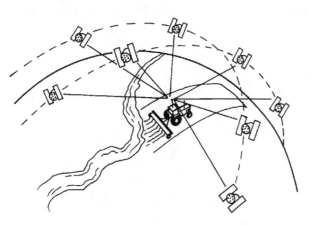

Fig. 26 — Only satellites "in view," or above the horizon, can be used for navigation

Fig. 27 — NAVSTAR satellite used for GPS

Of course we cannot actually see the satellites in orbit, but a GPS receiver must be able to pick up the satellites' signals sent to earth. The only satellites from which signals can be received are those that are "above the horizon" since the signals travel by line-of-sight and cannot be seen around the curvature of the earth.

MM61211,00012C7 -19-12JUL12-2/5

Each satellite, as shown in Figs. 26 and 27, is equipped with radio transmitters and receivers for sending and receiving radio waves. These radio waves are much like the signals received by your television set, but they are transmitted at a much higher frequency of around 1200–1500 MHz (million cycles per second). Your television operates between 60 and 500 MHz. Fig. 28 illustrates a radio wave and the relationship among wavelength, frequency, and cycles. Radio waves travel at the speed of light, which is 186,300 miles per second (300,000,000 m/s) in a vacuum, and at a slightly reduced speed through the Earth's atmosphere.

The satellites are also equipped with atomic clocks. The clocks are not powered by atomic or nuclear energy, but keep time based on natural periodic vibrations within atoms. These incredibly precise clocks are the critical components that make it possible to use the satellites for mapping and navigation. To make the system run adequately, each satellite needs only one atomic clock. However, since these clocks eventually fail, the DoD placed four clocks (two cesium and two rubidium) in the early NAVSTAR satellites and three rubidium clocks in the latest satellites.

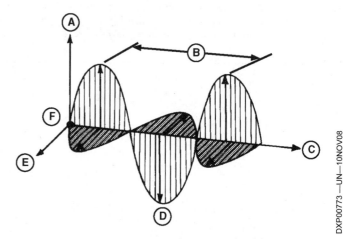

Fig. 28 — Radio waves travel as electromagnetic waves. Wavelength is the distance between successive peaks on a wave. Frequency, or cycles per second, tells how fast the oscillations occur.

A—Electric Field
B—Wavelength = 25 cm (Time = 0.83 Billionths of a Second
C—Distance
D—1200 MHz Radio Wave Travel 25 cm in 0.83 Billionths of a Second
E—Magnetic Field
F—Radiation Source

Continued on next page   MM61211,00012C7 -19-12JUL12-3/5

Control Segment

The GPS satellites are tracked and monitored by several facilities strategically located around the world. This network of monitoring stations is usually referred to as the **control segment** of GPS. The monitoring stations are located in Hawaii, Kwajalein Island in the South Pacific Ocean, Diego Garcia Atoll in the Indian Ocean, and Ascension Island in the Atlantic Ocean. A Master Control Monitor Station is located at Schriever Air Force Base (formerly Falcon AFB) in Colorado Springs, Colorado. The monitoring stations measure the radio wave signals that are continuously transmitted by the satellites and relay information to the Master Control Monitor Station. The Master Control Monitor Station uses this information to compute clock errors and the exact orbits of the satellites. Corrective information is then relayed back to each satellite to update their navigation signals.

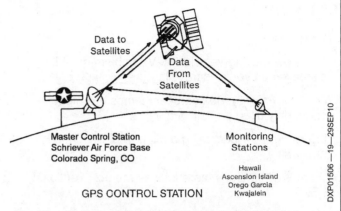

Fig. 29 — *Control segment of GPS includes several monitoring facilities located around the world. A master control station sends information up to satellites to update their navigation signals.*

MM61211,00012C7 -19-12JUL12-4/5

User Segment

The **user segment** includes the GPS receivers located on vehicles or carried by hand, which are used by civilians and military personnel who receive the GPS signals. Military GPS equipment has been integrated into almost every vehicle and soldier's equipment for navigation and target designation. Civilian GPS receivers are used in a wide range of applications, some of which include: surveying, automobile and aircraft navigation, rail traffic management, hiking, hunting, and, of course, precision farming. Civilian GPS receivers do not require a license to operate because they to do not send out or transmit radio signals. They only receive signals. Also, there is no direct charge or fee for using the basic GPS satellite signals.

Fig. 30 — *User segment of GPS includes the receivers located on vehicles or carried by hand*

MM61211,00012C7 -19-12JUL12-5/5

TEST YOURSELF

QUESTIONS

1. The slow-moving vehicle (SMV) emblem must be displayed on vehicles traveling _____ mph or less.

2. (True or False?) Sealed-beam lamps are most commonly used as indicator lights.

3. LED's are now becoming a big part of illumination, due what?

4. What is 1000 times more intense than conventional LED's?

5. (True or False?) Halogen bulbs require no special handling procedures.

6. (True or False?) Mechanical linkage are required to activate and deactivate an electromagnetic clutch.

7. (True or False?) Small AC electrical motors are used to perform auxiliary functions on some machines.

8. Gauge sending units are all _____ _____ type.

9. (True or False?) Horns and buzzers are basically the same in design and operation and only differ in the sound they make.

10. (True or False?) On an agriculture tractor and some industrial equipment lights are adjusted by the lamp brackets and not by the sealed-beam unit itself.

11. An ammeter is used to measure the strength of _____ _____.

12. A voltmeter is used to indicate the _____ of the electrical input in a circuit.

13. Glow plus are preheating devices used as a _____ _____ for a cold engine.

14. What is a general method of identifying and recording the location of a stationary object or moving vehicle?

15. The United States Space satellite constellation is called what?

16. The network of monitoring stations is usually referred as what?

(Answers are in the back of the textbook.)

OUO1082,0002CA2 -19-12JUL12-1/1

Connectors

INTRODUCTION

DXP02711 —UN—23FEB11

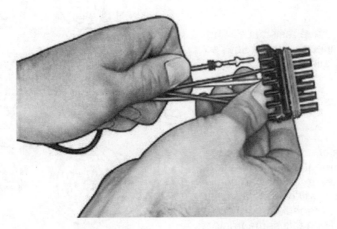

DXP03332 —UN—08NOV11

With the increasing use of electrical equipment and electronic monitoring systems on modern machines and implements, more and more connectors of all types, sizes, and shapes are being used. And with this more widespread use comes the need for improved skills in maintaining and repairing the connectors and their associated wiring, pins, and sockets.

Another contributing factor to the increased requirement for maintenance and repair is the harsh environment

in which these connectors must operate. Connectors on various types of equipment have been designed to operate in, but can be damaged by, extremes of heat and cold, dirt, dust, moisture, and even chemicals of both dry and wet types.

OUO1082,0002CB0 -19-03APR12-1/1

CURRENT FLOW IN CONNECTORS

The purpose of a connector is to pass current from one set of wires to another. To do this, connectors have what is known as mating halves, which are shown in Fig. 1. One mating half houses the male pin contacts and the other contains the female socket contacts. When the connector halves are mated, the pins fit inside the sockets and make contact, thus enabling the current flow to continue. Sounds simple.

But pins and sockets, when mated, have resistance. And as we learned earlier, resistance impedes current flow, so we strive for as little as possible by eliminating or at least minimizing the causes.

What are some causes of resistance in connectors?

CONTAMINANTS

Contaminants of all types are a major contributing factor to resistance in connectors. As we mentioned, connectors are used on equipment that operates in rather harsh environments. A tractor, for example, will operate in dusty fields pulling a planter that could be loaded with dry or liquid insecticides and herbicides. Then this same tractor could be used in the winter to remove heavy, wet snow. These contaminants along with oxide films and oils all contribute to increased resistance on the pins and sockets used in connectors.

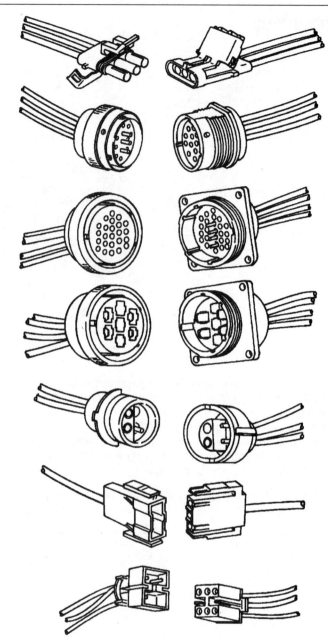

Fig. 1 — Common Types of Connectors

Continued on next page OUO1082,0002CB1 -19-12JUN12-1/4

ASPERITY

The pins and sockets used in connectors are merely extensions of the wires they are connected to. Their purpose is to pass or conduct the current in a continuing manner from one wire to the other. To do this, the surfaces of the pins must contact the surfaces of the socket.

When we look at and feel a pin contact, its surface seems very smooth. But the surface actually contains microscopic peaks and valleys, a condition known as asperity. The inside of the socket has this same condition. Because of this situation, when the pin and socket are mated, only about 1% of the actual surfaces contact each other. Fig. 2 illustrates this condition in an exaggerated form.

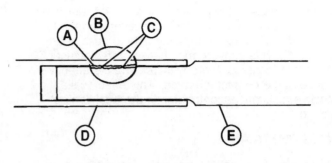

Fig. 2 — Asperity in Pin Contacts

A—No Contact
B—Condition of Asperity
C—Contact

D—Pin Contact Socket
E—Pin Contact

OUO1082,0002CB1 -19-12JUN12-2/4

A—Electrons Converging
B—Condition of Asperity
C—Contact

D—No Contact
E—Pin Contact Socket
F—Pin Contact

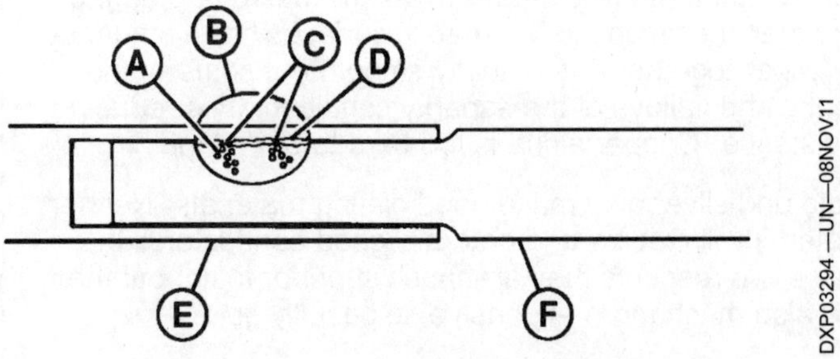

Fig. 3 — Electrons Converging at Asperity

Continued on next page

OUO1082,0002CB1 -19-12JUN12-3/4

When the surfaces of the pin and socket meet, electrons must converge to pass from one conducting surface to the other (Fig. 3), rather than being able to pass at any point (Fig. 4). This convergence causes the electrical path length to increase, thereby increasing the effective resistance at the contact interface. This effect, called constrictive resistance, contributes to the total contact resistance.

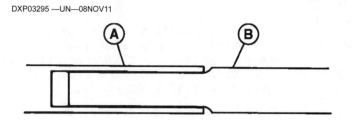

DXP03295 —UN—08NOV11

Fig. 4 — Electrons Able to Flow from Any Point

A—Pin Contact Socket　　　　**B—Pin Contact**

PLATING MATERIAL

In contact pins and sockets, we strive for minimum resistance. This is directly dependent on surface finish, contact pressure, and the kind of material used. Tin is soft enough to allow film-wiping but it has high resistivity. Conversely, copper has low resistivity but is hard. So striving for minimum resistance and thus reducing the asperity condition discussed previously, low-resistance copper contacts are often plated with tin or tin alloys.

What is film-wiping? As we just mentioned, tin is soft enough for this condition to occur. When a pin contact and socket that are plated with tin are mated or plugged together, the tin on the two mating surfaces has a tendency to "wipe" together and actually smooth out some of the peaks and valleys of the asperity condition, thus reducing resistance. Copper alone is too hard to permit this.

Gold and silver also make good plating materials. Neither material will oxidize and both are good conductors. In these two respects they are much superior to tin, but they are also much more expensive, especially gold.

ELECTRICAL CONNECTOR HANDLING

Electrical connectors must not be forcibly mated or unmated. All are designed to be mated easily. If you have to use tools, you may be doing something wrong. Prying

or forcing connectors may cause permanent damage to the locking mechanism, contacts, or both.

When working on connectors, make sure you are working on the correct terminal. Remember that male and female halves are mirror images of each other. Look for the terminal number on the connector body. The connection of improper electrical circuits can cause unusual electrical symptoms.

When an electrical connector is repaired, it is important that the proper terminals are used. In some of these connectors, different terminals are used to carry different currents. If contacts of different materials are mated, corrosion may develop that could affect performance.

When removing a terminal from a connector, it is very important to use the correct extraction tool and gently remove the terminal. The connector body can be damaged if terminals are just jerked out of it. The damage caused will prevent the new terminal from staying in the connector and will result in replacement of the connector body.

OUO1082,0002CB1 -19-12JUN12-4/4

COMMON TYPES OF CONNECTORS

In the remainder of this chapter, we will discuss seven common types of connectors used in electrical systems. There are many different types of connectors used in today's electrical systems; some common types are shown in Fig. 1.

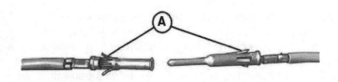

Connectors can be considerably different from one another because they are used in different applications. However, most will have the following characteristics in common:

- The two mating halves have a locking mechanism so they will not inadvertently disconnect.
- The mating halves have either a mating guide mechanism or a pin contact arrangement so the two halves cannot be connected wrong.
- Most connectors are designed so that an individual pin contact can be removed and replaced should it become bent or broken.

CIRCULAR PLASTIC CONNECTOR: PIN-TYPE CONTACTS

The circular plastic connector shown in Fig. 5 will accommodate 37 pin contacts. However, this same design of connector is available with many different pin contact configurations.

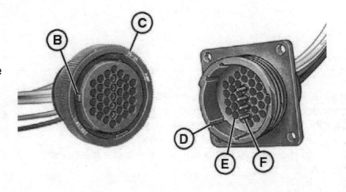

A—Locking Lance	D—Keyway
B—Guide Key	E—Vacant Pin Hole
C—Locking Flange	F—Pin Contact

Fig. 5 — Circular Plastic Connector for Pin-Type Contacts

OUO1082,0002CB2 -19-13JUL12-1/36

Fig. 6 shows a connector that will accommodate 16 pin contacts. Not all pin cavities in the connector have to be used as can be seen in Fig. 5. If you do not need all pin cavities, just make sure that the corresponding cavity in each mating half is used because the connector halves will mate only one way.

A—Pin Contact   B—Pin Contact Socket

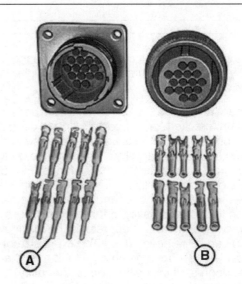

Fig. 6 — Connector Body, Pins, and Sockets

Continued on next page   OUO1082,0002CB2 -19-13JUL12-2/36

To mate the connector halves, align the guide keys with the keyways (Fig. 5), push the two halves together, and then turn the knurled connector half clockwise to engage the locking flange (Fig. 7). When turning the connector, you will feel an initial resistance. Turn past this point until you feel a solid resistance. You will then have a secure connection with practically no danger of it coming apart. This connector also has provisions for mounting the female half (which actually contains the male pin contacts) onto a panel, mounting flange, or bulkhead.

A—Ring Nut

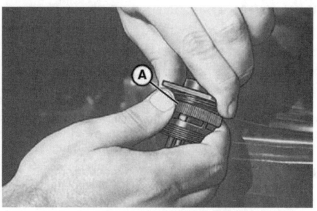

Fig. 7 — Mating the Connector Halves

OUO1082,0002CB2 -19-13JUL12-3/36

No special tools are required to install the pin contacts into the connector halves. Both female and male pin contacts are simply pushed through from the rear of the connector (Fig. 8). Just make sure that the pins are pushed far enough into the connector to engage the locking lances on the pin.

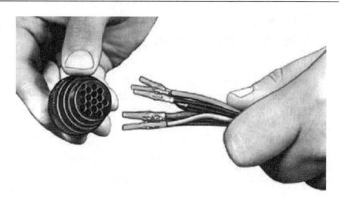

Fig. 8 — Inserting Pins or Sockets

OUO1082,0002CB2 -19-13JUL12-4/36

Fig. 9 shows a cutaway of the locking lance inside the connector cavity. Also, make sure that the proper pin contact is installed in the proper connector body.

It is not necessary to replace an entire connector body unless it is broken, cracked, or chipped. But quite often it is necessary to replace pin contacts because they become corroded, broken, or bent. Basically, all you have to do to remove a pin contact is depress the locking lance (Fig. 5) and pull the wire out from the rear. But you need a special tool to do this—one that will fit over and around the pin contact between the pin and cavity of the connector. As the tool is inserted over the pin, it depresses the locking lance so the pin can be removed (Fig. 9). So the size of the tool is critical. It must be large enough to fit over the pin, yet small enough to fit inside the connector cavity.

The following steps explain how to remove a pin contact.

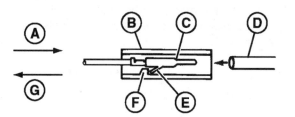

Fig. 9 — Pin Contact Locking Mechanism in Connector Body

A—Insert Pin in This Direction
B—Cutaway of Connector Cavity
C—Pin Contact
D—Extraction Tool Tip
E—Locking Lance
F—Connector Cavity Stop
G—Remove Pin in This Direction

Continued on next page   OUO1082,0002CB2 -19-13JUL12-5/36

1. Select the proper tool. Align the sleeve of the tool with the contact to be removed (Fig. 10).

A—Pin Contact   B—Sleeve

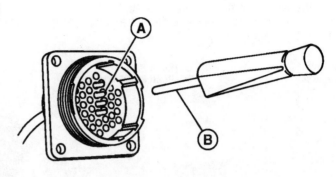

Fig. 10 — Remove Pin from Circular Plastic Connector Housing (Tool Not Inserted)

OUO1082,0002CB2 -19-13JUL12-6/36

2. Push wire in slightly (Fig. 11).

3. While holding the handle, insert the sleeve of the tool into the cavity until it bottoms (Fig. 11).

A—Connector   B—Extraction Tool

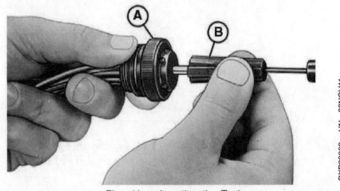

Fig. 11 — Inserting the Tool

OUO1082,0002CB2 -19-13JUL12-7/36

4. Allow the push rod to back out during insertion (Fig. 12).

5. Rotate the handle of the tool in either direction to ensure the release of the contact locking lances.

A—Rotate Handle   C—Sleeve Bottomed in Cavity
B—Depress Push Rod Button

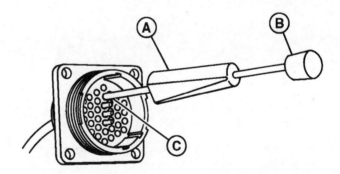

Fig. 12 — Removing Contact from Circular Plastic Connector Installing Blade-Type Contacts Housing (inserted)

Continued on next page   OUO1082,0002CB2 -19-13JUL12-8/36

6. Keep the sleeve firmly bottomed in the cavity and depress the push rod button to eject the contact (Fig. 13).

A—Sleeve   C—Push Rod
B—Handle   D—Push Rod Button

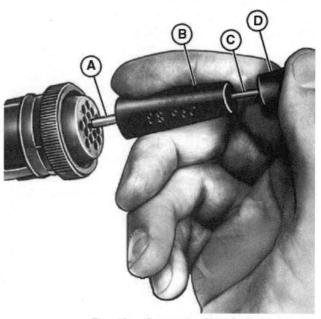

Fig. 13 — Depressing Push Rod

OUO1082,0002CB2 -19-13JUL12-9/36

NOTE: If you intend to reinstall the pin, pry the locking lance upward with a knife blade as shown in Fig. 14.

A—Locking Lance

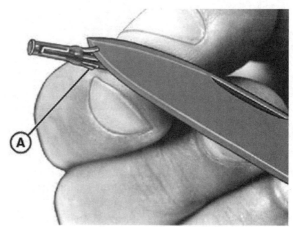

Fig. 14 — Reset Locking Lance with a Knife

Continued on next page   OUO1082,0002CB2 -19-13JUL12-10/36

CIRCULAR PLASTIC CONNECTOR: BLADE-TYPE CONTACTS

The circular plastic connector shown in Fig. 15 will accommodate seven blade contacts, although the one pictured shows only four installed with the three center cavities vacant. Again, like the connector with pin contacts, make sure that corresponding cavities in each connector half are used because they will mate only one way. Mating and locking the connector halves is the same as for the circular plastic connector with pin contacts.

INSTALLING BLADE-TYPE CONTACTS

Like pin contacts, blade contacts are also installed from the rear of the connector halves by simply pushing them in. Make sure that the male contacts are installed in the female connector half and vice versa just like for the circular plastic connector with pin-type contacts.

EXTRACTING BLADE-TYPE CONTACTS

1. Select the appropriate tool.

A—Extraction Tool Contact Flange
B—Guide Keys
C—Contact
D—Keyways
E—Locking Flange
F—Vacant Pin Holes
G—Locking Flange

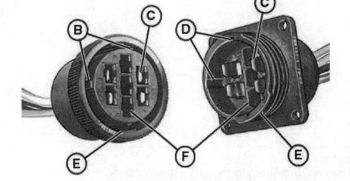

Fig. 15 — Circular Plastic Connector for Blade-Type Contacts

DXP03306 —UN—08NOV11

OUO1082,0002CB2 -19-13JUL12-11/36

2. Push the tips of the tool into the offsets in the cavity of the housing until they bottom. It may be necessary to wiggle the tool during insertion to get it to bottom completely. If it is necessary, be sure to wiggle the tool only in the direction of the arrows in Fig. 16. You may bend the tool tips if you work the tool up and down against the flat surfaces of the tool tips.

3. Carefully pull the wire lead to remove the contact.

A—Blade Contact
B—Tool Tips
C—Offsets in Cavity
D—Housing

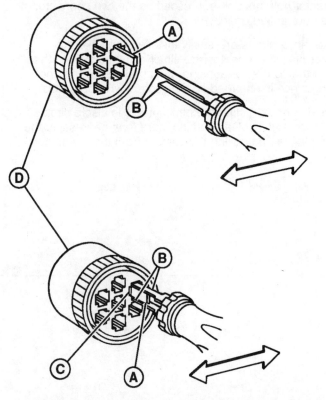

Fig. 16 — Removing the Blade-Type Contacts from the Connector

DXP03307 —UN—08NOV11

Continued on next page   OUO1082,0002CB2 -19-13JUL12-12/36

Another type of connector and pin contacts are shown in Fig. 17. Like most connectors, it has a safeguard so that it can be mated only one way. The locking mechanism consists of clips, and to separate the connector halves, the clips must be depressed while pulling them apart. The procedures for removing and installing pin contacts are the same as for the circular plastic connector for pin-type contacts discussed earlier.

A—Locking Lance
B—Locking Clips
C—Guide Keys

D—Pin Contacts
E—Keyways

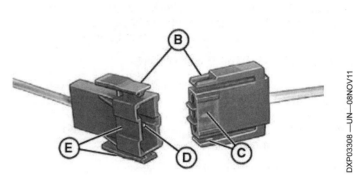

Fig. 17 — Connector and Pin Contacts

OUO1082,0002CB2 -19-13JUL12-13/36

The connector shown in Fig. 18 has provisions for six pin contacts, although in this picture, only three are installed. Like the other connectors, the female part of the contact or socket is installed in the male half of the connector body and the male part or pin, in the female half. The locking mechanism engages as the connector halves are mated. To disengage, the locking clips on the male connector half must be depressed as the two connector halves are pulled apart.

These pin contacts are easily installed, and like the circular plastic connector, simply pushed in from the rear of the connector housing. Just make sure that the locking lance is engaged so the contact will not pull out.

Removing or extracting the pin contacts is also a simple procedure that involves nothing more than depressing the locking lance and pulling the contact from the connector housing.

A—Locking Lance
B—Pin Contact

C—Locking Clips

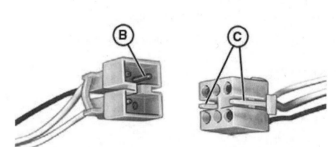

Fig. 18 — Connector and Pin Contacts

Continued on next page   OUO1082,0002CB2 -19-13JUL12-14/36

To remove the female pin contacts or sockets:

1. Push the socket into the cavity of the connector as far as it will go. Align the tool so that the tip is positioned opposite the socket seam (Fig. 19).

2. Bottom the tool in the cavity. Pull the wire to remove the contact.

A—Socket Contact
B—Tool Tip
C—Connector Housing
D—Contact Cavity
E—Seam
F—Wire

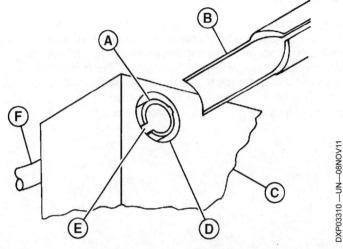

Fig. 19 — Removing Pin Contact Socket from Connector Housing

OUO1082,0002CB2 -19-13JUL12-15/36

To remove the male pin contacts or pins:

1. Push the pin into the cavity as far as it will go. Place the tool tip against the locking lance (Fig. 20).

2. Depress the locking lance with the tool tip and pull the wire to remove the pin contact.

Not all connectors use the same size pin contacts. Other tools that can be used to remove the contacts.

A—Wire
B—Pin Contact
C—Tool Tip
D—Locking Lance

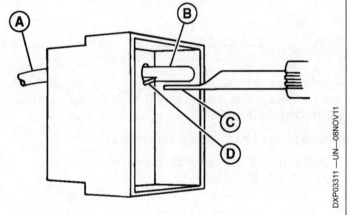

Fig. 20 — Removing Pin Contact from Connector Housing

Continued on next page

OUO1082,0002CB2 -19-13JUL12-16/36

SEALED CONNECTORS

One type of sealed connector and pin contacts is shown in Fig. 21. These types of connector housings also have provisions for accurate mating between the two halves, but instead of using guide keys and keyways, the connector bodies are molded such that they will not mate incorrectly.

A—Locking Flange   B—Pin Contact

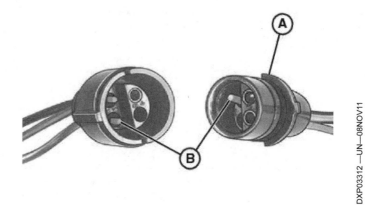

Fig. 21 — Connector and Pin Contacts

OUO1082,0002CB2 -19-13JUL12-17/36

Unlike the other connectors discussed in this chapter, these connectors require two special tools for installing the pin contacts (Fig. 22).

To install pin contact in this type of connector:

1. Determine the number of the hole in which the pin contact is to be installed.

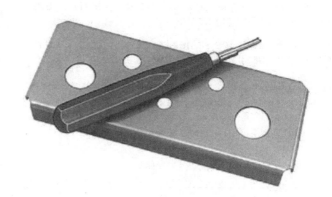

Fig. 22 — Insertion Tool and Holding Plate for Installing Pin Contacts in Connector

OUO1082,0002CB2 -19-13JUL12-18/36

2. Mate this connector half to the other connector half and place in the proper size hole of the holding plate (Fig. 23).

A—Connector Half   B—Mounting Hole

Fig. 23 — Connector and Holding Plate

Continued on next page OUO1082,0002CB2 -19-13JUL12-19/36

3. Start the contact into the connector (Fig. 24).

A—Contact Shoulder   B—Tool Shoulder

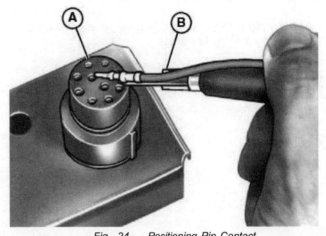

Fig. 24 — Positioning Pin Contact

OUO1082,0002CB2 -19-13JUL12-20/36

4. Position the wire inside the tip of the contact insertion tool (Fig. 25) so that the tip of the tool butts against the contact shoulder.

A—Wire Lead   C—Pin Contact
B—Insertion Tool

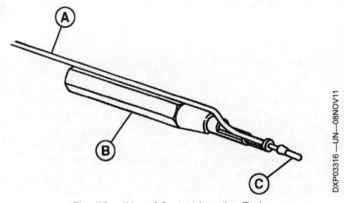

Fig. 25 — Use of Contact Insertion Tool

OUO1082,0002CB2 -19-13JUL12-21/36

5. Holding the insertion tool firmly, insert the contact into the cavity to the depth of the insertion tool shoulder (Fig. 26). Remove the tool and pull the wire slightly to ensure that the contact is properly seated.

A—Tool Shoulder

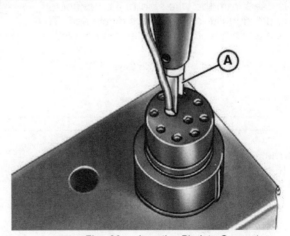

Fig. 26 — Inserting Pin into Connector

Continued on next page   OUO1082,0002CB2 -19-13JUL12-22/36

NOTE: *Plugs must be installed from the wire side.*

6. Install cavity plugs (Fig. 27 and Fig. 28) in all unused holes in the connector housings.

There is usually a special tool for removing the pin contacts from most sealed connector housings. If a contact is damaged, use a suitable tool to remove the contact from the connector housing.

A—Cavity Plug   B—Pin Contact Wire

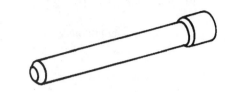

Fig. 27 — Connector Cavity Plug

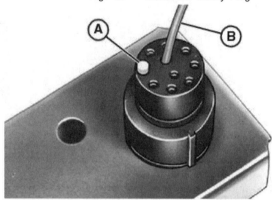

Fig. 28 — Connector with Cavity Plug Installed

OUO1082,0002CB2 -19-13JUL12-23/36

The connector (Fig. 29) is circular like the circular plastic connectors discussed earlier but is made from metal rather than plastic. It also has soft rubber around the cavity holes to seal out moisture, dust, or any other type of contaminant. This connector is available in different sizes to accommodate varying numbers of pin contacts, and some models will take two different sizes of pins.

Special extracting tools are available in different sizes to remove the pin contacts from the connectors. The size tool you use depends on the gauge of the wire lead. But note that this tool is used from the wire side of the connector rather than the pin side like all the others discussed. The following steps explain how to remove the pin contacts.

A—Locking Ring   C—Guide Keys
B—Keyway

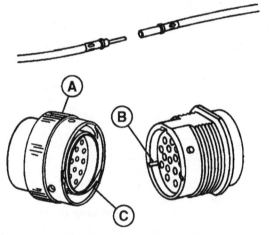

Fig. 29 — Connector and Pin Contacts

OUO1082,0002CB2 -19-13JUL12-24/36

1. Select correct size tool for the size of the wire to be removed (Fig. 30).

DXP03321 —UN—08NOV11

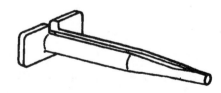

Fig. 30 — Extraction Tool for Connector Pins

Continued on next page   OUO1082,0002CB2 -19-13JUL12-25/36

2. Insert the wire into the tool starting at the handle end (Fig. 31).

   A—Handle

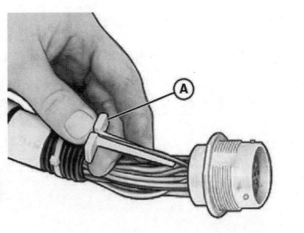

Fig. 31 — Starting Extractor Tool onto Wire

OUO1082,0002CB2 -19-13JUL12-26/36

3. Slide the tool rearward along the wire (away from the connector) allowing the wire to slide into the tool until the tool tip snaps onto wire (Fig. 32). You may have to spread the tool tips slightly with your fingernail, but be very careful not to break the tip.

   A—Tool Tip

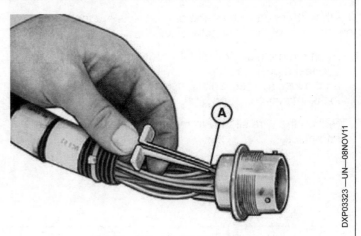

Fig. 32 — Wire Inside Extractor Tool

OUO1082,0002CB2 -19-13JUL12-27/36

IMPORTANT: Do not twist the tool when inserting into the connector. The twisting action may break the tool tips.

4. Slide the tool along the wire toward the connector and into the pin cavity until the tool bottoms inside the connector (Fig. 33).

   A—Connector   **B—Extractor Tool**

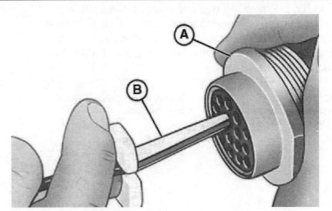

Fig. 33 — Inserting Extractor Tool into Connector

Continued on next page   OUO1082,0002CB2 -19-13JUL12-28/36

110112
PN=403

5. Pull the wire and the extraction tool from the connector body (Fig. 34).

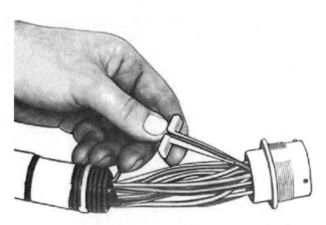

Fig. 34 — Removing Wire, Contact, and Tool from Connector

OUO1082,0002CB2 -19-13JUL12-29/36

Like the other connectors, the pin contacts are installed from the rear of the connector (Fig. 35).

1. Push pin contact straight into connector body until you feel a positive stop. You will also hear a soft click as the locking mechanism inside the connector body locks into place.

2. Pull on the wire slightly to make sure the pin is locked into place.

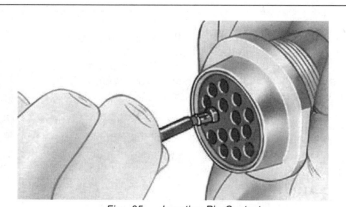

Fig. 35 — Inserting Pin Contact

OUO1082,0002CB2 -19-13JUL12-30/36

Some sealed connectors have a molded self-lubricating silicone seal that comes assembled to the male connector half (Fig. 36). When the two connector halves are mated, the seal creates an effective environmental seal between the connector halves. This connector, like the others, is equipped with a locking mechanism between the two halves.

A—Cable Seal
B—Locking Lance
C—Locking Clip
D—Wire and Contact Cover
E—Connector Seal

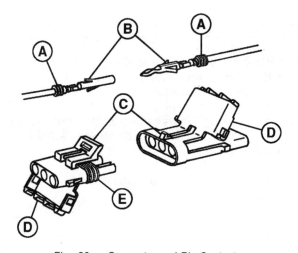

Fig. 36 — Connector and Pin Contacts

Continued on next page

OUO1082,0002CB2 -19-13JUL12-31/36

To keep moisture and other contaminants from entering the connector at the wire leads, cable seals (Fig. 37) are used on each wire lead. In vacant cavity holes, cavity plugs (also in Fig. 37) are installed.

These types of connectors also require a special tool to remove the pin contacts. The tool is similar to the one used for the circular plastic connector but does not have a plunger. However, the tool is hollow, even the handle, so that a nail or wire can be inserted all the way through the tool to push the pin contact out should it be necessary.

The procedure for removing the contact pins follows:

A—Cable Seal   B—Cavity Plug

Fig. 37 — Cable Seal and Cavity Plug for Connector

OUO1082,0002CB2 -19-13JUL12-32/36

1. Open the wire cover protector (Fig. 38).

   A—Wire Cover Protector

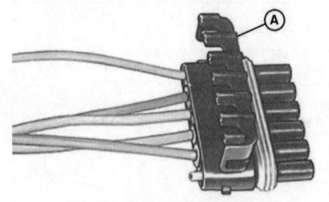

Fig. 38 — Connector with Wire Cover Open

OUO1082,0002CB2 -19-13JUL12-33/36

2. Insert the extractor tool over the pin contact in the connector body (Fig. 39). Make sure the tool bottoms in the connector so that the locking lances on the contact will be depressed.

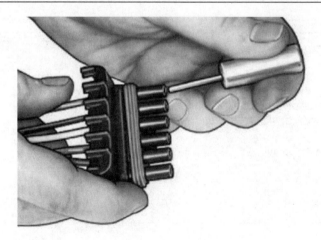

Fig. 39 — Inserting Extractor Tool

Continued on next page

OUO1082,0002CB2 -19-13JUL12-34/36

NOTE: *If the pin contact cannot be removed, insert a wire or nail through the tool handle and push the pin out.*

3. Hold the extractor tool fully seated (Fig. 40) and pull wire and pin contact from the connector body.

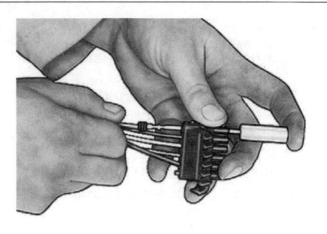

Fig. 40 — Removing Pin Contact

OUO1082,0002CB2 -19-13JUL12-35/36

To install pin contacts:

1. Push pin contact straight into connector body from the rear (Fig. 41) until you feel a positive stop. Make sure the cable seal is flush with the connector body.

2. Pull on the wire slightly to make sure the pin contact is locked into place.

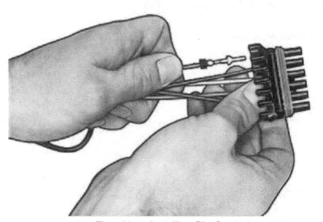

Fig. 41 — Installing Pin Contacts

OUO1082,0002CB2 -19-13JUL12-36/36

STRIPPING AND CRIMPING

In the remaining part of this chapter, we will discuss wire stripping and crimping terminals to wires using universal electricians pliers (Fig. 42) and the universal terminal applicator (Fig. 43).

A—Wire Stripping   **B—Terminal Crimping (Closed Barrel)**

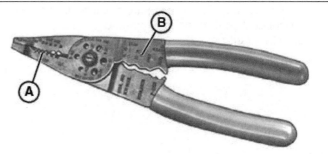

Fig. 42 — Universal Electricians Pliers

Continued on next page   OUO1082,0002CB3 -19-13JUN12-1/24

These tools, especially the universal terminal applicator, are practically indispensable when it comes to repairing electrical wiring and connectors. Even though they do have two common functions, you do need both tools, as only the terminal applicator will crimp open-barrel terminals, and only the electricians pliers will strip wires.

A—Open Barrel Wire Crimp
    Area
B—Front of Tool
C—Open Barrel Insulation
    Crimp Area

D—Closed Barrel Insulation
    Crimp Area
E—Closed Barrel Wire Crimp
    Area
F—Open Barrel Insulation
    Crimp Area

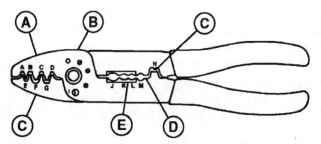

Fig. 43 — Universal Terminal Applicator

OUO1082,0002CB3 -19-13JUN12-2/24

Other types of tools for stripping and crimping wires are shown in Fig. 44.

A—Soldering Iron
B—Wire Stripper

C—Crimping Tool

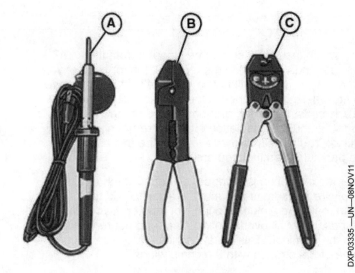

Fig. 44 — Special Tools

OUO1082,0002CB3 -19-13JUN12-3/24

WIRE STRIPPING

The electricians pliers (Fig. 42) makes wire stripping a simple task. But to use it properly, you have to know the gauge of the wire you intend to strip, because the pliers has several sizes of stripping holes. If you use a stripping hole that is too small, you will not only cut through the insulation but also cut through part of the wire strands. If the hole is too large, you will not cut through the insulation and then not be able to strip it off.

As we said, wire stripping is a simple task, but like anything else, the more practice you have, the better you will become at doing it. Generally, about all you have to do is match the gauge of the wire to the proper stripping hole on the pliers (Fig. 45), insert the wire, close the pliers, and pull the insulation off. Sometimes, the most difficult task is determining the gauge of the wire. If the gauge is not printed directly on the insulation, you will have to refer to the wiring diagram for whatever piece of electrical equipment or machine you are working on.

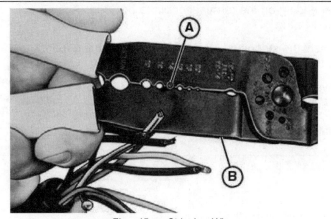

Fig. 45 — Stripping Wires

A—Wire Being Stripped   B—Wire Strippers

Continued on next page

OUO1082,0002CB3 -19-13JUN12-4/24

PN=407

Also, if you are replacing several pins in a connector, you should identify the wire according to the wiring diagram (Fig. 46). Do not depend solely on color. It may have faded or the wire may have grease or dirt on it.

IMPORTANT: The wires in any one connector may be of different gauges. More than likely, they are. Do not assume they are all the same gauge.

A—Tape Tabs on Each Wire

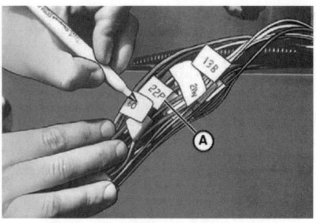

Fig. 46 — Identify Wires with Circuit Code Numbers

OUO1082,0002CB3 -19-13JUN12-5/24

How much insulation should be stripped from the wire? That depends entirely on the terminal, pin, or contact you will be using. If you will notice in Fig. 47, the pin has two points where it is crimped. One point is around the bare wire strands; the other, around the end of the insulation. So the amount of insulation stripped from the wire is critical. You will simply have to measure this amount on the particular terminal you are using.

After the insulation is stripped, do not twist the exposed bare wire strands as you may be accustomed to doing when replacing a plug on a lamp or toaster. If you twist the strands, they will overlap each other and not run parallel with the terminal. This situation may cause you to cut some of the strands with the crimp wings.

To review the wire stripping process, we can put it into four distinct steps:

1. Determine the amount of insulation to be stripped, depending on the terminal or pin to be used. Again, refer to Fig. 47.

2. Select the stripping hole on the pliers that corresponds to the gauge of the wire.

3. Insert the wire to the point determined in step 1 and cut the insulation. Release the pliers just slightly, rotate the wire about 180°, and again close the pliers to make sure that the insulation is cut all the way around.

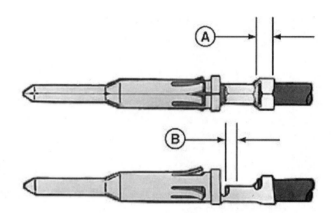

Fig. 47 — Relationship Between Stripped Wire and Pin Contact

A—Wire and Insulation   B—Bare Wire Strands

4. Pull the wire from the pliers to remove the cut insulation.

As we mentioned, with practice, wire stripping will become practically automatic. It would be a good idea to obtain several pieces of scrap wire of different gauges and practice stripping insulation of various lengths.

Continued on next page   OUO1082,0002CB3 -19-13JUN12-6/24

CRIMPING

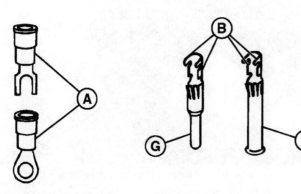 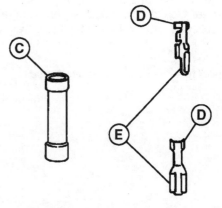

Fig. 48 — Closed- and Open-Barrel Terminals and Pin Contacts

A—Closed-Barrel Terminals
B—Crimp Wings
C—Closed-Barrel Splice Terminal

D—Crimp Wing
E—Open-Barrel Terminals
F—Open-Barrel Pin Contact Socket

G—Open-Barrel Pin Contact

In working with electrical connectors, wiring, and terminals, you will be faced with two types of crimping—open-barrel and closed-barrel. Both of these types are illustrated in

Fig. 48. The pin contacts shown in Fig. 35, which are installed in connector bodies, are of the open-barrel type. Most terminals are closed-barrel.

OUO1082,0002CB3 -19-13JUN12-7/24

OPEN-BARREL CRIMPING

Because the open-barrel pin contacts are installed in connector bodies, the crimping process is critical but certainly not difficult, at least not with a little practice. When using a universal terminal applicator, crimping these pin contacts is actually a two-step procedure, whereby you first crimp the bare wire strands in the wire barrel part of the contact, and then the tip of the insulation in the insulation barrel. The wire barrel part of the contact is toward the center of the contact and has shorter but wider crimp wings. The insulation barrel is on the end and has the long and narrow crimp wings.

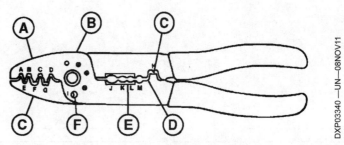

Fig. 49 — Universal Terminal Applicator

A—Open-Barrel Wire Crimp Area
B—Front of Tool
C—Open-Barrel Insulation Crimp Area
D—Closed-Barrel Insulation Crimp Area

E—Closed-Barrel Wire Crimp Area
F—Bolt Cutting Area
G—Open-Barrel Insulation Crimp Area

Continued on next page

OUO1082,0002CB3 -19-13JUN12-8/24

To perform the crimping procedure, you will need a crimping tool like the one shown in Fig. 49. Fig. 50 shows another type in actual use. When using a universal terminal applicator, follow these steps to obtain a good crimp.

A—Crimping Tool   B—Pin Contact

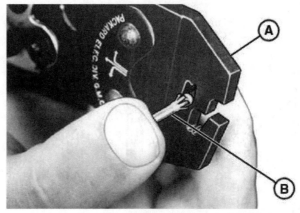

Fig. 50 — Crimping Pin Contact to Wire

OUO1082,0002CB3 -19-13JUN12-9/24

---

1. Position the connector in the best-suited area (A, B, C, or D) with the wire barrel opening facing the letter as shown in Fig. 51. Close the handles of the tool just enough to grasp the contact and hold it in place.

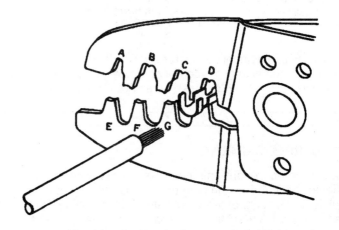

Fig. 51 — Position the Connector in the Tool

OUO1082,0002CB3 -19-13JUN12-10/24

IMPORTANT: The pin or socket must be positioned in the crimping tool with the crimp wings centered. Be certain that only the exposed wire is crimped. Do not insert the wire too far and crimp the wire barrel of the pin or socket on any insulation. Correct crimping is critical because of the low current flow in many of these circuits.

NOTE: *Unless you are very steady of hand, it is a good idea to rest the tool on a solid surface (table or workbench top) while grasping the contact and inserting the wire.*

2. Insert a properly stripped wire into the wire barrel (Fig. 52) and position it as shown in Fig. 47. Hold the wire in place and squeeze the tool handles to complete the crimp.

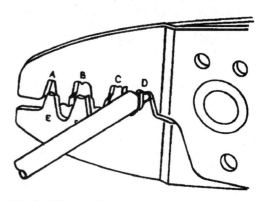

Fig. 52 — With the Wire and Connector in Position, Squeeze the Tool Handles to Crimp the Wire Strand Wings

Continued on next page   OUO1082,0002CB3 -19-13JUN12-11/24

The connector should now look like the one shown in Fig. 53.

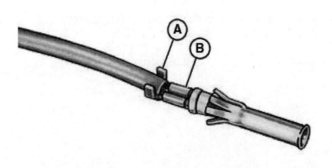

Fig. 53 — Connector After Crimping Wire Strand Wings but Before Crimping Insulation Wings

OUO1082,0002CB3 -19-13JUN12-12/24

1. Position the connector in the best-suited crimp area (E, F, G, or H) of the crimping tool (Fig. 54) with the opening of the insulation barrel facing the letter on the tool.

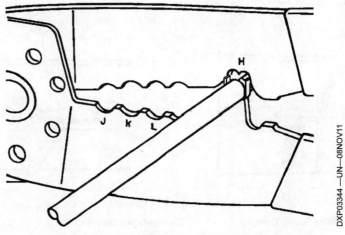

Fig. 54 — Position the Connector in the Tool to Crimp the Insulation Wings

OUO1082,0002CB3 -19-13JUN12-13/24

2. Hold the insulation and wire in place and squeeze the tool handles to complete the crimp (Fig. 55).

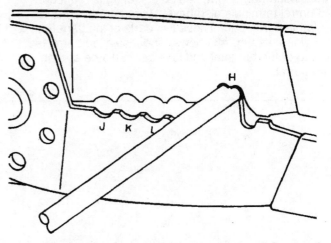

Fig. 55 — After the Connector Is Correctly Positioned, Squeeze the Tool Handles—Insulation Wings Are Now Crimped

Continued on next page

OUO1082,0002CB3 -19-13JUN12-14/24

3. After the completion of both crimps, the connector should look like the one shown in Fig, 56.

A—Insulation Crimp   B—Bare Wire Crimp

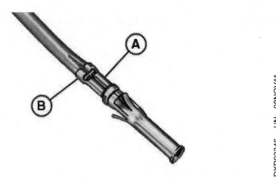

Fig. 56 — Electrical Connector After Both Crimps Have Been Made

OUO1082,0002CB3 -19-13JUN12-15/24

CLOSED-BARREL CRIMPING

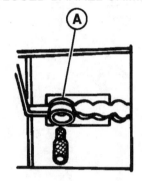
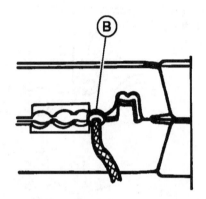
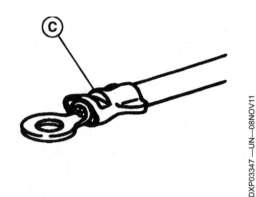

Fig. 57 — Closed-Barrel Crimping Using Universal Terminal Applicator Tool

A—Wire Barrel Crimper   B—Insulation Barrel Crimper   C—Crimped Terminal

Like open-barrel crimping, closed-barrel is also a two-step process. But closed-barrel crimps are usually associated with terminal connections like the two shown in Fig. 48. With the closed-barrel terminal, no soldering is required. Closed-barrel terminals also have a wire barrel part and an insulation barrel part. These two parts of the barrel are clearly evident as Fig. 48 shows. The insulation barrel is on the end of the terminal and is larger in diameter than the wire barrel.

Follow these steps to crimp a closed-barrel terminal using either the electricians pliers (Fig. 42) or the universal terminal applicator (Fig. 43).

1. Position the wire barrel of the terminal or contact in the best-suited area (J, K, or L) with the wire barrel centered in the crimping jaws as shown in Fig. 57. Squeeze the tool handles just enough to hold the terminal in place.

Continued on next page   OUO1082,0002CB3 -19-13JUN12-16/24

2. Insert a properly stripped wire into the wire barrel as shown in Fig. 58. Hold the wire in place and squeeze the tool handles to complete the crimp.

3. Position the insulation barrel in the crimp area marked M so that it is centered in the crimping jaws as shown in Fig. 57.

4. Hold the terminal in place and squeeze the tool handles to complete the crimp.

A—Insulation Crimp
B—Wire Crimp
C—Terminal Insulation
D—SPLICE TERMINAL
E—TERMINAL

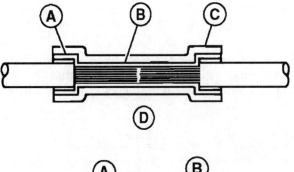
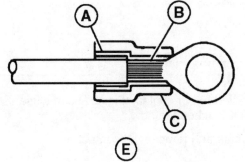

Fig. 58 — Cross-Section View of a Closed-Barrel Splice Connector and Terminal

OUO1082,0002CB3 -19-13JUN12-17/24

CRIMPING PIN CONTACTS USING SPECIALIZED CRIMPERS

A specialized crimping tool (Fig. 59) is required to crimp the pin contacts used in some connectors. Depending on the crimping tool used, the crimping procedure will vary.

Follow these steps for crimping contacts using the crimping tool shown in Fig. 59.

1. Strip 1/4 inch (6 mm) of insulation from wire.

2. Adjust wire size selector on crimping tool (Fig. 59) to correspond with the gauge of the wire.

3. Loosen the lock nut and turn the adjusting screw in until it stops.

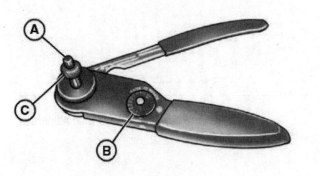

Fig. 59 — Specialized Crimping Tool

A—Adjusting Screw
B—Wire Size Selector
C—Lock Nut

Continued on next page

OUO1082,0002CB3 -19-13JUN12-18/24

4. Insert a pin contact and turn adjusting screw until the contact is flush with the cover (Fig. 60). Tighten lock nut.

5. Close handle on crimping tool just enough to hold pin contact snug. While doing this, observe that the contact is centered between the crimping indenters in the tool.

A—Lock Nut   C—Cover
B—Adjusting Screw   D—Pin Contact

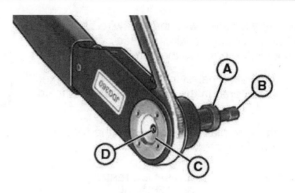

Fig. 60 — Adjusting Crimping Tool

OUO1082,0002CB3 -19-13JUN12-19/24

6. Insert wire into the pin contact (Fig. 61) and close handle until it touches the stop.

7. Release handle and remove the contact.

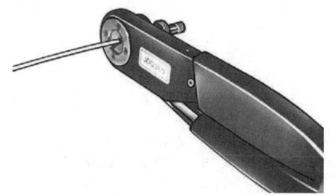

Fig. 61 — Inserting Wire and Crimping Pin Contact

OUO1082,0002CB3 -19-13JUN12-20/24

8. Inspect the contact (Fig. 62) to be certain that all wires are crimped in the barrel.

Fig. 62 — Pin Contact After Crimping

Continued on next page   OUO1082,0002CB3 -19-13JUN12-21/24

CRIMPING PIN CONTACTS WITH CABLE SEALS

The procedure for crimping contacts with cable seals is actually the same as for the others. However, we are providing it separately because another part (cable seal) is involved in the crimping (Fig. 63).

Cable seals are color coded for three sizes of wire.

- Green: 18 to 20 gauge wire
- Gray: 14 to 16 gauge wire
- Blue: 10 to 12 gauge wire

The procedure for crimping pin contacts with cable seals is as follows:

1. Slide the correct size cable seal onto wire. Refer to the color coding above.

2. Strip 1/4 inch (6 mm) of insulation from wire. Align cable seal with the edge of the insulation (Fig. 63).

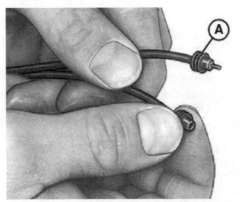

Fig. 63 — Installing Cable Seal

A—Cable Seal

OUO1082,0002CB3 -19-13JUN12-22/24

3. Position wire barrel of the contact in the crimping tool (Fig. 64). Close the handles of the tool just enough to grasp the contact and hold it in place. Be sure the crimp wings are centered.

4. Insert a properly stripped wire into the wire barrel of the contact. Squeeze the tool handles to complete the crimp.

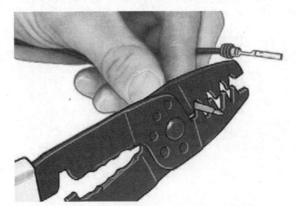

Fig. 64 — Crimping Insulation and Cable Seal

OUO1082,0002CB3 -19-13JUN12-23/24

5. Position the insulation barrel in the crimping tool. Make sure the small part of the cable seal is within the crimp wings of the contact as shown in Fig. 65. Close the tool handles to complete the crimp.

CRIMPING A SPLICE

To splice two wires, you will need to use a closed-barrel splice. As Fig. 48 shows, the splice, like the terminal, has an insulation crimp area and a wire crimp area. The difference is that the splice has an insulation crimp at each end. The procedure for crimping a splice is the same as for a closed-barrel terminal except that you repeat the procedure for each of the two wires you are splicing. In other words, each splice requires two wire crimps and two insulation crimps. Fig. 58 shows a cross section of a splice with the wires inserted.

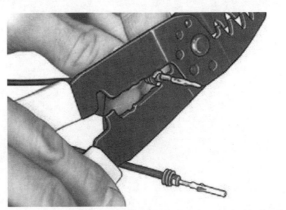

Fig. 65 — Crimping Insulation and Cable Seal

OUO1082,0002CB3 -19-13JUN12-24/24

SUMMARY

The electrical connectors discussed in this chapter are some of the more common types that are in use. These connectors all have a locking mechanism to keep the two mating halves from disconnecting and a mating guide mechanism or pin contact arrangement to prevent connecting them wrong. They are designed so that individual contacts can be replaced.

Specialized tools are required for repairing the connectors, particularly for removing and installing the contacts. Two universal tools that can be used with most connectors and wiring are the electricians pliers and universal terminal applicator. The electricians pliers is used primarily for stripping wire and the terminal applicator, for crimping terminals and splices.

Stripping wires and crimping terminals and pin contacts are critical processes in the repair of connectors, but are easily performed if you follow the procedures.

OUO1082,0002CB4 -19-03APR12-1/1

TEST YOURSELF

QUESTIONS

1. What is the purpose of a connector?

2. What is asperity?

3. What three characteristics do the types of connectors discussed in this chapter have in common?

4. (True or False?) It is not necessary to use all pin contact cavities in the connector bodies.

5. (True or False?) After stripping, the end of the wire should be twisted tightly before installing the terminal.

(Answers are in the back of the textbook.))

OUO1082,0002CB5 -19-10JAN12-1/1

INTRODUCTION

DXP02712 —UN—23FEB11

12

DXP03372 —UN—08MAR12

Maintaining the electrical system is not difficult—many of the components require little or no maintenance. However, there are parts that are extremely important, and some of these are often neglected. Regular maintenance takes little time and effort, and can prevent many problems.

Other chapters in this manual give you detailed descriptions of electrical components, as well as diagnosis and testing procedures. This chapter will be confined to regular maintenance—the care that will keep the system operating properly and ensure a long service life.

Before proceeding, review the safety information in previous chapters. Closely follow safety precautions when working with batteries and other electrical devices.

OUO1082,0002CBC -19-10APR12-1/1

STORAGE BATTERIES

The battery is the heart of the electrical system. It is perishable, but with the proper care you can keep it operating for the longest possible time.

Here are the most common causes of poor battery performance or failure:

- Low electrolyte level
- Low specific gravity
- External damage, dirt, and corrosion
- Faulty connections

Let's take a closer look at these.

CHECKING THE ELECTROLYTE LEVEL

Once a week, or after 50 hours of operation, make sure the electrolyte level is above the battery plates (Fig. 1). If the level is low, add water to each cell until the level rises to the bottom of the split ring in the vent well.

IMPORTANT: If the battery electrolyte level is allowed to stay low, the charging circuit will not work properly. Also, the battery plates will dry, and permanent damage may result.

Don't add water you wouldn't drink! If distilled water is available, use it. But remember that even using hard water is better than allowing the electrolyte level to get low.

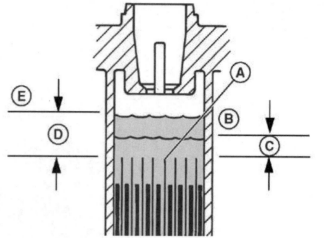

Fig. 1 — Proper Level of Battery Electrolyte

A—Plate Separators
B—Min.
C—1/4 in. (6 mm)

D—1/2 in. (13 mm)
E—Max.

Don't overfill—you'll lose electrolyte. Overfilling also can cause the electrolyte to splatter, causing acid burns. Always follow proper safety precautions when working with electrolyte.

OUO1082,0002CBD -19-03APR12-1/3

CHECKING THE SPECIFIC GRAVITY

The specific gravity reading tells you the battery charge. Check periodically using an accurate hydrometer (Fig. 2). Readings should be from 1.225 to 1.280, corrected per the electrolyte temperature as described in Chapter 5.

Never allow the specific gravity to fall below 1.225. Keep the battery at full charge to prevent sulfation and get longer service life.

On the other hand, don't overcharge the battery. A sign of this is when the battery uses too much water.

A—Hold Hydrometer Vertical
B—Do Not Draw In too Much Electrolyte

C—Read Scale at Eye Level
D—Float Must Be Free

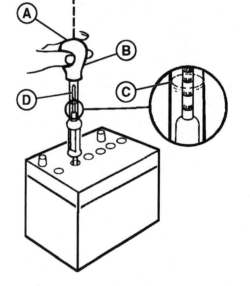

Fig. 2 — Checking the Specific Gravity

Continued on next page   OUO1082,0002CBD -19-03APR12-2/3

PREVENTING DAMAGE TO BATTERIES

When you service the battery, always check for external damage (Fig. 3). A broken case or cracked cell cover will result in battery failure. Battery hold-down clamps must be tight enough to hold the battery securely, yet not so tight as to warp the case.

KEEPING THE BATTERY CLEAN

If acid film, corrosion, and dirt are present on the top of the battery, current will flow between the terminals, causing slow discharge. Use diluted ammonia or baking soda and water solution to clean the battery; flush with clear water. Keep the vent plugs tight so that none of the solution gets into the cells.

When disconnecting the battery cables for cleaning, disconnect the ground strap first to prevent arcing. After cleaning, apply a coat of petroleum jelly to terminals and cable clamps to prevent further corrosion.

CHECKING THE BATTERY CONNECTIONS

Poor battery connections will impede the flow of current. Clamps should hold cables firmly to battery terminals. If necessary, remove some metal from the clamp jaws to ensure a snug fit when tightened.

LOW-MAINTENANCE BATTERIES

Visually inspect low-maintenance batteries and their cables as you would any other battery. Do not add water to these batteries. If the battery is of a type which allows viewing of the electrolyte levels in the cells, or is equipped with hydrometers which indicate electrolyte levels, replace the battery if the electrolyte levels are found to be low.

Low-maintenance batteries can be checked with a voltmeter. If voltage is below 12.4 volts, charge the battery

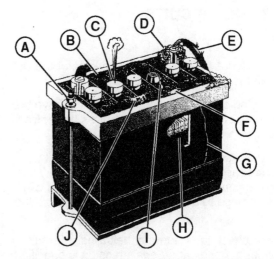

Fig. 3 — Maintenance Problems with Batteries

A—Loose Hold-Down	F—Sealing Compound Defect
B—Dirt	G—Cracked Case
C—Overfilling	H—Low Electrolyte
D—Corrosion	I— Cracked Cell Cover
E—Frayed or Broken Cable	J— Cell Connector Corrosion

as described in Chapter 5. The battery charger should include a charge duration control. If the battery fails to charge the first time, attempt to charge it again. If the battery fails to accept a second charge, replace it.

If voltage is 12.4 volts or above, load test the battery (see fixed load testing in Chapter 5). If voltage is less than the minimum specified in Chapter 5 replace the battery. If voltage is at or above minimum specified, return the battery to service.

OUO1082,0002CBD -19-03APR12-3/3

DC CHARGING CIRCUITS

GENERATOR

For detailed description, testing, and servicing of the DC generator, refer to Chapter 6 of this manual.

Aside from periodic lubrication and keeping the drive belt in proper adjustment, the generator requires no regular maintenance.

Every 200 hours, add SAE 10W or SAE 5W-20 oil to both front and rear generator oil cups (Fig. 4). Only 8 to 10 drops are required. Do not over lubricate! This can cause more damage to electrical components than a lack of lubrication.

Don't forget to check the generator belt tension at this time. The amount of flex at a certain tension is specified by the manufacturer.

Also note the condition of the belt. Excessive wear or glazing may mean replacement is necessary.

Remember that a V-belt should ride on the sides of the pulley grove—not on the bottom. If the belt bottoms in the pulley, it is either too tight or excessively worn.

If the generator brushes are visible, examine the commutator and brushes for dirt, oil, wear, and other defects.

Fig. 4 — Generator Oil Cups

REGULATOR

For complete instructions covering the generator regulator, refer to Chapter 6.

The regulator requires no periodic maintenance.

On a DC charging circuit, however, the generator must be polarized after the generator starting motor or battery has been disconnected for any reason.

Before starting the engine, momentarily touch a jumper lead to both the GEN and BAT terminals of the regulator. This will establish correct polarity. Failure to do this may damage the regulator or the wiring.

OUO1082,0002CBE -19-10JAN12-1/1

AC CHARGING CIRCUITS

AC charging circuits are covered in detail in Chapter 6.

ALTERNATOR

Most alternators need no regular maintenance. Bearing lubricant is sealed in at the factory—no further lubrication is required.

Check the fan or alternator belt for proper tension (Fig. 5).

Also note whether belt is worn or grazed, or bottoming in the pulley. Replace belt if necessary.

Loose or slipping belts can cause the battery to run down.

REGULATOR

The regulator normally requires no maintenance. For service and testing, see Chapter 6.

SAFETY RULES FOR AC CHARGING CIRCUITS

To prevent damage to the AC or alternator charging circuit, remember:

1. Disconnect the battery ground straps when working on the alternator or regulator. Damage could occur if terminals are accidentally grounded.

2. Never polarize the alternator. Never ground an alternator or regulator terminal, or connect a jumper wire to any terminal (unless recommended for a test).

3. if the alternator or regulator wiring is disconnected, connect it properly before connecting batteries.

Fig. 5 — Adjusting Fan or Alternator Belt Tension

A—Check Belt Tension Midway
on Side of Belt

4. Never disconnect or connect any alternator or regulator wiring with batteries connected or with alternator operating.

5. Always connect batteries or boosters in the correct polarity. Most AC electrical systems are negative-grounded.

6. Don't use a battery charger as a booster to start the engine.

7. Never disconnect the batteries when the engine is running and the alternator is charging.

OUO1082,0002CBF -19-10JAN12-1/1

STARTING CIRCUITS

Periodically check for corroded or loose terminals on the starting motor. Most starting motors require no other regular maintenance. (Some models may have armature shaft wicks that need regular oiling.) See Chapter 7 for complete information.

OUO1082,0002CC0 -19-10JAN12-1/1

IGNITION CIRCUITS

Ignition circuits are covered in detail in Chapter 8.

DISTRIBUTOR

Every 500 hours, check the condition of the distributor contact points. Rough or pitted contacts must be replaced when metal transfer is excessive.

Clean the points with a few strokes of a clean contact file. Don't try to remove all roughness—just scale or dirt. Never use emery cloth or sandpaper—particles will embed in the points and cause them to burn.

If the points are burned, find the cause before operating the machine. Contact point burning could be caused by one or more of the following:

- Too-high voltage
- Presence of oil or other foreign material
- Defective condenser
- Improper point adjustment

Check the distributor point gap periodically (Fig. 6). For the correct gap, see the machine Technical or Operator's Manual.

Also check the timing of the distributor. If it seems erratic, adjust as described in Chapter 8.

Inspect the distributor cap. If you find defects, replace the cap. Some of these defects are cracks, chips, carbon tracks, worn or corroded tower inserts, or worn or damaged rotor button. If the cap is still serviceable, clean it before installing.

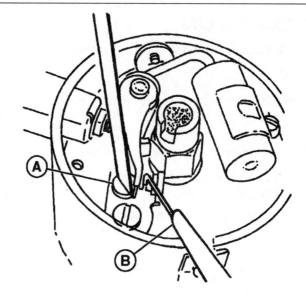

Fig. 6 — Adjusting Distributor Point Gap

A—Locking Screw   B—Use a Feeler Gauge to Check Gap

Periodically lubricate the distributor cam, using only a trace of cam lubricant or high-temperature grease. Too much lubricant will ruin the distributor points.

OUO1082,0002CC1 -19-03APR12-1/3

Some distributors also have an oil wick in the top of the cam (Fig. 7). In this case, place 4 or 5 drops of SAE 30 oil on the wick.

IGNITION COIL

Ignition coils don't require service, but check the coil for damage or carbon tracks.

A—Wick   B—Cam

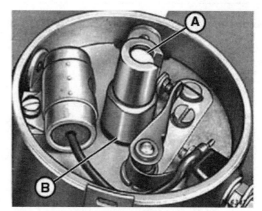

Fig. 7 — Lubricating the Distributor

Continued on next page   OUO1082,0002CC1 -19-03APR12-2/3

SPARK PLUGS

For the complete story on spark plugs, refer to Chapter 8, which covers description, installation, and testing.

Periodically check the external condition of the spark plugs (Fig. 8).

Look for carbon tracks or dirt which might contribute to poor performance.

If the ceramic insulator is cracked, the plug must be replaced.

When replacing plugs, remember:

- Use the right plug.
- Gap the plug as specified.
- Install properly, using a new gasket.
- Tighten the plug to the specified torque.

WIRING

When servicing electrical components, take the time to check all wiring.

Loose or corroded connections can contribute to poor performance, as can cracked or damaged insulation.

These conditions cause excessive voltage drops in the system because of high resistance.

Unless the connections are tight and wiring is in good condition, batteries may be undercharged and the spark plugs will misfire.

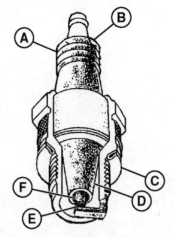

Fig. 8 — Spark Plug Maintenance

A—Check for Cracks
B—Wipe Clean
C—Replace Gasket
D—Clean Insulation until White
E—File and Re-Gap
F—Clean Electrodes

Also check the protective boots on the secondary ignition circuit. These can become cracked or oil-soaked, causing low ignition voltage. Carbon tracks inside the boots also permit current leakage. Replace faulty boots.

OUO1082,0002CC1 -19-03APR12-3/3

TEST YOURSELF

QUESTIONS

1. When connecting booster batteries, connect positive terminals to _____ terminals.

2. (True or False?) After disconnecting any part of the AC charging system, always polarize the alternator.

3. What difficulties can be caused by faulty wiring or poor connections?

4. Why is it necessary to remove acid film and dirt from the battery top? Why remove corrosion?

(Answers are in the back of the textbook.)

OUO1082,0002CC2 -19-14JUN12-1/1

Diagnosis and Testing of Systems

INTRODUCTION

DXP02713 —UN—23FEB11

DXP03369 —UN—08MAR12

"We've had some faulty regulators lately, so that must be your problem. We'll replace the regulator!"

"I don't really see what the owner's maintenance program has to do with troubleshooting!"

"I never talk to the operator. Operators sometimes know more about electrical systems than I do."

Here are three statements you might hear from "experienced" troubleshooters in a shop. Then again, maybe they aren't troubleshooters.

Regulator problems on the last job do not mean that the regulator is bad in every situation. What if the alternator had failed or a wiring lead was broken? The customer cannot afford the time and expense of replacing parts when unsure if a part is bad or requires replacement. That first quotation above wasn't made by a troubleshooter—it was made by a hit-or-miss parts replacer.

Is maintenance a key to troubleshooting? It certainly is. Problems are very likely to occur if the electrolyte level in a battery is never checked or if the alternator drive belt tension is never checked. The second quotation above couldn't have been made by a troubleshooter, because the effects of poor maintenance are being overlooked.

What was being done when the equipment broke down? Is the problem erratic, or does it happen every time? What was done after the breakdown? These are a few of the questions that can be answered by talking to the operator. These answers help the troubleshooter to re-create the problem and accurately diagnose the cause. The third quotation was not made by a troubleshooter either. In fact, the person who made this statement knows little about the system being worked on.

THEN WHAT IS A GOOD TROUBLESHOOTER?

Before answering this, let's realize that the electrical and electronic systems of today require diagnosis and testing at a minimum of cost. Equipment breakdown means a loss of time and money for the operator-owner, and we cannot expect the owner to absorb the extra cost due to poor troubleshooting.

So a good troubleshooter starts out by using common sense, getting all the facts and examining them until the trouble has been pinpointed. Then the troubleshooter checks out the diagnosis by testing it. And only then does the process of replacing parts begin.

With the complex systems of today, diagnosis and testing is the only way.

OUO1082,0002CCA -19-10APR12-1/1

SEVEN BASIC STEPS

A good program of diagnosis and testing has seven basic steps:

1. Know the System

2. Ask the Operator

3. Inspect the System

4. Operate the Machine (If Possible)

5. List the Possible Causes

6. Reach a Conclusion

7. Test Your Conclusion

We now have a formula for a troubleshooter:

TROUBLESHOOTER = COMMON SENSE + SEVEN BASIC STEPS.

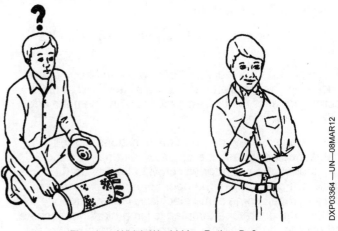

Fig. 1 — Which Would You Rather Be?

Now let's see what these seven basic steps mean.

OUO1082,0002CCB -19-03APR12-1/7

1. KNOW THE SYSTEM

In other words, do your homework. Find out all you can about the electrical and electronic systems of the machine. Is it a positive- or negative-grounded system? Is the starting system 12 or 24 volts? Answers to these and many other questions are in the machine Technical Manual. Study this manual, especially the diagrams of the system. Schematics are an important tool; you should know how to read them. The glossary at the end of this book explains the various terms and symbols used in electrical diagrams. Study them and be able to recognize them at a glance.

Be familiar with the key specifications for the system given at the end of each section or group in the machine Technical Manual.

Keep up with the latest service bulletins. Read and then file them. The problem on your latest machine may be in this month's bulletin, giving the cause and remedy.

You can be prepared for any problem by knowing the system.

Fig. 2 — Know the System

Continued on next page   OUO1082,0002CCB -19-03APR12-2/7

2. ASK THE OPERATOR

A good reporter gets the full story from a witness—the operator.

What work was the machine doing when the trouble was noticed? Is the trouble erratic or consistent? What did the operator do after the breakdown? Was an attempt made to fix the problem?

These are just a few of the many questions a good troubleshooter will ask the operator. Often a passing comment by the operator will provide the key to the problem. For example, the operator may have tried to adjust or repair some of the electrical system components. Perhaps the operator attempted to jump-start the machine and damaged the alternator or reversed the polarity of the system.

Ask about how the machine is used and when it was serviced. Many problems can be traced to poor periodic maintenance programs or abuse to the machine.

Fig. 3 — Ask the Operator

3. INSPECT THE SYSTEM

CHECKLIST FOR INSPECTING THE ELECTRICAL SYSTEM

- Bare Wires or Shorts
- Loose Wires or Opens
- Poor Connections
- Battery Electrolyte Level
- Alternator Belt Tension
- Overheated Components
- Other Trouble Signs

Carefully inspect the electrical and electronic components for clues about the malfunction. Check to see if the machine can be operated without further damage to the system.

Always check these items before turning on switches or running the machine:

- Look for bare wires that could cause grounds or shorts and dangerous sparks. Shorted wires can damage the charging system.
- Look for loose or broken wires. In the charging system, they can damage the regulator.
- Inspect all connections, especially battery connecting points. Acid film and dirt on the battery may cause

current flow between the battery terminals, resulting in current leakage. Check the battery ground strap for proper connection.
- Check the battery electrolyte level. Continued loss of electrolyte indicates overcharging.
- Check the generator or alternator drive belt tension.
- Inspect for overheated parts after the machine has been stopped for a while. They will often smell like burnt insulation. Put your hand on the alternator or regulator. Heat in these parts when the machine has not been operated for some time is a sure tip-off to charging circuit problems.

IN GENERAL, LOOK FOR ANYTHING UNUSUAL

Many electrical failures cannot be detected even if the machine is started. Therefore, a systematic and complete inspection of the electrical and electronic systems is necessary.

Many times the problem can be detected without turning on the switch or starting the machine.

While inspecting the electrical and electronic systems, make a note of all trouble signs.

Continued on next page   OUO1082,0002CCB -19-03APR12-3/7

4. OPERATE THE MACHINE (IF POSSIBLE)

If your inspection shows that the machine can be run, first turn the key switch to the accessory position. Try out the accessory circuits, lights, cigarette lighter, etc. How does each of these components work? Look for sparks or smoke which might indicate shorts.

Turn the key switch to the on position. The indicator lights should glow. (Some lights will also glow when the switch is in the start position.)

Now start the machine. Check all gauges for good operation and see if the system is charging or discharging.

Fig. 4 Operate the Machine (If Possible)

OUO1082,0002CCB -19-03APR12-4/7

5. LIST THE POSSIBLE CAUSES

Now we are ready to make a list of the possible causes. What were the signs you found while inspecting the machine? What is the most likely cause? Are there other possibilities? Remember that one failure often leads to another.

Fig. 5 — List the Possible Causes

Continued on next page   OUO1082,0002CCB -19-03APR12-5/7

6. REACH A CONCLUSION

Look over your list of possible causes and decide which are most likely and which are easiest to verify. Use the troubleshooting charts at the end of this chapter as a guide.

Fig. 6 — Reach a Conclusion

OUO1082,0002CCB -19-03APR12-6/7

7. TEST YOUR CONCLUSION

Before you repair the system, test your conclusions to see if they are correct. Many of the items can probably be verified without further testing. Maybe you can isolate the problem to a particular circuit, but not to an individual component. This is where test instruments will help you further isolate the trouble spot.

The next part of this chapter will tell you how to test the system and locate troubles.

But first let's repeat the seven steps for good troubleshooting:

1. Know the System

2. Ask the Operator

3. Inspect the System

4. Operate the Machine (If Possible)

5. List the Possible Causes

6. Reach a Conclusion

7. Test Your Conclusion

Fig. 7 — Test Your Conclusion

OUO1082,0002CCB -19-03APR12-7/7

TESTING THE SYSTEM

The use of many types of electrical test equipment is most effective after the failure has been isolated to a particular circuit in the system. Other types of test equipment are specialized and are designed to isolate problems in specific systems. See Chapter 17.

Chapter 13 lists the most common types of test equipment required to test circuits and components. Instruction manuals are also furnished with these special tools. Study this information and take all precautions. Improper use of test equipment can damage the electrical components.

Other chapters of this manual have sections on testing of components and circuits:

- Chapter 5—Storage Batteries
- Chapter 6—Charging Circuits
- Chapter 7—Starting Circuits
- Chapter 8—Ignition Circuits
- Chapter 9—Electronic Ignition and Fuel Injection
- Chapter 10—Lighting and Accessory Circuits
- Chapter 11—Connectors
- Chapter 17—Monitors and Controllers

REMEMBER THE BATTERY!

The battery is a prime factor in each circuit of any electrical or electronic system. However, it is often overlooked while troubleshooting the system.

Before you begin most circuit tests, remember to do the following.

- Check battery electrolyte level.

Fig. 8 — Electrical Testing

- Look for corroded terminals.
- Check for acid film and dirt on top of battery.
- Check battery polarity.
- Test the charge of the battery. For all battery tests, see chapter 5.

CONNECTOR AND GROUND CONNECTIONS

Other areas not to overlook while troubleshooting are ground and connector connections. Poorly crimped or corroded contacts and terminals can cause many different problems. Before beginning most circuit tests, visually check and perform a continuity check on applicable connection points, especially ground connections.

Continued on next page   OUO1082,0002CCC -19-05APR12-1/3

TESTING PROCEDURES

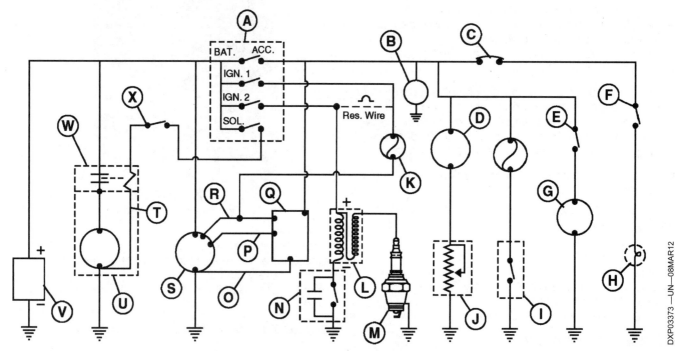

Fig. 9 — Layout of "Problem" Electrical System

DXP03373 —UN—08MAR12

A—Ignition Switch	G—Horn	N—Distributor	V—Battery
B—Cigarette Lighter	H—Lights	O—Ground	W—Starting Solenoid
C—Circuit Breaker	I—Pressure Switch	P—Field	X—Starting Safety Switch
D—Fuel Gauge	J—Sending Unit	Q—Voltage Regulator	
E—Horn Switch	K—Alternator Indicator Light	R—Auxiliary	
F—Light Switch	L—Coil	S—Alternator	
	M—Spark Plug	T—Output	
		U—Starter Motor	

Most problems with electrical systems require the same basic reasoning. Let's see how a good troubleshooter approaches an electrical problem and isolates the cause.

A sample problem follows. A schematic of the system is shown in Fig. 9.

PROBLEM

The troubleshooter, when first arriving on the scene, located the operator, asked what had happened and asked if the operator had noticed anything unusual about the operation of the machine.

"The battery was run-down yesterday morning after the machine had been idle overnight," said the operator. "So we started it with a slave battery. The alternator indicator light was okay—it stayed off during operation. We started the unit several times during the day without a slave battery. But this morning we tried to start it and it was discharged again."

After talking to the operator, the troubleshooter felt that a visual inspection would be helpful since the unit had not yet been started.

In checking the battery, the troubleshooter noticed that the electrolyte level was only slightly low. The battery terminals were not corroded and all connections were tight. Further inspection of the wiring did not provide any clues either.

The charging circuit was then checked.

The alternator was warm to the touch—not extremely hot or smoking, just moderately warm. This could possibly be the cause of the problem. A warm alternator in a case like this could mean that current is flowing in the alternator field circuit.

Since there didn't seem to be anything unusual that would hinder starting, the troubleshooter made an operational check of the unit. During this check the warm alternator was kept in mind.

When the key switch was turned on and the dash gauges checked, the engine oil pressure light was on, but it was very dim. This could be expected, since battery voltage was low. However, the alternator indicator light was out. This could be another clue to the malfunction. If the alternator light was out, current might be flowing in the charging circuit.

The troubleshooter asked the operator whether or not the light came on at all while starting. The operator hadn't noticed. But, even if it didn't come on, the machine still operated.

Continued on next page

OUO1082,0002CCC -19-05APR12-2/3

At this point the troubleshooter felt that a tentative conclusion could be made. One clue was that a shorted isolation diode in the alternator would discharge the battery even if the machine was idle. Also, there were two exact clues to a shorted diode: 1) the warm alternator, and 2) the indicator light that would not light.

To test this conclusion, the troubleshooter turned the switch off and, using a voltmeter, found that there was battery voltage at the alternator auxiliary terminal. (See Fig. 10.) This condition is not normal and is usually caused by a shorted isolation diode.

To clearly pinpoint the isolation diode as the problem, the troubleshooter asked the operator to start the machine.

Using a slave battery, the voltage drop across the isolation diode was checked. During normal operation there is a 1-volt drop across this diode. However, the test indicated no voltage drop at all.

This confirmed the troubleshooter's conclusion and pinpointed the trouble. The isolation diode was replaced and the voltage rechecked. The reading was normal, so the problem was corrected.

After correcting the problem, a second inspection was made of the charging circuit to be sure that other parts were not damaged.

The battery was then checked before the unit was started and returned to normal operation.

SUMMARY

Did you notice how the troubleshooter used the seven basic troubleshooting steps? Let's review the sequence of the story and look for these steps.

The first thing the troubleshooter did was to **Ask the Operator**. The machine operation and the symptoms of the malfunction were kept in mind. The troubleshooter did not assume the operator was correct, but tactfully

double-checked the operator's comments. Checking the indicator light was a good example of this.

The troubleshooter then proceeded to **Inspect the System**, for it was during this inspection that the first clues to the problem were obtained. To show the importance of inspecting the system, notice that the troubleshooter was able to reach a tentative conclusion without even starting the machine.

While inspecting the system, the troubleshooter checked on whether it was possible to **Operate the Machine** without further damage. Although the unit was not actually started, the troubleshooter knew that it could be successfully and safely started.

There are many ways to **List the Possible Causes**. This troubleshooter made a mental list of clues to the malfunction.

We should also point out that the troubleshooter did **Know the System**. When a clue became apparent, the cause and effect were recognized as well as how one symptom was related to another. Because of knowledge of the system, the troubleshooter was able to **Reach a Conclusion** from these clues.

The last of our seven basic steps is to **Test Your Conclusion**. The troubleshooter did not assume that the first test had pinpointed the cause. An extra test was made to confirm that there was only one trouble spot and that it was definitely the cause of the trouble. Only after positive proof of malfunction was the isolation diode replaced.

We can see from the example that the seven basic steps fall easily into place during troubleshooting. Proper troubleshooting can save the machine owner time and money. The time spent in replacing many parts suspected of being faulty can be better utilized in diagnosis. Through proper diagnosis, the trouble spot can be quickly identified. Then time can be spent in correcting the problem without wasting time and money.

OUO1082,0002CCC -19-05APR12-3/3

TROUBLESHOOTING CHARTS

Use the charts on the following pages to help in listing all the possible causes of trouble when you begin diagnosis and testing of the electrical system.

Once you have located the cause, check the item in the chart again for the possible remedy.

When you have pinpointed the problem to one circuit or component, refer to the other chapters of this manual for more details.

The Technical Manual for each machine supplements all these charts by giving more detailed and specific causes and remedies.

BATTERIES

LOW BATTERY OUTPUT

High Resistance in Circuit.

• Check for resistance with voltmeter. See machine Technical Manual for maximum permissible voltage drop.

Low Electrolyte Level.

• Add distilled water to proper level.

Low Specific Gravity.

• See "Low Battery Charge."

Defective Battery Cell.

• Replace battery.

Cracked or Broken Battery Case.

• Replace battery.

Low Battery Capacity.

• Always replace battery with one of adequate capacity.

BATTERY USES TOO MUCH WATER

Cracked Battery Case.

• Replace battery.

Overcharged Battery.

• See "High Charging Circuit Voltage." (A shorted cell in a 24-volt system may cause other batteries to be overcharged.)

LOW BATTERY CHARGE

Excessive Loads from Added Accessories.

• Remove excessive loads.

Excessive Engine Idling.

• Idle engine only when necessary.

Lights or Accessories Left On.

• Be sure electrical switches are off before leaving machine.

Continuous Drain on Battery.

• Check for leakage on dirty battery top. Disconnect battery ground and connect voltmeter between the ground battery terminal and a good ground. (On a 24-volt split-load system, also place voltmeter in the series connection between batteries to test for defective circuits that are not grounded. Disconnect circuits until the grounded or shorted component is located.)

Faulty Charging Operation.

• See "Low Charging Circuit Voltage" or "Low Charging Circuit Output."

CHARGING CIRCUITS

LOW CHARGING CIRCUIT VOLTAGE

High Resistance in Charging Circuit Connections.

• Check voltage drop to locate resistance. Be sure to use pin connector at battery to locate resistance between battery post and battery cable.

Defective Wiring.

• Check voltage drop in wire to locate broken wire strands or undersized replacement wire.

Low Amperage Output of Generator or Alternator.

• See "Low Charging Circuit Output."

Poor Regulator Ground.

• Clean regulator ground connection.

Dirty Voltage Regulator Contact Points.

• Clean points or replace regulator. (Broken resistors will cause excessive pitting of contact points.)

Regulator Out of Adjustment.

• Adjust to specifications.

Dirty Cutout Relay Points.

• Clean points or replace regulator.

Defective Regulator.

• Replace regulator.

Open-Circuited Isolation Diode in Alternator.

• Replace isolation diode assembly.

LOW CHARGING CIRCUIT OUTPUT

Slipping Drive Belts.

• Adjust belt tension.

Excessively Worn or Sticking Brushes.

• Repair or replace. Check commutator or slip rings.

Continued on next page   OUO1082,0002CCD -19-10JAN12-1/5

Dirty or Out-of-Round Commutator or Slip Rings.

• Clean commutator or slip rings.

Grounded Field Circuit (24-Volt, Split-Load System).

• Repair or replace defective component.

  NOTE: This defect places continuous drain on battery.

Dirty Current Regulator Contact Points.

• Clean points or replace regulator.

Defective Diodes in Alternator.

• Replace diode or diode plate assembly.

Defective Electrical Windings in Generator or Alternator.

• Repair or replace windings. (If alternator stator windings are defective, be sure regulator will control alternator voltage.)

HIGH CHARGING CIRCUIT VOLTAGE

Grounded Generator Field Wire or Field Terminal.
(Does not apply to 24-volt generator on split-load system.)

• Repair or replace wire or terminal.

High Resistance at Alternator-Regulator Connections.

• Clean and tighten connections.

Defective Alternator Regulator.

• Replace regulator.

Faulty Regulator.

• Check and clean voltage regulator points as necessary. Adjust voltage regulator. Replace regulator if it does not respond to adjustment.

EXCESSIVE GENERATOR OUTPUT (DC CIRCUITS)

Grounded Generator Field Wire or Field Terminal.
(Does not apply to 24-volt generator on split-load system.)

• Repair or replace wire or terminal.

Faulty Current Regulator in Generator Regulator.

• Check and clean current regulator points if necessary. Adjust current regulator. Replace regulator if it does not respond to adjustment.

NOISY GENERATOR OR ALTERNATOR

Defective or Badly Worn Drive Belt.

• Replace belt. Adjust to proper tension.

Generator Brushes Not Seated.

• Seat brushes with No. 00 sandpaper or brush seating stone.

Generator Commutator Needs Reconditioning.

• Turn and undercut commutator.

Worn or Defective Bearings.

• Replace bearings.

Loose Mounting or Loose Drive Pulley.

• Tighten mounting and pulley.

Misaligned Drive Belt or Pulley.

• Check pulley condition. Align pulley.

Alternator Rectifier Shorted or Open.

• Replace diode or diode plate assembly.

BUZZING IN ALTERNATOR-REGULATOR FIELD RELAY (AC CIRCUITS)

Open Negative Diode in Alternator Causing Reduced Voltage to Relay Winding.

• Replace rectifier assembly.

SLUGGISH STARTING MOTOR OPERATION

Low Battery Charge.

• Charge battery and check specific gravity. If battery does not respond to charging, install a new one.

High Resistance in Circuit.

• Clean and tighten all connections. Repair or replace faulty wiring.

Defective Starter Motor.

• Service and repair starter motor where necessary.

Starter Motor Bearings Dry.

• Lubricate bearings with oil of proper viscosity.

Excessive Engine Drag Due to Tight Bearings.

• Recheck engine overhaul procedures. If problem still exists after break-in period, test and service starting circuit.

Extremely Cold Weather.

• Warm up battery before starting the engine.

Too-High Engine Oil Viscosity.

• Drain oil and replace with lower viscosity oil as recommended.

STARTER MOTOR WILL NOT OPERATE

Low Battery Charge.

• Charge battery and check specific gravity. If battery does not respond to charging, install a new battery.

Starter Safety Switch Open.

• Put shift lever in neutral or park position.

Continued on next page   OUO1082,0002CCD -19-10JAN12-2/5

Improperly Adjusted or Defective Starter Safety Switch.

• Adjust or replace switch.

Defective Starter Switch.

• Replace switch.

High Resistance in Starting Circuit or Defective Wiring.

• Clean and tighten all connections and replace faulty wiring.

Faulty Solenoid Switch on Starter Motor.

• Repair or replace switch.

Faulty Starter Motor.

• Service and repair motor.

STARTER MOTOR SOLENOID SWITCH FLUTTERS

Low Battery Charge.

• Charge battery and check specific gravity. If battery does not respond to charging, install a new battery.

High Resistance in Circuit.

• Clean and tighten all connections and replace faulty wiring.

Open Circuit in Starter Solenoid Hold-In Winding Circuit.

• Repair or replace solenoid or wires.

MISFIRING OF ENGINE

Improper Spark Plugs Heat Range.

• Replace with "hotter" or "colder" plugs as required.

Worn Spark Plug Electrodes or Dirty Spark Plugs.

• Clean, file, and regap plugs. Replace if necessary.

Defective Spark Plug.

• Replace spark plug.

Incorrect Distributor Timing.

• Reset timing.

Insufficient High-Tension Voltage Available to Spark Plug.

• See "Low Available Voltage at Spark Plug."

Cold Starting Conditions.

• Warm battery before starting engine.

LOW AVAILABLE VOLTAGE AT SPARK PLUG

Worn or Improperly Spaced Distributor Points.

• Reset point gap.

Dirty, Burned, or Pitted Points.

• Clean or replace points.

Defective Condenser (Leakage, Shorts, High Resistance, or Wrong Capacity).

• Replace condenser.

Dirt or Moisture in Distributor Cap.

• Clean distributor cap.

Cracked Rotor or Distributor Cap.

• Replace cap or rotor.

Too-Wide Distributor Rotor Gap.

• Replace rotor. Replace cap if deep path is worn on contacts.

Paint Covering Ignition Cables.

• Remove paint. Replace defective wiring if necessary.

Faulty Spark Plug Cables.

Defective Ignition Coil.

Loose Coil Tower—High-Tension Cable or Primary Coil Leads.

• Clean and tighten all connections. Replace faulty wiring.

Cracked Coil Cap or Carbon Tracks on Cap.

• Clean and tighten all connections. Replace faulty parts.

Defective Wiring.

• Check all connections. Replace faulty wiring.

Low Battery Charge.

• Charge battery and check specific gravity. If battery does not respond to charging, install a new battery.

High Resistance in Resistor Wire to Coil.

• Replace resistor wire.

BROKEN OR CHIPPED DISTRIBUTOR CAP

Cocked Distributor Cap.

• Replace distributor cap and install correctly.

HIGH-RESISTANCE CORROSION ON DISTRIBUTOR CAP TERMINALS

Arcing Inside the Cap Tower Due to Exposed Leads.

• Push all leads snugly into cap towers.

FLUTTER OR "FANNING" OF IGNITION TIMING MARKS WHEN TIMING

Excessive Wear in Bushing or Distributor Drive Train.

• If flutter exceeds 3 degrees, replace worn parts.

BUILDUP OF MATERIAL ON DISTRIBUTOR POINTS

Continued on next page OUO1082,0002CCD -19-10JAN12-3/5

Over-Capacity Condenser: Causes buildup of metal on stationary contact with negative-grounded battery, or on movable contact with positive-grounded battery.

• Replace with condenser of proper capacity.

Under-Capacity Condenser: Causes buildup of metal on movable contact with negative-grounded battery, or on stationary contact with positive-grounded battery.

• Replace with condenser of proper capacity.

EXCESSIVE WEAR ON DISTRIBUTOR CONTACT POINTS

Improper Method of Cleaning Points.

• Use contact file, crocus cloth, or lint-free tape to clean points.

EXCESSIVELY CONTAMINATED DISTRIBUTOR POINTS

Improper Cam Lubricant or Too Much Lubricant.

• Use proper amount of specified lubricant.

Excessive Lubrication of Breaker Plates or Distributor Advance Mechanism.

• Use proper amount of lubricant.

Clogged Oil Filler Breather Cap.

• Clean breather cap.

Clogged Filters in Crankcase Vent Pipe.

• Clean filters.

Worn Drive Shaft Bushing Letting Oil Fumes Enter Distributor.

• Replace bushing.

ARCING AND BURNING OF DISTRIBUTOR CONTACT POINTS

Loose Lead or High Internal Resistance in Condenser.

• Tighten lead or replace condenser.

Improper Method of Cleaning Distributor Points.

• Use proper contact file and polish with stone or crocus cloth. Use lint-free tape to clean parts.

Points Improperly Adjusted.

• Readjust points.

Oil or Other Foreign Material on Contacts.

• Clean and remove all foreign material. Correct the cause (see "Excessively Contaminated Distributor Points").

High Voltage Due to Faulty or Improperly Adjusted Voltage Regulator.

• Adjust voltage regulator. Replace unit if faulty.

Shorted Bypass Resistor.

• Replace resistor.

Wrong Capacity Condenser.

• Replace condenser.

DAMAGE TO METAL TERMINALS IN DISTRIBUTOR CAP DUE TO ARCING

Ignition Cable Leads Loose.

• Clean terminals. Push leads snugly into cap towers. Replace cap if erosion is severe.

DIM LIGHTS

High Resistance in Circuit or Poor Ground on Lights.

• Clean and tighten all connections. Replace faulty wiring.

Low Battery Charge.

• Charge battery and check specific gravity. If battery does not respond to charging, install a new battery.

Defective Light Switch or Starting Switch.

• Replace switch.

Defective Battery Ground Wire (24-Volt Split-Load System).

• Repair or replace ground wire.

LIGHTS BURN OUT PREMATURELY

Excess Voltage Due to Faulty Regulator or Ground Wire on Alternator or Generator "F" Terminal.

• Adjust or replace regulator. Replace faulty wiring.

Defective Battery Ground Wire (24-Volt Split-Load System).

• Repair or replace ground wire.

GENERATOR OR ALTERNATOR INDICATOR LAMP GLOWS DIMLY OR INTERMITTENTLY

Excessive Resistance in Battery Lead to Generator Regulator.

• Clean and tighten all connections. Replace faulty wiring.

Excessive Internal Resistance in Generator Regulator.

• Clean and adjust cutout relay contact points.

Excessive Internal Resistance in Alternator Regulator.

• Replace regulator.

Defective Generator or Alternator.

• Service or replace unit.

OIL PRESSURE INDICATOR LAMP WILL NOT LIGHT

Burned-Out Bulb.

Open Circuit or Excessive Resistance in Wiring.

• Clean and tighten all connections. Replace faulty wiring.

Continued on next page OUO1082,0002CCD -19-10JAN12-4/5

Defective Lamp Body.

Faulty Oil Pressure Switch.

• Replace switch.

OIL PRESSURE LAMP REMAINS ON WITH STARTING SWITCH OFF

Defective Lamp Body.

Grounded Wire to Oil Pressure Switch.

• Repair or replace wiring.

Faulty Oil Pressure Switch.

• Replace switch.

OUO1082,0002CCD -19-10JAN12-5/5

TEST YOURSELF

QUESTIONS

1. Give the seven basic steps for good troubleshooting.

2. During which of the seven steps should you begin replacing parts?

3. What electrical component should be checked out even before testing most circuits?

(Answers are in the back of the textbook.)

OUO1082,0002CCE -19-10JAN12-1/1

INTRODUCTION

DXP02714 —UN—23FEB11

14

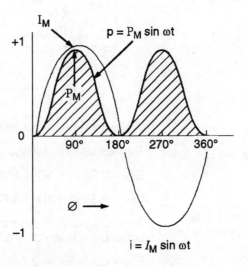

$p = P_M \sin \omega t$

$i = I_M \sin \omega t$

SW03989,00010BC -19-05APR12-1/1

DC VOLTAGE DIVIDER NETWORKS

SERIES DC VOLTAGE DIVIDER RULE

We can use the voltage divider rule to supply lower voltages to other circuits. In chapter 2, we calculated the following using the voltage divider rule (Fig. 1):

- V_{R1}, between points A and B = 2.4 V
- V_{R2}, between points B and C = 3.6 V
- V_{R3}, between points C and D = 6.0 V
- I_t = 1.2 A

A—Point A   C—Point C
B—Point B   D—Point D

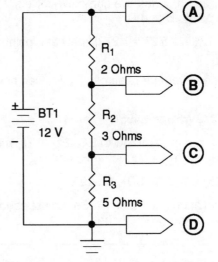

Fig. 1 — Series Voltage Divider Network

Continued on next page
Continued on next page   OUO1082,0002CD4 -19-10JAN12-1/3

PARALLEL DC VOLTAGE DIVIDER RULE

When a load is applied to the circuit shown in Fig. 1, the circuit changes to a series-parallel circuit shown in Fig. 2 and dramatically affects the circuit current and voltages.

The mathematical symbol for parallel-to is ||. Review the equations for parallel circuits in chapter 2, if needed.

We can make the calculations with the addition of R_4 as follows:

Total resistance is: $R_t = R_1 + [(R_2 + R_3) \| R_4]$

We must first solve for the parallel resistance:

$R_P = 8\Omega \| 5\Omega = 3.077\Omega$

Now we can solve for total resistance:

$R_t = 2\Omega + 3.077\Omega = 5.077\Omega$

Since we know total voltage and resistance, we can now solve for current (I_t):

$I_t = E_t/R_t = 12V/5.077\Omega = 2.364A = I_{R1}$

Since the R_1 resistor is in series, all the current flows through it. We can now solve for the voltage drop across the R_1 resistor.

$E_{R1} = I_{R1} \times R_1 = 2.364A \times 2\Omega = 4.727V$ between points A and B

Since R1 and R_4 are in series, we can solve for the voltage between points B and D:

$E_{R4} = E_t - E_{R1} = 12V - 4.727 = 7.273V$ between points B and D

Since we know the voltage drop across R_4, we can now solve for current at R_4:

$I_{R4} = E_{R4}/R_4 = 7.273V/5\Omega = 1.455A$

Since E_{R2} and E_{R3} are in parallel with E_{R4}, $E_{R2} + E_{R3}$ must equal E_{R4}. We can solve for current at R_2 and R_3:

$I_{R2} = E_{R4}/(R_2 + R3) = 7.273V/8\Omega = 0.909A$

To check our calculations, It = 2.364A. So It must equal I_{R1} + IR4 (the sum of the two branches):

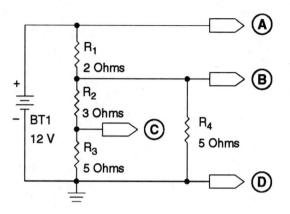

Fig. 2 — Parallel Voltage Divider Network

1.455A + 0.909A = 2.364 = It

To calculate the voltage drop across R_2 and R3:

$E_{R3} = 0.9091 \times 5\Omega = 4.546V$

$E_{R2} = 0.9091 \times 3\Omega = 2.727V$

To check our calculations, the sum of E_{R2} and E_{R3} must equal the voltage drop across the resistor R_4.

$E_{R2} + E_{R3} = E_{R4} = 2.727V + 4.546V = 7.273V$

Table 1 — Comparison of Circuits Shown between Figs. 1 and 2		
PARAMETER	**Fig. 1 Circuit**	**Fig. 2 Circuit**
Between A and B	2.4 V	4.727 V
Between B and C	3.6 V	2.727 V
Between C and D	6 V	4.546 V
Between A and D	12 V	12 V
Between B and D	9.6 V	7.723 V
Between C and D	6 V	4.546 V
Total Circuit Current	1.2 A	2.364 A

In review, we can see that adding a load to a voltage divider changes the complexity of the circuit by a large amount. By studying Table 1, you will see the changes to circuit current and voltage drops.

Continued on next page   OUO1082,0002CD4 -19-10JAN12-2/3

VOLTAGE DIVIDER USING A POTENTIOMETER

Now let's explore what happens when we replace the fixed resistor R2 with a 300Ω potentiometer (pot) (Fig. 3). We have changed the values of the other resistors in the circuit to provide some more mathematics practice.

The total resistance (R_t) will vary with the setting of the pot. We can analyze the circuit with the pot set at both extremes, giving us a clear picture of how it will affect the circuit.

SOLUTION FOR R_2 PIN 2 POSITIONED AT PIN 1.

$R_t = R_1 + [1/(1/R_2 + R_3) + (1/R_4)]$

$R_t = 100Ω + (300Ω \| 100Ω) = 100 + [1/(1/300 + 1/100)] = 175Ω$

$I_t = E_t/R_t = 12V/175Ω = 68.57mA$

$V_{R1} = I_t/R_1 = 68.57mA \times 100Ω = 6.857V$

$V_{R4} = V_t - V_{R1} = 12V - 6.957V = 5.143V$

$I_{R1} = I_t = 68.57mA$

$I_{R4} = V_{R4}/R4 = 5.143V/100Ω = 51.43mA$

$I_{R3} = V_{R4}/(R_2 + R_3) = 5.143V/300Ω = 17.14mA$

$V_{R3} = I_{R3}/R_3 = 17.14mA/100Ω = 1.714V$

$V_{R2} = I_{R2}/R_2 = 17.14mA/200Ω = 3.428V$

SOLUTION FOR R_2 PIN 2 POSITIONED AT PIN 3.

$R_t = R1 + R2 + [1/(1/R3) + (1/R4)]$

$R_T = 100Ω + 200Ω + (100Ω \| 100Ω) = 300 + [1/(1/100 + 1/100)] = 350Ω$

$I_t = E_t/R_t = 12V/350Ω = 34.29mA$

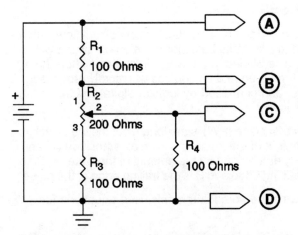

Fig. 3 — *Potentiometer Loaded Voltage Divider Network*

$V_{R1} = I_t \times R_1 = 34.29mA \times 100Ω = 3.429V$

$V_{R2} = I_t \times R_2 = 34.29mA \times 200Ω = 6.857V$

$V_{R4} = V_t - V_{R1} - V_{R2} = 12V - 3.429V - 6.857V = 1.714V$

$V_{R3} = V_{R4} = 1.714V$

$I_{R1} = I_{R2} = It = 34.29mA$

$I_{R3} = I_{R4} = It/2 = 34.29/2 = 17.14mA$

Table 2 — Comparison of Potentiometer Extremes			
POSITION OF PIN 2	R_t	V_{R4}	I_t
Pin 2 at Pin 1	175 Ω	5.143 V	68.57 mA
Pin 2 at Pin 3	350 Ω	1.714 V	34.29 mA

We can summarize the results using Table 2.

OUO1082,0002CD4 -19-10JAN12-3/3

DC PULSES

A pulse is a sudden on and off of direct current flow within a circuit (Fig. 4). In its basic form, an on-off switch will cause a pulse of electron flow within a circuit when the switch is turned on and off. Pulses are mostly processed, generated, and controlled by logic or digital electronic circuit devices.

The width of a pulse (PW) is the length of time the switch is on. The height of the pulse is known as amplitude (v) and is generally determined by the amount of the voltage. Side A is the leading edge and B is the trailing edge of the pulse.

The following are some commonly used equations for pulses:

- Cycle time (T) = Pulse Width (PW) + Space Width (SW)
- Frequency (f) = 1/T
- Duty Cycle = (PW/T)100%

A—Leading Edge
B—Trailing Edge
C—Volts = 1 V/Div
D—Time = 10µs/Div

PW—Width of Pulse
SW—Space Width
T—Time

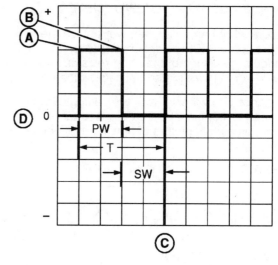

Fig. 4 — A Theoretical Pulse

OUO1082,0002CD5 -19-13JUN12-1/2

Since pulses are generated and processed by components that are not ideal, we tend to have pulses that look like Fig. 5 rather than the one in Fig. 4.

We can see from Fig. 5 that this pulse has T equal to 40 µs. Using the equation for frequency, we can determine that the frequency is equal to 25 kHz. The pulse's amplitude is 3 VDC because it does not go negative (below the 0 line).

A—Volts = 1V/Div

B—Time = 10µs/Div

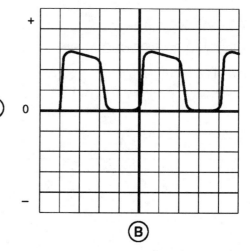

Fig. 5 — Typical Pulse as Viewed on an Oscilloscope

OUO1082,0002CD5 -19-13JUN12-2/2

RESISTOR AND CAPACITOR (RC) CIRCUITS

INTRODUCTION

There are two types of resistor and capacitor (RC) circuits used to reshape incoming waves or pulses for signals. They are the integrator circuit and the differentiator circuit. The product of the RC in these circuits is the RC time constant.

RC TIME CONSTANTS

It is important to understand RC time constants (the charging and discharging of capacitors through resistors) because this is the basis of filter, oscillator and timing circuits. These circuits are extensively employed in electronics. Some examples are:

- Delayed headlight turnoff
- Timing circuits for controllers and microcomputers
- Square wave generators
- Clock circuits

A time constant is the time it would take the voltage (potential difference) across the capacitor to rise to the same value as the applied voltage, if it continued to rise at its initial rate of change for the whole time interval. This calculated time constant is the amount of time it takes a capacitor to reach 63.2% of its full charge or to discharge to 36.8% of its initial voltage.

The letter symbol for time constant is the Greek letter τ (tau).

In Fig. 6 is shown capacitor voltage (V_C) in relation to the applied voltage as it rises over time. As we can see from the chart, if the initial rate of change of voltage (slope) were to remain constant, we could calculate the time constant for the capacitor using the following equation:

$$v = \tau(\text{initial } d_v/d_t)$$

Where:

$\tau = C_R$ in seconds

initial $d_v/d_t = E/CR$

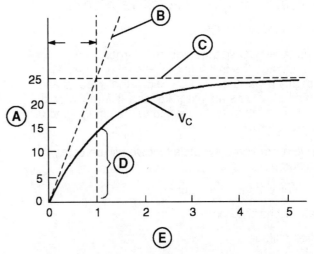

Fig. 6 — Charging Curve for an RC Circuit

A—Voltage
B—Slope = d_v/d_t
C—Applied Voltage (E_{app})
D—63.2% of E
E—Time after switch is closed (seconds)

And:

τ = length of time in seconds defined as a time constant

C = the capacitance of the capacitor in farads

R = the resistance through which the capacitor charges in ohms

Full charge on the capacitor equals five time constants (5τ). This is because the capacitor voltage increases exponentially. At the end of the first time constant, the voltage is 63.2% of the applied voltage. At the end of the second time constant, the voltage is 86.5% of the applied voltage, which is 63.2% of the remaining applied voltage (applied voltage minus voltage of first time constant). This continues until the capacitor voltage is 99.3% of the applied voltage, which is considered a full charge.

OUO1082,0002CD6 -19-16OCT12-1/16

EXAMPLE (after S_1 is closed)

1. What is the initial rate of change (initial d_v/d_t) of voltage across the capacitor in Fig. 7?
2. How long will it take the capacitor in Fig. 7 to charge to 63.2% of its full charge?
3. How long will it take the capacitor to fully charge?

SOLUTION

1. Initial $dv/d_t = E/CR = 24V/(1\mu F \times 2M\Omega) = 12V/s$
2. $\tau = CR = 1\mu F \times 2M\Omega = 2s$
3. Full Charge = 5τ = 5 x 2s = 10s

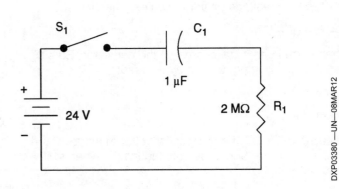

Fig. 7 — A Typical Series RC Network

Continued on next page OUO1082,0002CD6 -19-16OCT12-2/16

CALCULATING CAPACITOR VOLTAGE VS. TIME

CHARGING CAPACITORS

When a constant DC voltage source charges a capacitor through a resistor, the instantaneous level of capacitor voltage at any given time can be calculated (Figs. 8 and 9). When employed as an integrator or a differentiator, the circuit time constant must be related to the time period of the input waveform.

The following are some symbols that we will be using in our calculations:

e_c = capacitor voltage at instant t

i_c = capacitor charging current

E = applied voltage

E_o = initial charge on the capacitor

ε = exponential constant = 2.718

t = time from commencement of charge

C = capacitance being charged

R = charging resistance

Note that when a symbol is shown in lower case, it designates a measurement at a specific instant in time while the value is changing.

In Fig. 8, with V_C = 0V at the instant that switch S_1 is closed, then V_R at t = 0 is:

$V_R = E - e_c = 10V$

We can now solve for the charging current through R_1 at t = 0. We will use the following equation:

$i_C = i_R = V_{R1}/R_1$

$= (E - e_c)/R$

$= (10V - 0)/1k\Omega = 10mA$

Once the capacitor begins to charge (Fig. 9), it does so at a rapid rate initially and then the rate decreases as the capacitor voltage increases. This is because the resistor voltage decreases as the voltage at the capacitor increases, causing the current to also decrease.

The capacitor voltage ec follows an exponential law:

$e_c = E - (E - E_o)\varepsilon^{-t/CR}$

When there is no initial charge on the capacitor (Eo = 0) then the following equation may be used:

$ec = E(1 - \varepsilon^{-t/CR})$

EXAMPLE 1

Calculate the level of ec (capacitor voltage) across C1 in the circuit for Fig. 8 at 4 ms from the instant when switch S1 is closed.

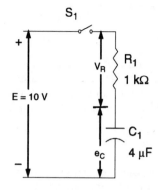

Fig. 8 — Series RC Circuit

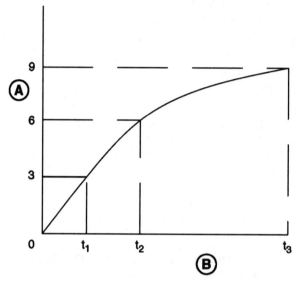

Fig. 9 — ec Plotted vs. Time

A—Volts   **B—Time**

SOLUTION 1

At t = 4ms

$e_c = E(1 - \varepsilon^{-t/CR})$

$= 10V(1 - 2.718^{-4ms/(4\mu F \times 1K\Omega)})$

$= 10V(1 - 2.718^{-1})$

$= 10V(1 - 0.3679) = 10V(0.6321) = 6.32V$

EXAMPLE 2

Determine the instantaneous level of charging current in the circuit of Fig. 8 at 4 ms after switch S1 is closed.

SOLUTION 2

$i_C = i_R = V_{R1}/R_1$

$= (E - e_c)/R$

$= (10V - 6.32V)/1K\Omega = 3.68mA$

Continued on next page
OUO1082,0002CD6 -19-16OCT12-3/16

DISCHARGING CAPACITORS

Once the capacitor in Fig. 10 is charged to the same level of voltage as the applied voltage, current will no longer flow. If the applied voltage is turned off, with switch S1 still closed, the capacitor will discharge past the circuitry of the applied voltage source and through resistor R1.

In order to calculate the voltage of the capacitor at a specific time during discharge, we will use the following equation:

$e_c = Ee^{-t/CR}$

Where E equals the starting value of the charged capacitor.

EXAMPLE

Calculate the level of ec (capacitor voltage) across C1 in the circuit for Fig. 10 at 4 ms from the instant when switch S1 is switched to position 2 with the capacitor fully charged.

SOLUTION

At t = 4 ms

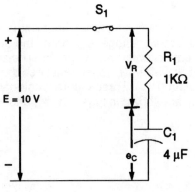

Fig. 10 — Series RC Circuit

$$e_c = E\varepsilon^{-t/CR}$$
$$= 10V \times 2.718^{-4ms/(4\mu F \times 1K\Omega)}$$
$$= 10V \times 2.718^{-1}$$
$$= 10V \times 0.3679 = 3.68V$$

OUO1082,0002CD6 -19-16OCT12-4/16

As we can see by Fig. 11, the discharge curve is similar to the charging curve. That's because the discharge curve is also exponential in shape. Once five time constants have been completed, the capacitor is said to be fully discharged.

A—Voltage (E)
B—Charge
C—Discharge
D—Time in seconds (CR)

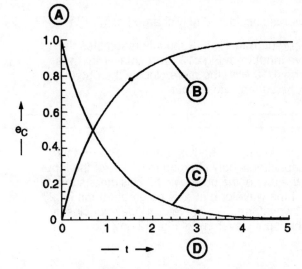

Fig. 11 — Charge and Discharge Curves for an RC Circuit

Continued on next page   OUO1082,0002CD6 -19-16OCT12-5/16

INTEGRATOR CIRCUIT

In Fig. 12 we have an R_C circuit showing input voltage as a square wave and an output voltage (e_c). Since the output is taken across the capacitor it is an integrator. The shape of the output voltage waveform is dependent upon the ratio of τ (CR) to pulse width (PW). Three different categories of output waveforms are shown in Figs. 13, 14, and 15.

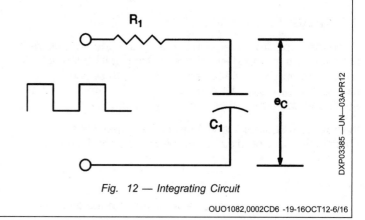

Fig. 12 — Integrating Circuit

OUO1082,0002CD6 -19-16OCT12-6/16

In Fig. 13 is shown a waveform where $\tau \leq 1/10$ PW. We know that the capacitor is charged at 99.3% of the input voltage at t = 5 CR. Therefore, we can write the following equation:

e_c = 99.3% of E at τ = 5(1/10PW)

Since e_c equals 99.3% of E when the capacitor is fully charged, we can write the equation as follows:

$e_c \approx$ E at τ = 1/2PW

The capacitor is considered fully charged at 1/2 PW.

The wave output from Fig. 13 roughly resembles the square wave input from Fig. 12. The smaller that τ is made (< than 1/10 PW) the more closely the output resembles the square wave input.

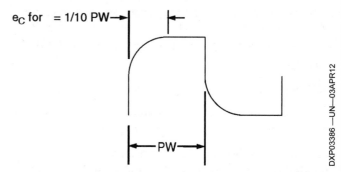

Fig. 13 — Output Waveforms Where $\tau \leq 1/10$ PW

OUO1082,0002CD6 -19-16OCT12-7/16

The waveform in Fig. 14 shows e_c for τ = PW. In this case, the capacitor is only charged to 63.2% of the input voltage by the end of the pulse-width. This means that the amplitude of the waveform at e_c is no greater than 63.2% of the input waveform. The waveform does not closely resemble the input waveform of Fig. 12 any more.

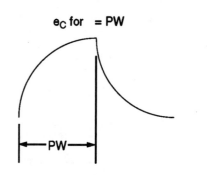

Fig. 14 — Output Waveforms Where τ = PW

Continued on next page

OUO1082,0002CD6 -19-16OCT12-8/16

When τ ≥ 10 PW, then the waveform of Fig. 15 results and we have an integrator. To understand an integrator, it is necessary to calculate the output voltage levels in relation to time. When τ ≥ 10 PW, use the following equation:

$$e_{ct2} \approx E - (E - E_0)\varepsilon^{-1PW/10PW}$$

Since $E_0 \approx 0$, we can use the following equation:

$$e_{ct2} \approx E\varepsilon^{-t/CR}$$

$$e_{ct2} \approx E(1 - \varepsilon^{-1PW/10PW})$$
$$\approx E(1 - 0.90)$$
$$\approx E(0.10)$$

To calculate e_{ct1} at 1/2 PW:

$$e_{ct1} \approx E(1 - \varepsilon^{-\frac{1}{2}PW/10PW})$$
$$\approx Eve - \varepsilon^{-1/20})$$
$$\approx E(1 - 0.95)$$
$$\approx E(0.05)$$

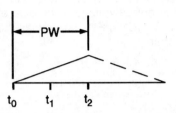

Fig. 15 — Output Waveforms Where τ ≥ 10 PW

This shows that after time to $e_c = E(0.05)$ and that after time to $e_c = E(0.1)$ or $e_c = 2(t1)$. The capacitor voltage is growing almost linearly.

To examine the output waveform when RC is 10 (or more) times the pulse width, consider the following example:

EXAMPLE

OUO1082,0002CD6 -19-16OCT12-9/16

The circuit shown in Fig. 16 has the following pulse inputs applied:

1. E = 10 V, PW = 1 ms
2. E = 5 V, PW = 2 ms
3. E = 10 V, PW = 2 ms

Calculate the level of ec at the end of each pulse. Since the initial voltage on C is zero, use the following equation:

$$e_c \approx E(1 - \varepsilon^{-t/CR})$$

Since the charging current remains substantially constant during the input PW, this problem can also be solved by using the following equation:

$$V = I_t/C = E/R \times t/C = (E \times t)/(R \times C)$$

SOLUTION

1. 50 mV
2. 50 mV
3. 100 mV

IN CONCLUSION:

• When the pulse width is doubled, the output voltage is doubled.

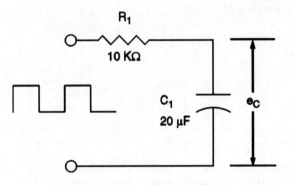

Fig. 16 — Integrator Circuit

• The charging rate is (almost) linear.
• The output amplitude is proportional to the pulse width.
• When the pulse amplitude is doubled, the output voltage is doubled.
• The output voltage is proportional to the pulse area = pulse width (PW) x pulse amplitude (PA). $e_c \propto PA \times PW$
• When we integrate a sine wave, it produces a negative cosine wave. The mathematics to support this are very complex and will not be discussed in this text.

Continued on next page   OUO1082,0002CD6 -19-16OCT12-10/16

DIFFERENTIATOR CIRCUIT

When the output (e_R) of an RC circuit is across the resistor (R_1), as in Fig. 17, the output voltage is the differential of the input. The ratio of τ (RC) to PW determines the shape of the output waveforms.

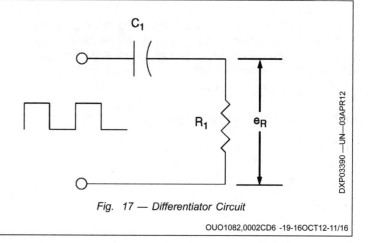

Fig. 17 — Differentiator Circuit

OUO1082,0002CD6 -19-16OCT12-11/16

The voltage drop across R_1 equals $e_R = i_c \times R$. When $\tau =$ 10 PW, the capacitor charges very little during the pulse width time. The charging current decreases very little from its initial level (Fig. 18). Thus, eR remains almost constant during the PW. During the space width, the capacitor is discharged, and i_c is a negative quantity. The resistor voltage is negative and remains nearly constant for the discharge time.

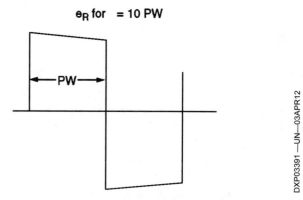

Fig. 18 — Differentiator Pulse for $\tau \geq$ 10 PW

OUO1082,0002CD6 -19-16OCT12-12/16

If t = PW, the capacitor is charged to approximately 60% of the input voltage during the pulse time. Consequently, the charging current falls by about 60% of its initial value, giving an output waveform with a very pronounced tilt (Fig. 19).

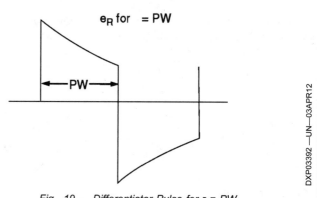

Fig. 19 — Differentiator Pulse for $\tau =$ PW

Continued on next page   OUO1082,0002CD6 -19-16OCT12-13/16

When τ ≤ 1/10 PW, the capacitor is charged very rapidly. The resulting waveform of eR is a series of positive and negative spikes at the pulse leading and lagging edges, respectively (Fig. 20). The differential of a quantity is a measure of the rate of change of the quantity. During both the pulse width and the space width, the input voltage does not change at all. Thus, it is seen the positive and negative spikes with intervening spaces (Fig. 20) do indeed represent a differentiated square wave.

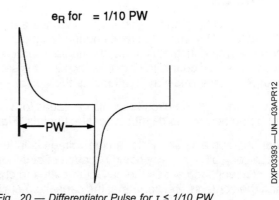

Fig. 20 — Differentiator Pulse for τ ≤ 1/10 PW

OUO1082,0002CD6 -19-16OCT12-14/16

In Fig. 21 is shown a differentiation circuit with a t = 100–9s (100 nanoseconds). It has a square wave pulse input of 10 volts. The input and output pulses of this circuit are shown in Fig. 22.

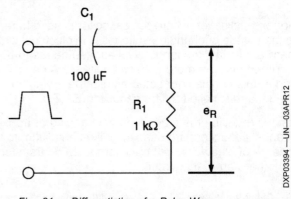

Fig. 21 — Differentiation of a Pulse Wave

OUO1082,0002CD6 -19-16OCT12-15/16

This equation may be applied in the case of pulse waveforms with known rise and fall times, as illustrated in Fig. 22.

EXAMPLE

Calculate the amplitude of the differentiated output waveform for the circuit and input pulse shown in Fig. 22.

e_R = RC x (rate of change of input)

SOLUTION

e_R = C_R x (slope)

e_{R1} = CR x (E_{max}/t_r) = 100pF x 1kΩ x 10V/µs = 1V

e_{R2} = CR x (E_{max}/t_f) = 100pF x 1kΩ x (10V/3µs) = 0.3V

When we differentiate a sine wave we will get a cosine wave.

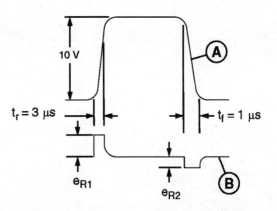

Fig. 22 — Differentiated Pulse Wave

A—Input Wave   **B—Output Wave**

OUO1082,0002CD6 -19-16OCT12-16/16

RC FILTERS

When the discharging time constant is long, the ripple out of a peak rectifier may be small enough to ignore. But when the time constant is short, the ripple is large and we have to use additional filtering to reduce it. This section is about RC filters, one way to attenuate the ripple.

Consider an ignition circuit in which a capacitor is connected across the distributor contact points (Fig. 23).

When the contacts separate, a high voltage is induced in the ignition coil primary winding because of self-induction. This high voltage causes the capacitor plates to charge when the contacts first separate; the capacitor acts initially like a short circuit and current flows into the capacitor to minimize arcing at the contacts.

DXP03396 —UN—03APR12

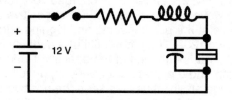

Fig. 23 — Capacitor in Ignition Circuit

High voltages originating when a circuit is opened may exist for a very short interval of time, such as 1 microsecond, and are called transient voltages.

OUO1082,0002CD7 -19-05APR12-1/3

Another application where the capacitor is used to reduce the magnitude of changing voltages is in electrical circuits, where a constantly changing voltage (A) needs to be smoothed out to a more constant voltage. A capacitor used in this way is connected across the changing voltage, and is called a filter capacitor (B) (Fig. 24).

Besides reducing the magnitude of changing or transient voltages, capacitors are used in ignition amplifiers to store a charge of electricity until the charge can be transferred to another part of the circuit.

A—Changing Voltage   C—With Capacitor
B—Filter Capacitor   D—Without Capacitor

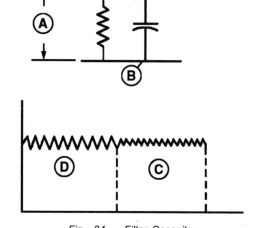

Fig. 24 — Filter Capacitor

Continued on next page OUO1082,0002CD7 -19-05APR12-2/3

Another application, Fig. 25 shows an RC filter between the input capacitor and load resistor. By deliberate design, R_F is much greater than X_C. Therefore, the circuit acts like an A_C voltage divider (voltage drop of C_F is in parallel with RL). Because R is much greater than X_C, the output ripple is much smaller than the input ripple. Typically, R_F is at least 10 times X_C; this means the output ripple is attenuated or reduced by a factor of at least 10.

We can use more than one section. Since each section acts like an AC voltage divider, the overall attenuation equals the product of the individual attenuations; if each section reduces the ripple by a factor of 15, the overall attenuation is 225.

This means one section reduces the ripple by a factor of 15, two sections by 225, and three sections by 3300.

The main disadvantage of an RC filter is the loss of DC voltage across resistance R_F. Since R_F is in series with R_L, we get voltage-divider action. On the one hand, we need a large R_F for good filtering action. On the other, we need a small R_F to prevent excessive loss of DC voltage. These conflicting requirements mean the RC filter is practical only for small load currents (large R_L).

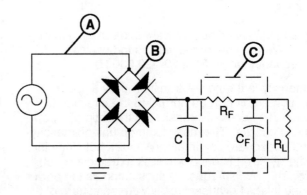

Fig. 25 — One-Section RC Filter Application

A—Generator   **C—RC Filter Section**
B—Full Wave Rectifier

OUO1082,0002CD7 -19-05APR12-3/3

DECIBELS

Sound is a longitudinal mechanical wave traveling through a medium. We are concerned with sound waves in the audible frequency range from 20—20,000 Hz.

Sound intensity is the power transferred by a sound wave through a unit of area normal to the direction of propagation. The units of intensity are the ratio of a power unit to a unit of area. The most common unit of intensity is the watt per square centimeter (W/cm2), but since the rate of energy flow in sound waves is extremely small, the microwatt (μW) is frequently substituted as the power unit. Sound intensity varies directly with the square of the frequency (Ä) and with the square of the amplitude (A) of a given sound wave. The formula for Intensity (I) is:

$$I = 2\pi^2 f^2 A^2 pv$$

Where:

f = the frequency of the sound

A = the amplitude of the sound wave

p = the density of the medium

v = the sound velocity

The intensity of the faintest audible sound (I_0) is calculated at 10^{-16}W/cm^2. This intensity is the hearing threshold and is referred to by acoustic experts as the zero of sound intensity. The hearing threshold represents the standard zero of sound intensity. Its value is $10^{-10}\mu$W/cm^2 at a frequency of 1000 Hz.

$$I_0 = 10^{-10}\mu\text{W/cm}^2 = 10^{-16}\text{W/cm}^2$$

The pain threshold represents the maximum intensity that the average ear can record without feeling or pain. Its value is 100μW/cm2 or 10–4 W/cm2

$$I_p = 100\mu\text{W/cm}^2 = 10^{-4}\text{W/cm}^2$$

The decibel scale is established by the following rule:

When the intensity (I_1) of one sound is 10 times as great as the intensity (I_2) of another, the ratio of intensity is said to be 1 bel (B).

When comparing the intensities of two sounds, the difference in intensity levels is given by:

$$B = \log(I_1/I_2)$$

Where:

I_1 = the intensity of one sound

I_2 = the intensity of a second sound

Example 1

Two sounds have intensities of 15 and 1500 μW/cm^2. Compute the difference in intensity levels in bels.

Solution 1

$$B = \log(I_1/I_2) = \log(1500\mu\text{W/cm}^2/15\mu\text{W/cm}^2)$$
$$= \log 100 = 2B = 20\text{dB}$$

A decibel (dB) is defined as one-tenth of a bel.

By using the standard zero of intensity (I_0) as a standard for comparing all intensities, a general scale has been devised for rating any sound. The intensity level in decibels of any sound of intensity (I) can be found using the following formula:

$$dB = 10 \log(I/I_0)$$

Where:

I_0 is the intensity at the hearing threshold (10^{-16}W/cm^2).

Example 2

Compute the intensity level in decibels of a sound whose intensity is at the pain threshold (10^{-4}W/cm2).

Solution 2

$$dB = 10\log((10^{-4}\text{W/cm}^2)/(10{-}16\text{ W/cm}^2))$$
$$= 10\log 10^{12} = 10 \times 12$$
$$= 120\text{dB}$$

We must remember that a 40 dB sound is much more than twice as intense as a 20 dB sound. A sound which is 100 times as intense as another, is only 20 dB larger.

Table 3 — Intensity Levels for Common Sounds	
SOUND	**Intensity Level (dB)**
Hearing threshold	0 dB
Rustling leaves	10 dB
Whisper	20 dB
Quiet radio	40 dB
Normal conversation	65 dB
Busy street corner	80 dB
Subway car	100 dB
Pain threshold	120 dB
Jet engine	140—160 dB

Refer to Table 3 for several examples of intensity levels for common sounds.

OUO1082,0002CD8 -19-05APR12-1/1

HOW SINE WAVES ARE PRODUCED

A SIMPLE ROTATING GENERATOR

In Chapters 2 and 4, we discussed a second method of generating a voltage, based on electromagnetic induction. As an electric conductor rotates in a magnetic field, it cuts across magnetic lines of force inducing a voltage in the conductor. In order to maintain a potential difference by this method, we must keep the conductor in motion within a stationary magnetic field.

We can achieve this by the arrangement shown in Fig. 26. The electric conductor is in the form of a loop and rotates continuously within the magnetic field in the air gap between a north and a south pole. Slip rings and brushes maintain electrical connection to the rotating loop.

The two sides of the rotating loop must always cut across the magnetic lines of force in opposite directions, resulting in the two induced voltages being connected in series so that the brushes receive the sum of the two voltages. By connecting a load resistor to the brushes of this simple generator, the induced voltage causes current to flow in the closed circuit consisting of the loop and the load. The electric energy that is converted into heat energy in the

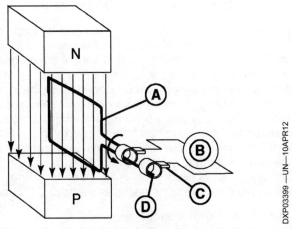

Fig. 26 — A Simple AC Generator

A—Conductor
B—Load
C—Brush
D—Slip Ring

load resistance is generated directly at the expense of the mechanical energy maintaining the rotation of the loop.

Continued on next page OUO1082,0002CD9 -19-13JUN12-1/7

THE NATURE OF THE INDUCED VOLTAGE

A conductor is said to have completed one full cycle once it has rotated through the magnetic lines of force for one complete revolution (360°). First, it will cut the magnetic field in one direction and then back through the same magnetic field in the opposite direction. Since the induced voltage appearing at the brushes of this simple generator reverses its polarity with each half-revolution, the basic generator for converting mechanical energy into electric energy develops an alternating voltage and current. Since most of our electrical energy is generated by rotating machines, it is necessary for us to understand and analyze AC circuits just as easily as we have DC circuits.

In Fig. 27 is shown a sectional view of the simple generator from Fig. 26. Only one conductor is shown during one full rotation in order to relate the rotation of the conductor to numerical calculations. It is conventional to consider the normal or positive direction of rotation as being counterclockwise, starting from an angular position representing three o'clock.

In Fig. 27 it describes one rotation of our simple generator, which is known as one electrical cycle (revolution). A typical generator will complete many electrical cycles per one mechanical revolution. This is because generators are built with many field windings.

The time taken to complete one electrical cycle is the period of the waveform.

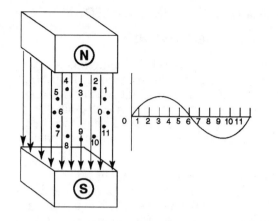

Fig. 27 — Nature of Induced Voltage

Table 4 shows the position of the conductor in relation to the magnetic lines of force, polarity and induced voltage.

Table 4 — Relationship of Conductor Between Cutting Lines of Force and Graph			
Position	Relation to Magnetic Lines of Force	Induced Voltage	Polarity
0	Parallel	Minimum	Starting +
1	Starting to cut lines of force	Yes	+
2	Cutting more lines of force	Yes	+
3	Cutting at right angles	Maximum	+
4	Starting to decrease	Yes	+
5	Decreasing more	Yes	+
6	Parallel	Minimum	Starting −
7	Starting to cut lines of force	Yes	−
8	Cutting more lines of force	Yes	−
9	Cutting at right angles	Maximum	−
10	Starting to decrease	Yes	−
11	Decreasing more	Yes	−
0	Parallel	Minimum	Starting +

Continued on next page   OUO1082,0002CD9 -19-13JUN12-2/7

THE SINE WAVE

We can show the continual change by plotting a graph showing the magnitude and polarity of the induced voltage at any position of the loop, as shown in Fig. 27. In order to analyze the AC circuit we must be able to determine exactly what the induced voltage is at any instant during the rotation of the conductor.

We replace the sectional view in Fig. 27 with a much simpler diagram, as shown in Fig. 28. The straight line OX represents the rotating conductor pivoted at point O (for origin). The free end is free to rotate (A) and is indicated by an arrowhead. We call this representation of the rotating conductor a phasor. We have not shown the magnetic lines of force for reasons of simplicity.

Mathematical convention requires this phasor to rotate in a CCW direction, starting from a position of three o'clock (reference axis). The position of the phasor at a certain instant in time is located by stating the phase angle (Ø) through which it has rotated from the reference axis.

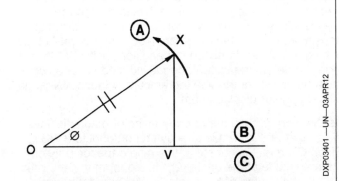

Fig. 28 — Phasor Representation of the Rotating Conductor

A—Rotation   C—Axis
B—Reference

Continued on next page OUO1082,0002CD9 -19-13JUN12-4/7

The voltage induced in a rotating conductor is directly proportional to the rate at which it cuts across the magnetic lines of force. We will assume a uniform flux density and a constant angular velocity so the rate of cutting will depend only on the angular position of the loop. To determine instantaneous induced voltage, we must be able to determine the amount of induced voltage at any angular displacement.

As the loop rotates, the rate of cutting of magnetic lines of force at any instant is directly proportional to XV/OX. Since OX remains constant, this ratio depends only on the magnitude of the angle (Ø). In trigonometry, the ratio XV/OX is the sine of the angle Ø. We can determine accurately the ratio of XV/OX for any magnitude of the angle (Ø) by using the sin key of an electronic calculator.

The voltage induced into the rotating conductor at any point is directly proportional to the sine of the angle through which the loop has rotated from the reference axis.

We can plot an accurate graph of the instantaneous variations in an alternating voltage by plotting the readings from a sine table or calculator (at approximately 5° intervals) on a sheet of graph paper and then joining the plots to form a smooth curve. The result (Fig. 29) is a sine curve and the alternating voltage that varies in accordance with this sine curve is a sine wave.

THE PEAK VALUE OF A SINE WAVE

The greatest value the induced voltage can attain occurs at Ø = 90°, when the rate of cutting of magnetic lines of force is maximum. When Ø = 270°, the same maximum value is attained but the polarity of the induced voltage is reversed. The numerical value that the alternating voltage attains at these two angles is termed the peak value of the AC waveform.

The designation for the peak value of an alternating source voltage is E_m (m for maximum).

This peak value is a numerical quantity in volts without polarity, since it occurs at both 90° and 270°. It is also independent of time, since it always appears at 90° and 270° and is a constant for a given generator. We refer to E_m as a scalar quantity that has a numerical magnitude but has no direction (positive or negative) associated with it.

In the simple AC generator, the peak voltage will depend on:

- The total number of lines of force in the magnetic field
- The angular velocity of the loop
- The number of turns of wire in the loop

Faraday's law states, when a conductor cuts across magnetic lines of force at the rate of one weber per second, an emf of one volt is induced in that conductor.

THE INSTANTANEOUS VALUE OF A SINE WAVE

Instantaneous values are snapshots in time of a constantly changing variable and are represented by lower case letters.

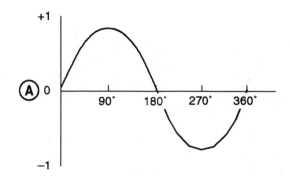

Fig. 29 — The Sine Curve

A—Sine Ø

As depicted in Fig. 27, it takes one complete revolution for the voltage to vary through the complete possible range of values. The same series of events recurs on every 360° rotation of the generator shaft. Every 360° of shaft rotation produces one cycle of a sine wave. The period of a sine wave is equal to the time (T) it takes to complete one electrical rotation (cycle) of the generator. The number of cycles completed in one second is the frequency of the sine wave.

The letter symbol for frequency is f.

The hertz is the SI unit of frequency. The unit symbol for hertz is Hz.

Hertz and electrical cycles per second are numerically synonymous.

In Fig. 26, one mechanical revolution generated one cycle or one sine wave of voltage. Generators that are more practical have more than two poles. In this situation, we must take into account there will be 360° of electrical rotation for every pair of poles. A six-pole generator will have 3 x 360° = 1080° of electrical rotation for every 360° of mechanical rotation.

Example 1

At what speed is the shaft of a four-pole 60-Hz alternator turning?

Solution 1

With two pairs of poles, one mechanical revolution generates two electrical cycles.

Therefore, the shaft speed is:

60/2 = 30rps x 60 = 1800rpm

Instantaneous voltage is never constant. Its exact magnitude at any instant is directly proportional to sin. Instantaneous voltage for any particular angle of rotation can be calculated from:

$e = E_m \sin(Ø)$

Continued on next page   OUO1082,0002CD9 -19-13JUN12-5/7

We can express this equation in a more useful form as:

$e = E_m \sin(360ft)°$

Where:

e = the instantaneous source voltage at a given instant in time

E_m = the peak value of the sine wave in question

sin = the sine of the angle expressed in electrical degrees

f = the frequency of the sine wave in hertz

t = the elapsed time in seconds.

Example 2

What is the instantaneous value of a 60-Hz sine wave whose peak voltage is 120 V, 5 ms after the instantaneous voltage passes through zero volts?

Solution 2

$e = E_m \sin(360ft)°$

= 120 sin(360 x 60 x 0.005)°

= 120 sin(108°) = 114.13VAC

OUO1082,0002CD9 -19-13JUN12-6/7

THE RADIAN

The Babylonian 360° system of angular measurement works very well in geometry and trigonometry. However, it is not well-suited for working with linear velocity and angular velocity. The linear velocity of the conductor governs the rate of cutting lines of force. For electrical purposes, we need to have a unit of angular distance, which is related to the distance traveled by the free end of a rotating phasor. The radian is that unit of angular distance and is the SI unit for a plane angle. By definition:

One radian = the angular distance through which the phasor travels when its free end X in Fig. 30 travels through a linear distance equal to the length (OX) of the phasor.

A phasor represents the radius of a circle. The circumference of a circle equals 2 pr. There are 2 p radians in one 360° revolution (electrical or mechanical). The significance of radian measure (Fig. 30) will become apparent as we deal with the behavior of certain AC circuits in later chapters. Most engineering calculators can solve trigonometric functions in either degrees or radians.

1 cycle = 360°

Therefore:

2π radians = 360°

We can solve for one radian by completing the calculation:

1 radian = 360°/2π

= 360°/(2 x 3.14) = 57.3°

1 radian degree = degree x (3.14/180 degrees)

In radian measure, angular velocity is expressed in radians per second.

The letter symbol for angular velocity in radians per second is the Greek small letter omega (ω).

Expressed in radian measure, we write the instantaneous voltage equation as follows:

$e = E_m \sin(\omega t)°$

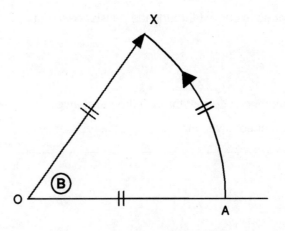

Fig. 30 — The Radian

B—1 Radian

Since there are 2π radians in a cycle:

$\omega = 2\pi f$

Therefore, we write the equation as:

$e = E_m \sin(2\pi p ft)°$

The angle is numerically expressed in radians.

Example

Write the general equation for the instantaneous voltage of a 400-Hz generator whose peak voltage is 120 V.

Solution

$e = E_m \sin(2\pi ft)°$

Since:

2πf = 2 x 3.14 x 400

= 2512 radians/second (rps)

Therefore:

$e = 120 \sin(2512t)°$

OUO1082,0002CD9 -19-13JUN12-7/7

INTRODUCTION TO AC CURRENT, VOLTAGE AND REACTANCE (RESISTANCE TO AC)

INSTANTANEOUS CURRENT IN A RESISTOR

We can determine the nature of the current that flows when we connect resistance to the generator terminals in a simple AC circuit (Fig. 31). If we consider only one particular instant, there is no difference between the simple AC circuit of Fig. 26 and the equivalent DC circuit. The real difference between them is that AC is an instantaneous voltage and the DC voltage remains constant over time. If we consider any particular instant in time, all the Ohm's law equations developed in Chapter 2 apply to the AC circuit of Fig. 31.

The instantaneous current through the resistance in Fig. 31 will be:

$i = e/R$

Where:

i = the instantaneous current through the resistance

e = the instantaneous voltage applied to the resistance

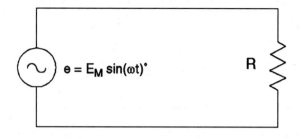

Fig. 31 — A Simple Alternating Current Circuit

R = the resistance of the circuit (constants use capitol letters).

The value of resistance is governed by physical factors such as:

- Type of material
- Length
- Cross section
- Temperature

Continued on next page

OUO1082,0002CDA -19-13JUN12-1/5

110112
PN=456

Since R is a constant, instantaneous voltage and instantaneous current must maintain the relationship required by Ohm's law. The instantaneous voltage must track the instantaneous current and must reach their peak value at the same instant. This relationship is depicted in Fig. 32 and the current is in phase with the voltage. This is always true of a resistor at low frequency.

We know that the general equation describing a sine-wave alternating applied voltage is:

$e = (E_m/R) \sin \omega t$.

We can substitute to solve for current in the following manner:

$I_m = (E_m/R)$

Therefore:

$i = I_m \sin \omega t$

Since the peak value of the instantaneous current depends on the peak value of the applied voltage:

$i_m = E_m R$

Therefore:

$i = I_m \sin \omega t$

Where:

i = the instantaneous current through a resistor when a sine wave of voltage is applied

I_m = the peak current as determined by the relationship $I_m = E_m/R$.

INSTANTANEOUS POWER IN A RESISTOR

If we still think in terms of instantaneous values, we may apply the Ohm's Law Power formulas from Chapter 2 to an AC circuit. Therefore:

$p = vi = i^2 R = v^2/R$

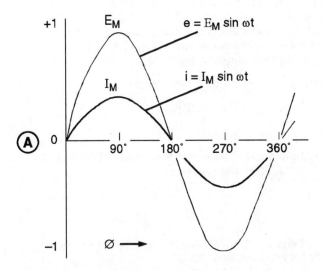

Fig. 32 — Instantaneous Current Through a Resistor

A—Instantaneous Values

Where:

p = the instantaneous power in a resistor in watts

v = the instantaneous voltage drop across the resistance in volts

i = the instantaneous current through the resistance in amperes

R = the resistance of the circuit ohms

With R constant, and since the instantaneous voltage and current are both sine waves, the instantaneous power must be a sine-squared wave.

Continued on next page   OUO1082,0002CDA -19-13JUN12-2/5

We can plot a graph of instantaneous power by obtaining sine values from a calculator at 5° intervals and plot the squares of these values on a linear graph. We will get a shape similar to the one shown in Fig. 33. Note that squaring a negative quantity results in a positive quantity.

By substituting i = Im sin(ωt)°, we obtain:

$p = R[I_m \sin(ωt)°]^2 = R[\sin2(ωt)°]I_m^2$

Where:

p = the instantaneous power in a resistance when a sine wave of current flows through it

$P_m = I_m^2 R$

Where:

P_m = the peak power (maximum instantaneous value) as determined by the relationship

From trigonometry, we can show that:

$\sin^2 ωt = 0.5[1 - \cos2(ωt)°]$

Therefore:

$p = 0.5P_m - 0.5Pm \cos2(ωt)°$

This relationship tells us three things about the instantaneous power waveform, which we can check by referring to Fig. 33.

1. In any right-angled triangle, the cosine of one acute angle is also the sine of the other acute angle. Therefore, the general shape of the cosine curve and the sin curve are the same. Consequently, the

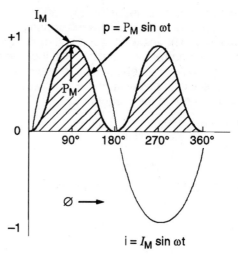

Fig. 33 — *Instantaneous Power Through a Resistor*

fluctuations in instantaneous power are sinusoidal in nature.

2. Since 2 ω is twice the angular velocity of ω, the frequency of the sinusoidal variation is twice as great as the frequency of the instantaneous voltage and current.

3. Since the limits of the value of a cosine are +1 when ∅= 0° and –1 when ∅= 180°, the value of the expression 0.5 [1 – cos2(ωt)°] can vary between 0 and + 1. Therefore, the instantaneous power waveform for a resistance is always positive.

Continued on next page   OUO1082,0002CDA -19-13JUN12-3/5

PERIODIC WAVES

We have studied only one form of alternating current, the sine wave, which is by far the most important AC waveform, and the only one we shall consider in detail in this book. In electronic circuits, a periodic wave refers to any repeating, time-varying function such as voltage, current, or power. The time interval required for the functions to repeat themselves is the period of the waveform. Fig. 34 shows how six typical periodic waves vary as a function of time. The graphs of the sine wave Fig. 34, (K) and sine-squared wave Fig. 34, (L) are repetitions of the two waves shown in Fig 33. All graphs in Fig. 34 show two complete cycles.

An oscilloscope is required to study the waveforms depicted in Fig. 34.

THE AVERAGE VALUE OF A PERIODIC WAVE

By definition, an alternating current (or voltage) is one in which the average of the instantaneous values over a period is zero. By examining the waveforms from Fig. 34, we can determine that the sine wave, square wave, and sawtooth wave are alternating currents or voltages. We can also determine that the sine-squared wave, pulse wave, and half-wave rectified wave are not alternating currents because their instantaneous values are always above zero.

To find the average value of a sine wave, calculate the sine of 5°, 10°, 15°, etc., continuing in increments of five degrees up to 180° (1/2 cycle). Calculating the average value of the sine wave over one half-cycle using a calculator is:

22.9/36 = 0.636

If we average the half-cycle of a sine wave by integration (area under the curve method), we arrive at a slightly more accurate result, expressing average value as 2/p or 0.6366.

Since:

$i = I_m \sin(\omega t)°$

Therefore:

$I_{av} = I_m \times 0.6366$

The half-cycle average value of a sine wave is:

$I_{av} = (0.636)I_m = 2/p - I_m$

Or:

$E_{av} = (0.636)E_m = (2/p)I_m$

The sine-squared wave of Fig. 34 will have a half-cycle average value of one-half the peak value of the sine-squared wave. The pulse waveform will have an average value that depends on the ratio of the pulse duration to the time interval between pulses. The half-wave rectified sine wave will have a full-cycle average value which, in turn, is the average of $0.636E_m$ for one half-cycle and zero for the next half cycle or $0.3183E_m$.

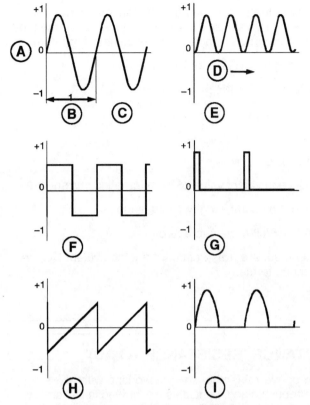

Fig. 34 — Typical Periodic Waves

A—Instantaneous Values
B—Period
C—Sine Wave
D—Time
E—Sine-Squared Wave
F—Square Wave
G—Pulse Wave
H—Sawtooth Wave
I— Half-Wave Rectified Wave

THE RMS VALUE OF A SINE WAVE

Instantaneous values of alternating current are not suitable for calculation purposes and full-cycle average values of sine waves are zero. Half-cycle average values are only useful for applications where we are concerned with a half-cycle of a sine wave.

DC circuits do not have these problems since the voltage, current, and power in a resistive circuit remains constant for a considerable period. As for converting electric energy into light, it makes no difference whether DC or AC is applied: the lamp still emits light. We can establish equivalent steady state values for alternating current and voltage that allow us to use the same interrelationships among voltage, current, resistance, power, work, etc., as we did in DC circuits.

The basis for finding the DC equivalent is to look at the amount of heat energy in a certain time interval. We can translate this into average work per unit time or simply average power. To determine average power in a resistive AC circuit, start with the following equation:

$p = i^2R$

Continued on next page OUO1082,0002CDA -19-13JUN12-4/5

We compute the square of the instantaneous current at small time intervals over a full cycle and then calculate the average or mean value of all these i2 values. Therefore:

P_{av} = (full-cycle average of i^2) x R

In a DC circuit, $P = i^2R$

In an AC circuit, $P = I^2R$

Where:

P = the average power

I = the DC equivalent value of the alternating current

Solving for I by combining two equations:

$I = \sqrt{(P/R)} = \sqrt{\text{full-cycle average of } I^2}$

Root-mean-square (rms), effective and equivalent DC are synonymous terms.

$P = 0.5P_m$

From this, we can derive:

$I = I_m/2 = 0.707I_m$

The rms value of a sine wave is $1/\sqrt{2}$ or 0.707 of the peak value.

$V = V_m/2 = 0.707V_m$

Also:

$V_m = \sqrt{2}V = 1.414V$

All currents and voltages are rms values unless stated otherwise, for the rest of this chapter.

Example

What is the peak voltage of the 120-V, 60-Hz electric service?

Solution

$E_m = 1.414E = 1.414 \times 120V = 170V$

OUO1082,0002CDA -19-13JUN12-5/5

REACTANCE (RESISTANCE TO AC)

As long as we remember we are working with instantaneous values, principles we studied in DC circuits must also hold true for AC circuits. Ohm's law takes the form:

$i = v/R$

Where:

Both v and i are instantaneous values.

As far as this equation is concerned, resistance is a constant and instantaneous current is directly proportional instantaneous voltage.

Since the instantaneous current in a resistor reaches its peak value at the same instant as the instantaneous voltage across the resistance, we are also able to state Ohm's law in the form $I_m = V_m/R$. The most useful form of Ohm's law is simply:

$I = V/R$

Where:

I = the rms value of the sine wave current through a resistor

V = the rms value of the sine wave voltage across the resistor

THE NATURE OF THE INSTANTANEOUS CURRENT IN AN IDEAL INDUCTOR

To calculate the instantaneous current that flows in the circuit in Fig. 35, we assume:

- The resistance is so small that we can neglect it
- Think of the inductor as a load connected across a voltage source

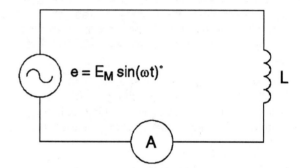

Fig. 35 — Inductance in an Alternating Current Circuit

To satisfy Kirchhoff's voltage law the inductive voltage across the coil in Fig. 35 must exactly equal the applied voltage. Therefore:

$V_L = e = E_m \sin(\omega t)°$

Any voltage drop that appears across the terminals of an inductor must be due to the voltage induced in the coil by a changing current through it. We can express this instantaneous voltage that appears across the inductor in Fig. 35 as:

$v_L = L/(d_I/d_t)$

We can substitute:

$E_m \sin(\omega t)° = d_I/d_t$

Therefore:

$v_L = (E_m/L) \sin(\omega t)°$

Kirchhoff's voltage law requires the voltage across the inductor in Fig. 35 to be exactly equal to the applied voltage at every instant in time.

Continued on next page   OUO1082,0002CDB -19-13JUN12-1/5

14-24

Instantaneous voltage v_L across the inductor is represented by the sine wave starting at 0° in Fig. 36.

Faraday's law of electromagnetic induction states, the magnitude of the inductive voltage is directly proportional to the rate of change of current through the coil at that instant. At the instant when we require maximum positive voltage across the inductor (at the 90° point in Fig. 36), the current must be changing at the greatest rate in a positive direction. Hence, maximum rate of change is indicated in the instantaneous current graph of Fig. 36 by the steepest slope.

For a sine-wave voltage drop to appear across an ideal inductor, the current through it must be a sine wave, which lags the inductive voltage drop by 90°.

Since the angle ωt is expressed in radians, we must represent 90° as p/2 radians. We can write an equation for the instantaneous current in the circuit of Fig. 36.

$i_L = I_m \sin(\omega t - (\pi/2))° \text{ rad}$

INDUCTIVE REACTANCE

If we input a sine wave to the circuit of Fig. 35, we get a sine wave current in the inductor of some definite rms value and a constant reading on the AC ammeter. For a given alternating voltage and a given inductance, the ratio V/I is a constant.

In discussing Ohm's law, we established that a constant V/I ratio represents resistance of the circuit. We say that the constant V_L/I_L ratio in Fig. 35 represents the opposition of the inductance to AC. We cannot call this opposition resistance because the current and voltage are not in phase. The inductor does not convert energy into heat, as does a resistor. Therefore, we must call this opposition by another name, which suggests opposition to AC.

Inductive reactance is the opposition of inductance to alternating current. The letter symbol for inductive reactance is X_L

This is expressed as:

$X_L = V_L/I_L$

Inductive reactance is a V/I ratio just as is resistance. We can use the ohm as the unit of inductive reactance.

An AC circuit has an inductive reactance of one ohm when one ampere of rms current through the inductor creates a voltage drop of one volt rms across the inductor.

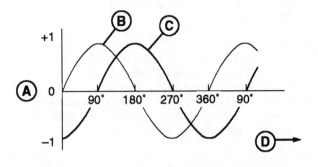

Fig. 36 — Instantaneous Current in an Inductor

A—Instantaneous Values   C—Current
B—Voltage   D—Time

FACTORS GOVERNING INDUCTIVE REACTANCE

Assuming the input waveform in the circuit in Fig. 35 remains sinusoidal, there are three variables. Remembering that $X_L = V_L/I_L$, analyze the following statements:

- The magnitude of the applied alternating voltage has no effect on the inductive reactance of an AC circuit.
- Inductive reactance is directly proportional to frequency.
- Inductive reactance is directly proportional to the inductance.

The most commonly used formula for inductive reactance is:

$X_L = 2\pi f L$

Where:

X_L = inductive reactance in ohms

f = frequency in hertz

L = inductance in henrys

We can substitute ω for $2\pi f$ giving us:

$X_L = \omega L$

Where:

ω = angular velocity in radians per second

Continued on next page   OUO1082,0002CDB -19-13JUN12-2/5

THE NATURE OF THE INSTANTANEOUS CURRENT IN A CAPACITOR

We can connect a capacitor across a sine-wave voltage source (Fig. 37). But in order to satisfy Kirchhoff's voltage law, the voltage across the capacitor must be the same as the applied voltage at that instant. The capacitor in Fig. 37 must charge and discharge in such a manner that the voltage across it is a sine wave equal to the applied voltage at every instant in time. Therefore:

$i = C(d_v/d_t)$

Capacitance is assumed as a constant.

Instantaneous current is always directly proportional to the rate at which the voltage across the capacitor is changing.

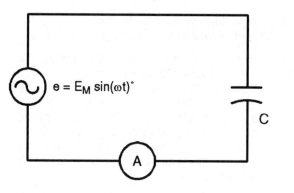

$e = E_M \sin(\omega t)°$

Fig. 37 — Capacitance in an AC Circuit

DXP03410 —UN—10APR12

Continued on next page

OUO1082,0002CDB -19-13JUN12-3/5

Examining the sine curve of Fig. 38, representing the instantaneous voltage across the capacitor, we note the maximum potential difference across the capacitor and the maximum rate of change of voltage occur 90° apart in time.

For a sine-wave voltage to be developed across a capacitor, the current through it must be a sine wave which leads the instantaneous voltage by 90°.

From this equation:

$i_C = I_m \sin(\omega t + \pi/2)° \text{ rad}$

CAPACITIVE REACTANCE

When we connect a capacitor across a sine-wave voltage source, the instantaneous current takes on a sine wave form, leading the voltage sine wave by 90° in order to produce a voltage sine wave across the capacitor.

For a given source of alternating voltage and a given capacitance, the ratio V/I is a constant. As in the case of resistance and inductive reactance, this constant V/I ratio represents the opposition of the capacitor to alternating current. Therefore:

Capacitive reactance is the opposition of capacitance to alternating current. The letter symbol for capacitive reactance is X_C.

And:

$X_C = V^C/I_C$

An AC circuit has a capacitive reactance of one ohm when one ampere of rms current creates a voltage of one-volt rms across the capacitance of the circuit.

FACTORS GOVERNING CAPACITIVE REACTANCE

The three factors that govern capacitive reactance are:

• The magnitude of the applied voltage does not affect the capacitive reactance in an AC circuit.
• Capacitive reactance is inversely proportional to frequency.
• Capacitive reactance is inversely proportional to the capacitance.

The most commonly used formula for capacitive reactance is:

$X_C = 1/(2\pi f C)$

Where:

X_C = capacitive reactance in ohms

f = frequency in hertz

C = capacitance in farads

We can substitute ω for $2\pi f$ giving us:

$X_C = 1/\omega C$

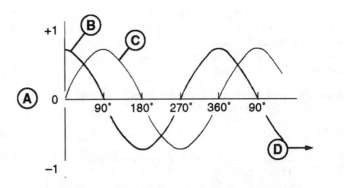

Fig. 38 — Instantaneous Current in a Capacitor

COMPARING RESISTANCE, INDUCTIVE REACTANCE, AND CAPACITIVE REACTANCE

There are some commonalities between R, X_L, and X_C:

• All are defined in terms of a V/I ratio.
• All are expressed in ohms.
• For a given circuit and frequency, the opposition is a constant, and is independent of time.
• All are scalar quantities represented by uppercase letter symbols.

However, there are significant differences in the behavior of resistance, inductance, and capacitance in AC circuits, which we must constantly keep in mind:

• Whereas resistance converts electric energy into heat, inductance and capacitance alternately store energy during the charging quarter cycle, only to return this energy to the circuit during the next (discharging) quarter cycle;
• Resistance is independent of frequency, but inductive reactance is directly proportional to frequency, and capacitive reactance is inversely proportional to frequency
• Whereas the current through a resistor is in phase with the voltage across it, the current through an ideal inductor lags the voltage across it by 90° and the alternating current through a capacitor leads the voltage across it by 90°. These characteristics are summarized in the following table.

Table 5 — Comparison of Resistance, Inductive Reactance and Capacitive Reactance		
R, L, AND C IN ALTERNATING CURRENT CIRCUITS		
Resistance	$R = V_R/I_R = R\Omega$	I_R in phase with V_R
Inductive Reactance	$X_L = V_L/I_L = \omega L\Omega$	I_L lags V_L by 90°
Capacitive Reactance	$X_C = V_C/I_C = 1/\omega C\Omega$	I_C leads V_C by 90°

Continued on next page

OUO1082,0002CDB -19-13JUN12-4/5

It is vital to clearly identify the type of opposition when making statements about AC circuits. There is considerable difference between an AC circuit containing inductive reactance and one containing capacitive reactance as Table 5 illustrates.

The following examples will illustrate how to use letter symbols and subscripts.

Example 1

What is the resistance of a 1000 W toaster operated from a 120 V, 60 Hz source?

Solution 1

$R = E^2/P$

$\quad = (120V)_2/1000W$

$\quad = 14.4\Omega$ (resistive)

Example 2

What is the inductor's reactance when there is 100 V induced with a current through it of 200 mA rms?

Solution 2

$X_L = V_L/I_L$

$\quad = 100V/200mA$

$\quad = 500\Omega$ (inductive)

Example 3

What is the capacitive reactance of a 120 pF capacitor when it is used in a 5 MHz circuit?

Solution 3

$X_C = 1/(2\pi f C)$

$\quad = 1/(2\pi \times 5MHz \times 120pF)$

$\quad = 265.4\ \Omega$ (capacitive)

OUO1082,0002CDB -19-13JUN12-5/5

NUMBERING SYSTEMS

DECIMAL

Reviewing the numbering system we are most familiar with, the decimal or base 10 system. The placeholders in this system are powers of 10.

Let's analyze the number 1234.567 which we know to represent one thousand, two hundred, thirty four and five hundred sixty seven thousandths. We also know that 1 is the most significant digit (MSD) and 7 is the least significant digit (LSD).

Table 6 — Comparison Between Decimal Numbering System and Scientific Notation								
10^3	10^2	10^1	10^0	.	10^{-1}	10^{-2}	10^{-3}
1	2	3	4	.	5	6	7
MSD							LSD

Let's see how this number is broken down using scientific notation (Table 6).

Scientific Notation		Decimal Equivalent
10^3	=	1000.000
10^2	=	200.000
10^1	=	30.000
10^0	=	4.000
10^{-1}	=	0.500
10^{-2}	=	0.060
10^{-3}	=	0.007
Total	=	1234.567

HEXADECIMAL

Another numbering system which is commonly used in computer software systems is the hexadecimal numbering system.

The hexadecimal system uses both numbers and letters as placeholders. The placeholders are powers of 16.

Table 7 — Comparison Between Hexadecimal Numbering System and Decimal Numbering System	
Hexadecimal Value and Decimal Equivalent	Hexadecimal Value and Decimal Equivalent
0 = 0	8 = 8
1 = 1	9 = 9
2 = 2	A = 10
3 = 3	B = 11
4 = 4	C = 12
5 = 5	D = 13
6 = 6	E = 14
7 = 7	F = 15

Table 7 shows each hexadecimal value and the decimal equivalent.

Table 8 — Comparison Between Hexadecimal Numbering System and Exponential Notation					
16^5	16^4	16^3	16^2	16^1	16^0
F	A	0	1	6	8
MSD					LSD

Lets take a look at the example, FA0168, in Table 8:

Hexadecimal Value		Exponential Notation		Decimal Equivalent
F00000	=	15×16^5	=	15,728,640
A0000	=	10×16^4	=	655,360
0000	=	0×16^3	=	0,000
100	=	1×16^2	=	256
60	=	6×16^1	=	96
8	=	8×16^0	=	8
FA0168		=		16,384,360

The advantage of using the Hexadecimal system is it takes only a few numbers and letters to represent a very large number. Most scientific calculators will perform hexadecimal conversions.

BINARY

All computers use the binary system which has only two numbers, 0 (low) and 1 (high). The binary system is a base two system.

Table 9 — Comparison Between Binary Numbering System and Exponential Notation									
2^9	2^8	2^7	2^6	2^5	2^4	2^3	2^2	2^1	2^0
1	0	1	0	1	0	1	0	1	1
MSB									LSB

Let's look at another example (1010101011) in Table 9 which has a most significant bit (MSB) of 1 and a least significant bit (LSB) of 1.

Binary Value		Exponential Notation		Decimal Equivalent
1000000000	=	1×2^9	=	512
000000000	=	0×2^8	=	0
10000000	=	1×2^7	=	128
0000000	=	0×2^6	=	0
100000	=	1×2^5	=	32
00000	=	0×2^4	=	0
1000	=	1×2^3	=	8
000	=	0×2^2	=	0
10	=	1×2^1	=	2
1	=	1×2^0	=	1
1010101011		=		683

Continued on next page OUO1082,0002CDC -19-05APR12-1/2

110112
PN=465

Table 10 — Comparison Between Decimal, Hexadecimal and Binary Numbering Systems

Decimal	Hexadecimal	Binary
0	0	0000
1	1	0001
2	2	0010
3	3	0011
4	4	0100
5	5	0101
6	6	0110
7	7	0111
8	8	1000
9	9	1001
10	A	1010
11	B	1011
12	C	1100
13	D	1101
14	E	1110
15	F	1111

We know how the Hex and Bin numbering systems work, why we have them and how we use them. The relationships of each are clearly shown in Table 10.

Table 11 — Relationship Between Bits, Nibbles, Bytes and Words in Computer Busing

Bit_{15}	Bit_{14}	Bit_{13}	Bit_{12}	Bit_{11}	Bit_{10}	Bit_9	Bit_8	Bit_7	Bit_6	Bit_5	Bit_4	Bit_3	Bit_2	Bit_1	Bit_0
MSB															LSB
Most Significant Nibble				Least Significant Nibble				Most Significant Nibble				Least Significant Nibble			
MSB			LSB	MSB			LSB	MSB			LSB	MSB			LSB
Most Significant (High) Byte								Least Significant (Low) Byte							
MSB															LSB
Word															
MSB															LSB

Table 11 shows a typical micro-controller which has a 16-bit- wide bus organized into four nibbles, two bytes and one word. It should be noted each nibble is four bits wide and its value can be represented by a single Hex digit. The value of a byte is represented by two Hex digits and the value of the word by four Hex digits. The most significant bit (MSB) and least significant bit (LSB) is indicated just below each grouping.

OUO1082,0002CDC -19-05APR12-2/2

POSITIVE AND NEGATIVE NUMBERS

Table 12 — Negative and Positive Numbers

Negative Numbers								Positive Numbers								
−8	−7	−6	−5	−4	−3	−2	−1	0	1	2	3	4	5	6	7	8

In electronics, we use negative numbers and they must, at times, be combined with positive numbers. As a rule all negative numbers are preceded by a negative sign (−) and positive may or may not be preceded by a plus sigh (+). All negative numbers are shown in brackets, thus a negative 2 is shown as (−2). Look at the rules for using negative numbers in (addition and subtraction) and (multiplication and division).

ADDITION AND SUBTRACTION

The rules for addition are as follows:

- If the numbers have like signs, add them together and the result will carry the sign.
- If one of the numbers is negative, change the sign of the negative number and subtract. The result carries the sign of the larger.

Study the following examples:

6 + 2 = 8

7 + (−2) = 7 − (+2) = 5

(−7) + 2 = (+7) − 2 = (−5)

(−10) + (−5) = (−15)

The rules for subtraction are as follows:

- If the numbers have like signs, Subtract them and the result will carry the sign.
- If one of the numbers is negative, change the sign of the negative number and add. The result carries the sign of the larger.

Study the following examples:

6 − 2 = 4

7 − (−2) = 7 + (+2) = 9

(−7) − 2 = 7 + 2 = (−9)

(−10) − (−5) = (−5)

MULTIPLICATION AND DIVISION

The rules for like signs are as follows:

- If you multiply two numbers, the product will be positive.
- If you divide two numbers, the quotient will be positive.

Study the following examples:

6 x 2 = 12

(−6) x (−2) = 12

6/2 = 3

(−6)/(−2) = 3

The rules for unlike signs are as follows:

- If you multiply two numbers, the product will be negative.
- If you divide two numbers, the quotient will be negative.

Study the following examples:

6 x (−2) = (−12)

(−6) x 2 = (−12)

(−6)/2 = (−3)

6/(−2) = (−3)

OUO1082,0002CDD -19-13JUN12-1/1

BOOLEAN ALGEBRA

Since our digital world only has ones and zeros we can use a mathematical tool known as Boolean algebra to analyze how digital systems will work. In Boolean algebra there are only three basic logic operations. They are:

• Logical addition, which is called the OR operation
• Logical multiplication, which is called the AND operation
• Logical complementation or inversion, which is called the NOT operation

LOGICAL OR OPERATION

Table 13 — Logical OR Truth Table and Schematic Symbol				
A	OR	B		X = A OR B
0	+	0	=	0
0	+	1	=	1
1	+	0	=	1
1	+	1	=	1

A and B are independent variables and can be combined using OR addition as depicted in Table 13. We can see from the table that if either A or B is a 1 (high) then X will also be 1 (high).

LOGICAL AND OPERATION

Table 14 — Logical AND Truth Table and Schematic Symbol				
A	AND	B		X = A OR B
0	x	0	=	0
0	x	1	=	0
1	x	0	=	0
1	x	1	=	1

A and B are independent variables and can be combined using AND multiplication as depicted in the table above. We can see from Table 14 that if either A or B is 0 (low) then X will also be 0 (low).

LOGICAL NOT OPERATION

Table 15 — Logical NOT Truth Table and Schematic Symbol	
A	X = A NOT
0	1
1	0

A is an independent variable and can have the NOT operation applied as depicted in Table 15. We can see from the table that if A is 0 (low) then X will be 1 (high).

OUO1082,0002CDE -19-10JAN12-1/1

TEST YOURSELF

QUESTIONS

1. Replace the values in Fig. 2 with R1 = 75 Ω, R2 = 500 Ω, R3 = 100 Ω and R4 = 200 Ω. If the battery has a 24 VDC output, what are the voltages between points A and D, B and D, and C and D?

2. Using the same resistor values as in the previous question, what are the voltages between points A and D, B and D, and C and D if the battery voltage were 12 VDC?

3. (True or False) The purpose of R2 in Figure 3 is to allow us to change the voltage and current supplied to point C.

4. In Fig. 8, what will the charge be equal to, 3 ms after S1 is closed?

5. If we have a 24-pole generator running at 2,000 RPM, what is the frequency?

6. 300° is equal to _____ radians?

7. Convert 60 cycles per second to radians per second. (22.623 RPS)

8. What is the Hex value of 1000d (decimal)?

9. What is the Hex value of 1000b (binary)?

10. (True or False) To check the MSB on a 16 bit address bus you would check A15.

11. Add the following 30 + (−15) + 30 + (−10) + 50.

12. (True or False) 0 OR 1 = 0.

13. (True or False) 0 AND 1 = 1.

14. (True or False) 0 OR 1 AND 1 = 1.

(Answers are in the back of the textbook.)

OUO1082,0002CDF -19-10JAN12-1/1

PRECAUTIONS WHEN WORKING WITH ELECTRONICS

DXP02715 —UN—23FEB11

INTRODUCTION

DXP03414 —UN—09NOV11

In addition to procedures relating to personal safety, electronic boards and components require special handling and procedures to prevent damaging components due to electrostatic discharge (ESD) and other factors.

There are three main safety concerns to be aware of while working on electronic equipment:

• A clean, safe work environment
• Personal safety
• Equipment safety

WORK ENVIRONMENT

The reason for placing a clean work environment first is that it influences the other two safety concerns greatly. It is important to have a clean, safe place to work on electronics. A cluttered workbench is an invitation to an accident to yourself or the equipment you are working on. You should have a separate work area for electronics, which has the proper ESD work mat and wrist straps. This mat will be destroyed if used on the mechanical workbench. It is important to have a quiet area where you can concentrate and work. The workbench should also have an electrical insulating rubber mat on the floor in front of it.

PERSONAL SAFETY

You should read and understand all of the operator's manuals that come with the various test instruments you use. The manufacturers will recommend the best and safest ways to use their equipment. It is a very good idea to use the "one hand rule", keep one hand in your pocket, whenever practical. It is not so important with the low-voltage electronics, but low voltage can still kill. The use of caution and common sense never hurts.

EQUIPMENT SAFETY

We will explore several areas of concern regarding equipment safety. The following are some factors affecting equipment safety:

• Electrostatic discharge (ESD)
• Unintentional grounding
• Improperly connecting test equipment
• Connecting supply voltages improperly

ELECTROSTATIC DISCHARGE (ESD)

Static electricity is generated by the interaction of various common materials. When working on electronic components, static electricity present on a person or workstation could discharge to the component(s) or board, damaging the component(s). Proper handling of electronic components is essential to prevent electrostatic discharge (ESD).

Continued on next page OUO1082,0001330 -19-03APR12-1/3

Components that are susceptible to electrostatic discharge are identified using the ESD susceptibility symbol (Fig. 1). Components or circuit boards displaying this symbol must be handled using proper ESD precautions. Failure to handle the component or circuit board properly may result in damage.

Components or circuit boards susceptible to electrostatic discharge will be packaged in specialized bags that protect the components during transport. The bags should be opened only at an ESD workstation, or by following the proper ESD precautions.

Fig. 1 — ESD Susceptibility Symbol

OUO1082,0001330 -19-03APR12-2/3

An ESD workstation (Fig. 2) is constructed so that all surfaces and equipment are grounded to a common electrical ground point (F). This common ground point is then connected to the equipment ground (E) or the third wire (green) electrical ground connection of the building's electrical system.

The workstation also includes provisions for the technician to be connected to the common ground using wrist (B) and/or ankle straps. Workstations may also include provisions for grounding additional equipment and accessories.

Additionally, the workstation is connected to an auxiliary ground (water pipe, building frame, ground stake) that will minimize differences in potential between the two grounds (building's electrical system and auxiliary ground).

UNINTENTIONAL GROUNDING

Unintentional grounding can only happen while working on energized equipment. When probing with a meter lead, you must be careful to touch only the energized terminal you are probing and not touch a ground with the same lead. Sometimes when you are making an adjustment with a screwdriver, it will slip off and short something to ground. This type of accident can cause failure to some components.

IMPROPERLY CONNECTING TEST EQUIPMENT

Some measuring devices have the negative terminal connected directly to ground. If you place the negative probe on an energized component, it could cause a short circuit and possible damage to the device under test (DUT). If you hook the digital multimeter (DMM) to a powered circuit and it is set to measure current, you will damage the meter or the DUT or both.

CONNECTING SUPPLY VOLTAGES IMPROPERLY

Connecting supply voltages improperly will normally cause severe damage to the DUT and possibly the power source. If it becomes necessary to power up a device when

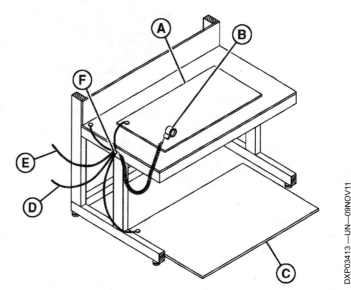

Fig. 2 — Typical ESD Workstation

A—ESD Protective Work Surface
B—Wrist Strap Ground Connection
C—ESD Protective Mat
D—To Auxiliary Ground
E—To Equipment Ground
F—Common Ground Point

working on the bench, always double-check the power supply connections. Remember, it pays to be cautious.

SUMMARY: ELECTRICAL SAFETY

- Follow safe shop practices and work habits.
- Pay attention to signal words like DANGER, WARNING, and CAUTION.
- Be aware of hazards that could occur while working on an electrical system.
- Although battery acid is diluted, it can still cause severe burns. Always wear gloves and eye protection when servicing batteries.
- Always keep one hand away from the voltage source when working on a circuit.

OUO1082,0001330 -19-03APR12-3/3

INTEGRATED CIRCUITS

An integrated circuit (IC) (Fig. 3) is a device that contains circuits composed of resistors, diodes, transistors, and capacitors. Sometimes referred to as "chips," they are unique because of their small size and the amount of work performed. They can contain a few components to form a simple circuit or can be made into a complex circuit with up to hundreds of thousands of components. It is not uncommon for an IC to have more than 250,000 transistors on a silicon chip that is only 1/4-inch square! ICs have made possible video games, digital watches, affordable personal computers, and microcomputers for use on agricultural and industrial machines.

Most failures in integrated circuits occur during initial usage when they are new. For this reason, manufacturers perform an operational "burn in" on new ICs to isolate defective components before they are sold. After this initial

Fig. 3 — An Integrated Circuit Assembly

"burn in," very few IC failures occur until environmental factors start to take effect after a number of years.

OUO1082,0001331 -19-03APR12-1/6

HOW INTEGRATED CIRCUITS ARE MADE

All IC components are assembled on pure crystal silicon of N or P type known as wafers (Fig. 4). Grooves are made in the wafers and filled with doped silicon (silicon with impurities). Pure crystal silicon is an extremely high-resistive material. Therefore, to allow electron flow, differing concentrations of impurities and silicon (P or N type) are added to the grooves to form components.

Previously, we became familiar with how these conventional electronic components were made. Let's look at how these components are made on silicon wafers to make integrated circuits.

A—Aluminum Conductor
B—Insulator (Silicon Dioxide)
C—Wire Lead
D—Silicon Substrate

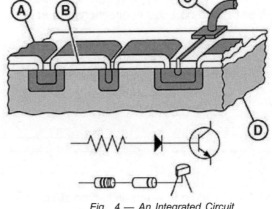

Fig. 4 — An Integrated Circuit

OUO1082,0001331 -19-03APR12-2/6

IC RESISTOR

An IC resistor (Fig. 5) is made by adding a strip of P-type "doped" silicon that is arranged between two metal connections over a silicon wafer (P type). The P-type silicon wafer and N-type silicon sections seen in Fig. 5 serve primarily for physical reasons only because, as we will soon see, other components are made of the same kind of wafer. The top of the resistor is covered with an insulator such as silicon oxide.

A—Connections
B—Silicon Oxide
C—P-Type Silicon Wafer

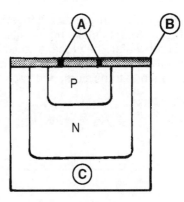

Fig. 5 — An IC Resistor

Continued on next page   OUO1082,0001331 -19-03APR12-3/6

IC DIODE

An IC diode (Fig. 6) is made by layering two strips of "doped" silicon, one P type and the other N type, over a silicon wafer. Each section will have its own connection and the diode is covered with an insulator. You will note in comparing the IC diode to the IC resistor, the only thing different are the connection locations.

A—Connections   C—P-Type Silicon Wafer
B—Silicon Oxide

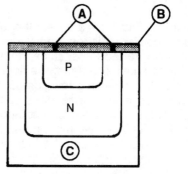

Fig. 6 — An IC Diode

OUO1082,0001331 -19-03APR12-4/6

IC TRANSISTOR

An IC transistor (Fig. 7) can be made by adding another strip of N-type silicon over the P-type strip that could have been used for the resistor or diode. Rearranging the connections to each strip makes an NPN transistor. Note that the emitter, base, and collector connections are at the top of the wafer.

A—Base   D—Silicon Oxide
B—Emitter   E—P-Type Silicon Wafer
C—Collector

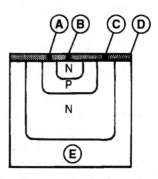

Fig. 7 — An IC Transistor

OUO1082,0001331 -19-03APR12-5/6

IC CAPACITOR

An IC capacitor (Fig. 8) is made when an N-type silicon is doped to act as a plate. The silicon oxide covering acts as the insulator. The other plate of the capacitor is a larger metal connection mounted above the insulator. Needless to say, a capacitor of this type can be constructed only with values above a few hundred picofarads.

Such IC components are then connected together, usually with aluminum conductors, to make up circuits. However, within a P-type silicon wafer, the process could have been repeated with different types of silicon to form circuits of various diodes, resistors, transistors, and capacitors into a single unit.

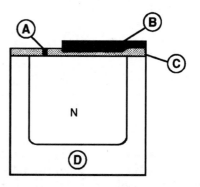

Fig. 8 — An IC Capacitor

A—Connections   C—Silicon Oxide
B—Connection Plate   D—P-Type Silicon Wafer

OUO1082,0001331 -19-03APR12-6/6

ANALOG IC

Analog ICs are circuits composed to produce, amplify, or respond to *variable voltages*. They include timers, oscillators, operational amplifiers and voltage regulator chips.

TIMERS

Some of the many timing circuits required for modern day electronics are monostable multivibrators, astable multivibrators, ramp generators, op-amps, and sequential timers. These tasks may be implemented with discrete component circuitry or by the use of dedicated IC chips. Timer IC chip circuitry design is far more commonplace in today's electronics because of the ease of design, reliability, and fewer components required.

555 TIMERS

One of the most commonly used timers is the 555 (Fig. 9). The data sheets for the 555 are available online from any of the IC manufacturers. You can download and study these data sheets as an aid to understanding them.

Here are some applications for the 555 timer:

- Precision timing
- Pulse generation
- Sequential timing

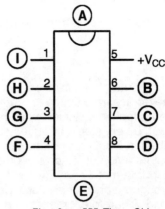

Fig. 9 — 555 Timer Chip

A—555 Timer
B—Discharge
C—Threshold
D—Control Voltage
E—Top View
F—Reset
G—Output
H—Trigger
I— Ground

- Time delay generation
- Pulse width modulation
- Pulse position modulation
- Linear ramp generator

OUO1082,0001332 -19-14JUN12-1/10

With the 555 timer chip connected as in Fig. 10, we will have a free running (astable) multivibrator. The pulse width (PW) is controlled by $R_{L\text{"On"}}$ and the space width (SW) is controlled by $R_{L\text{"Off"}}$. The frequency (f) is controlled by the ratio of R_A and R_B.

The formulas for working with 555 timer circuits connected in this fashion are:

Charge time (output high):

$$t_1 = 0.693(R_A + R_B) \times C$$

Discharge time (output low):

$$t_2 = 0.693(R_B) \times C$$

Total Period:

$$T = t_1 + t_2 = 0.693(R_A + 2R_B) \times C$$

Frequency:

$$f = 1/T = 1.44/(R_A + 2R_B) \times C$$

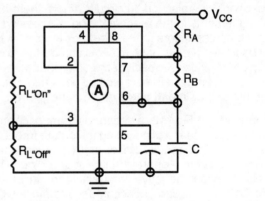

Fig. 10 — 555 Timer Circuit Connected as an Astable Multivibrator

A—555 Timer

Continued on next page   OUO1082,0001332 -19-14JUN12-2/10

In Fig. 11 the waveforms are shown from the circuit in Fig. 10.

CLOCK CIRCUITS

555 timers are accurate but not accurate enough for keeping time. Whenever accurate timing is required, clock circuits are used. Real time clock circuits require oscillators that maintain a very stable frequency output over wide temperature and input voltage ranges. There is a variety, but the most common use a crystal or ceramic wafer that is packaged in a metal can. By sending a 32.768 kHz pulse through a series of dividers, we get a pulse every 0.5 second. Therefore, timekeeping is an easy task with pulse counting.

System clocks for normal PCs and embedded systems have speeds up to several hundred mHz. We will discuss what clock circuits do later in this chapter.

CRYSTAL OSCILLATOR CIRCUITS

Crystals are designed to be series or parallel resonant.

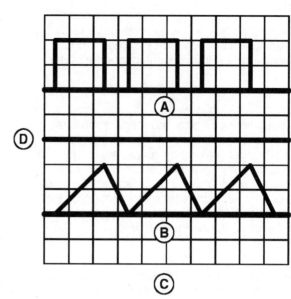

Fig. 11 — *Astable Multivibrator Waveforms*

A—Pin 3 Output @ 5V/Div   C—Time/Div
B—Pin 5 Capacitor @ 1V/Div   D—Volts/Div

OUO1082,0001332 -19-14JUN12-3/10

Series Circuit

Series resonant crystals work in circuits where there are no reactive elements in the feedback loop. Series crystal circuits have no capacitors in the feedback loop. Series resonant oscillator circuits have minimal component count. These circuits provide feedback paths other than through the crystal unit. In the event of crystal failure, such a circuit may continue to oscillate at some arbitrary frequency.

As is apparent from Fig. 12, a series resonant oscillator circuit provides no means of adjusting the output frequency should adjustment be required. Resistor R1 biases the inverter and causes it to operate in its linear region. This resistor also provides negative feedback to the inverter. Capacitor C1 is a coupling capacitor, used to block DC voltage. Resistor R2 adjusts the drive current seen by the crystal Y1. Therefore, we must use caution not to choose too small of a value. Crystal unit Y1 is a series resonant crystal, specified to operate at the desired frequency and with the desired frequency tolerance and stability.

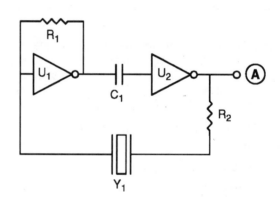

Fig. 12 — *Typical Series Crystal Oscillation Circuit*

A—Output

Continued on next page   OUO1082,0001332 -19-14JUN12-4/10

Parallel Circuit

A parallel resonant oscillator circuit uses a crystal that will operate with a specified value of load capacitance. This will result in a crystal frequency that is higher than the series resonant frequency, but lower than the true parallel resonant frequency. These circuits do not provide paths other than through the crystal unit to complete the feedback loop. In the event of crystal unit failure, the circuit will not continue to oscillate.

The values for the components in Fig. 13 are:

C_1 = 22 pF

C_2 = 22 pF

R_1 = 10 mΩ

R_2 = 330 kΩ

U_1 = TC 4069P

Y_1 = ECS 3X8

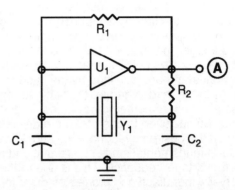

Fig. 13 — *Typical Parallel Crystal Oscillation Circuit*

A—Output

Table 1 — Typical Values for a Parallel Circuit			
Frequency (mHz)	C_1 and C_2 (pF)	R_2 (Ω)	C_L (pF)
3—4	27	5.6k	16
4—5	27	3.9k	16
5—6	27	2.7k	16
6—8	18	2.7k	12
8—12	18	1.8k	12
12—15	18	10k	12
15—20	15	560	10
20—25	12	560	10

This circuit uses a single inverter, with two capacitors in the feedback loop. These capacitors comprise the load capacitance and together with the crystal unit, establish the frequency at which the oscillator will operate. As the value of the load capacitance is changed, so is the output frequency of the oscillator. Therefore, this circuit provides a convenient means of adjusting the output frequency, should adjustment be required.

The resistors R_1 and R_2 serve the same functions as detailed for the series resonant circuit shown in Fig. 12. The two load capacitors (C_1 and C_2) serve to establish the frequency at the crystal unit; therefore, the oscillator will operate. Crystal unit Y1 is a parallel resonant crystal unit, specified to operate with a specified value of load capacitance, at the desired frequency and with the desired frequency tolerance and stability.

Load Capacitance

Load capacitance is the value of capacitance, either measured or calculated, present in the oscillator circuit, across the connection points of the crystal. In the case of a series resonant circuit, there is no capacitance present between the connecting points of the crystal unit. Therefore, load capacitance is not specified for a series resonant crystal unit. In the case of a parallel resonant oscillator circuit, capacitance is present. As a direct measurement of this capacitance is impractical, it is usually necessary to calculate the value. Use the following equation:

$$C_{Load} = ((C_1 \times C_2)/(C_1 = C_2)) + C_{Stray}$$

Where C_1 and C_2 are the load capacitors and C_{Stray} is the circuit stray capacitance, usually 3.0–5.0 pF.

Drive Level

The drive level is the power dissipated by the crystal unit while operating. The power is a function of the applied current and is expressed in terms of milliwatts or microwatts. Crystal units are specified as having certain maximum values of drive level, which change as functions of the frequency and mode of operation. It is advised to consult with the crystal unit vendor as to the maximum value of drive level allowed for a particular crystal unit. Exceeding the maximum drive level for a given crystal unit may result in unstable operation, increased aging rates and, in some cases, catastrophic damage. The drive level may be calculated by the following equation:

$$Power = (I_{rms}^2 \times R_{Crystal})$$

Where I is the rms current through the crystal unit and $R_{Crystal}$ is the maximum resistance value of the specific crystal unit in question, this equation is simply Ohm's law for power.

Frequency vs. Mode

The physical dimensions of the vibrating quartz element limit the frequency of a quartz crystal unit. In some cases, the limiting dimensions are the length and width. In the case of the most popular crystal unit, the "AT" cut crystal unit, the limiting dimension is the thickness of the vibrating quartz element. As the thickness is diminished, the frequency is increased. At some point usually around 30 MHz, the thickness of the quartz plate becomes too thin for processing.

Continued on next page

OUO1082,0001332 -19-14JUN12-5/10

Should it be desired to develop an oscillator at a frequency higher than the limiting frequency, advantage must be taken of the fact that quartz crystal units will oscillate at odd integer multiples of their fundamental frequency. These multiples of the fundamental frequency are called overtones and are identified by the integer of multiplication, as in the third overtone, the fifth overtone, etc. When use at an overtone frequency is required, the crystal unit must be specified to operate at the desired frequency and on the desired overtone. One should never attempt to order a fundamental mode crystal unit and then operate it at an overtone frequency. This is due to the fact that the crystal manufacturing processes differ for fundamental and overtone crystal units.

Design Considerations

For good operation of an oscillator circuit, certain design considerations should be followed. In all cases, it is recommended that parallel traces be avoided in order to reduce circuit stray capacitance. All traces should be kept as short as possible and components should be isolated in order to prevent coupling. Ground planes should be used to isolate signals.

Negative Resistance

Procedures for Negative Resistance Measurement

1. Open either end of the crystal unit in the main circuit used and insert a variable resistor in series with the crystal unit. Change the resistance value to examine the limits of oscillation and resistance in ohms observed at that time. In this case, power must be turned on and off without fail.

NOTE: *This measurement should be carried out at the upper and lower limits of the operating temperature range.*

2. Negative resistance (–R) in the circuit is the sum of the value obtained by step 1 and the resonant resistance R1 of the crystal.

3. C1 and C2 should be used within the range of 10–30 pF. If C1 and C2 are used below 10 pF or above 30 pF, oscillation performance may be easily affected. Drive level may increase or negative resistance may decrease, thus failure to maintain oscillation.

For good reliable circuit operation, the negative resistance should be a minimum of five times the specified maximum resistance value of the crystal unit.

OUO1082,0001332 -19-14JUN12-6/10

OPERATIONAL AMPLIFIERS (OP-AMP)

Op-Amps produce, amplify, or respond to variable voltages. They are included in the design of many kinds of amplifier circuits that involve analog-to-digital conversion, timers, oscillators, and voltage regulators.

Some of the components in an integrated Op-Amp are IC diodes, capacitors, transistors, and resistors. Op-Amps are available in packages of single, dual, and quad circuits to an IC.

In Fig. 14 depicts the symbol for an Op-Amp. The input marked with a negative sign (–) is the inverting input and the input marked with the plus sign (+) is the non-inverting input. The output pin is on the right side of the device.

How Op-Amps Work

Op-Amps amplify the difference between voltages or signals applied to their inverting and non-inverting inputs. The input signals can be AC, DC or a combination. The

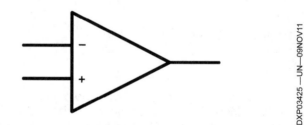

Fig. 14 — Symbol for an Op-Amp

output voltage is equal to the potential difference between the two inputs multiplied by the gain of the amplifier. The ideal Op-Amp has a gain of infinity but practically they are in the range of 50,000 to 100,000. The supply voltage of the device usually limits the output of an Op-Amp. These are typically in the ±10-volt to ±15-volt range. The actual output will be slightly less than the supply voltage.

Continued on next page
OUO1082,0001332 -19-14JUN12-7/10

Inverting

By connecting the AC voltage input to the inverting input of an Op-Amp, and the non-inverting input is connected to ground, the output voltage will be amplified and the signal will be inverted as in Fig. 15. Notice that the input and output do not look alike. This is because the output has been distorted. With such a high gain, almost as soon as the input starts going positive, the output will have reached the highest voltage that it can amplify, or in common terms, the output is railed.

Let us assume that the operating voltages of our Op Amp are ±15 VDC and a gain of 30,000.

$V_{Out} = V_{In} \times$ Gain

Therefore:

$V_{In} = V_{Out}$/Gain = 15VDC/30,000 = 500 µVDC

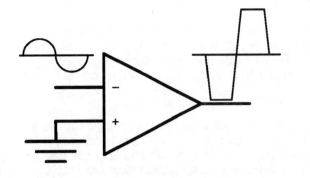

Fig. 15 — An Inverting Op-Amp

We can see that in this configuration the input on the Op-Amp will be limited to ± 500 µVDC, which would render our Op-Amp very impractical.

OUO1082,0001332 -19-14JUN12-8/10

Non-Inverting

With the incoming voltage connected to the non-inverting input of an Op-Amp and the inverting input connected to ground, the output voltage is amplified to the extent that the top and bottom of the waveform will be clipped off because of the high gain of the amplifier (Fig. 16). The input and output waves will remain in phase with each other. By this we mean that at the exact instant the input starts going positive, the output also goes positive. Since the input and output are in phase, this is a non-inverting Op-Amp.

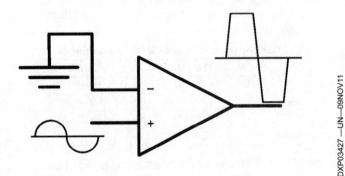

Fig. 16 — A Non-Inverting Op-Amp with Railed Output

OUO1082,0001332 -19-14JUN12-9/10

Op-Amp Output Control

To make the Op-Amp a useful tool requires a means of controlling the gain of these circuits. We have noted the a gain of 30,000 restricts the input to ± 500 µVDC or less. We can connect the output of the amplifier back to the input, through R_2 to allow some negative feedback. This voltage is 180° out of phase with the input voltage. The amount of feedback is controlled by the ratio of R_1 and R_2.

In Fig. 17 is shown an inverting Op-Amp with gain control. The formula for finding the output of the circuit is:

$V_{Out} = V_{In} \times (R_2/R_1)$

Other uses of Op-Amps

There are many more uses of Op-Amps than can be discussed in this text. It is one of the most widely used IC on the market and for that reason one of the most important to understand. There are whole textbooks devoted solely

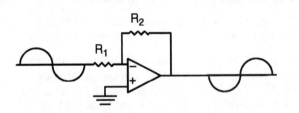

Fig. 17 — An Inverting Op-Amp with Gain Control Resistors

to the understanding and use of the Op-Amp. There are also many application notes on manufacturers' Internet sites. Some common applications for the Op-Amp are:

- Integrator circuits
- Differentiator circuits
- Filter circuits
- Oscillator circuits

OUO1082,0001332 -19-14JUN12-10/10

DIGITAL IC

Digital ICs are composed of circuits that produce voltage signals or pulses that have only two levels: ON and OFF. They include microprocessors, memories, microcomputers, and many kinds of simpler chips.

LOGIC GATES

To process data electronically, the use of logic circuits is required. Logic circuits rely on the binary number system, which we discussed in Chapter 14. The Boolean algebra system was developed as a mathematical tool for the analysis and design of digital circuits and systems. The usefulness of this mathematical tool is universal in the digital field, since it permits the design of a digital circuit or instrument to be performed in a logical manner. In addition, Boolean algebra allows an engineer or technician to easily follow the operation of someone else's design.

Boolean algebra has only two possible values, 0 and 1. A Boolean variable is a quantity that may, at different times, be equal to either 0 or 1. Boolean variables are often used to represent the voltage level present on a wire or at the input/output terminals of a circuit.

Table 2 — Comparison of TTL and CMOS Logic Families		
	TTL (74)	CMOS
Logic 0	0.0—0.8	0.0—0.8
Undefined	0.9—1.9	0.9—1.8
Logic 1	2.0—5.0	1.9—5.48
Input Power	4.5—5.25	2.0—6.0

For example, in a Transistor-Transistor Logic (TTL) digital system, the Boolean value of 0 may be assigned to any voltage in the range between 0.0 and 0.8 V while the Boolean value of 1 may be assigned to any voltage between 2 and 5 V. TTL was most commonly used until recently, when CMOS technology gained the lead. Table 2 shows a comparison between TTL and CMOS.

Voltages between 0.8 and 2 V are undefined (neither 0 nor 1) and under normal circumstances should not occur.

Thus, Boolean 0 and 1 do not represent actual numbers but instead represent the state of a voltage variable or what is called its logic level. A voltage in a digital circuit is to be at the logic level 0 or the logic level 1 depending on its actual numerical value. In digital logic design, several other terms are used synonymously with 0 and 1.

Table 3 — Logic Levels	
Logic 0	Logic 1
Low (Lo)	High (Hi)
False	True
Off	On
No	Yes
Open Switch	Closed Switch

Table 3 lists common terms used to describe logic levels.

Boolean algebra can express the effects that various digital circuits have on logic inputs and determine the best method to implement a design. In Boolean algebra, there are only three basic operations which are:

1. Logical addition is called OR addition or OR operation. The common symbol for this operation is the plus sign (+).

2. Logical multiplication is called AND multiplication or AND operation. A common symbol for this operation is the multiplication sign (·).

3. Logical complementation or inversion is called the NOT operation. The common symbol for this operation is the overline ($^-$). Sometimes a bar over an input is used ($\bar{A}$). This means NOT A.

There are seven basic types of logic gates used as parts of logic digital ICs to control data flow. They are:

- AND gate
- OR gate
- NOT gate
- NAND gate
- NOR gate
- EXCLUSIVE OR (XOR) gate
- EXCLUSIVE NOR (XNOR) gate

AND GATE

The operation of a logic gate is described by its truth table (Fig. 18). Looking at the top row of the truth table for the AND gate, the logical operation is described. In the second row we see if A is low AND B is low, then X will be low. The first line of the truth table would be read, for A = 0 AND B = 0, then X = 0 and the last line would be read as A = 1 AND B = 1, then X = 1.

Continued on next page

OUO1082,0001333 -19-14JUN12-1/15

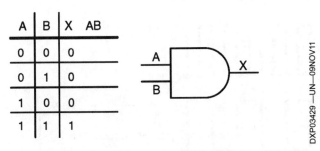

A	B	X AB
0	0	0
0	1	0
1	0	0
1	1	1

DXP03429 —UN—09NOV11

Fig. 18 — AND Gate Symbol and Truth Table

OUO1082,0001333 -19-14JUN12-2/15

Look at the waveforms for inputs A and B (Fig. 19). Verify the output X using the truth table in Fig 18. The truth table tells us that output X will only be high when both A and B are high.

DXP03430 —UN—09NOV11

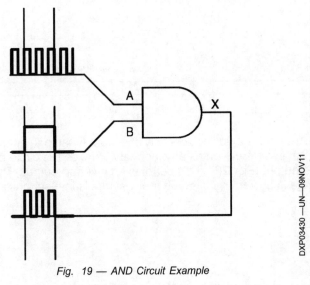

Fig. 19 — AND Circuit Example

OUO1082,0001333 -19-14JUN12-3/15

OR GATE

The truth table for the OR gate (Fig. 20) is read like the AND gate. Looking at line two, since A is low OR B is high, then X is high.

A	B	X = A + B
0	0	0
0	1	1
1	0	1
1	1	1

DXP03431 —UN—09NOV11

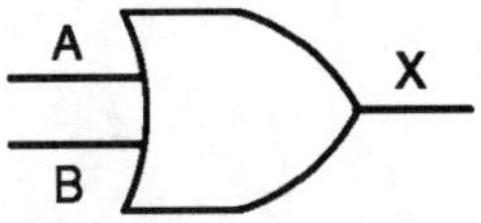

Fig. 20 — OR Gate Symbol and Truth Table

Continued on next page

OUO1082,0001333 -19-14JUN12-4/15

Look at the waveforms for inputs A and B (Fig. 21). Verify the output X using the truth table in Fig. 20. The truth table tells us that the output X will be high if either A or B is high.

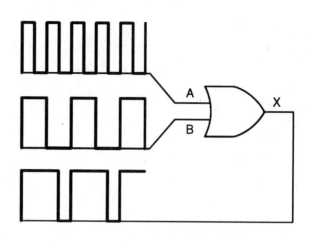

Fig. 21 — OR Circuit Example

DXP03432 —UN—09NOV11

OUO1082,0001333 -19-14JUN12-5/15

NOT GATE

An inverter is a device with only one input A and one output B. An inverter reverses any input at A. Notice the circle on the output (Fig. 22). This denotes an inverted output. The circle is universally used on many symbols in electronics.

A	X = $\overline{A}$
1	0
0	1

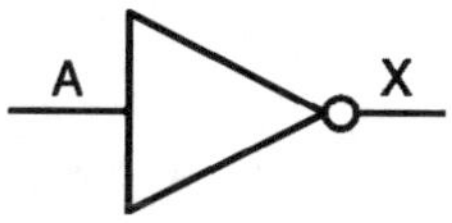

Fig. 22 — NAND Gate Symbol and Truth Table

DXP03433 —UN—09NOV11

OUO1082,0001333 -19-14JUN12-6/15

Referring to the truth table in Fig. 22, we can see in Fig. 23 that if input A is low, then output X will be high.

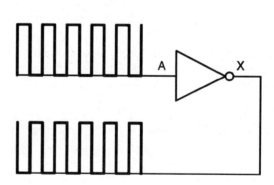

Fig. 23 — Inverter Circuit Example

Continued on next page

DXP03434 —UN—09NOV11

OUO1082,0001333 -19-14JUN12-7/15

NAND GATE

The inverter is used with any gate device to invert its output. By combining an AND gate with an inverter, we make a device known as a NAND gate (Fig. 24). Looking at the truth table for a NAND gate, you will note that it is the inverse of the truth table for an AND gate (Fig. 18).

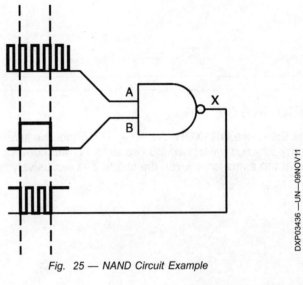

A	B	$X = \overline{AB}$
0	0	1
0	1	1
1	0	1
1	1	0

DXP03435 —UN—09NOV11

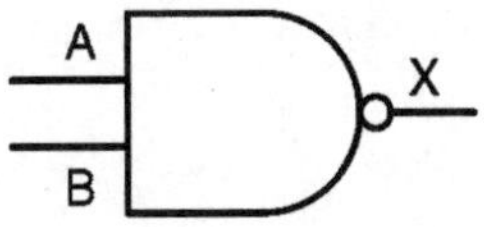

Fig. 24 — NAND Gate Symbol and Truth Table

OUO1082,0001333 -19-14JUN12-8/15

Look at the truth table in Fig. 24 and verify output X of the NAND gate (Fig. 25).

DXP03436 —UN—09NOV11

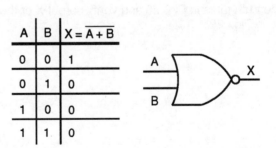

Fig. 25 — NAND Circuit Example

OUO1082,0001333 -19-14JUN12-9/15

NOR GATE

In this case the inverter is used in combination with an OR gate to make a device known as a NOR gate. Looking at the truth table for a NOR gate in Fig. 26, you will note it is the inverse of the truth table for an OR gate (Fig. 20).

A	B	$X = \overline{A+B}$
0	0	1
0	1	0
1	0	0
1	1	0

DXP03437 —UN—09NOV11

Fig. 26 — NOR Gate Symbol and Truth Table

Continued on next page

OUO1082,0001333 -19-14JUN12-10/15

Look at the truth table in Fig. 26 and verify output X of the NOR gate in Fig. 27.

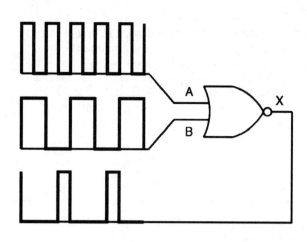

Fig. 27 — NOR Circuit Example

OUO1082,0001333 -19-14JUN12-11/15

EXCLUSIVE OR GATE

The Exclusive OR (XOR) gate (Fig. 28) is not the inverse of any other gate we have studied so far. When both A or B are at the same logic level, the output X is exclusively low.

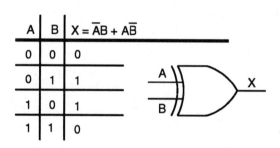

A	B	$X = \bar{A}B + A\bar{B}$
0	0	0
0	1	1
1	0	1
1	1	0

Fig. 28 — XOR Gate Symbol and Truth Table

OUO1082,0001333 -19-14JUN12-12/15

Look at the truth table in Fig. 28 and verify output X of the NOR gate in Fig. 29.

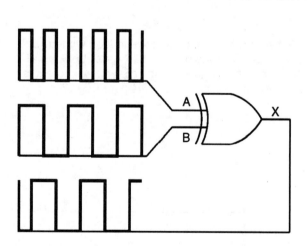

Fig. 29 — XOR Gate Circuit Example

Continued on next page OUO1082,0001333 -19-14JUN12-13/15

EXCLUSIVE NOR GATE

The Exclusive NOR (XNOR) gate (Fig. 30) is the inverse of the XOR gate we have just studied. When both A or B are at the same logic level, output X is exclusively high.

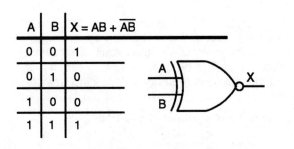

A	B	$X = AB + \overline{AB}$
0	0	1
0	1	0
1	0	0
1	1	1

Fig. 30 — XNOR Gate Symbol and Truth Table

OUO1082,0001333 -19-14JUN12-14/15

Look at the truth table in Fig. 30 and verify output X of the XNOR gate in Fig. 31.

COMBINATIONAL LOGIC CIRCUITS

Logic gates are rarely used alone in a circuit. Combinations of logic circuits will be covered later in this chapter and in chapter 17 — Computers and Programmable Controllers.

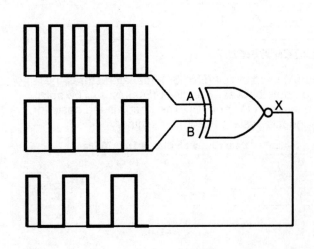

Fig. 31 — XNOR

OUO1082,0001333 -19-14JUN12-15/15

SEQUENTIAL LOGIC (FLIP-FLOP) CIRCUITS

The output of a sequential logic circuit is determined by the previous state of the input (pulses). Bits of data move through sequential circuits step by step. Data (memory) advances a step each time a steady stream of pulses occur at the input. This steady stream of pulses is a clock pulse. The building block (gates) of a sequential logic circuit is the flip-flop circuit.

RESET-SET (RS) CIRCUITS

The basic circuit of all sequential circuits is the RS (reset-set) flip-flop circuit (Fig. 32). In this circuit, the two outputs always are opposite of each other and two low inputs are not allowed. If there are two high inputs, the outputs do not change. This is sometimes called a latch circuit.

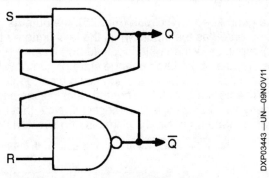

Fig. 32 — Basic Reset-Set Flip-Flop Circuit

Table 4 — Basic Reset-Set Flip-Flop Circuit Truth Table			
S	R	Q	Q
0	0	Disallowed	
0	1	1	0
1	0	0	1
1	1	No Change	

Continued on next page   OUO1082,0001334 -19-14JUN12-1/8

CLOCK LATCH CIRCUITS

In a clock (A) latch (RS flip-flop) circuit (Fig. 33), the latch ignores any data input at S and R until a stream of pulses (clock) triggers the operation of the circuit. This circuit will not allow S and R to be both on 1. This circuit is the basis for random access memory (RAM), discussed later in this chapter.

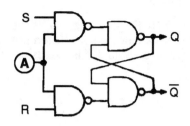

Fig. 33 — Clock Latch Circuit

A—Clock

Table 5 — Clock Latch Circuit Truth Table			
S	**R**	**Q**	**Q**
0	0	No Change	
0	1	1	0
1	0	0	1
1	1	Disallowed	

OUO1082,0001334 -19-14JUN12-2/8

DATA LATCH CIRCUIT

In a data (A) latch circuit (Fig. 34), the latch stores the present outputs between the clock (B) pulses. The data input is either on (1) or off (0). This circuit is the basis for a self-diagnosis system used on machinery.

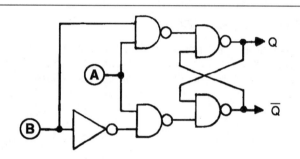

Fig. 34 — Data (A) Latch Circuit

Table 6 — Data (D) Latch Circuit Truth Table		
D	**Q**	**Q**
0	0	1
1	1	0

A—Clock   **B—Data**

OUO1082,0001334 -19-14JUN12-3/8

JUMP-KEEP LATCH CIRCUIT

In a jump-keep (JK) circuit (Fig. 35), the outputs keep the same on/off as the inputs while the latch ignores the clock (A) impulses. When both inputs (J and K) are on (1), then the outputs of the latch change state or "jump" with each clock pulse. This jump is also known as a toggle. This circuit acts like a switch to control clock pulses and is used mostly as a basis for a counter circuit. Note that this circuit is also made up of two NOR gates and two AND gates.

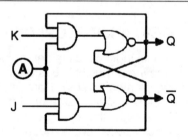

Fig. 35 — Jump-Keep Latch Circuit

A—Clock

Table 7— Jump-Keep Latch Circuit Truth Table			
J	**K**	**Q**	**Q**
0	0	No Change	
0	1	1	0
1	0	0	1
1	1	Disallowed	

Continued on next page

OUO1082,0001334 -19-14JUN12-4/8

When the sequential circuits become complicated, a named box is used as a symbol. Fig. 36 shows the box symbols for the RS latch (E), the D latch (D), and the JK latch (C) circuits.

A—Clock
B—Data
C—RS Latch Circuit

D—D Latch Circuit
E—JK Latch Circuit

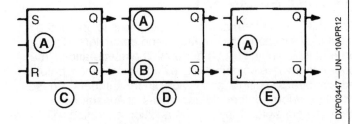

Fig. 36 — Latch Circuit Symbols

OUO1082,0001334 -19-14JUN12-5/8

TOGGLE LATCH CIRCUIT

A toggle latch circuit (Fig. 37) has its outputs change state with every input pulse and has no restrictions.

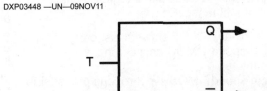

Fig. 37 — Toggle Latch Circuit Symbol

OUO1082,0001334 -19-14JUN12-6/8

Toggle circuits can be made from any of the three latch circuits previously shown by changing the connections (Fig. 38).

A—Clock
B—Data
C—Will Accept On Pulses Only

D—RS Latch to Toggle Latch
E—Data Latch to Toggle Latch
F—JK Latch to Toggle Latch

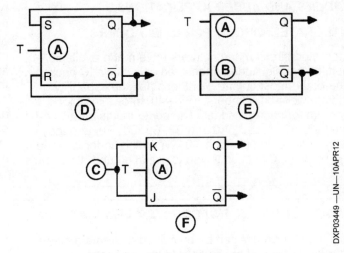

Fig. 38 — Toggle Latch Circuits

OUO1082,0001334 -19-14JUN12-7/8

For every other input (A) on/off pulse on a toggle latch circuit, the outputs (B) change their state. In other words, the output of a toggle latch is one half of its input pulse (Fig. 39). Therefore, the input pulses are divided by two.

A—Input Pulses
B—Ouput Pulses

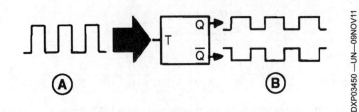

Fig. 39 — Toggle Latch Input and Output Pulses

OUO1082,0001334 -19-14JUN12-8/8

ARITHMETIC CIRCUITS

The ability to perform arithmetic operations is one of the most vital functions of computers and controllers. The arithmetic logic unit (ALU) performs these operations in a computer, where combinations of logic gates and flip-flops add, subtract, multiply, and divide binary numbers. These circuits perform arithmetic operations at speeds not humanly possible. Typically, an addition operation will take less than 1μs.

In this section, we will study some of the basic arithmetic circuits that perform these arithmetic operations. The circuits are commercially available in integrated-circuit form. A short list of arithmetic ICs are:

• 74LS283—4-bit binary full adders with fast carry
• 74HC161—high-speed CMOS asynchronous presettable counters
• 74HC163—high-speed CMOS synchronous presettable counters
• 74HC191—synchronous up/down counters with mode control
• 74HC193—presettable synchronous 4-bit up/down counters
• 74LS181—4-bit arithmetic logic unit with carry

ADDERS AND ADDER APPLICATIONS

INTEGRATED-CIRCUIT PARALLEL ADDERS

Integrated-circuit manufacturers have made available multi-bit parallel adders fabricated as a single IC package. One of the most common of these has the capability of adding two 4-bit numbers. (Fig. 40) shows the block diagram for such an adder. The adder inputs are two 4-bit numbers A3, A2, A1, A0 and B3, B2, B1, B0, and they carry into the first position C0. When the adder is in the first position, C0 is connected to digital ground. Its outputs

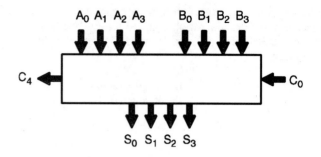

Fig. 40 — A 4-Bit Parallel Adder

are the sum bits, S3, S2, S1, S0 and they carry out of the last position C4. The adder block consists of full adders and their interconnections. If it is a high-speed adder, it will also contain extra logic gates for reducing carry propagation time, such as the look-ahead carry design. In all the work to follow, we will use this block symbol to represent the 4-bit parallel adder, for clarity.

CASCADING PARALLEL ADDERS

Two or more parallel adder blocks may be connected in cascade to accommodate the addition of larger binary numbers. Two 4-bit parallel adders can be connected to add two 8-bit numbers. One adder adds the four least-significant bits (LSB) of the numbers. The C0 output of this adder is connected to digital ground. The C4 output of this adder is connected as the input carry (C0) to the first position of the second adder, which adds the four most-significant bits (MSB) of the numbers. The eight sum outputs represent the resultant sum of the two 8-bit numbers. C4 is the carry out of the last position (MSB) of the second adder. C4 can be used as an overflow bit or as a carry into another adder stage if larger binary numbers are to be handled.

OUO1082,0001335 -19-14JUN12-1/3

BINARY COUNTER AND COUNTER APPLICATIONS

Toggle latch circuits can be combined to create a binary counter. Let's look at how four toggle or T latch circuits can be formed to create a four-bit binary counter (Fig. 41). Each T latch circuit divides the incoming pulses by two.

Table 8 — Truth Table for a 4-Bit Binary Counter																
Input	0	1	2	3	4	5	6	7	8	9	10	11	12	13	14	15
D	0	0	0	0	0	0	0	0	1	1	1	1	1	1	1	1
C	0	0	0	0	1	1	1	1	0	0	0	0	1	1	1	1
B	0	0	1	1	0	0	1	1	0	0	1	1	0	0	1	1
A	0	1	0	1	0	1	0	1	0	1	0	1	0	1	0	1
Output	0	1	2	3	4	5	6	7	8	9	A	B	C	D	E	F

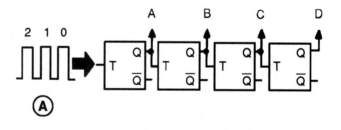

Fig. 41 — A 4-Bit Binary Counter

A—Input Pulses

Table 8 shows us a truth table in which we see a 4-bit binary count of 0000 (0) to 1111 (F). Please note the output of this counter in the bottom row, as it can also serve as a HEX counter. The count will recycle after the 16th incoming

pulse and restart. This type of circuit can count pulses up to 20,000,000 times per second! There are many types of IC counters, most of which have special features that count up, count down, add, subtract, divide, rest, etc.

Continued on next page   OUO1082,0001335 -19-14JUN12-2/3

ARITHMETIC LOGIC UNITS (ALU)

All arithmetic operations take place in the ALU of a computer. A block diagram (Fig. 42) shows the major elements included in a typical ALU. The main purpose of the ALU is to accept binary data from the memory (B) and perform arithmetic operations on this data, as instructed by the control unit (E).

The ALU usually contains at least three registers:

- A Register (accumulator) (B)
- B Register (E)
- C Register (F)

It also contains combinatorial logic, which performs the arithmetic operations on the binary numbers in different registers. A typical sequence of operations may occur as follows:

1. The control unit receives an instruction from memory. A number stored in a particular memory (address) location is to be added to a number stored in another particular memory (address) location. These memory locations are usually contained in the instructions from memory to the control unit.

2. One number is transferred from memory to the B register. The other number may be placed directly in the accumulator or placed in the C register. The number may also be in the accumulator from a previous operation. In this example let us assume the accumulator is empty.

3. The number in the B register and the number in the C register are added together in the logic circuits (upon command from the control unit). The resulting sum is placed in the accumulator to be temporarily stored.

4. The new number in the accumulator can remain there to act as a number for the next instruction. Or, if the

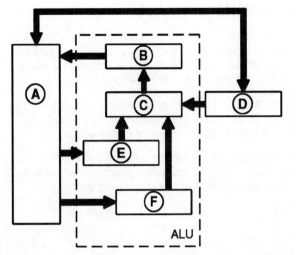

Fig. 42 — Diagram of an Arithmetic Logic Unit

A—Memory Unit	D—Control Unit
B—A Register	E—B Register
C—Logic Circuits	F—C Register

particular arithmetic process is finished, it can be transferred to memory for long-term storage.

These steps should make it apparent how the accumulator (A register) derives its name. This register accumulates the results that occur when performing successive mathematics operations between new numbers acquired from memory and the previously accumulated results. In fact, for any arithmetic problem containing several steps, the accumulator always contains the results of the intermediate steps as they are completed, as well as the final result when the problem is finished.

OUO1082,0001335 -19-14JUN12-3/3

DATA HANDLING CIRCUITS

Data and processor instructions for all digital systems are in some form of binary code, and are continually processed in some manner. In this section, we will examine various types of digital circuits whose applications include:

- Changing data from one form to another
- Selecting one out of several groups of data
- Distributing data to one of several destinations

We will investigate how they are used alone or in combination to perform various operations on digital data. Some of the operations that are discussed are:

- Decoding
- Encoding
- Code conversion
- Multiplexing
- Demultiplexing
- IC Registers
- Memory

DECODERS

A decoder is a logic device that selects one unique output for a given input. A dual 2-line (input) to 4-line decoder symbol is shown in Fig 43. This decoder may be referred to in several ways. It can be called a 2-line to 4-line decoder, because it has two input lines and four output lines. It is also sometimes referred to as a 1- of 4-line decoder, because only one of the four outputs is activated at one time.

Table 9 — 74AC11239 Truth Table						
Enable Not G	**Select Inputs**		**Outputs**			
	A	**B**	**Y_0**	**Y_1**	**Y_2**	**Y_3**
H	X[a]	X	L	L	L	L
L	L	L	H	L	L	L
L	H	L	L	H	L	L
L	L	H	L	L	H	L
L	H	H	L	L	L	H

[a]An X indicates that the associated input is ignored and another input will determine the output.

Table 9 shows the truth table for the dual 2-line to 4-line decoder.

OPEN-COLLECTOR OUTPUTS

Some decoders such as the 7445 have open-collector outputs. For these types of decoders, each output is normally OFF, providing a high-resistance path to ground.

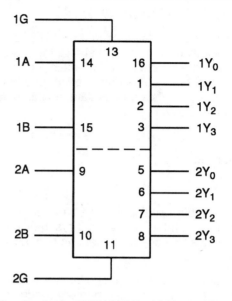

Fig. 43 — Symbol for 74AC11239 Dual 2-Line to 4-Line Decoder

The output becomes a low-resistance path to ground when its corresponding input code is applied to the decoder inputs. These open-collector outputs are usually designed to operate at higher current and voltage limits than a normal TTL device. For example, the 7445 outputs can sink up to 80 mA in the LOW state and can tolerate voltages up to 30 V in the HIGH state.

ENABLE INPUTS

Some decoders have one or more enable inputs that are used to control the operation of the decoder. It might be worth noting at this time that active-low inputs and outputs are often represented on a logic diagram with an inversion over-bar.

There are several reasons for including enable inputs on decoder circuits. One is to allow the selection of one of several decoders in a system by means of signals applied to the various enable inputs. Another is to allow the decoder to be used as a demultiplexer, which we will discuss shortly. Still another is to provide a means for turning off the decoder while the input code is in a transition state. Thereby eliminating the possibility of decoding glitches at the decoder outputs. We can call it a strobe input rather than enable. Both terms are used for this particular type of input. In this text we will use the term enable.

Continued on next page OUO1082,0001336 -19-14JUN12-1/13

ENCODERS

The opposite of the decoding process is encoding and it is performed by a logic circuit called an encoder. An encoder has a number of input lines, only one of which is active at a given time, and produces an output code, depending on which input is active.

In Fig. 44 is the diagram for a 74HC148 priority encoder with eight inputs and three outputs. Here the inputs are active low, which means they are normally high.

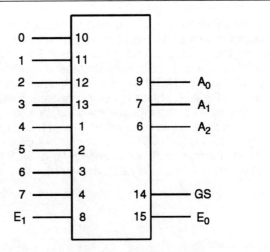

Fig. 44 — 74HC148 Priority Encoder Symbol

Table 10 — 74HC148 Priority Encoder Truth Table													
Inputs									Outputs				
E_1	0	1	2	3	4	5	6	7	A_0	A_1	A_2	GS	E_0
H	X	X	X	X	X	X	X	X	H	H	H	H	H
L	H	H	H	H	H	H	H	H	H	H	H	H	L
L	X	X	X	X	X	X	X	L	L	L	L	L	H
L	X	X	X	X	X	X	L	H	L	L	H	L	H
L	X	X	X	X	X	L	H	H	L	H	L	L	H
L	X	X	X	X	L	H	H	H	L	H	H	L	H
L	X	X	X	L	H	H	H	H	H	L	L	L	H
L	X	X	L	H	H	H	H	H	H	L	H	L	H
L	X	L	H	H	H	H	H	H	H	H	L	L	H
L	L	H	H	H	H	H	H	H	H	H	H	L	H

Notice that an all high input is not allowed, indicated by a LOW on E_0. Also take note, a low on the highest input (0 to 7) will have the highest priority output and it will be validated by a HIGH on E_0.

OUO1082,0001336 -19-14JUN12-2/13

This priority encoder has eight input lines and produces a 3-bit binary output code. Its circuitry is shown in Fig. 45. If more than one of the input lines is made HIGH at one time, the one with the highest priority (D_0) will have its address presented to A_0, A_1 and A_2. The circuit is designed so that when D_0 is LOW, the binary code 111 is generated at the output; when D1 is LOW, the binary code 011 is generated; when D_2 is LOW, the code 101 is generated. Table 10 shows the complete list of codes.

EXAMPLE

Describe the structure and operation of a decimal-to-BCD (binary coded decimal) encoder with active LOW inputs.

SOLUTION

A—PTO ON
B—Hitch Locked
C—Headlights
D—4-Ways
E—R-Turn Signal

F—L-Turn Signal
G—Back-up Alarm
H—Clutch
I— Enable

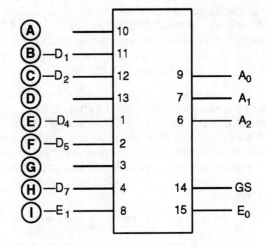

Fig. 45 — 74HC148 Priority Encoder Circuit

Continued on next page

OUO1082,0001336 -19-14JUN12-3/13

This encoder takes ten input lines, with active LOW inputs and produces a 4-bit BCD output code. Since there are four outputs, the circuitry contains four gates. The gates used are NAND gates because the outputs are to be normally LOW and go HIGH when any of their inputs is made LOW. In Fig 46 it shows the block diagram for this encoder. When one of the inputs is made LOW, the 4-bit code corresponding to this input will appear at the outputs. For example, if A8 is held LOW, the outputs will be $O_3 O_2 O_1 O_0 = 0111$. Perform an Internet search for a 74LS147 and using the truth table, verify this statement.

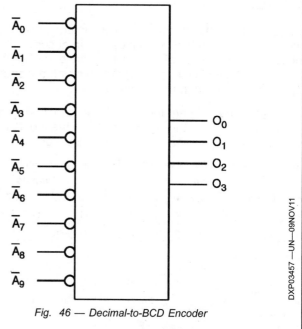

Fig. 46 — *Decimal-to-BCD Encoder*

OUO1082,0001336 -19-14JUN12-4/13

MULTIPLEXERS (DATA SELECTORS)

A multiplexer or data selector is a logic circuit that accepts several data inputs and allows only one of them at a time to get through to the output. The routing of the desired data input to the output is controlled by (A, B, C) inputs (sometimes referred to as ADDRESS inputs). In Fig. 47 it shows the symbol for an 8-to-1 multiplexer (MUX). In this diagram the inputs and outputs are drawn as large arrows to indicate that they may be one or more lines.

The multiplexer acts like a digitally controlled multiposition switch where the digital code applied to the address inputs controls which data input will be switched to the output. For example, output Y will equal the data input of the particular selected input code. Stated another way, a multiplexer selects one out of eight input data sources and transmits the selected data to a single output channel. This is multiplexing.

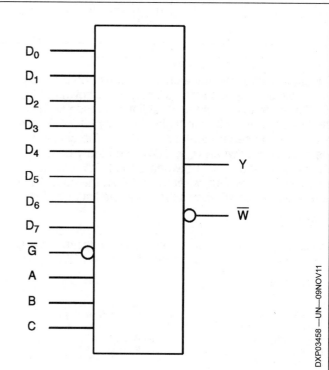

Fig. 47 — *Symbol for a 74HC151 Digital Multiplexer (MUX)*

Table 11 shows the inputs and outputs for the 74HC151 multiplexer.

Table 11 — Truth Table for the 74HC151 Digital Multiplexer (MUX)					
Input				Output	
Select			Strobe Not G	Y	W
C	B	A			
$D_0, D_1...D_7$ = The Level of the Respective D Input					
X	X	X	H	L	H
L	L	L	L	D_0	NOT D_0
L	L	H	L	D_1	NOT D_1
L	H	L	L	D_2	NOT D_2
L	H	H	L	D_3	NOT D_3
H	L	L	L	D_4	NOT D_4
H	L	H	L	D_5	NOT D_5
H	H	L	L	D_6	NOT D_6
H	H	H	L	D_7	NOT D_7

Continued on next page   OUO1082,0001336 -19-14JUN12-5/13

BASIC 2-INPUT MULTIPLEXER

In Fig. 48 shows the logic circuitry for a 2-input (or 2-channel) multiplexer with data inputs A and B and SELECT input S. The logic level applied to the S input determines which AND gate is enabled so its data input passes through the OR gate to output Z. Looking at it another way, the Boolean expression for the output is:

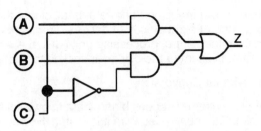

Fig. 48 — A 2-Input Multiplexer

Table 12 — A 2-Input Multiplexer	
Select	Output (Z)
0	Z = B
1	Z = A

A—Data A
B—Data B

C—Select

Z = AS + B NOT S

With S = 0, this expression becomes

Z = A x 0 + B x 1 = B

Which indicates that Z will be identical to input signal B, which can be a fixed logic level or a time-varying logic signal. With S = 1, the expression becomes:

Z = A x 1 + B x 0 = A

Showing that output Z will be identical to input signal A.

MULTIPLEXER APPLICATIONS

Multiplexer circuits find numerous and varied applications in digital systems of all types. These applications include data selection, data routing, operation sequencing, parallel-to-serial conversion, waveform generation, and logic-function generation. We will investigate some of these applications here.

Data Selection and Routing

Multiplexers can route data from one of several sources to one destination.

The purpose of the multiplexing technique is to time-share an output device between two input devices rather than have a separate set of output circuits for each input device. This results in a significant savings in the number of wiring connections. Even more importantly, it represents a significant decrease in power consumption, because two circuits typically draw twice the amount of current from the Vcc supply. Of course, this technique has the limitation of only one input circuit content can be displayed at a time. However, in many applications this is not a drawback. A mechanical switching arrangement could have been used to perform the function of switching first one input and then the other to the output.

Continued on next page

OUO1082,0001336 -19-14JUN12-6/13

The circuit shown in Fig. 49 shows a small circuit that will display one of eight pieces of data as directed by the address from the central processing unit (CPU). A strobe or latch signal is sent to the display to lock in the data.

Parallel-to-Serial Conversion

Many digital systems process binary data in parallel form (all bits simultaneously) because it is faster. However when this data is to be transmitted over relatively long distances, the parallel arrangement becomes undesirable because it requires a large number of transmission lines. For this reason, binary data or information that is in parallel form is often converted to serial form before being transmitted to a remote destination.

A—PTO rpm
B—Engine rpm
C—Battery Voltage
D—Oil Pressure
E—Speed
F—Engine Temperature
G—Oil Temperature

H—Alarm Code
I— Strobe
J— Address 0
K—Address 1
L—Address 2
M—CPU
N—Display

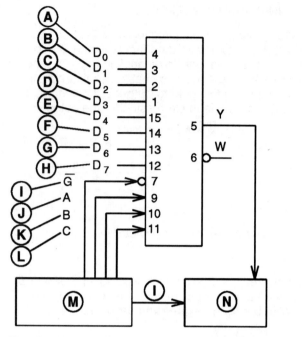

Fig. 49 — Sample Circuit for a 74HC151 Multiplexer (MUX)

OUO1082,0001336 -19-14JUN12-7/13

One method for performing this parallel-to-serial conversion uses a multiplexer, as illustrated in Fig. 50.

The data is present in parallel form at the inputs (D_0 to D_7) to the latched storage register and is latched onto the output. They are then fed to the 8-input MUX. A 3-bit (three JK flip-flops) counter that can count from 0 to 8 in binary code (MOD-8) is used to provide the select code bits (S_0, S_1, S_2) so that they cycle from 000 to 111 as clock pulses are applied. In this way, the output of the multiplexer will be X0 during the first clock period, X_1 during the second clock period, and so on. The output Z is a waveform that is a serial representation of the parallel input data. The waveforms in Fig. 50 are for the case where X_0, X_1, X_2, X_3, X_4, X_5, X_6, X_7 = 10101101. This conversion process takes a total of eight clock cycles. Note, X_0 (the LSB) is transmitted first and the X_7, (MSB) is transmitted last.

A—Storage Register
B—8-Input MUX

C—Latch
D—Clock

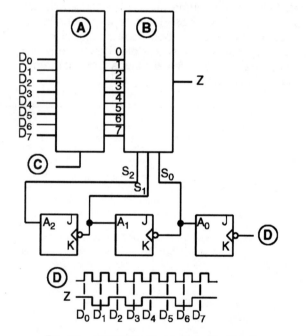

Fig. 50 — Parallel-to-Series Example Circuit

Continued on next page   OUO1082,0001336 -19-14JUN12-8/13

DEMULTIPLEXERS (DATA DISTRIBUTORS)

A multiplexer takes several inputs and transmits one of them to the output. A demultiplexer performs the reverse operation; it takes a single input and distributes it over several outputs.

The circuit shown in Fig. 51 will take a 3-bit address and decode it to select one of eight devices or processes. For instance, the address of 010 will turn on the hydraulic pump. This is a very common task for a controller and is easily accomplished very quickly.

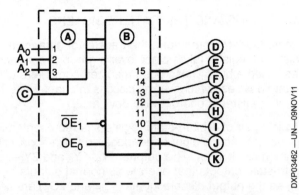

Fig. 51 — Data Selection Example for a 74HC137 Digital Demultiplexer (MUX) with Latch

A—3-Bit Latch
B—1-of-8 Decoder
C—Latch Enable
D—Memory Address Latch
E—Data Address Latch
F—Hydraulic Pump
G—A/D Conversion Enable
H—D/A Conversion Enable
I— GPS Steering Enable
J—PTO Enable
K—Raise Bucket Enable

Table 13 shows the inputs and outputs for the 74HC137 demultiplexer.

Table 13 — Truth Table for a 74HC137 Digital Demultiplexer (MUX) With Latch

Inputs						Outputs							
L-E	OE_0	Not EO_1	A_2	A_1	A_0	Y_0	Y_1	Y_2	Y_3	Y_4	Y_5	Y_6	Y_7
X	X	H	X	X	X	H	H	H	H	H	H	H	H
X	L	X	X	X	X	H	H	H	H	H	H	H	H
L	H	L	L	L	L	L	H	H	H	H	H	H	H
L	H	L	L	L	H	H	L	H	H	H	H	H	H
L	H	L	L	H	L	H	H	L	H	H	H	H	H
L	H	L	L	X	H	H	H	H	L	H	H	H	H
L	H	L	H	L	L	H	H	H	H	L	H	H	H
L	H	L	H	L	H	H	H	H	H	H	L	H	H
L	H	L	H	H	L	H	H	H	H	H	H	L	H
L	H	L	H	H	H	H	H	H	H	H	H	H	L
H	H	L	X	X	X	Depends upon the address previously applied while LE as at a logic low.							

OUO1082,0001336 -19-14JUN12-9/13

IC REGISTERS

Many types of flip-flop registers are used in digital systems to temporarily store data or to assist in transmitting data from one location to another. We will now look at some of the numerous types of registers that are available as off-the-shelf ICs.

DATA-LATCHING REGISTERS

Fig. 52 is a type of register that uses D-type latches discussed earlier. The clock input is common to each latch and causes the data outputs Q_3, Q_2, $Q1$, and Q_0 to respond to the data inputs D_3, D_2, D_1, and D_0 as follows:

1. While clock is high, each Q output follows the logic levels present in its i; corresponding D input (e.g., Q_3 follows D_3).

2. When clock goes low, each Q output latches (holds) the last D value and cannot change even if the D input changes.

The CLEAR input is used to clear each output to 0 simultaneously on a low level.

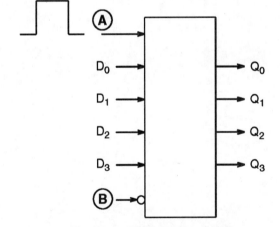

Fig. 52 — A 4-Bit Latching Register

A—Clock

B—Clear

Continued on next page

OUO1082,0001336 -19-14JUN12-10/13

DATA BUSING AND TRI-STATE REGISTERS

In most modern computers, the transfer of data from register to register takes place over a group of connecting lines called a bus. These bus-organized computers utilize tri-state devices, which we will discuss in chapter 17. The tri-state register is one of these devices.

A typical pair of 4-bit tri-state registers is represented in Fig. 53. It contains eight edge-triggered D flip-flops with a common clock input. The outputs $1Y_0$–$1Y_3$ and $2Y_0$–$2Y_3$ are tri-state outputs that operate as normal outputs as long as the output disable inputs ($1O_E$ and $2O_E$) are kept LOW. A HIGH on $1O_E$ and $2O_E$ places the outputs in the HIGH impedance (Hi-Z) state.

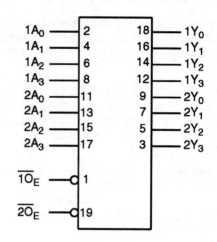

Fig. 53 — 74ACT244 Octal Buffer/Driver with Tri-State Outputs

Table 14 shows the inputs and outputs for the 74ACT244 octal buffer/driver.

Table 14 — 74ACT244 Octal Buffer/Driver Truth Table		
Inputs		Output
Not $1O_E$ and Not $2O_E$	A	Y
L	L	L
L	H	H
H	X	Z[a]

[a]*High Impendance*

Continued on next page   OUO1082,0001336 -19-14JUN12-11/13

In Fig. 54 we have a typical 16-bit bus that has a 74ACT244 as the bus buffer/driver. The typical operation would be for these drivers to pass the input through to the output in normal operation. If you wished the address on the bus to come from another place, there would be another set of 74ACT244s hooked to the common address bus and one of them would always be in the tri-state mode. So only one would be driving the bus at one time.

MEMORY

All machinery that has an onboard computer contains some form of memory. Several basic types of memory include:

- Dynamic random access memory (DRAM)
- Static random access memory (SRAM)
- Programmable read only memory (PROM)
- Erasable programmable read only memory (EPROM)
- Electrically Erasable Programmable Read-Only Memory (EEPROM)
- Non-volatile random access memory (NVRAM)

Memory in computers fulfills many purposes, such as program storage, temporary data storage and long-term data storage.

DYNAMIC RANDOM ACCESS MEMORY (DRAM)

DRAM is used for temporary data and program storage. If the power to the memory is turned off, all data will be lost. This type of memory is mature in design and is not used much anymore. SRAM has replaced the DRAM in common use.

STATIC RANDOM ACCESS MEMORY (SRAM)

SRAM is very similar to DRAM except that it does not have to be refreshed like the older DRAM. It is used in the same ways as DRAM was used. It will retain its data as long as the power is on. The power to this type of RAM is never turned off.

PROGRAMMABLE READ ONLY MEMORY (PROM)

PROM is used to permanently store programs within integrated circuits and cannot be changed or affected by normal operational inputs. They are obtained from the manufacturer blank and are programmed with the data by the end user. Commercially available programmers are used to program the information in the chip.

ERASABLE PROGRAMMABLE READ ONLY MEMORY (EPROM)

EPROM is used to permanently store programs within integrated circuits and cannot be changed or affected by normal operational inputs. They are obtained from the manufacturer blank and are programmed with the data

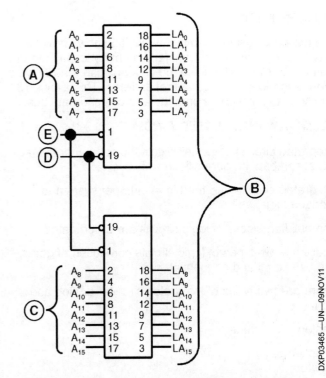

Fig. 54 — 74ACT244 Octal Buffer/Driver Data Example Circuit

A—Low Data Byte
B—Latched Data Address
C—High Data Byte
D—Enable
E—Clock

by the end user. The main difference between PROM and EPROM is that information on the EPROMs can be erased by the use of a high-intensity UV light. After that, they can be reused. This type of memory is used more often in Proto-Type work.

Electrically Erasable Programmable Read-Only Memory (EEPROM)

EEPROM is used to store data that must be saved when power is turned off. Unlike the previous discussed EPROM that needs to be removed, EEPROM's can be erased and reprogrammed repeatedly one byte at a time with an electrical charge and without the need be taken out of the computer or electronic device.

NON-VOLATILE RANDOM ACCESS MEMORY (NVRAM)

The main use of NVRAM is for storage of data and programs that may be changed remotely. This can be accomplished by a modem connected to the computer unit. A loader program is either stored in the NVRAM or it can be part of the program that is sent via the modem.

Continued on next page
OUO1082,0001336 -19-14JUN12-12/13

MEMORY BUSING

The memory busing example in Fig. 55 shows how the data bus (A_0 to A_{15}) can transfer a memory location to the memory bus and latch it, so the data bus can read or write information to the device at that address. This allows 16 DIO lines to function as both the address and data bus.

SUMMARY: INTEGRATED CIRCUITS

Integrated circuits are small electronic components that are assembled on pure silicon wafers.

Integrated circuits use the binary number system to produce logic.

The building blocks of logic circuits are called gates.

There are two types of logic circuits composed of gates: combinational and sequential.

There are two types of integrated circuits: analog and digital.

Analog ICs include:

• Op-Amps
• Filters

Digital ICs include:

• Logic
• Counters
• Timers
• Buffers
• Multiplexers
• Demultiplexers

Types of memory include:

• Dynamic random access memory (DRAM)
• Static random access memory (SRAM)

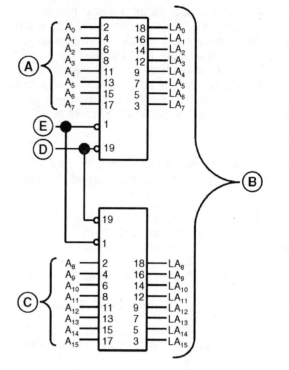

Fig. 55 — 74ACT244 Octal Buffer/Driver Data Example Circuit

A—Low Memory Byte   D—Enable
B—Latched Memory Address   E—Clock
C—High Memory Byte

• Read only memory (ROM)
• Programmable read only memory (PROM)
• Electrical programmable read only memory (EPROM)
• Non-volatile random access memory (NVRAM)

OUO1082,0001336 -19-14JUN12-13/13

COMMUNICATIONS INTERFACE CHIPS

CAN (CONTROLLER AREA NETWORK) BUS CHIPS

PCA 82C251, SAE 81C90, SJA 1000 and COP 87L84BC are some of the stand-alone CAN chips. You can search the Internet for these parts and download a data sheet for that part. We will be talking more about these parts in chapter 17.

These are stand-alone controller chips for the Controller Area Network (CAN) used within automotive and general industrial environments. Some of these support the CAN 2.0B protocol specification with several new features.

RS-232 CHIPS

A typical example is the MAX 222. These chips are designed to provide an RS-232 serial link to other devices. This method of communications was limited to a speed of 19.5 kilobits per second (kbit/s) but it can now be used in excess of 119 kbit/s.

The MAX222 consists of two line drivers, two line receivers, and a dual charge-pump circuit with ±15-kV ESD protection pin to pin (serial-port connection pins, including GND). This device meets the requirements of TIA/EIA-232-F and provides the electrical interface between an asynchronous communication controller and the serial-port connector. The charge pump and four small external capacitors allow operation from a single 5-V supply. This device operates at data signaling rates up to 200 kbit/s and a maximum of 30V/s driver output slew rate. By using enable, all receivers can be disabled.

RS-422 CHIPS

The MC3487 is a typical example of an RS-422 protocol communication chip.

The MC3487 offers four independent differential line drivers designed to meet the specifications of ANSI TIA/EIA-422-B and ITU Recommendation V.11. Each driver has a TTL-compatible input buffered to reduce current and minimize loading.

The driver outputs utilize 3-state circuitry to provide high-impedance states at any pair of differential outputs when the appropriate output enable is at a low logic level. Internal circuitry is provided to ensure the high-impedance state at the differential outputs during power-up and power-down transition times, provided the output enable is low.

The MC3487 is designed for optimum performance when used with the MC3486 quadruple line receiver. It is supplied in a 16-pin dual-in-line package and operates from a single 5-V supply.

RS-485 CHIPS

The SN65HVDO5 is a typical example of an RS-422 protocol communication chip.

It combines a 3-state differential line driver and differential line receiver. They are designed for balanced data transmission and interoperate with ANSI TIA/EIA-485-A and ISO 8482E standard-compliant devices. The driver is designed to provide a differential output voltage greater than that required by these standards for increased noise margin. The drivers and receivers have active-high and active-low enables respectively, which can be externally connected together to function as direction control.

The driver differential outputs and receiver differential inputs connect internally to form a differential input/output (I/O) bus port that is designed to offer minimum loading to the bus whenever the driver is disabled or not powered. These devices feature wide positive and negative common-mode voltage ranges, making them suitable for party-line applications.

OUO1082,0001337 -19-04NOV11-1/1

PRINTED CIRCUIT BOARDS (PCBS OR PWBS)

PURPOSE

Printed circuit boards are used to hold components in place and to provide current paths from component to component. They are usually designed to fulfill a specific purpose.

LAYOUT

The lines on a printed circuit board never touch each other. If they did, they would cause a short in the circuit. Current-carrying lines are routed from one side of the board to the other by a plated through hole called a via (A).

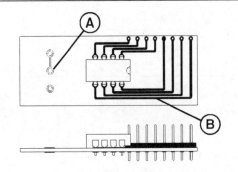

Fig. 56 — PC Board Drawing

A—Via   B—Trace

Continued on next page   OUO1082,0001338 -19-04NOV11-1/2

CONSTRUCTION

Printed circuit boards are manufactured by a photographic process combined with acid etching of copper pathways.

After the boards are manufactured, components are added and soldered into place.

Printed circuit boards are relatively inexpensive for large numbers of devices and eliminate mistakes that could occur with hand wiring.

Problems include difficulty in repairing damaged pathways and great expense to modify circuit design once in production.

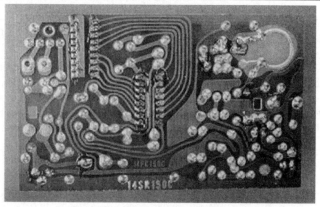

Fig. 57 — Lines of a Printed Circuit Board

OUO1082,0001338 -19-04NOV11-2/2

DISPLAY DEVICES

There are several types of display devices that are used in agricultural vehicles. We will spend some time discussing them.

ANALOG GAUGE

The most familiar type of display device is the analog gauge (Fig. 58). A varying signal causes a mechanical change in the position of a needle.

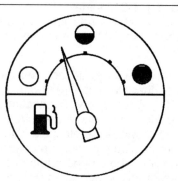

Fig. 58 — An Analog Fuel Gauge

OUO1082,0001339 -19-04NOV11-1/6

LIGHT-EMITTING DIODE (LED)

A light-emitting diode (LED) is a solid-state display device (Fig. 59). LEDs are self-illuminating, but have relatively high energy consumption, making them undesirable for some applications.

Fig. 59 — A Typical LED

Continued on next page   OUO1082,0001339 -19-04NOV11-2/6

LIQUID CRYSTAL DISPLAY (LCD)

Liquid crystal displays (LCDs) are used on modern machinery instrument panels to show data output from integrated circuits (Fig. 60).

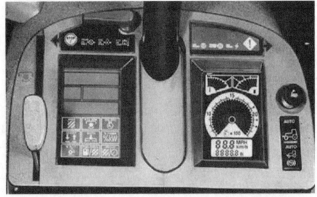

Fig. 60 — Instrument Panel of Liquid Crystal Displays

OUO1082,0001339 -19-04NOV11-3/6

LCDs use a special fluid medium to allow segmented displays (Fig. 61). When no current is applied to the conductive plates below and above the crystal fluid medium (E), the crystal elements float in random orientation.

Since LCDs do not provide their own light, only the relatively low power required to orient the crystals is consumed by their operation. For night operation, LCDs require some kind of illumination from behind.

There is a polarizing screen (B) above the crystal layer. Light can travel freely through the screen and the crystal, and be reflected by the mirror (D) at the bottom of the display back to the viewer.

When a signal turns on the plates for a segment, the crystals snap into alignment, the polarized light is polarized again at a 90° angle, and light no longer reaches the mirror. A dark segment forms.

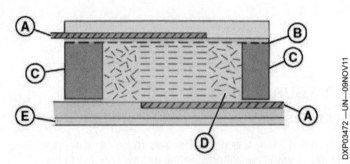

Fig. 61 — Side View of a Liquid Crystal Display

A—Conductor
B—Polarizing Screen
C—Spacer
D—Medium
E—Mirror

OUO1082,0001339 -19-04NOV11-4/6

VACUUM FLUORESCENT DISPLAY (VFD)

Vacuum fluorescent displays (VFDs) (Fig. 62) are instrument displays that give off their own light.

Fig. 62 — Panel Displaying a Vacuum Fluorescent Display

Continued on next page

OUO1082,0001339 -19-04NOV11-5/6

VFDs work in the manner of neon lights, where output data from integrated circuits directs streams of electrons to strike phosphorescent segments. Displayed information is controlled by turning on and off anodes below the phosphor coating (Fig. 63).

SUMMARY: DISPLAY DEVICES

An analog gauge operates by varying signals.

Light-emitting diodes are self-illuminating, but have high energy consumption.

Liquid crystal displays do not provide their own light and use low power to operate.

Vacuum fluorescent displays give off their own light and operate in the manner of neon lights.

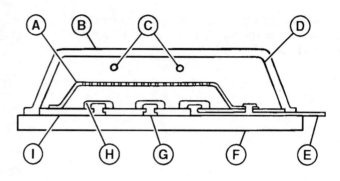

Fig. 63 — Side View of a Vacuum Fluorescent Display

A—Grid
B—Glass Face
C—Filament (Cathode)
D—Film Coating
E—Lead
F—Glass Substrate
G—Anode
H—Phosphor Coating
I— Insulating Layer

OUO1082,0001339 -19-04NOV11-6/6

TEST YOURSELF

QUESTIONS

1. (True or False) It is not necessary to be careful when working with low voltage because it will not hurt you.

2. (True or False) It is always necessary to ground all electronic equipment that you are working on at the bench.

3. (True or False) It is very difficult to identify ESD susceptible equipment and parts.

4. Integrated circuits use the _____ number system to produce _____ .

5. What are the building blocks of logic circuits called?

6. Using Fig. 17, Input the following values. R_1 and R_2 each equal 10 kΩ. The input is 8 VDC. What is the output?

7. (True or False) When the ENABLE input on a chip is active, it can not receive inputs.

8. (True or False) On an HC148, D_0 has a lower priority than D_7.

9. Using Fig. 47, the inputs on pins A–C of 74HC151 are 101 and pin 7 is 0. What data input would appear on the output?

10. (True or False) LCDs provide their own light.

(Answers are in the back of the textbook.))

OUO1082,000133A -19-16MAY11-1/1

Sensors

INTRODUCTION

DXP02716 —UN—23FEB11

16

DXP03498 —UN—24MAY11

In this chapter, we will discuss several kinds of sensors. Sensors are used in machinery for all types of monitoring and reading. The types of sensors we will discuss are these:

- Strain Gauges
- Pressure Sensors
- Temperature Sensors
- Proximity Sensors
- Flow Sensors
- Level Sensors
- Speed Sensors

OUO1082,0002CF7 -19-05APR12-1/1

STRAIN GAUGES

A strain gauge is an instrument that measures deformation (strain) of an object. The most common type is the bonded metallic strain gauge. This type of strain gauge uses a metallic foil that is etched onto a flexible backing. An adhesive is then used to attach the strain gauge to the object that will be measured.

The foil of the bonded metallic strain gauge relies on a change of resistive value which is proportional to the amount of deformation of the object. The foil of the strain gauge is included as one of the resistors of a Wheatstone bridge.

STRAIN GAUGE MEASUREMENT

In practice, the strain measurements rarely involve quantities larger than a few millistrain.

To measure such small changes in resistance, strain gauges are almost always used in a Wheatstone bridge.

A Wheatstone bridge (Fig. 1) consists of a power source (V_{EX}), four resistors equally divided into a two-branch parallel circuit and a voltage metering device (V_M) that connects the two parallel branches.

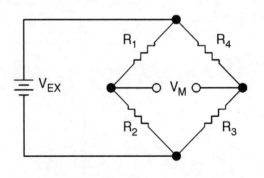

DXP03475 —UN—24MAY11

Fig. 1 — Wheatstone Bridge

When the resistance in the first parallel branch (R_1 and R_2) is equal to the resistance in the second parallel branch (R_3 and R_4), the V_M will indicate zero volts.

If we replace R_4 in Fig. 1 with an active strain gauge, any changes in the strain gauge resistance will cause a differential voltage between the two branches and a non-zero voltage output will result.

OUO1082,0002CF8 -19-04APR12-1/1

PRESSURE SENSORS

BELLOWS AND BOURDON TUBES

Bellows and bourdon tubes are mechanical devices that are used to mechanically measure pressure. A bellows is a sealed unit that will expand or contract as pressure or vacuum is applied. A bourdon tube is a long tube that is elliptical in shape. One end of the tube is connected to the pressure source and the other end is sealed. They typically are formed into a spiral or helical shape. As the pressure inside the bourdon tube changes, so does the shape of the tube.

POTENTIOMETRIC PRESSURE SENSORS

When a precision potentiometer is added to a bellows or boudon tube, a simple method for obtaining an electronic output from a mechanical pressure device is created. However, the mechanical nature of this sensor introduces unavoidable errors. Temperature effects cause additional errors because of the differences in thermal expansion coefficients of the metallic components of the system. Errors also develop due to mechanical wear of the components and of the contacts.

Potentiometric pressure sensors are inexpensive and can detect pressures between 5 and 10,000 psi. Their accuracy is between 0.5% and 1%, not including drift and the effects of temperature.

CAPACITIVE PRESSURE SENSORS

Capacitive pressure sensors have the ability to measure low pressures with high accuracy. These sensors rely on applied pressure to alter the distance between two electrodes of a capacitor, resulting in a change in capacitance. Generally, the position of one electrode is fixed while the second electrode moves in relation to the first electrode.

PIEZORESISTIVE PRESSURE SENSORS

Piezoresistive pressure sensors are currently more common than any other technology. They can handle pressure ranges between approximately 1.0 and 20,000 psi.

This type of pressure sensor consists of a piezoresistive strain gauge diffused onto a micro-machined silicon diaphragm. The piezoresistive material changes resistance when subjected to stress. This, in principal, is the same as a standard foil-type strain gauge. But a piezoresistive strain gauge is as much as 50 times more sensitive.

A signal conditioning circuit is used to compensate for offset, temperature variations and manufacturing. It is also used to amplify the output signal.

OUO1082,0002CF9 -19-10JAN12-1/1

TEMPERATURE SENSORS

There are generally three major categories of temperature sensors. They are thermocouples, resistance temperature detectors (RTDs) and thermistors.

THERMOCOUPLE SENSORS

A thermocouple consists of two dissimilar metals joined together at one end. When the junction of the two metals is heated or cooled, a voltage is produced that can be correlated back to the temperature.

RESISTANCE TEMPERATURE DETECTOR SENSORS (RTDS)

RTDs are wire wound and thin film devices that measure temperature because of the physical principle of the positive temperature coefficient of electrical resistance of metals. The hotter they become, the higher the value of their electrical resistance.

The most popular RTD is the platinum resistance temperature detector (PRTD). The PRTD is nearly linear over a wide range of temperatures, and some are small enough to have response times of a fraction of a second.

THERMISTOR SENSORS

A thermistor, like the RTD, is a temperature-sensitive resistor. However, the thermistor is much more sensitive. It exhibits, by far, the largest parameter change with temperature.

Thermistors can be divided into two different categories—negative temperature coefficient (NTC) and positive temperature coefficient (PTC).

- NTC thermistors will have their resistive values decrease as the sensing temperature increases.
- PTC thermistors will have their resistive values increase as the sensing temperature increases.

NTC THERMISTORS

NTC thermistors are temperature-dependent semiconductor resistors. They are manufactured from the oxides of transition metals—manganese, cobalt, copper and nickel. They can operate in a range of −200°C to +1000°C and are supplied in glass bead, disc, chip and probe formats.

The temperature coefficient (TC) for an NTC thermistor can be as large as several percent for each degree Celsius. This allows the NTC thermistor circuit to detect very small changes in temperature that could not be detected by a thermocouple or RTD.

NTCs are chosen when a continuous change of resistance is required over a wide temperature range. They offer mechanical, thermal and electrical stability, together with a high degree of sensitivity.

Performance and price has led to the extensive use of NTCs in applications such as temperature measurement and control, temperature compensation, surge suppression and fluid flow measurement.

PTC THERMISTORS

PTC thermistors are temperature-dependent resistors that are manufactured from barium titanate. They are used when a drastic change in resistance is required at a specific temperature or current level. PTCs can operate in the following modes:

- Temperature sensing, switching at temperatures ranging from 60°C to 180°C. Example: protection of windings in electric motors and transformers.
- Solid state fuse to protect against excess current levels, ranging from several milliamps to several amps (25°C ambient) and continuous voltages up to 600V and higher. Example: power supplies for a wide range of electrical equipment.
- Liquid level sensor.

OUO1082,0002CFA -19-10JAN12-1/1

PROXIMITY SENSORS

DXP03476 —UN—24MAY11

INDUCTIVE PROXIMITY SENSORS

Inductive proximity sensors are ideally used for virtually all metal-sensing applications. They operate under the principle of electromagnetic induction, which we covered in depth in Chapter 2. Construction of an inductive proximity sensor includes a coil, an oscillator, a detection circuit and an output circuit.

When current is introduced into the sensor, the oscillator creates a fluctuating magnetic field around the coil. Once a metal object moves into the sensor's range, a small voltage is built up in the metal object. The magnetic field created by the voltage in the metal object reduces the magnitude of the magnetic field from the coil and oscillator. The detection circuit will then send a signal to the output circuit once the oscillator has been sufficiently dampened.

CAPACITIVE PROXIMITY SENSORS

Capacitive proximity sensors can sense both metallic and non-metallic materials. They can also be adjusted to see through an object in order to sense another object behind the first one.

A capacitive proximity sensor generates an electrostatic field and detects changes in this field caused when a target approaches the sensing face.

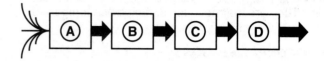

Fig. 2 — Block Diagram of a Capacitive Proximity Sensor

A—Probe
B—Oscillator
C—Rectifier Filter
D—Output Circuitry

The sensor consists of a capacitive probe, an oscillator, a signal rectifier, a filter circuit and an output circuit.

In the absence of a target, the oscillator is inactive. As a target approaches, it raises the capacitance of the probe system. When the capacitance reaches a specified threshold, the oscillator is activated. This triggers the output circuit to change between ON and OFF.

Continued on next page
OUO1082,0002CFB -19-04APR12-1/3

HALL-EFFECT SENSORS

The Hall-effect sensor relies on a magnetic field to sense motion. The principle is based on the Hall effect, which was discovered by Edwin H. Hall in 1879.

If current flows through a conductor within a magnetic field (Fig. 3), the magnetic field will exert a transverse force (a force at right angles) on the moving charge carriers, which tends to push them to one side of the conductor. This causes a small potential difference between the two sides, which can be measured.

Hall-effect sensors can sense either an external magnet or a ferrous object (metal object containing at least 50 percent iron).

PHOTOELECTRIC SENSORS

Photoelectric sensors are used in many applications and industries to provide accurate detection of objects without physical contact.

These sensors operate by sensing a change in the amount of light that is either reflected or blocked by an object to be detected. This change in light could be the result of the presence or absence of the target, or as the result in a change of the size, shape, reflectivity, or color of a target.

Photoelectric sensors operate effectively at distances from less than 5 mm (0.2 in.) to over 250 m (820 ft.).

Successful sensing with a photoelectric sensor requires the following must be clearly understood:

• The requirements
• The environment
• The specifications of the sensor

There are many factors that need to be considered when working with photoelectric sensors. They are:

• Form, reflectivity and opacity of the target
• Response time of the sensor
• Mounting requirements
• Physical requirements
• Load requirements such as voltage, current, load impedance
• Power requirements
• Ambient temperature
• Environmental conditions

There are a vast number of photoelectric sensors from which to choose. Each offers a unique combination of sensing, performance, output characteristics and mounting options. Many sensors also offer unique embedded logic or device networking capabilities.

This introduction will help you select the optimal photoelectric sensor for each application.

BASIC CONCEPTS AND COMPONENTS

There are four basic components to any photoelectric sensor:

1. Light source

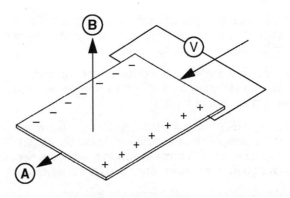

Fig. 3 — Hall Effect

A—Magnetic Field   B—Direction of conventional current flow

2. Light detector

3. Lens

4. Output switching device

LIGHT SOURCE

Different LED colors offer different desirable characteristics. Infrared LEDs are the most efficient; they generate the most light and the least heat of any LED color.

LIGHT DETECTOR

A photodiode or phototransistor is used as a detector for the infrared LED source.

Photodetectors are more sensitive to certain wavelengths of light. The response of the detector is in the 0.9 to 0.95 micron range.

The photodetector and associated circuitry are referred to as the receiver.

LENS

Lenses increase the sensing distance of photoelectric sensors. The light beam from an LED and lens combination is typically conical in shape. The area of the cone increases with distance.

OUTPUT SWITCHING DEVICE

Once the sensor has detected the target, an output device switches the electrical power in the user's control circuit. The output is either ON or OFF, making the sensor a digital device.

ULTRASONIC SENSORS

An ultrasonic proximity sensor works by transmitting ultrasonic (inaudible) pulses of sound. It then measures the length of time it takes those pulses to hit nearby objects and return as echos. The longer the time, the farther away the object.

Continued on next page   OUO1082,0002CFB -19-04APR12-2/3

The controller usually performs the counting and distance computations. The sensor takes care of transmitting and detecting the ultrasonic pulses.

The sensing range of an ultrasonic sensor can vary greatly among sensors. Typically, they can sense from just over 2 in. to about 32 ft.

A blind zone exists with ultrasonic sensors. This is an area that the sensor can't accurately detect the target object. The blind zone is immediately in front of the sensor and can range from approximately 6 to 80 centimeters.

The angle of the target with respect to the sensor must also be considered when working with ultrasonic sensors. The target must not deflect the signal from the sensor more than 3 degrees, or the signal will not echo back toward the sensor.

Certain environmental influences can affect the operational performance of the sensor. They are:

• Temperature—Most sensors can adjust for current temperature conditions.

• Pressure—The altitude at which the sensor is operated can affect performance. The speed of sound will change depending on atmospheric pressure. The sensor can be adjusted for the altitude at which it will be used.
• Humidity—The speed of sound increases as humidity increases. There is about a 2-percent change in velocity from dry air to humid air.
• Wind—Wind speeds under approximately 30 mph will have no effect. Wind speeds between about 31 and 62 mph can give erroneous results. Wind speeds over 62 mph will not allow the echo of the sensor to return toward the sensor.
• Precipitation—Rain or snow will not normally affect the sensor operation.
• Dust—Dusty environments can lower the range of the sensor 25 to 33 percent.
• Gas—Sensors are designed for the atmosphere in which they will be operated. If heavy concentrations of a different gas are present, measurement errors will result.

OUO1082,0002CFB -19-04APR12-3/3

AIRFLOW SENSORS

The most common airflow sensors are based on the following technologies:

- Vane
- Karman vortex
- Hot wire
- Thin film

VANE AIRFLOW SENSORS

The vane airflow sensor monitors the volume of air entering the engine by means of a spring-loaded mechanical flap. It also measures the temperature in order to determine the mass of air entering the engine. The flap is forced open by an amount of air that is proportional to the amount of air entering the engine. Attached to the flap is an arm that is also attached to a potentiometer. As the flap opens, the resistance of the potentiometer changes.

Vane airflow sensors are also vulnerable to dirt. Unfiltered air passing through a torn or poor-fitting air filter can allow dirt to build up on the flap shaft, causing the flap to bind or stick.

Some vane sensors have an anti-backfire valve built into the flap which is supposed to vent the explosion. But the anti-backfire valve itself can become a source of trouble if it leaks, because it can affect the air/fuel mixture.

KARMAN VORTEX AIRFLOW SENSORS

This airflow sensor relies on the Karman vortex principle. When air flows past a stationary object, a turbulence (vortex) is created behind the object. As the airflow increases, so does the turbulence.

A small object is placed in the path of the incoming air to generate turbulence. The turbulence is typically measured by the use of light or sound waves. The light or sound waves are passed at right angles to the airflow in order to detect changes in pressure at the vortex.

HOT WIRE AIRFLOW SENSORS

The hot wire airflow sensor uses an exposed wire (hot wire) and a thermistor that are both positioned within the airstream to be measured. The hot wire is heated to a constant temperature by an electronic control circuit. The thermistor measures the temperature of the incoming air.

As airflow is increased through the airflow sensor, more heat will dissipate from the hot wire. The electronic circuitry in the sensor will detect the heat loss in the hot wire and increase current to the hot wire in order to maintain a constant temperature.

To keep the hot wire clean and free from deposits, the wire is momentarily heated when the ignition is switched off to remove dirt deposits.

The electronic control circuit will monitor the current flow through the hot wire and put out a voltage signal that is proportional to the current flow.

THIN FILM AIRFLOW SENSORS

Thin film sensors contain thin film resistance temperature detectors (RTDs) in a Wheatstone-bridge arrangement. The RTDs are fabricated on a thin airfoil in order to minimize airflow disturbance and is more durable than hot wire sensors. Thin film sensors work by converting the temperature difference seen at each leg of the wheatstone bridge into an electrical signal.

Current is applied to the upstream leg of the bridge, which causes an increase in the temperature of that leg. The air passing over that leg has a cooling effect that reduces the leg's temperature and leads to reduced electrical resistance for that leg. The air, which has picked up the heat from the upstream leg, continues and passes over the downstream leg of the bridge. The heated air raises the temperature of this leg, which increases its electrical resistance. The resistance difference between the upstream and downstream legs unbalances the bridge, causing a voltage difference that can be amplified and calibrated to the airflow rate. Separate temperature sensors measure the temperature of the airflow and are used to complete the calculation for the mass of air passing by the sensor.

OUO1082,0002CFC -19-10JAN12-1/1

LEVEL SENSORS

The most common level sensors are based on the following technologies:

- Float
- Capacitive
- Ultrasonic

FLOAT LEVEL SENSORS

The float level sensor consists of a float, metal rod and variable resistor. The float is attached to the metal rod. At the other end of the metal rod is the variable resistor. The float follows the surface of the fluid as the fluid level in the tank changes. This causes the rod to move a wiper arm on the variable resistor, changing the resistance value of that resistor.

CAPACITIVE LEVEL SENSORS

Capacitive level sensors measure the capacitance between two electrodes immersed in a liquid or between one electrode and the electroconductive tank's wall.

Each type constitutes a capacitor having a capacitance, the value of which is dependent on both the liquid level and the dielectric constant of the liquid. The ratio of capacitance is proportional to the liquid level.

Capacitive level sensors can give erroneous readings if the fluid tank is tilted. Compensation for tilt angle of the tank can be provided through the addition of a second (or more) level sensor. Then an average of the capacitance values of the level sensors can be used to give an accurate fluid level reading.

Another cause of erroneous readings of capacitance sensors is the presence of contaminants in the tank. Contaminants, such as water in a fuel tank, can cause the capacitance reading in the tank to fluctuate drastically. Therefore, it is important to periodically check for and remove any water or other settled contaminates in the tank.

ULTRASONIC LEVEL SENSORS

Several sensing techniques are used in ultrasonic level sensors, including:

- Oscillations of quartz, ceramic or magnetostrictive elements at an ultrasound frequency have a greater amplitude in gas than in liquid. Wetting the elements causes a decrease in the amplitude, providing the detection of the liquid level.
- Point-level or continuous-level sensing is provided by measuring the time lapse between the transmission and reception of the ultrasound pulses generated by ceramic crystals at the bottom of the tank. Usually one crystal acts, alternately transmitting and receiving pulses that pass along the liquid height and are reflected from the surface back to the tank bottom. Some constructions contain separate elements for generating and receiving the pulses.
- A point-level detection is also performed by two piezoceramic crystals oriented toward each other across the inside of a tank. One of the crystals transmits ultrasonic waves and the other one receives them. The transmission is intensified when the liquid wets the crystals. The increase in the output voltage of the receiving crystal indicates that the level has reached the specific point.

OUO1082,0002CFD -19-10JAN12-1/1

SPEED SENSORS

Most conventional speed sensors are of the inductive or Hall-effect type. These sensors use gear teeth or a notch on a rotating shaft in order to detect the speed of the shaft. The signal is sent to the controller for various calculations, including wheel speed. Examples of conventional speed sensors are:

- Crankshaft speed sensors
- Camshaft speed sensors
- Transmission shaft speed sensors
- Wheel speed sensors

For more information on inductive or Hall-effect sensors, review Proximity Sensors earlier in this Chapter.

RADAR (RADIO FREQUENCY) SENSORS

The Doppler Radar Speed Sensor is used in vehicle ground speed and distance measurements. The sensor measures relative motion of the vehicle over the ground. The advantage of radar over conventional wheel rpm measuring systems is that the radar sensor gives accurate ground speed regardless of wheel slip.

Radar sensors emit radio beams that bounce off the ground. They compute ground speed based on the speed at which objects are passing in front of the sensor. Updates are extremely quick and radar sensors usually emit a pulse for every 0.3 inch of travel. Radar sensors will work in all temperature ranges, and dust does not affect the accuracy of the radar sensor.

The output of the sensor is a digital pulse. The frequency of the pulse can be used to determine vehicle speed, or the pulses can be added to determine distance traveled.

OUO1082,0002CFE -19-10JAN12-1/1

TEST YOURSELF

QUESTIONS

1. (True or False) Wheatstone Bridge circuits are used to measure small changes in resistance.

2. (True or False) The thermistor is a device for measuring temperature.

3. (True or False) An NTC thermistor's resistance increases with an increase in temperature.

4. (True or False) Inductive proximity sensors are ideally used for virtually all metal and non-metal sensing applications.

5. The Hall-effect sensor relies on a _____ _____ to sense _____.

6. What are the four basic components of any photoelectric sensor?

7. Thin film sensors work by converting the temperature difference seen at each leg of the _____ _____ into an _____ _____.

8. (True or False) Contaminants, such as water in a fuel tank, can cause the capacitance reading in a capacitive type fluid level sensor to fluctuate drastically.

(Answers are in the back of the textbook.)

OUO1082,0002CFF -19-10JAN12-1/1

INTRODUCTION

DXP02717 —UN—23FEB11

17

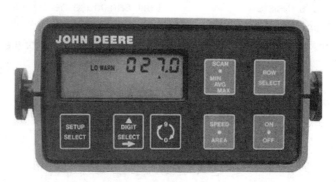

DXP03495 —UN—24MAY11

We will discuss two types of electronic devices: controllers and monitors.

- Controllers cause a particular function of a machine to operate in a programmed and automatic manner to help the operator obtain greater productivity from the machine.
  Some of the basic functions that controllers perform are the following:
  - Analog to digital conversion (A/D)
  - Digital to analog conversion (D/A)
  - Pulse width modulation (PWM)
  - Counters
  - Timers
  - Communications
  - Mathematics
- Monitors keep track of the performance of a function of the machine and signal the operator when something goes wrong.

In this chapter, we are going to examine each of the following in varying degrees of detail:

- Computer chip theory
- Port A operation
- Port B operation
- Port C operation
- Port D operation
- Port E operation
- Controller system theory
- CAN bus
- Serial buses
- Parallel buses
- Controller system applications
  – Tractors
- Monitor system applications
  – Combines
    • Grain loss monitors
    • Tachometer speed monitoring system
    • Low shaft speed monitoring system
  – Planter monitor
  – Round balers
    • Bale size-monitoring system
  – Tractors
    • Engine, hydraulic, and power train monitors
  – Motor graders
    • Automatic blade control system
  – Scrapers
    • Automatic transmission control system

OUO1082,0002D09 -19-04APR12-1/1

COMPUTER CHIP THEORY

Our discussion in this chapter will apply to a typical 8-bit processor with an 18-bit address bus. We will discuss the major sections of this microprocessor chip in general terms before we try to incorporate it into a controller. Most of them have the following areas:

- Control register
- Data register
- Address register
- Control unit
- Arithmetic logic unit
- Internal ROM
- Internal RAM
- X-register
- Y-register
- Accumulator
- Data bus
- Address bus
- Control bus

CONTROL REGISTER

A control register stores a control word made up of at least 4 bits. Some are larger than this in the 16-, 32-, and 64-bit processors. It contains signals like read (RD), write (WR), memory request (MREQ), interrupt (Int), and non-maskable interrupt (NMI).

DATA REGISTER

A data register (port) can be read from or written to. One of the ways of classifying microprocessors is by bus width. So an 8-bit controller would have a data bus 8 bits wide.

ADDRESS REGISTER

An address register (port) is as wide as the address bus. These are often separated into 8-bit segments for ease of hardware implementation. In other words, a 16-bit address bus would be implemented as two address ports (Port A and Port B).

CONTROL UNIT

A control unit deciphers the instructions that are being fetched by the control unit from the internal RAM or ROM memory sections.

ARITHMETIC LOGIC UNIT

The arithmetic logic unit (ALU) performs all mathematical and logic functions.

INTERNAL ROM

The internal ROM sections hold all of the program instructions (code) for the processor.

INTERNAL RAM

The internal RAM (scratchpad RAM) section holds all of the temporary instructions and data.

X-REGISTER

The X-register is a general-purpose register that holds one of the numbers used in an arithmetic or logic operation.

Y-REGISTER

The Y-register is a general-purpose register that holds the other number used in an arithmetic or logic operation.

ACCUMULATOR

The accumulator holds the result of the operation.

DATA BUS

The data bus is usually 8 or 16 bits wide and carries all of the data to the outside world and instructions to the control unit. Bus width is commonly indicated by a slash through the bus line and a number beside it denoting the bus width (8).

ADDRESS BUS

The address bus carries addresses to both the internal and the external memories and other devices.

CONTROL BUS

The control bus carries all control signals to the control register and the ALU.

Continued on next page

OUO1082,0002D0A -19-29OCT12-1/2

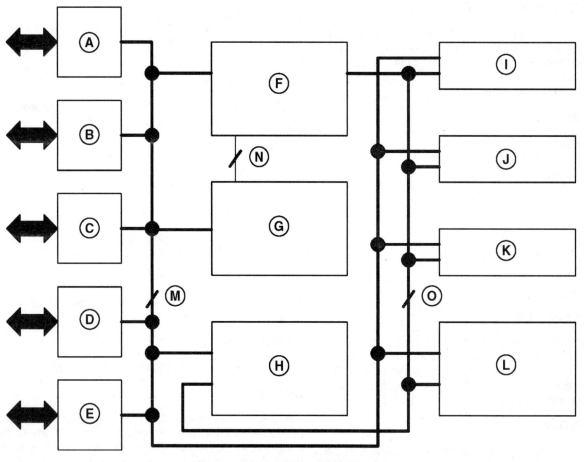

Fig. 1 — Microprocessor Block Diagram

A—I/O Port A 8 Bit	E—I/O Port E 4 Bit	I— X-Register	N—10 Internal Control Bus
B—I/O Port B 8 Bit	F—Control Unit	J— Y-Register	O—16 Internal Control Bus
C—I/O Port C 8 Bit	G—Arithmetic Logic Unit	K—Accumulator	
D—I/O Port D 8 Bit	H—Internal ROM	L—Internal RAM	
		M—8 Internal Control Bus	

Now that we have some sections of the chip defined, we can see how they work together (Fig. 1). The first task is to find out what to do! There is a starting address programmed in the internal ROM that tells the processor where to start looking for its program. This address varies with manufacturers, but the data sheet will always tell the programmer where it is. The control unit will read this address from the internal ROM (N) and place it in the address register. The control section will then issue a read command and the data at that external memory address is transferred to the data bus. This will usually be half of an address and is placed in one of the registers (X or Y). The address in the address register will be incremented by one and the other half of the address word read and placed in the unused register. The processor will then issue a jump command that sends the program to a different address, at the beginning of the program segment in memory (more about memory allocation later), to start processing the instructions.

As a simplified example, let us trace the operation of adding 2 to 4. We will assume the two numbers are stored at memory address 200h and 201h, respectively, and we wish to store the results at 202h. We will further assume that the start-up jump goes to address 100h.

1. Instruction at 100h tells the control unit (F) to read data at 200h and place it in the X-register (G).

2. Control unit increments to address 101h, which tells the control unit to read data at 201h and place it in the Y-register (J).

3. Control unit increments to 102h, which tells the control unit to instruct the ALU to add the X- and Y-registers and place the result in the accumulator (K).

4. Control unit increments to 103h, which tells the control unit to store the accumulator in address 202h.

5. Control unit increments to 104h, which tells the control unit to jump to a wait routine.

These instructions are written in a pseudo code, called mnemonics, by the software engineer. They are then compiled and linked to the system. They are then downloaded to, or programmed into, the system's memory. The mnemonics and the methods of compiling and linking vary, depending on manufacturer.

OUO1082,0002D0A -19-29OCT12-2/2

This will conclude the discussion of internal (to the chip) devices. For the rest of the chapter we will discuss only external buses and devices.

OUO1082,0002D0A -19-29OCT12-3/2

INTRODUCTION TO PORTS

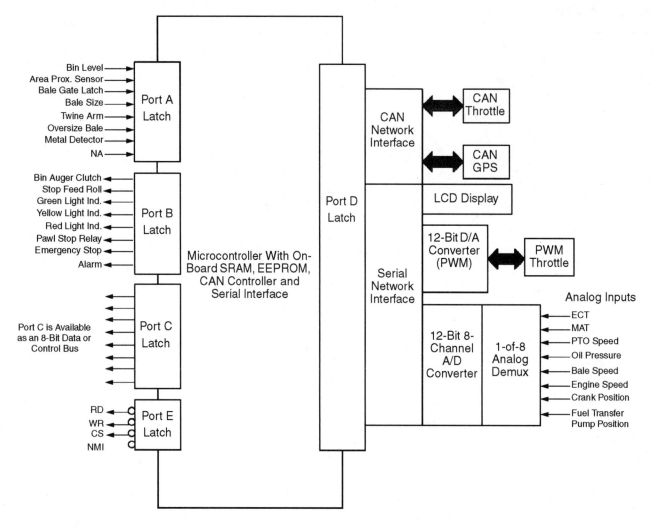

Fig. 2 — Example of a Controller

Ports are the way that microprocessors get and send information from the outside world. Most ports are configured as input or output purposes. Many ports will allow you to configure a nibble for input and a nibble for output. Some ports are dedicated to a single purpose, like control rather than being for general purpose (I/O). Each manufacturer allows different configurations of its ports, so it is very important to read the data sheet. We will discuss ports by using our theoretical controller system in Fig. 2. All of our ports are shown with the LSB at the top of the port.

PORT A OPERATION

Port A is set up as a digital latched input port. By monitoring this port, we can quickly check the status of our machine. Through the attached sensors we can learn if the grain bin is full, there is metal in the chopper feed, or the bale is oversized, to name just a few facts.

PORT B OPERATION

Port B is set up as a digital latched output port. The output acts as a driver chip so that the processor port would be protected from over-current and to boost the power of the signal. This would allow us to drive relays, solenoids, and indicator LEDs directly from the chip.

PORT C OPERATION

In our theoretical model, port C is not used. It would be available to use for any input or output function.

PORT D OPERATION

Port D is set up as two nibbles. One nibble is the CAN interface to which the CAN throttle controller and the GPS module are connected. The other nibble is the serial interface to which the LCD display, 12-bit A/D converter and 12-bit D/A converter are connected.

Continued on next page

OUO1082,0002D0B -19-15OCT12-1/4

PORT E OPERATION

Port E is set up as one control nibble. The pins are assigned to the following:

RD — the read command is an active low signal that tells the device connected to it that the controller chip desires to read data from the selected device.

WR — the write command is an active low signal that tells the device connected to it that the controller chip desires to write something to the selected device.

CS — the chip select command is an active low signal that tells the device connected to it that the controller chip desires to do something (read, write or disconnect from the bus) to that chip.

NMI — the non-maskable interrupt is an input to the processor that allows it to react to some type of process (engine over temp) that requires immediate action.

OUO1082,0002D0B -19-15OCT12-2/4

PORT I/O EXPANSION

There are times when the digital ports require expansion. For instance, by adding a couple of latching register chips to the port as indicated in Fig. 3, we can expand the data bus by two. A scheme like this would be used if you wished to control two entirely separate data bus structures that are independent from each other. Because one 74AC11244 has an inverter (74LS04) in its enabling pins, only one may be active at a time and the other will be in tri-state. Whatever data is in Port C will be sent out the active 74AC11244 and onto its data bus.

A—Port C   B—Port E

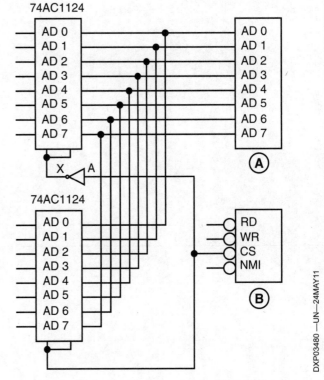

Fig. 3 — Digital Output Port Expansion Scheme (DIO Multiplexer)

Continued on next page
OUO1082,0002D0B -19-15OCT12-3/4

The expansion scheme in Fig. 4 controls 16 devices from Port C. In this case Port C would be set up to work with two nibbles. As an example, let us say we wanted to turn on whatever was connected to AD0 of the upper 74HC237 (Ô237). We would send an 8h (1000b) out the lower nibble of Port C. After a couple of processor clock cycles we would have port E issue a chip select. At this point the output of the inverter would go from low to high and the inputs to the upper AND gate would have two positive inputs so the output would go high. This would tell the Ô237 to latch the input address and we would get an active low signal on AD0 of the upper Ô237. It would remain there as long as the latch enable stayed high.

A—Port C   **B—Port E**

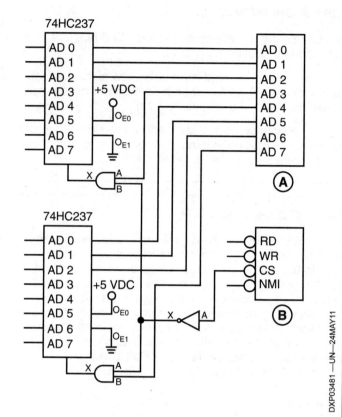

Fig. 4 — Another Digital Output Port Expansion Scheme (DIO Multiplexer)

OUO1082,0002D0B -19-15OCT12-4/4

110112
PN=516

CONTROLLER SYSTEM THEORY

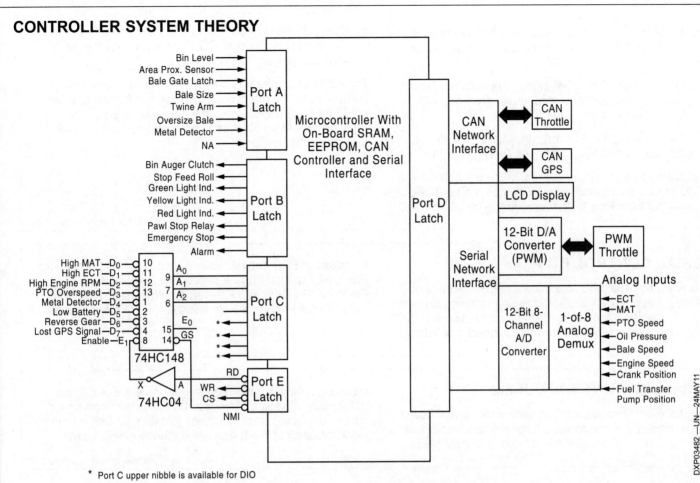

* Port C upper nibble is available for DIO

Fig. 5 — Typical Microcontroller System Block Diagram

The following discussion will be in reference to Fig. 5. The following assumptions were made about the microcontroller chip:

- Microcontroller has large enough on-board SRAM
- Microcontroller has large enough on-board EEPROM
- Microcontroller has on-board CAN controller
- Microcontroller has on-board serial interface
- Microcontroller has 4 on-board I/O ports
- Microcontroller has 1 on-board control port
- All ports are latched so that the output will stay there until it is changed

This is a theoretical layout and not supposed to duplicate the real one

Some general points regarding the general layout:

- Port A is configured as a digital input port
- Port B is configured as a digital output port
- Port C is available for any general use (DIO)
- Port D is divided into 2 nibbles, 1 for the CAN network and 1 for the serial interface
- Port E is configured as the control port

Computers and controllers are very fast at what they do, but they are very dumb. They can do nothing on their own and continuously have to be told what to do. This task usually falls to a piece of software called the operating system.

There are two basic types of operating systems. One is the normal system, which processes information as fast as it can. The second is the real-time operating system (RTOS) which is a very specialized system that handles events in real time. The former is the type found in most general-purpose computers like desktops, laptops, and hand helds. The latter is for controllers that are designed to do very specific tasks, such as monitoring machinery, fly aircraft and control factories.

Consider this for a moment: the metal detector in an agricultural harvester tells the controller that there is metal in the feeder. Upon receipt of this information, the controller acknowledges the information but does not have time to do anything about it for 5 seconds. In the meantime, the metal would have already passed, and, upon checking, the detector would find no metal present. So it just goes on doing what it was doing. This is not an acceptable condition for us. So we must rely on a controller with an RTOS so that it can work in real time.

Now the controller can react to the above situation in the following manner. This is a very simplistic explanation because the way that it does this in software is very complicated and beyond the scope of this manual.

1. The metal detector will send a signal to the priority encoder connected to Port C.

Continued on next page

OUO1082,0002D0C -19-04APR12-1/2

2. The 74HC148 encoder would send an interrupt signal on GS pin 14 to the non-maskable interrupt pin of Port E.

3. Upon receipt of the NMI signal, the software would cause the processor to execute instructions at a special address set aside for NMI.

4. The first thing that the software would do is decode the address on pins 6(L), 7(H), and 9(H) of the 74HC148.

5. This address (3h) would then cause the software to jump to a subroutine that would stop the feed belt with a signal from Port B and remove the metal from it.

6. The subroutine would then check to see that the interrupt was cleared, GS pin is high, and the metal detector pin on Port A is high.

From this example, you can see how microcontrollers are interfaced to the real world and how a software solution could be implemented to solve these problems. The thinking processes of these controllers have to be built into the software.

OUO1082,0002D0C -19-04APR12-2/2

SERIAL CONTROL BUSES

The RS-232 serial bus was one of the first means of communications with applications or processes outside of the immediate control system. It is slow, usually 19.2 kbps, and very susceptible to noise. It had a practical limitation of 50 ft. maximum line length. It has pretty much given way to faster, more secure systems such as USB, FireWire, RS-485, and RS-422 architectures. However, most of these schemes are not suitable for off-road use.

OUO1082,0002D0D -19-10JAN12-1/1

PARALLEL CONTROL BUSES

About the only real application of parallel control buses these days is the centronics printer port on a computer or controller. The parallel control bus is largely being replaced by the smaller and faster universal serial bus (USB) bus. This is an important consideration on small controller boards because there just is not much room to incorporate all of the hardware on these small boards.

OUO1082,0002D0E -19-10JAN12-1/1

CAN BUS

The controller area network (CAN) is a serial communications protocol that efficiently distributes real-time control (data) with great data integrity. In other words, it efficiently sends and receives data in a binary code between controllers.

In Chapter 16 we looked at the physical CAN chips. Now we are going to explore the CAN bus in more detail. The controller area network (CAN) controller has 7 defined layers, which we will name and define each function, so that you will have a fuller understanding of how the CAN bus works. The International Organization for Standardization (ISO) Open Systems Interconnect (OSI) defines these layers.

1. Physical Layer — defines the electrical and mechanical characteristics of the communications system.

2. Data Link Layer — controls and protects communication on a frame level.

3. Network Layer — controls the logical communications through a physical communications system.

4. Transport Layer — controls the packeted information exchange between two applications.

5. Session Layer — is responsible for the synchronization between the communicating applications.

6. Presentation Layer — transforms data to an application independent form.

7. Application Layer — provides the interface to the actual application requesting communication.

In (Fig. 6) is a visual summary of the seven CAN-bus layers. CAN bus is very fast at 500 kilobits per second (500 kbps) and can address as many as 63 nodes (sensors) on one bus. It is very rugged and not susceptible to outside noise and interference, making it ideal for use on off-road machines, trucks, buses and automobiles. Many microcontroller chips have a CAN-bus interface onboard, making it very easy to implement in software applications.

CAN SYSTEM HARDWARE INFORMATION

All controllers within a CAN bus system continually carry broadcast data while the system is energized. Some controllers broadcast more frequently than others, depending on the type of data.

There are typically four wires involved in the CAN bus system. They are:

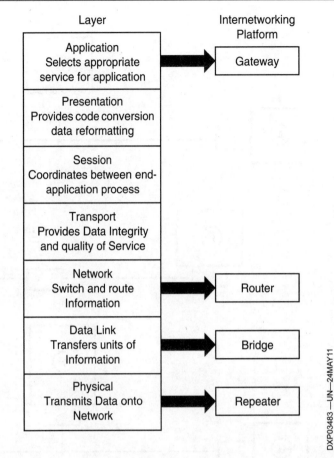

Fig. 6 — ISO/OSI CAN Layers

- CAN– (also called CAN lo)
- CAN+ (also called CAN hi)
- 12V Power wire
- Ground wire

Communications are sent on the CAN lo and CAN hi wires. These wires are protected from electromagnetic interference by twisting them together. The other two wires are the power supply and ground.

Terminating resistors are located at the beginning and end of the CAN-bus communication lines. Terminating resistors are required to reduce faults in the communication lines. There are two types of terminating resistors: the 6-terminal (active type) and 4-terminal (passive type). The two types have the same layout, serve the same function, and are interchangeable. The 6-terminal type resistor has a 12V switched and a ground circuit that allows the active terminator to set up the other CAN-bus lines.

Continued on next page

OUO1082,0002D0F -19-29OCT12-1/4

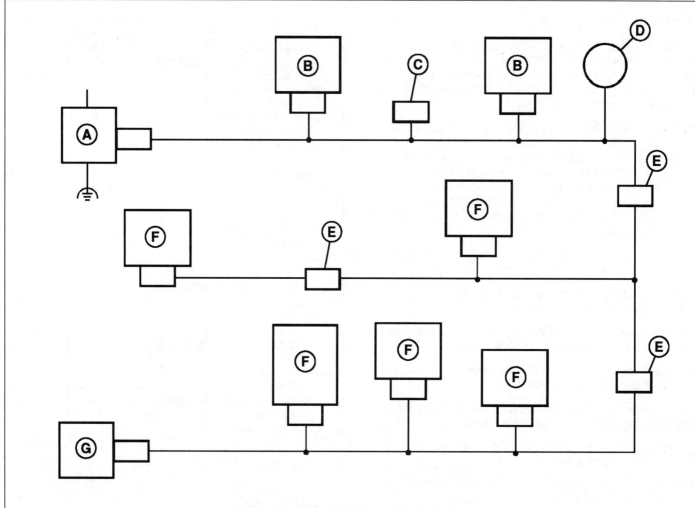

Fig. 7 — Typical CAN Network Block Diagram

A—CAN Active Terminator	C—Optional Display Connector	E—Interconnect
B—Display	D—Diagnostic Port	F—Control Unit
		G—CAN Passive Terminator

CAN SYSTEM SOFTWARE INFORMATION

Basically, electronic control units consist of two elements:

- Electronic control unit
- Interface controller

The electronic control unit is fully occupied with performing its tasks, such as receiving inputs from sensors and sending signals to drive relays, solenoids, and indicator LEDs.

The interface controller manages the vast amount of data that is broadcast and recalled via the CAN-bus communication lines. The data it passes on to the electronic control unit is only the data that the control unit actually requires.

The electronic control units share their monitoring, operational, and display data with each other by continually broadcasting it on the CAN-bus line.

Continued on next page

OUO1082,0002D0F -19-29OCT12-2/4

DXP03484 —UN—22OCT12

In CAN-bus systems, addresses are allocated according to the importance of the data. In order to transmit data on the CAN-bus system, a data frame (A) is required. The data frame consists of seven fields.

The start signal (B) indicates the start of the data frame and synchronizes all the electronic control units. (This will be low voltage for a set time.)

The assignment field (C) consists of an identifier and a control bit.

• The identifier indicates the priority according to the data. During transmission of this field, the sender checks that it has the right to transmit, or if priority should be given to another electronic control unit.
• The control bit indicates whether the data is a question or answer.

The control field (D) contains information of the size of the data in the data field. It lets the other controllers know the length of the message.

The data field (E) contains the actual data.

The cyclic redundancy check (CRC) field (F) is used to check for any errors that may occur in transmission. This field contains a code name. This code name must be known by every electronic control unit.

The acknowledgment field (G) contains the acceptance signals from data that has been received without error by the various electronic control units (it keeps track that the message was received okay.)

The end signal (H) lets the other controllers know the message is finished.

The sending electronic control unit initiates a data transfer by sending a data frame. However, the receiving electronic control unit can also request data from the sender. To do this, the receiver issues a request. Request (question) and answer both have the same identifier. The only difference is in the control bit.

An acceptance check is carried out within the electronic control units. This means that only data with an identifier stored in a list is actually accepted by the control units. The code numbers that are otherwise required for data transmission are thus eliminated.

The identifier determines the priority with which the data is transmitted. Each electronic control unit can transmit its data, provided the CAN communication lines are free. If several want to transmit at the same time, the data sent first is the one with the highest priority. The other electronic control units then go automatically to

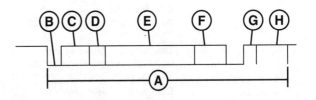

Fig. 8 — Data Frame

A—Data Frame
B—Start Signal
C—Assignment Field
D—Control Field
E—Data Field
F—Cyclic Redundancy Check (CRC) Field
G—Acknowledgment Field
H—End Signal

the receive mode and do not send their data until the CAN-bus communication lines are free.

If a malfunction is registered, the electronic control unit interrupts the current transmission. The electronic control units are capable of telling the difference between malfunctions that persist. This is achieved by making a statistical assessment of the error situation.

Diagnostic trouble codes (DTCs) that are generated by the control unit are based on the CAN ISO and J1939 SAE standards. These are worldwide standards for automotive and off-highway vehicles and are controlled by an ISO industry committee. They set up the definition of the codes. Two main parts provide a DTC:

SPN (suspect parameter number) — This is intended to identify where the problem exists. An example is "94," which the standard defines as "fuel delivery system." All automotive and off-highway vehicles using the "94" in the DTC will therefore be defining a problem with the fuel delivery system. The list of possible SPNs is too large to provide here, but basically, codes assigned lower numbers, currently below about 5000, are assigned numbers that are set standards. SPNs that contain 6 digits, such as 524255, are called proprietary and are set up in blocks (such as 520,000–540,000) might be assigned to John Deere to use for parameters that are not already defined. At some point, if these proprietary numbers are approved by SAE and the CAN committee, they may be assigned a lower number and become available industry-wide.

FMI (failure mode indicator) — This is a standard set of numbers that defines how the SPN failed. FMIs are defined by the J1939 standard as:

Continued on next page

OUO1082,0002D0F -19-29OCT12-3/4

Table 1 — Failure Mode Indicators	
00	Data valid but above normal operating range — most severe level
01	Data valid but below normal operational range — most severe level
02	Data erratic, intermittent or incorrect
03	Voltage above normal, or shorted to high source
04	Voltage below normal, or shorted to low source
05	Current below normal or open circuit
06	Current above normal or grounded circuit
07	Mechanical system not responding or out of adjustment
08	Abnormal frequency or pulse width or period
09	Abnormal update rate
10	Abnormal rate of change
11	Root cause not known
12	Bad intelligent device or component
13	Out of calibration
14	Special instructions
15	Data valid but above normal operating range — least severe level
16	Data valid but above normal operating range — moderately severe level
17	Data valid but below normal operating range — least severe level
18	Data valid but below normal operating range — moderately severe level
19	Received network data in error
20—30	Reserved for SAE assignment
31	Too long

By assigning the SPN and FMI, the code 94.03 would mean the fuel delivery system input voltage is high. With the universal standard, this would apply to any CAN vehicle, whether a car, a tractor, or a combine.

OUO1082,0002D0F -19-29OCT12-4/4

TRACTOR CAN BUS CONTROLLER SYSTEM APPLICATIONS

ELECTRO-HYDRAULIC CONTROLLER GENERAL INFORMATION

The electro-hydraulic controller (EHC) (A) is a single box that houses software for various applications. It is mounted on the inner side of the left fender and is used only on machines with PowrReverser™ transmissions. Besides controlling operation of the PowrReverser™ transmission, the EHC controls the following options:

- Electro-Hydraulic (EH) Hitch
- EH PTO
- EH MFWD

Fig. 9 — *Electro-Hydraulic Controller*

A—Electro-Hydraulic Controller (EHC)

PowrReverser is a trademark of Deere & Company

Continued on next page

OUO1082,0002D10 -19-15OCT12-1/6

Either Service ADVISOR™ (A) or a performance monitor (B) can be connected to the EHC via the Service ADVISOR™ connector located in the left console for isolated open operator station and cab tractors and behind the VEC cover located next to the left foot plate on straddle mount tractors. These devices provide access to the diagnostic trouble codes (DTC) stored by the EHC. They also provide access to a list of addresses for viewing current controller inputs and outputs and also for calibration purposes.

The stored DTCs and addresses within the EHC are divided by software applications. The following is a list of acronyms for these software applications and the functions they control:

- CCU — Central Control Unit. This software controls sensor excitation, hydraulic oil temperature and optional EH PTO and EH MFWD operation.
- HCU — Hitch Control Unit. This software controls the optional EH Hitch.
- PTR — Power Train Reverser Control Unit. This software controls the PowrReverser™ Transmission.

NOTE: There are no addresses associated with the performance monitor (PRF). DTCs associated with the performance monitor should be ignored. They do not indicate any problems with the tractor or EHC. They are simply communication faults between the EHC and performance monitor such as turning the key switch on and off.

DIAGNOSTIC TROUBLE CODE LISTING

The electro-hydraulic controller monitors certain electrical circuits for which it is responsible. The controller then stores a relevant diagnostic trouble code (DTC) if there is a malfunction (error) or if the operator makes a mistake. However, not all of the diagnostic trouble codes indicate a current problem, since most of the circuits are monitored only at the actual moment of activation or when they are actually activated (switched on). To make sure that the diagnostic trouble code you are troubleshooting is active, you should proceed as follows:

1. Access diagnostic trouble codes.

2. Note and clear the diagnostic trouble code(s).

3. Activate the circuit affected (functional check).

4. Access the diagnostic trouble codes again and diagnose any problems.

If it is not possible to reproduce a relevant diagnostic trouble code by means of a functional check and the problem is still present in the circuit, diagnose the codes you noted earlier.

RECOVERY FAULT TYPES

If the PTR detects a problem, a diagnostic trouble code will be stored and one of the following fault conditions will occur:

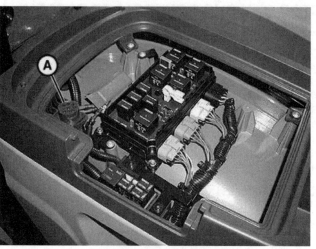

Fig. 10 — Service ADVISOR™

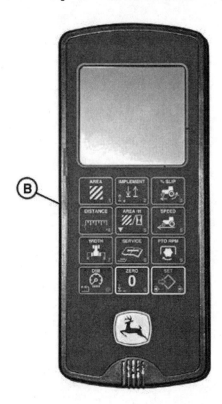

Fig. 11 — Performance Monitor

A—Service ADVISOR™ Connector   B—Performance Monitor

- Neutral Recoverable Fault (NR) — This fault will force the transmission to the NEUTRAL position, and will be canceled when the reverser lever is returned to neutral.
- Power-up Recoverable Fault (PuR) — This fault will force the transmission to NEUTRAL position, and cannot be canceled until the tractor is restarted.

Continued on next page   OUO1082,0002D10 -19-15OCT12-2/6

- **Recoverable Fault** — This fault will store a diagnostic trouble code and illuminate the appropriate light. Once the fault no longer exists, the light will go out, but the DTC will remain stored.
- **Miscellaneous Fault** — This fault will not force the transmission to neutral.

Choose from the following list for the desired controller DTCs:

- PRF Code List
- CCU Code List
- HCU Code List
- PTR Code List

PRF CODE LIST

NOTE: These codes represent a communication fault detected by the Performance Monitor during certain transient conditions such as turning the key switch on or off. These codes are to be ignored. They do not indicate a problem with the tractor or the EHC controller and will not cause any problems.

Table 2 — PRF Diagnostic Trouble Codes

TLA	DTC	Description
PRF	000639.13	CAN Warning Limit Exceeded
PRF	000639.19	CAN Data Received in Error

CCU CODE LIST

Table 3 — CCU Diagnostic Trouble Codes

TLA	DTC	Description	Recovery Type	Fault Indicator
CCU	000629.12	CCU Control Unit Fault	Miscellaneous	None
CCU	000639.12	CAN Lost Message	Miscellaneous	None
CCU	000639.14	CCU CAN Error Limit Exceeded	Miscellaneous	None
CCU	001638.00	Hydraulic Oil Temperature Very Hot	Miscellaneous	Hydraulic Oil Temperature Light
CCU	001638.03	Hydraulic Oil Temperature Sensor Circuit Voltage High	Miscellaneous	Hydraulic Oil Temperature Light
CCU	001638.04	Hydraulic Oil Temperature Sensor Circuit Voltage Low	Miscellaneous	Hydraulic Oil Temperature Light
CCU	001883.00	Rear PTO Overspeed (Disabled)	Miscellaneous	None
CCU	001883.01	Rear PTO Underspeed	Miscellaneous	None
CCU	523922.31	Not Currently Used	Miscellaneous	None
CCU	524016.04	CCU Switched Supply Voltage Low	Miscellaneous	None
CCU	524037.02	MFWD Switch Circuit Fault	Miscellaneous	None
CCU	524224.14	Rear PTO Disabled	Miscellaneous	None
CCU	524235.05	MFWD Solenoid Circuit Fault	Miscellaneous	None
CCU	524252.05	Rear PTO Solenoid Circuit Fault	Miscellaneous	None
CCU	600006.31	Default DTC	—	—

HCU CODE LIST

Table 4 — HCU Diagnostic Trouble Codes

TLA	DTC	Description	Recovery Type	Fault Indicator
HCU	000158.04	HCU Switched Supply Voltage Low	Recoverable	Hitch
HCU	000168.04	HCU Unswitched Supply Voltage Low	Recoverable	HCU
HCU	000190.02	Rear Hitch Calibration Fault/Engine Speed Low	Calibration	HCU
HCU	000629.12	HCU Control Unit Fault	Power-Up Recoverable	HCU
HCU	000630.13	HCU Calibration Fault/Not Calibrated	Calibrate	HCU
HCU	001079.03	HCU Sensor Supply Voltage High	Power-Up Recoverable	HCU

Continued on next page OUO1082,0002D10 -19-15OCT12-3/6

Table 4 — HCU Diagnostic Trouble Codes

TLA	DTC	Description	Recovery Type	Fault Indicator
HCU	001079.04	HCU Sensor Supply Voltage Low	Power-Up Recoverable	HCU
HCU	001638.02	HCU Calibration Fault/Hydraulic Oil Temperature Low	Calibration	HCU
HCU	001873.03	Rear Hitch Position Sensor Circuit Voltage High	Power-Up Recoverable	HCU
HCU	001873.04	Rear Hitch Position Sensor Circuit Voltage Low	Power-Up Recoverable	HCU
HCU	001873.13	HCU Calibration Fault/Rear Hitch Position Sensor Circuit	Calibrate	HCU
HCU	001881.03	Rear Hitch Draft Sensor Circuit Voltage High	Power-Up Recoverable	HCU
HCU	001881.04	Rear Hitch Draft Sensor Circuit Voltage Low	Power-Up Recoverable	HCU
HCU	001881.13	HCU Calibration Fault/Rear Hitch Draft Sensor Circuit	Calibrate	HCU
HCU	521000.02	Rear Hitch External Switch Circuit Fault	Power-Up Recoverable	HCU
HCU	521000.31	Rear Hitch External Switch Circuit Fault	Power-Up Recoverable	HCU
HCU	521001.02	HCU Calibration Fault/Rear Hitch Raise Valve Gain	Calibration	HCU
HCU	521001.05	Rear Hitch Raise Solenoid Current Low	Power-Up Recoverable	HCU
HCU	521001.06	Rear Hitch Raise Solenoid Current High	Power-Up Recoverable	HCU
HCU	521001.07	HCU Calibration Fault/Rear Hitch Raise Valve	Calibrate	HCU
HCU	521001.11	HCU Calibration Fault/Rear Hitch Raise Valve	Calibrate	HCU
HCU	521001.13	HCU Calibration Fault/Rear Hitch Raise Valve	Calibrate	HCU
HCU	521002.05	Rear Hitch Lower Solenoid Current Low	Power-Up Recoverable	HCU
HCU	521002.06	Rear Hitch Lower Solenoid Current High	Power-Up Recoverable	HCU
HCU	521002.07	HCU Calibration Fault/Rear Hitch Lower Valve	Calibrate	HCU
HCU	521002.11	HCU Calibration Fault/Rear Hitch Lower Valve	Calibrate	HCU
HCU	521002.13	HCU Calibration Fault/Rear Hitch Lower Valve	Calibrate	HCU
HCU	523832.03	Rear Hitch Rate-of-Drop Sensor Circuit Voltage High	Power-Up Recoverable	HCU
HCU	523832.04	Rear Hitch Rate-of-Drop Sensor Circuit Voltage Low	Power-Up Recoverable	HCU
HCU	523833.03	Rear Hitch Height-Limit Sensor Circuit Voltage High	Power-Up Recoverable	HCU
HCU	523833.04	Rear Hitch Height-Limit Sensor Circuit Voltage Low	Power-Up Recoverable	HCU
HCU	523834.03	Rear Hitch Control Lever Sensor Circuit Voltage High	Power-Up Recoverable	HCU
HCU	523834.04	Rear Hitch Control Lever Sensor Circuit Voltage Low	Power-Up Recoverable	HCU
HCU	523834.13	Hitch Calibration Fault/Hitch Control Lever	Calibrate	HCU
HCU	523842.03	Rear hitch Load/Depth Sensor Circuit Voltage High	Power-Up Recoverable	HCU

Continued on next page

OUO1082,0002D10 -19-15OCT12-4/6

Table 4 — HCU Diagnostic Trouble Codes

TLA	DTC	Description	Recovery Type	Fault Indicator
HCU	523842.04	Rear hitch Load/Depth Sensor Circuit Voltage Low	Power-Up Recoverable	HCU
HCU	523843.02	Rear Hitch Raise/Lower Switch Circuit Fault	Power-Up Recoverable	HCU
HCU	523910.02	HCU Control Unit Fault	Calibrate	HCU
HCU	523952.31	Rear Hitch Disabled/HCU Configuration	Calibrate	HCU
HCU	524016.04	HCU Switched Supply Voltage Low/Rear Hitch Solenoids	Recoverable	HCU

PTR CODE LIST

Table 5 — PTR Diagnostic Trouble Codes

TLA	DTC	Description	Recovery Type	Fault Indicator
PTR	000162.02	Hi/Lo Switch Circuit Conflict	Miscellaneous	Transmission
PTR	000162.30	Hi/Lo Switch Stuck On	Miscellaneous	Transmission
PTR	000168.01	PTR Unswitched Supply Voltage Low	Neutral Recoverable	Transmission
PTR	000190.18	Engine Speed Low	Neutral Recoverable	Neutral
PTR	000191.00	Transmission Overspeed During Calibration	Neutral Recoverable	Transmission
PTR	000191.17	Transmission Underspeed	Neutral Recoverable	Transmission
PTR	000598.02	Clutch Disengaged Switch/Clutch Pedal Sensor Circuit Conflict	Neutral Recoverable	Transmission
PTR	000598.04	Clutch Disengaged Switch/Transmission Enable Sensor Circuit Conflict	Miscellaneous	Transmission
PTR	000628.02	EOL Data Fault	Power-Up Recoverable	Transmission
PTR	000630.07	PTR Calibration Fault/Tractor Movement	Neutral Recoverable	Transmission
PTR	000630.14	PTR Not Calibrated	Miscellaneous	Transmission
PTR	000734.05	Forward Solenoid Circuit Fault	Neutral Recoverable	Transmission
PTR	000735.05	Reverse Solenoid Circuit Fault	Neutral Recoverable	Transmission
PTR	000736.05	Hi/Lo Solenoid Circuit Fault	Miscellaneous	Transmission
PTR	000752.03	Shuttle Sensor Circuit Voltage High	Miscellaneous	Transmission
PTR	000752.04	Shuttle Sensor Circuit Voltage Low	Miscellaneous	Transmission
PTR	001079.03	Sensor Reference Circuit Voltage High	Neutral Recoverable	Transmission
PTR	001079.04	Sensor Reference Circuit Voltage Low	Neutral Recoverable	Transmission
PTR	001504.30	Seat Switch Circuit Fault	Miscellaneous	Transmission
PTR	523959.31	Operator Left Seat With Directional Reverser Lever in Gear	Neutral Recoverable	Transmission
PTR	523960.31	Operator Not Seated During a Directional Reverser Lever Command	Neutral Recoverable	Transmission
PTR	524017.07	Gearshift Lever in Park With Directional Reverser Lever in Gear	Neutral Recoverable	Transmission
PTR	524020.31	Directional Reverser Lever in Gear at Power-Up	Neutral Recoverable	Transmission

Continued on next page   OUO1082,0002D10 -19-15OCT12-5/6

	Table 5 — PTR Diagnostic Trouble Codes			
TLA	**DTC**	**Description**	**Recovery Type**	**Fault Indicator**
PTR	524021.31	Directional Reverser Lever Switch Circuit Fault	Neutral Recoverable	Transmission
PTR	524029.02	Clutch Pedal Sensor Circuit Conflict	Neutral Recoverable	Transmission
PTR	524029.15	Clutch Pedal Sensor Circuit Voltage High	Miscellaneous	Transmission
PTR	524029.16	Clutch Pedal Sensor Circuit Voltage High, NR	Neutral Recoverable	Transmission
PTR	524029.17	Clutch Pedal Sensor Circuit Voltage Low	Miscellaneous	Transmission
PTR	524029.18	Clutch Pedal Sensor Circuit Voltage Low, NR	Neutral Recoverable	Transmission
PTR	524060.03	Transmission Enable Signal High During Operation	Power-Up Recoverable	Transmission
PTR	524060.04	Transmission Enable Signal Low During Operation	Neutral Recoverable	Transmission
PTR	524081.31	Come-Home Mode Active	Power-Up Recoverable	Neutral
PTR	524160.02	Not Neutral Signal Conflicts With Neutral Signal	Neutral Recoverable	Neutral
PTR	524230.05	Enable Solenoid Circuit Fault	Neutral Recoverable	Neutral
PTR	524230.07	Enable Valve Stuck Open	Power-Up Recoverable	Neutral
PTR	524234.03	Enable Pressure Sensor Circuit Voltage High	Miscellaneous	Transmission
PTR	524234.04	Enable Pressure Sensor Circuit Voltage Low	Miscellaneous	Transmission
PTR	600006.31	Default DTC	—	—

Service ADVISOR is a trademark of Deere & Company

OUO1082,0002D10 -19-15OCT12-6/6

CONTROL UNIT ADDRESSES

Choose from the following list for desired controller addresses:

- CCU Address List
- HCU Address List
- PTR Address List

Addresses are divided by display type. The following are a list of display types and their meanings.

- Display: Indicates that the address is for display only. No entry is ever allowed at the address.

- Beep: Indicates that the address is for display only and will generate an audible beep when the displayed value changes quickly.

NOTE: Tech mode is entered by entering into diagnostic mode within five seconds after powering up the performance monitor.

- Tech: Indicates that address will allow technician entry in technician diagnostic mode.
- Cal: Indicates that address will allow interactive calibration in technician diagnostic mode.
- Input: Indicates that address will allow entry in operator or technician diagnostic mode.

CCU ADDRESS LIST

		Table 6 — CCU Address List	
TLA	Address	Address Type	Description
CCU	000	—	Initial Address/EOL Programming
CCU	001	—	Recall/Clear Stored Diagnostic Trouble Codes
CCU	002	Beep	CCU System Beep Mode With Speed Sensors
CCU	003	Beep	CCU System Beep Mode Without Speed Sensors[a]
CCU	004	Beep	Engine and Rear PTO Speed Sensor Status
CCU	005	Beep	Wheel and True Vehicle Speed Sensor Status[b]
CCU	006	Beep	Rear PTO Switch Status
CCU	007	Beep	MFWD Switch Status
CCU	008	Beep	Secondary Hand Brake Switch, Left Brake Switch, Right Brake Switch-Status[c]
CCU	009	Beep	Sensor Supply Status
CCU	010	Beep	Hydraulic Oil Temperature Sensor Voltage
CCU	030	Display	System Voltage
CCU	031	Display	CCU Sensor Supply Voltage
CCU	032	Display	Engine Speed
CCU	033	Display	Rear PTO Speed
CCU	034	Display	Wheel Speed
CCU	035	Display	True Vehicle Speed[b]
CCU	036	Display	Hydraulic Oil Temperature
CCU	060	Input	MFWD Configuration
CCU	061	Input	Rear PTO Setup #1
CCU	062	Input	Rear PTO Setup #2
CCU	063	Input	Engine Pulses Per Revolution Configuration
CCU	064	Input	Rear PTO Pulses Per PTO Shaft Revolution Configuration
CCU	065	Input	Wheel Speed Pulses Per Axle Revolution Configuration
CCU	066	Input	Tire Rolling Circumference Configuration
CCU	067	Input	Radar Sensor Speed Configuration[b]
CCU	069	Input	Diagnostic Code Purge Setting
CCU	223	Display	Second EOL Software Part Number
CCU	224	Display	Second EOL Software Version Number
CCU	225	Display	Software Part Number Configuration
CCU	226	Display	Software Version Number Configuration
CCU	227	Display	CCU Boot Block Program Part Number
CCU	228	Display	CCU Boot Block Program Version Number
CCU	229	Display	EOL Software Part Number

[a]Address 3 is identical to address 2 except that engine speed, wheel speed and PTO speed are not included in address 3. This is eliminate the intrusion of frequency inputs when trying to troubleshoot problems with the engine running.
[b]True Vehicle Speed is not currently available.

Continued on next page OUO1082,0002D11 -19-10JAN12-1/4

[c]*Secondary Hand Brake is not currently available.*

HCU ADDRESS LIST

Table 7 — HCU Address List

TLA	Address	Address Type	Description
HCU	001	—	Recall/Clear Stored Diagnostic Trouble Codes
HCU	002	Beep	HCU System Beep Mode
HCU	005	Beep	Rear Hitch Draft Sensor Voltage
HCU	006	Beep	Rear Hitch Load/Depth Mix Control Voltage
HCU	007	Beep	Rear Hitch Control Lever Voltage
HCU	008	Beep	Rear Hitch Position Sensor Voltage
HCU	009	Beep	Rear Hitch Height-Limit Control Voltage
HCU	010	Beep	Rear Hitch Rate-of-Drop Control Voltage
HCU	011	Beep	Rear Raise/Lower Switch Voltage
HCU	012	Beep	Rear Hitch External Switch
HCU	013	Beep	Rear Hitch Sensor Supply Voltage
HCU	014	Tech	Rear Hitch Slip Control Enable
HCU	015	Tech	Rear Hitch Dampening Enable
HCU	016	Tech	Rear Hitch Enable
HCU	017	Display	Rear Hitch Raise/Lower Valve Commands
HCU	018	Beep	Display: 12 V Hitch Valve Supply Voltage
HCU	019	Display	Hydraulic Oil Temperature
HCU	020	Cal	HCU Calibration
HCU	021	Tech	Rear Hitch Raise Valve Threshold Adjustment
HCU	022	Tech	Rear Hitch Lower Valve Threshold Adjustment
HCU	023	Tech	Rear Hitch Raise Maximum Current Adjustment
HCU	024	Tech	Rear Hitch Raise Rate Adjustment
HCU	025	Tech	Rear Hitch Lower Draft Sensor Gain Adjustment
HCU	026	Tech	Rear Hitch Draft Sensor Zero Voltage Adjustment
HCU	027	Tech	Rear Hitch Minimum Rockshaft Position Voltage Adjustment
HCU	028	Tech	Rear Hitch Maximum Rockshaft Position Voltage Adjustment
HCU	029	Tech	Rear Hitch Minimum Lever Position Voltage Adjustment
HCU	030	Tech	Rear Hitch Maximum Lever Position Voltage Adjustment
HCU	031	Input	Rear Hitch Raise Solenoid Current Feedback
HCU	032	Input	Rear Hitch Lower Solenoid Current Feedback
HCU	033	Input	Off Command Frequency
HCU	180	Input	For Use by Engineering Personnel Only
HCU	181	Display	For Use by Engineering Personnel Only
HCU	182	Display	For Use by Engineering Personnel Only
HCU	183	Display	For Use by Engineering Personnel Only
HCU	184	Display	For Use by Engineering Personnel Only
HCU	185	Display	For Use by Engineering Personnel Only
HCU	186	Display	For Use by Engineering Personnel Only
HCU	187	Display	For Use by Engineering Personnel Only
HCU	188	Display	For Use by Engineering Personnel Only
HCU	189	Display	For Use by Engineering Personnel Only
HCU	190	Display	For Use by Engineering Personnel Only
HCU	191	Display	For Use by Engineering Personnel Only
HCU	192	Display	For Use by Engineering Personnel Only
HCU	193	Display	For Use by Engineering Personnel Only
HCU	194	Display	For Use by Engineering Personnel Only
HCU	195	Display	For Use by Engineering Personnel Only
HCU	196	Display	For Use by Engineering Personnel Only

Continued on next page   OUO1082,0002D11 -19-10JAN12-2/4

Table 7 — HCU Address List

TLA	Address	Address Type	Description
HCU	227	Display	HCU Boot Block Program Part Number
HCU	228	Display	HCU Boot Block Program Version Number
HCU	229	Display	EOL Data Part Number
HCU	230	Display	EOL Data Version Number
HCU	232	Display	Operating System Software Version Number
HCU	233	Display	HCU Software Part Number
HCU	234	Display	HCU Software Version Number
HCU	235	Display	HCU Part Number
HCU	236	Display	HCU Serial Number
HCU	237	Display	Software Assembly Part Number
HCU	238	Display	Software Assembly Version Number
HCU	245	Display	CAN Bus Off Retries Number
HCU	246	Display	CAN Bus Offs Interval
HCU	251	Display	Current Vehicle John Deere PIN

PTR ADDRESS LIST

Table 8 — PTR Address List

TLA	Address	Address Type	Description
PTR	000	—	Initial Address/EOL Programming
PTR	001	—	Recall/Clear Stored Diagnostic Trouble Codes
PTR	002	Beep	PTR System Beep Mode With Speed Sensors
PTR	003	Beep	PTR System Beep Mode Without Speed Sensors[a]
PTR	004	Beep	Engine and Countershaft Speed Sensor Status
PTR	005	Beep	Transmission Enable Relay Status
PTR	006	Beep	Neutral, Not Neutral, Forward and Reverse Switches
PTR	007	Beep	Hi/Lo Switches
PTR	008	Beep	Park Switch
PTR	009	Beep	Seat Switch
PTR	010	Beep	Clutch Disengaged Switch
PTR	011	Beep	Infinitely Variable Shuttle Sensor Voltage
PTR	012	Beep	Enable Pressure Sensor Voltage
PTR	013	Beep	Clutch Sensor A Voltage
PTR	014	Beep	Clutch Sensor B Voltage
PTR	022	Display	Automatic Overfill Protection Setting
PTR	030	Display	PTR Switched Supply Voltage
PTR	031	Display	PTR Sensor Supply Voltage
PTR	032	Display	Clutch Pedal Position Status
PTR	033	Display	Clutch Pedal Pressure Command
PTR	034	Display	Enable Pressure
PTR	035	Input	Countershaft Pulses Per Revolution
PTR	036	Display	Countershaft Speed
PTR	037	Display	Hydraulic Oil Temperature
PTR	060	Input	Transmission Configuration
PTR	061	Input	Hydraulic Oil Type Selection
PTR	062	Input	Temperature Adjustment for Non-JD20C Oil
PTR	063	Cal	PTR Transmission Calibration
PTR	064	Display	Transmission Fill Pressure and Fill Volume Calibration Values
PTR	065	Input	Forward Valve Fill Pressure Adjustment
PTR	066	Input	Reverse Valve Fill Pressure Adjustment
PTR	067	Input	Forward Valve Fill Time Adjustment
PTR	068	Input	Reverse Valve Fill Time Adjustment

Continued on next page OUO1082,0002D11 -19-10JAN12-3/4

Table 8 — PTR Address List

TLA	Address	Address Type	Description
PTR	069	Input	Infinitely Variable Shuttle Setup
PTR	070	Input	Below Wheel Speed Threshold Pressure
PTR	071	Input	Wheel Speed Threshold
PTR	072	Display	Forward and Reverse Starting Pressure Offset
PTR	073	Input	Coefficient for V^2 Shift Logic
PTR	074	Input	Starting Pressure for V^2 Shift Logic
PTR	075	Input	Maximum Shift Pressure for V^2 Shift Logic
PTR	076	Input	Tractor Model Configuration
PTR	080	Input	Forward and Reverse Valves Test Mode
PTR	081	Input	Enable Valve Test Mode
PTR	082	Display	Enable Pressure
PTR	083	Input	Hi/Lo Switch Setup
PTR	084	Input	Park Switch Polarity
PTR	085	Input	Seat Switch Polarity
PTR	100	Input	Come-Home Mode Enable
PTR	223	Display	Second EOL Software Part Number
PTR	224	Display	Second EOL Software Version Number
PTR	225	Display	Software Part Number
PTR	226	Display	Software Version Number
PTR	227	Display	PTR Boot Block Program Part Number
PTR	228	Display	PTR Boot Block Program Version Number
PTR	229	Display	PTR EOL Software Part Number
PTR	230	Display	PTR EOL Software Version Number
PTR	232	Display	Operating System Software Version Number
PTR	233	Display	EOL Software Part Number
PTR	234	Display	EOL Software Version Number
PTR	235	Display	PTR Part Number
PTR	236	Display	PTR Serial Number
PTR	237	Display	Software Assembly Part Number
PTR	238	Display	Software Assembly Version Number
PTR	245	Input	CAN Bus Off Retries Number
PTR	246	Input	CAN Bus Offs Intervals
PTR	247	Input	Current Vehicle Model Number
PTR	248	Input	Current Vehicle Serial Number
PTR	251	Display	Current Vehicle John Deere PIN

[a]*Address 3 is identical to address 2 except that engine speed and countershaft speed are not included in address 3. This is to eliminate the intrusion of frequency inputs when trying to troubleshoot problems with the engine running.*

OUO1082,0002D11 -19-10JAN12-4/4

CAN NETWORK VOLTAGE CHECKS

CHECK CAN LO (—) AND CAN HI (+) VOLTAGES

1. Turn key switch to RUN position (engine off).

2. Use a multimeter to measure CAN Hi and CAN Lo voltages at the connector and compare with the following specifications:

Specifications:—Specification

CAN Hi Circuit (A to C)—Voltage.. 2.50—3.50 V

CAN Lo Circuit (A to D)—Voltage.. 1.50—2.49 V

- If CAN Hi or CAN Lo voltages are not within specification, check for short or grounded circuits and for corroded connectors and bent connector pins.
- If CAN Hi and CAN Lo voltages are within specification, proceed to Compare CAN Hi and CAN Lo Voltages.

COMPARE CAN HI AND CAN LO VOLTAGES

NOTE: The CAN bias voltage is 2.5 V. To evaluate the CAN Hi and CAN Lo circuits, the voltage recorded for each must be calculated in reference to this bias.

Calculate voltages as given below:

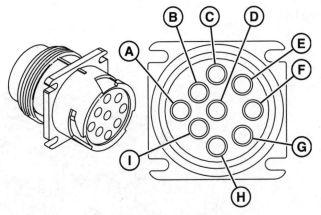

Fig. 12 — SERVICE ADVISOR Connector

A—12-V Battery	F—Open
B—Open	G—Open
C—Open	H—CAN Lo
D—Ground	I— CAN Hi
E—Open	

Table 9 — CAN Hi Recorded Value

	Recorded Value	Subtract Bias Voltage	Results
CAN Hi Voltage		– 2.5 V =	

Table 10 — CAN Lo Recorded Value

	Recorded Value	Subtract Bias Voltage	Results
CAN Lo Voltage	2.5 V –		=

Compare results from CAN Hi and CAN Lo calculations. Values must be within 35% of each other. Use the following chart to evaluate:

Table 11 — Comparison of Hi and Lo Calculations

If CAN Hi Result Was:	CAN Lo Result Must Be:
0.1 V	0.6—0.14
0.2 V	0.13—0.27
0.3 V	0.21—0.40
0.4 V	0.26—0.54
0.5 V	0.33—0.67
0.6 V	0.39—0.81
0.7 V	0.46—0.94
0.8 V	0.52—1.00
0.9 V	0.59—1.00
1.0 V	0.65—1.00

- If CAN Hi and CAN Lo voltages are not within specification, check for short or grounded circuits and for corroded connectors and bent connector pins.
- If CAN Hi and CAN Lo voltages are within specification, test is complete.

OUO1082,0002D12 -19-15OCT12-1/1

MONITOR SYSTEM APPLICATIONS

The applications of electronic monitor systems used in off-road equipment that will be presented and examined in detail in this chapter include:

- Combines
  - Grain loss monitors
  - Tachometer speed monitoring system
  - Low shaft speed monitoring system
- Planter monitors
- Seeder monitors
- Round balers
  - Bale size-monitoring system
- Forage harvesters
  - Metal detection system
- Tractors
  - Engine, hydraulic, and power train monitors
- Motor graders
  - Automatic blade control system
- Scrapers
  - Automatic transmission control system

OUO1082,0002D13 -19-10JAN12-1/1

COMBINES

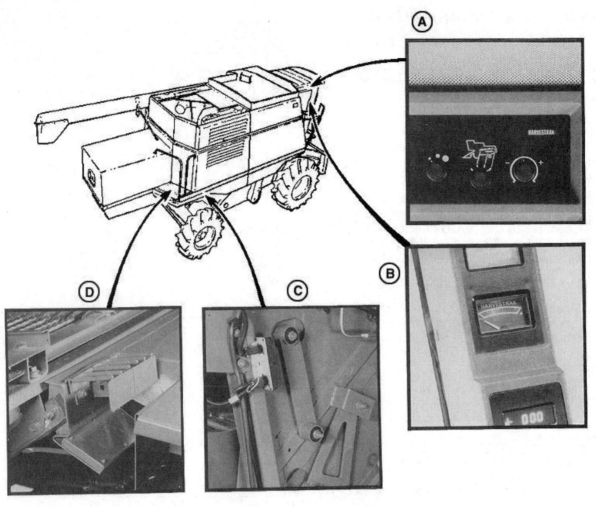

Fig. 13 — Components of a Grain Loss Monitor

A—Control Panel	**B—Monitor**	**D—Sensors (4)**
	C—Pre-Amplifier	

GRAIN LOSS MONITOR

Some combines use this type of monitor (Fig. 13) to check the performance of the combine, which enables the operator to use maximum combine capacity. The operator adjusts the combine and header to an acceptable loss level and then adjusts the display needle to the green arc. Sensors (A) at the straw walkers and cleaning shoes sense the level of grain loss and relay this information to the monitor (C) inside the cab. Based on the preset loss level, the operator knows whether to increase or decrease ground speed of the combine.

The monitor can also detect plugged or closed straw walkers, sieves and chaffers. A sudden move to the plus (+) side of the meter, when field conditions are unchanged, can indicate that one of these components is plugged or closed. It is then necessary to stop the combine and correct the problem.

Grain loss monitors assess grain loss by measuring a representative sample of losses over the cleaning shoes

and straw walkers. The monitor system consists of an ignition switch and electric clutch switch, a control panel, preamplifier circuit box, two cleaning shoe sensors, and two straw walker sensors. These sensors are connected with a wiring harness. Any change in the loss rate is indicated by the meter on the control panel.

The monitor continuously keeps track of combine performance to enable the operator to use maximum combine capacity. After the operator has adjusted the combine and header to a loss level that is acceptable, the monitor can then be set to this level indicating whether to increase or decrease ground speed.

The four sensors detect impacts from grain coming off the cleaning shoe and straw walkers and transmit these impacts as electrical impulses to the preamplifier. The preamplifier eliminates or filters out those signals that result from impacts on the sensors from straw stems, chaff, or cobs.

Continued on next page   OUO1082,0002D14 -19-15OCT12-1/7

110112
PN=534

The sensors detect grain by a principle similar to that used in a microphone. When grain strikes the sensor board, it causes the board to vibrate. This vibration is then transmitted to an electric element inside the sensor, causing the element to distort. The distortion causes the electric element to send out a voltage signal whose amplitude and frequency are characteristic of the material striking the sensor board. The difference in voltage signals tells the preamplifier whether the sensor board was struck by a kernel of grain or a piece of cob.

Next, the control panel inside the cab receives the impulses from the preamplifier and displays the grain loss on the monitor.

OPERATIONAL CHECK

A very simple and fast operational check can be carried out on the grain loss monitor by performing the nine steps listed below. An advantage to this check is that each of the four sensors and the individual leads of the wiring harness from the sensors are checked individually.

1. Turn the ignition switch of the combine to ON, but do not start the engine.

2. Turn on the header drive switch.

3. Turn the grain size knob to the small grain position.

4. Turn the sensor selection knob to the cleaning shoe symbol.

5. Turn the meter zone adjustment knob to the + symbol.

6. Tap rapidly and lightly on the left cleaning shoe sensor with a hard object such as a small screwdriver while

another person watches the meter needle. The needle should move into the green scale. Repeat for the right cleaning shoe sensor.

7. Turn the sensor selector knob to the straw walker symbol B. Check both straw walker sensors in the same manne

8. Turn the light switch to the fourth position (field lights). Check both straw walker sensors in the same manner.

9. Turn off the key switch, separator and header.

The operational check can lead to further diagnostic testing. For example, if tapping the left cleaning shoe sensor causes the monitor to read correctly but tapping the right one causes no reading at all, probably one of two things is wrong. Either the wiring harness lead to that sensor is bad or the sensor itself has failed. No needle movement at all from tapping all of the sensors would probably indicate no power, bad harness connection at the preamplifier, a malfunctioning preamplifier or a bad meter. The sensors would probably be all right since it is not likely that all four would fail at the same time.

REPAIR OF GRAIN LOSS MONITOR

The control panel, preamplifier and sensors are sealed units and can't be repaired. If found defective, they must be replaced. Environmental factors have little or no effect on the sensors. However, they should be kept clean because excessive dirt could cause them to lose sensitivity.

Continued on next page   OUO1082,0002D14 -19-15OCT12-2/7

TACHOMETER SPEED MONITORING SYSTEMS

Combines use this system (Fig. 14) to ensure proper operation of the machine. Sensors located on the engine, cylinder drive, cleaning fan, and transmission monitor rpm and ground speed (C). This information is then available on a digital display inside the cab.

The tachometer in many combines displays four different functions on a digital display. Engine (B) and separator (F) hours are also available for display.

The tachometer is accurate within ±1 0 rpm in displaying all three rpm functions and is accurate within ± 1/2 km/h (1/10 mph) in displaying ground speed. If ground speed drops below 3/4 km/h (1/2 mph), the digital display shows 0.0.

The engine and separator hour meters are accurate to ± 1 hour. Only full hours are shown, but the computer memory is updated in quarter-hours.

The digital display dims by 50 percent when the headlights are turned on and can be dimmed even more with the dimmer switch on the light panel.

DIGITAL TACHOMETER ENGINE CONTROL DIAGNOSTIC CODES

On some combines, the tachometer may display a number of diagnostic codes relating to engine operation.

The diagnostic codes will appear as –E on the tachometer. If any of these codes appear, you can continue to operate the combine, but write the code on a piece of paper and call your dealer at your earliest convenience. However, certain codes may appear which indicate that the combine engine might die or may not start.

After making a written note of the code, press the desired speed symbol to return the tachometer to normal operation. The diagnostic code will not appear again until the engine is turned off, restarted, and the problem occurs again.

TACHOMETER OPERATION

When the key is turned on, the tachometer first shows ground speed.

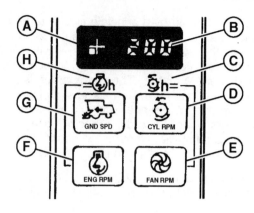

Fig. 14 — Tachometer Speed Monitoring System

A—Selector Symbol
B—Digital Display
C—Separator Hours
D—Cylinder RPM
E—Cleaning Fan RPM
F—Engine RPM
G—Ground Speed
H—Engine Hours

Select the function to be shown and press that symbol. The selector symbol square will move to show the function displayed.

The engine hour meter shows whole hours when ground speed and engine rpm symbols are touched at the same time.

The separator hour meter shows whole hours when cylinder rpm and cleaning fan rpm symbols are touched at the same time.

The tachometer also sends an alarm to the light and buzzer in the overhead panel for low engine speed and low cylinder speed.

The engine alarm turns on when rpm drops below a certain level.

The cylinder speed alarm turns on when speed drops below 80 percent of setting and engine is at full rpm with header drive engaged.

Continued on next page   OUO1082,0002D14 -19-15OCT12-3/7

SENSOR LOCATIONS

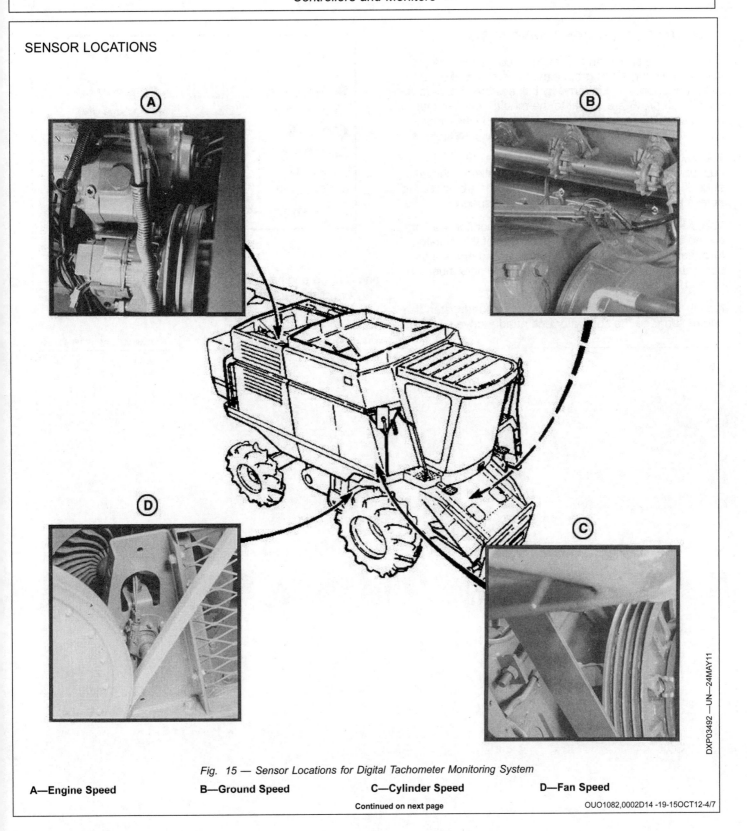

Fig. 15 — Sensor Locations for Digital Tachometer Monitoring System

A—Engine Speed   **B—Ground Speed**   **C—Cylinder Speed**   **D—Fan Speed**

Continued on next page   OUO1082,0002D14 -19-15OCT12-4/7

DXP03492 —UN—24MAY11

LOW SHAFT SPEED MONITORING SYSTEM

The five drive shafts on a combine—conveyor augers, tailings elevator, clean grain elevator, straw walkers and straw chopper are monitored by this system. Sensors on each shaft provide a signal to the monitor system that activates a light and buzzer inside the cab when these shafts are operating at less than their designed speeds.

The low shaft speed monitor shows with lights and a buzzer when the straw chopper, straw walkers, conveyor augers, grain elevator and tailings elevator are operating at less than 70 percent of their designed speed.

The electric clutch and low shaft speed monitor are both on the same circuit. To check operation of the monitor, turn the key to on (do not start engine) and engage the separator and header drive switches. All lights must turn on and the buzzer must sound.

If all the lights come on and the buzzer sounds, start the engine, engage the separator and header drive switches,

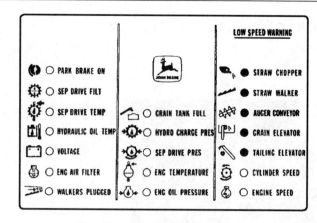

Fig. 16 — Low Shaft Speed Monitor

and run the engine at fast idle. If the lights continue to stay on, disengage the separator and header switches and idle the engine.

Continued on next page   OUO1082,0002D14 -19-15OCT12-5/7

SENSORS

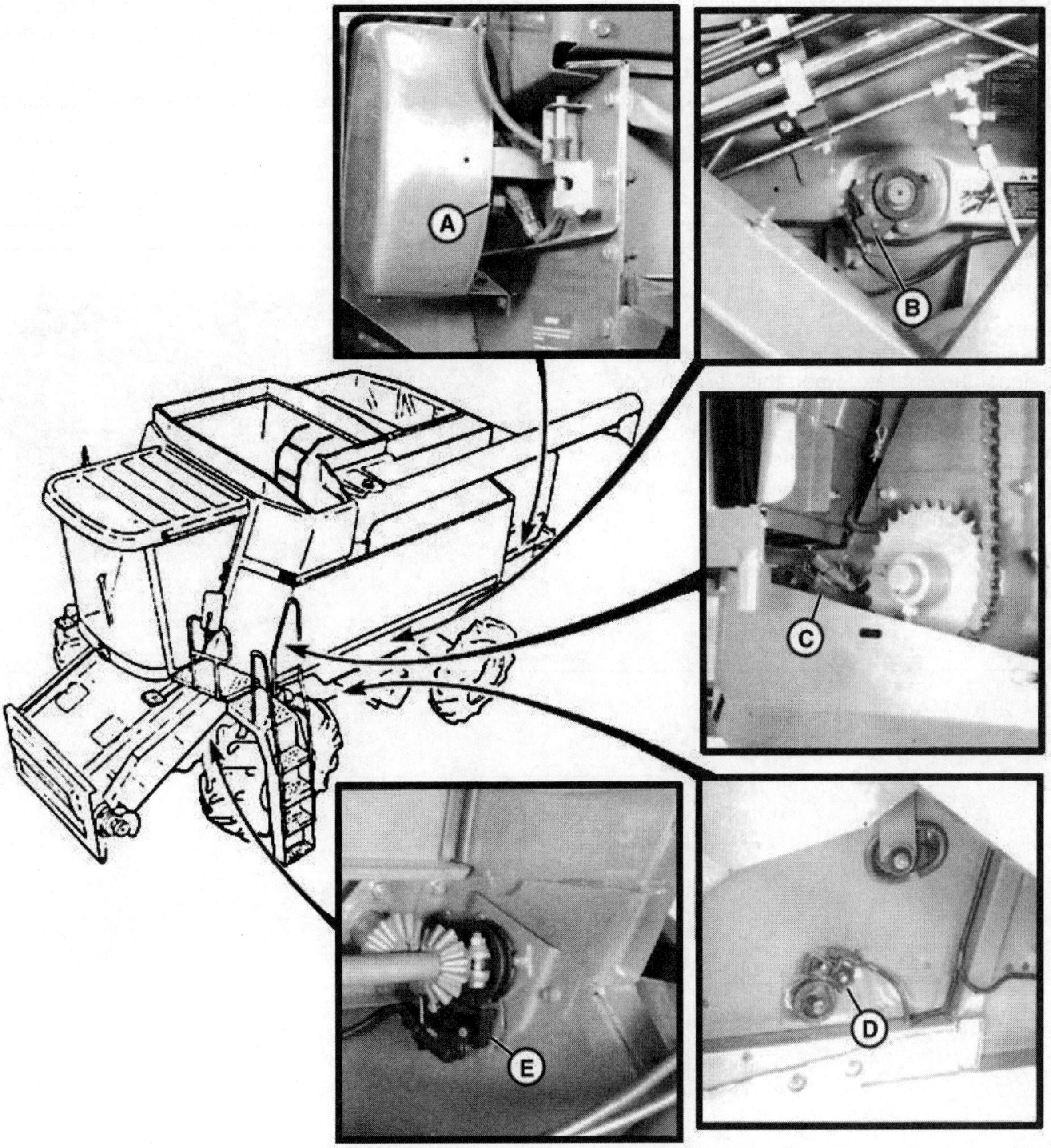

Fig. 17 — Sensor Locations for Low Shaft Speed Monitoring System

A—Straw Chopper Sensor   C—Tailings Elevator Sensor   E—Conveyor Augers
B—Straw Walker Sensor   D—Clean Grain Elevator Sensor

The five sensors are the following:

1. Straw chopper sensor (A)

2. Straw walker sensor (B)

3. Tailings elevator sensor (C)

4. Clean grain elevator sensor (D)

5. Conveyor augers (E)

The five sensors (Fig. 17) are not adjustable. If the combine is not equipped with a straw chopper, be certain the sensor leads are connected to ground plugs to prevent a false alarm.

LOW SHAFT SPEED MONITOR TROUBLESHOOTING

Continued on next page   OUO1082,0002D14 -19-15OCT12-6/7

110112
PN=539

A yellow light comes on and the buzzer sounds whenever any of these five functions are running below proper speed. The separator and header drive switches must be on to turn on this system.

When the buzzer sounds, check for plugged straw chopper, straw walkers or augers, or a broken belt.

Then check for:

• Broken or disconnected sensor wires

• Damaged sensor
• Loose sensor actuator on shaft collar

If the light and buzzer still stay on after checking those items, short both sensor wires to ground. If the light and buzzer then go out, replace that sensor.

If after replacing the sensor, the light and buzzer still stay on, see your dealer.

OUO1082,0002D14 -19-15OCT12-7/7

PLANTER MONITOR

Used on multi-row planters, these monitors (Fig. 18) keep track of the performance of each planting unit on the planter and signal the operator when this performance level is not being met. Some highly sophisticated monitors keep track of the number of rows planted, number of acres, and size of each field. Some newer monitors are equipped with a tractor-mounted radar sensor to indicate ground speed or plant population.

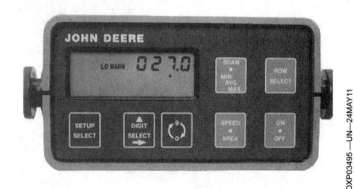

Fig. 18 — Planter Monitor

Continued on next page

OUO1082,0002D15 -19-29OCT12-1/21

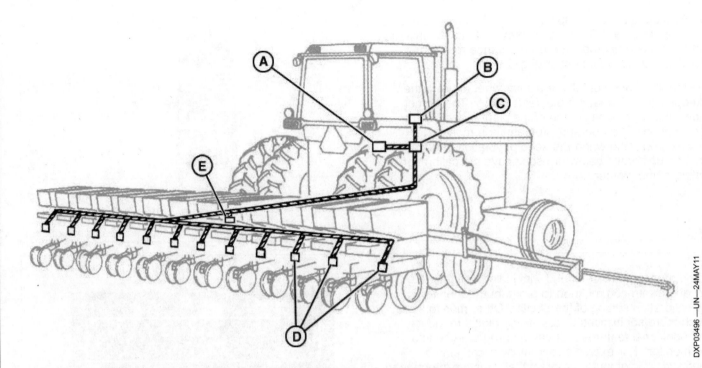

Fig. 19 — Components of a Planter Monitor

A—Radar Distance Sensor   **C—Power Module**   **E—Distance Wheel Sensor**
B—Monitor Console   **D—Seed Sensors**

Planter monitors let the operator know if the planter is actually doing its job. The monitor constantly checks each planting unit on the planter (Fig. 19) so that the operator knows whether or not any of the units are plugged. With today's highly sophisticated planters (some plant up to 24 rows at a time), the farmer has to know that the correct amount of seed at the proper spacing is going into the ground.

The monitor system consists of a sensor located at each planter unit, a monitor console (C) and power module (D) inside the tractor cab, and associated wiring harnesses.

OUO1082,0002D15 -19-29OCT12-2/21

The actual sensing device is located inside the seed tube. It is a photoelectric cell (Fig. 20) that senses the presence of each seed as it falls through the seed tube and relays this information to the monitor inside the tractor. Without a monitor, a planter unit could be clogged and the farmer could miss planting an entire row on each pass and not know it until he stopped to fill the seed hoppers.

Fig. 20 — Seed Tube Sensor

Continued on next page

OUO1082,0002D15 -19-29OCT12-3/21

On monitors that give a digital display of corn population per acre, distance information is provided to the console either from a sensor located on a distance measuring wheel or from a radar sensor (Fig. 21).

The monitor does not tell the planter what to do: rather, it keeps track of what the planter is doing. The farmer knows the calibration setting of the planter and tractor combination. The operator programs the monitor to provide a warning when the seed population in each planting unit drops below or rises above the calibration setting of the planter.

Fig. 21 — Planter Radar Sensor

OUO1082,0002D15 -19-29OCT12-4/21

Some monitors are equipped with indicator lights (Fig. 22) and a rate control knob to program the monitor to the calibration setting of the planter. Other monitors are much more sophisticated, containing digital readouts and additional features that can be programmed into the monitor. For example, one monitor contains a sophisticated computer program that uses the information programmed into the monitor by the operator. Row width, number of rows, high and low warning limits, and distance calibration are used to compute and display speed, area planted, individual row and average population, as well as to alert the operator when population has gone outside the programmed limits. There are also monitors that will even keep track of different field sizes and then total them when planting is complete.

TROUBLESHOOTING PLANTER MONITORS

Console operates intermittently.

• Monitor is not receiving 12 volts.

One row shows failure.

• Seed tube is clogged.
• Unit roller chain is off sprocket.
• Wrong seed plate is installed.
• Unit is not planting
• Photocells in shank are dusty.
• Fingers are malfunctioning.
• Sensor or planter harness is shorted.

Failure is shown for half of planter units.

Fig. 22 — Planter Monitor With Indicator Lights

• Drill shaft pin is sheared.

All rows fail.

• Drive chain in center of planter is off sprockets.
• Sensor or planter harness is shorted.

Failure is shown intermittently.

• Dampness is in coupler or connectors.
• Electrical interference coming from gasoline engine.
• Interference coming from alternator or generator.
• Sensor or planter harness is shorted.

Continued on next page   OUO1082,0002D15 -19-29OCT12-5/21

110112
PN=542

TESTING PLANTER MONITORS

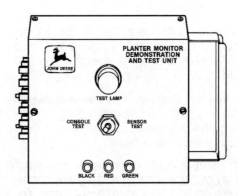

Fig. 23 — Standard Test Set for Planter Monitoring Systems

OUO1082,0002D15 -19-29OCT12-6/21

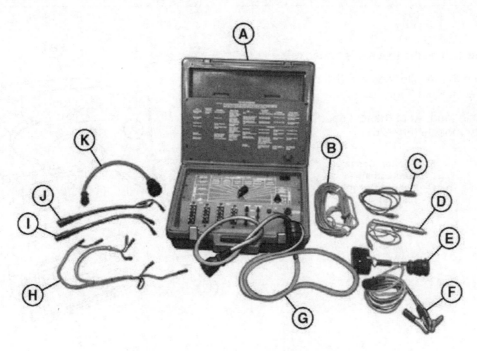

Fig. 24 — Deluxe Test Set Showing Attachments

A—Test Unit
B—Extension Lead
C—Negative Lead
D—Positive Lead

E—Adapter
F—External Battery Connector
G—Harness Lead

H—Seed Harness Adapter
I—Seed Sensor Adapter
J—Planter Harness Adapter

K—Power Module Adapter

Since planter monitors (G) use highly sophisticated seed and distance detection systems, specialized test sets (Fig. 23 and Fig. 24) have been developed for testing all components of the monitor systems.

The test unit actually simulates seed and distance signals to allow the technician to determine whether the components of the main system are performing satisfactorily.

Testing is divided into three separate phases:

• Connecting to power source.
• Preliminary setup.
• Functional tests.

Continued on next page

OUO1082,0002D15 -19-29OCT12-7/21

CONNECTING TO POWER SOURCE

If possible, perform the test with the console connected to the tractor on which it is used. If not, attach the power module (B) battery leads to a well-charged 12-volt battery or to a 120V AC-12V, DC converter (A) (Fig. 25).

Make certain that the positive (+) console power lead goes to the positive terminal and that the negative (–) lead goes to the negative terminal. Also, be certain the power module has two good 3-amp fuses.

IMPORTANT: NEVER USE A BATTERY CHARGER FOR A POWER SUPPLY. IF THE BATTERY YOU INTEND TO USE IS CONNECTED TO A CHARGER, DISCONNECT THE CHARGER DURING THE TEST.

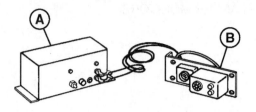

Fig. 25 — Hookup of Power Module

A—120V AC-12V, DC Converter   B—Power Module

OUO1082,0002D15 -19-29OCT12-8/21

PRELIMINARY SETUP

Make sure the selector switch on the test set is turned off.

1. Connect lead (C) from the monitor console (F) to the fuse side of the power module (Fig. 26).

2. Connect the to console lead (A) of the test set (G) to the back of the power module (Fig. 26).

A—Test Set to Console
B—Converter
C—Leads to Converter
D—Power Module

E—Monitor Console Connection
F—Monitor Console
G—Test Set

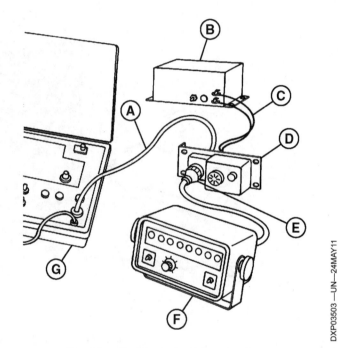

Fig. 26 — Test Setup for Planter Monitor

Continued on next page   OUO1082,0002D15 -19-29OCT12-9/21

Turn HI-Lo switch (E) on the monitor console to low and power switch on (Fig. 27).

A—Row 1 Lamp
B—Row Monitor Lights
C—Tuning Knob
D—On-Off Switch
E—Hi-Lo Switch

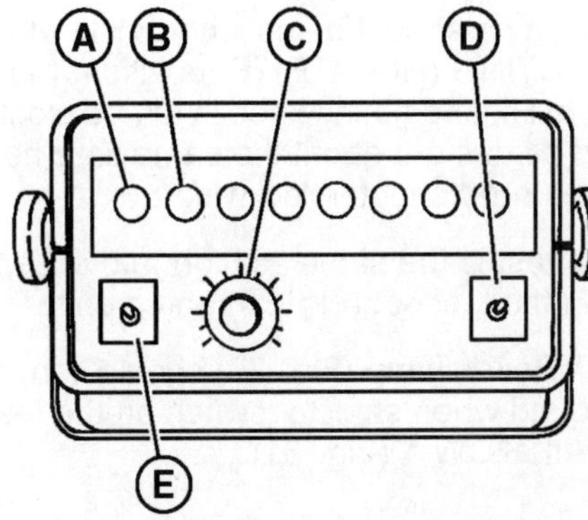

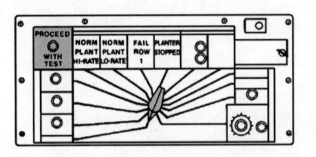

Fig. 27 — Planter Monitor Console

OUO1082,0002D15 -19-29OCT12-10/21

Turn tuning knob (Fig. 27) as far as it will go clockwise. All row monitor lights should be on and the PROCEED WITH TEST light (Fig. 28) should come on. If not, check the fuses, make sure the monitor console is connected to 12 volts, and make sure that the leads are not damaged. If the light still does not come on, either the monitor console or power supply is defective.

FUNCTIONAL TESTS

You are now ready for the functional tests. However, if at any point the monitor console or power module does not perform as described, the power module must be checked first before you proceed any further. Test the monitor console for:

Fig. 28 — Proceed With Test Light Must Be On

Continued on next page

OUO1082,0002D15 -19-29OCT12-11/21

- High rate. All lamps should be on when test set is in NORMAL PLANTING (HI-RATE) (E) position (Fig. 29), monitor is set to HI, and tuning knob is turned clockwise. Lamps should all dim out about the same time as the tuning knob is turned counterclockwise.

- Low rate. This test is the same as high rate except for the settings on the test set (Fig. 30) and monitor.

- Row 1 failure. Row 1 lamp (Fig. 27) should light and alarm must sound when selector switch on the test set is turned to FAIL ROW 1 (Fig. 31).

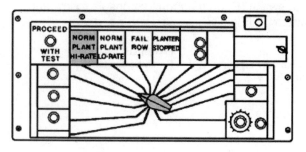

Fig. 29 — High Rate Test

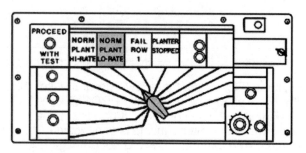

Fig. 30 — Low Rate Test

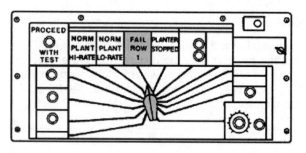

Fig. 31 — Failure Row 1 Test

OUO1082,0002D15 -19-29OCT12-12/21

Planter stopped. All lamps must light and alarm sound briefly when selector switch is turned to PLANTER STOPPED (Fig. 32).

If a problem occurred during any one of the four tests above, your first task is to determine which unit is defective—the power module or monitor console. Substitute another power module or console and repeat the tests. If the problem was eliminated, the unit that was replaced is defective.

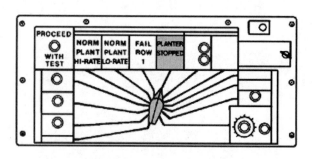

Fig. 32 — Planter Stopped Test

Continued on next page   OUO1082,0002D15 -19-29OCT12-13/21

SEEDER MONITOR

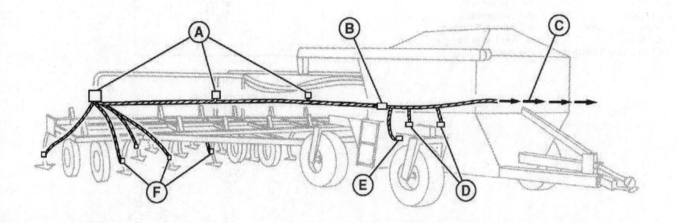

Fig. 33 — Components of Seeder Monitor

A—Sequencers
B—Splitter Unit

C—To Control Unit in Tractor
D—Bin Level Sensors

E—Area Proximity Sensor
F—Impact Sensors

The monitor (Fig. 33) provides the operator with information on the functions of the seeder. Each seed tube is monitored to ensure normal flow of seed, the seed bin sections in the seeder are monitored to prevent running out of seed or fertilizer, and the area seeded can be measured and displayed.

The seed flow monitoring system consists of six basic components in addition to the wiring harnesses:

• Control unit (C)
• Impact sensors (F)
• Sequencers (A)
• Splitter unit (B)
• Bin level sensors (D)
• Area proximity sensor (E)

Continued on next page

OUO1082,0002D15 -19-29OCT12-14/21

PN=547

Control unit (Fig. 34) is a block diagram of the system.

A—Control Unit
B—Power Cable
C—Breakaway Coupler
D—Frame Cable
E—Area Proximity Sensor

F—Splitter Unit
G—Sequencers
H—Impact Sensors
I— Bin Level Sensors
J— Tractor Cable

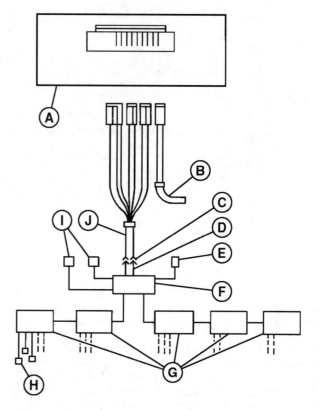

Fig. 34 — Block Diagram of Seeder Monitor

Continued on next page
OUO1082,0002D15 -19-29OCT12-15/21

IMPACT SENSORS

The impact sensors (Fig. 35) consist of a stainless steel pin with a vibration sensing crystal unit mounted and sealed in a plastic sensor assembly. The sensor (A) is mounted on the seed boot (B) with the steel pin (E) inserted directly into the flow of seed (F) (Fig. 36). Each time a seed or fertilizer particle strikes the steel sensor pin, the sensing crystal detects the vibration and sends a signal pulse to the sequencer. These sensors should be checked periodically because they can become encrusted and lose sensitivity.

A—Sensor
B—Seed Boot
C—Lead
D—Seed Tube
E—Steel Pin
F—Seed

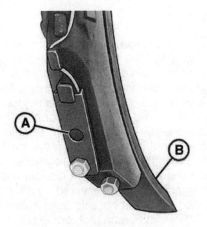

Fig. 35 — Impact Sensor on Seed Boot

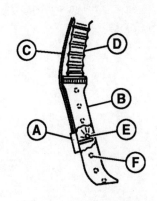

Fig. 36 — Steel Pin Inserted in Seed Boot

Continued on next page   OUO1082,0002D15 -19-29OCT12-16/21

SEQUENCERS

Groups of individual impact sensors are connected to one sequencer (B) (Fig. 37). The sequencer samples each impact sensor in order, starting at sensor number one and proceeding to the last one (Fig. 38). Each sensor is sampled for a fixed period of time, which is adjustable from about one-half second to seven seconds. The sequencer indicates which sensor is being sampled at any time. When a signal is received from the impact sensor being sampled, the sequencer progresses to the next sensor in the sequence. However, if at the end of the sample time, no signal has been received from the sensor being sampled, the sequencer halts its scan at that sensor and signals the splitter unit that a problem exists.

A—Sequencer   B—Impact Sensors

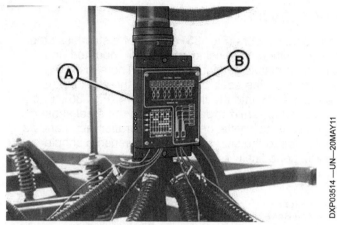

Fig. 37 — Sequencer Showing Connection of Impact Sensors

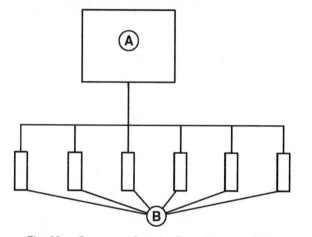

Fig. 38 — Sequencer Samples Each Sensor in Order

Continued on next page   OUO1082,0002D15 -19-29OCT12-17/21

SPLITTER UNIT

The splitter unit (D) (Fig. 39) receives signals from the sequencers (A), bin level sensors (B), and area proximity sensor (C). After processing the signals from the bin level sensor and the area proximity sensor, the input from all the sources (including sequencers) is transmitted to the control unit mounted inside the tractor cab (Fig. 40).

A—Sequencers
B—Bin Level Sensors
C—Area Proximity Sensor

D—Splitter Unit
E—Control Unit

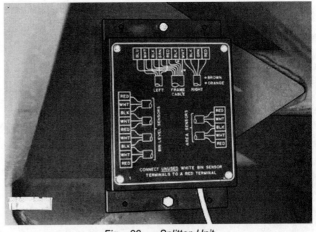

Fig. 39 — Splitter Unit

Fig. 40 — Splitter Unit Receives and Processes Signals and Sends to Control Unit

OUO1082,0002D15 -19-29OCT12-18/21

BIN LEVEL SENSORS

The bin level sensor (Fig. 41) is an optoelectronics device that projects a beam of light of invisible frequency across a gap near the bottom of the seed bin section. As long as material is present to block the passage of the light beam, no signal is created. However, if the material level drops below the light beam, the bin level sensor detects the completion of the light circuit and transmits a low bin level warning signal to the splitter unit. These sensors are located inside the seed bins. The optical lens should be kept clean because excessive contamination could block the beams, just as a high level of seed in the bin would block the beam.

A—Seed Bin Cross Section
B—Light Beam (Invisible)
C—Optical Sensor (Receiving)

D—Low Seed Level
E—Optical Sensor (Sending)

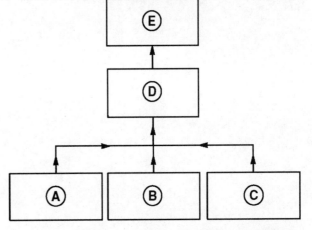

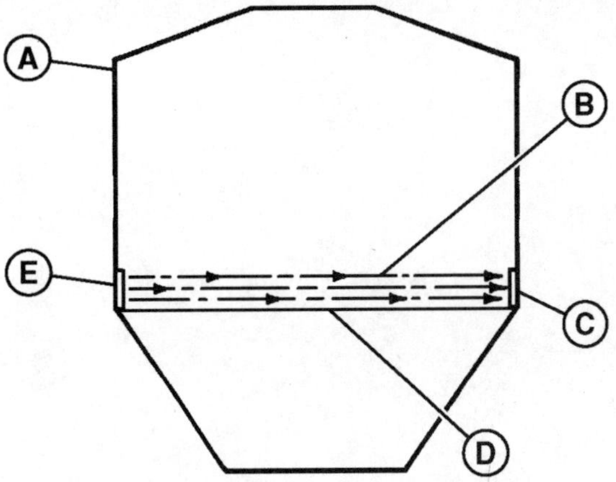

Fig. 41 — Optical Bin Level Sensor Operation

Continued on next page

OUO1082,0002D15 -19-29OCT12-19/21

AREA PROXIMITY SENSOR

The feed roll transmits the seed from the bin to the seed tubes. The area proximity sensor (C) (Fig. 42) signals each revolution of the feed roll on the seeder by electronically detecting the passage of a target cap screw (B) on the feed roll shaft. As the target cap screw passes the sensor tip, a small LED (light-emitting diode) on the sensor body blinks and a signal is transmitted to the splitter unit.

A—Jam Nuts   C—Proximity Sensor
B—Target Cap Screw

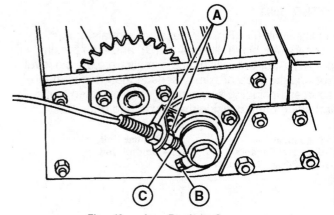

Fig. 42 — Area Proximity Sensor

Continued on next page   OUO1082,0002D15 -19-29OCT12-20/21

CONTROL UNIT

The control unit (Fig. 43) receives input from the splitter unit and signals the operator with lights and alarm when problem conditions exist at either the low bin level sensors or the impact sensors on the seed boots. The control unit also displays the area count (calculated from revolutions of the feed roll), adjusts the time interval for the impact sensors, and controls the power to the other components of the monitor.

SEEDER MONITOR TROUBLESHOOTING CHART

Control unit lights are off even though power switch is on and machine is not seeding

- Tractor key switch is off.
- Power cable is broken or shorted.
- Power cable is improperly connected.
- One or more sequencers are shorted.
- Splitter unit is shorted.
- One or more sensors are faulty.

Seeder lights on only one side of monitor flash while seeder is not seeding.

- Cables are faulty to that side of monitor.
- Sequencers are faulty on that side.
- Control unit is defective.

Tractor key switch is on, but no seeder lights come on after power switch is turned on.

- Breakaway connector is not making connections.
- Power cable is faulty.
- Control unit is defective.
- Cable between control unit and splitter unit is defective.

Low bin level light flashes, but both bins are full.

- Bin sensors are defective.
- Tractor or frame cable is damaged.
- Connectors are damaged.
- Cables are improperly connected.
- Splitter unit is defective.
- Control unit is defective.

Low bin level indicator on. Control unit does not light when bin is empty.

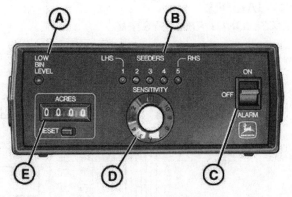

Fig. 43 — Control Unit

A—Low Bin Level Indicator
B—Seeder Indicator
C—Power Switch
D—Sensitivity Control
E—Area Meter

- Light path between two halves of bin level sensor is obstructed.
- Sensor cable, frame cable, tractor cable, or connectors are damaged.
- Cables are improperly installed.
- Sensor is defective.
- Splitter unit is defective.

One or more seeder lights flash while seeding.

- Seed tubes are plugged or not attached.
- Main seed tube is plugged or leaking.
- Sensitivity setting is too low.
- Applicable sequencer is not receiving power.
- Applicable sequencer is defective.
- Sensor unit wire is broken.
- Sensor pin is blocked or is contaminated.
- Sensor is defective.

All seeder lights flash while seeding.

- Seed bins are empty. (Bin level light should be flashing.)
- Fan and metering system is not functioning properly.
- Sensitivity setting is too low.
- Control unit is defective (sensitivity rheostat).

OUO1082,0002D15 -19-29OCT12-21/21

ROUND BALERS
BALE SIZE MONITORING SYSTEM

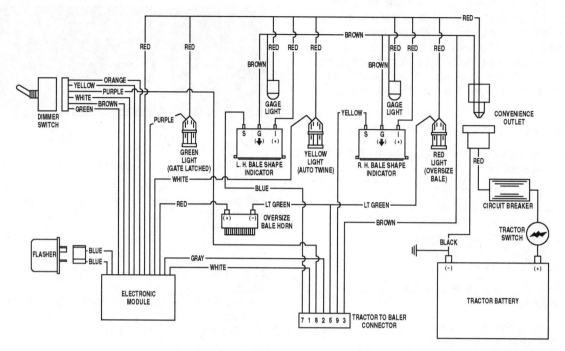

Fig. 44 — Bale Size Monitoring System

OUO1082,0002D16 -19-15OCT12-1/13

The bale size monitoring system (Fig. 44) found on some round balers monitors both the size and shape of round hay bales. The system consists of a monitor (Fig. 45) mounted inside the tractor, four switches, two potentiometers, and a wiring harness. It monitors the following functions:

• Gate latched
• Bale near completion
• Twine wrap starting
• Oversized bale
• Bale shape

Fig. 45 — Bale Monitor

Continued on next page

OUO1082,0002D16 -19-15OCT12-2/13

The gate latch switches (Fig. 46) are located on the right and left sides of the baler, behind the bale tension spring. When the gate is latched, the switch contact will be depressed and the green light will indicate that the gate is latched.

A—Gate Latch Switch

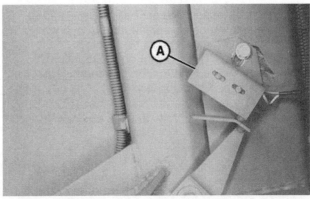

Fig. 46 — Gate Latch Switch

OUO1082,0002D16 -19-15OCT12-3/13

The bale size switch (A) (Fig. 47) is activated when the bale size adjustment knob (B) reaches the end of the slot in the linkage. It depresses the switch contact and causes the yellow light on the bale monitor to flash. This flashing light tells the operator that the bale is approaching the preset size and that the pointer indicators should be evened and preparations made to stop.

A—Bale Size Switch   **B—Bale Size Adjusting Knob**

Fig. 47 — Bale Size Switch

OUO1082,0002D16 -19-15OCT12-4/13

The twine arm switch (A) (Fig. 48) is depressed during most of the baling cycle. When the twine-wrapping cycle begins, the twine arm moves and activates the switch. This changes the flashing yellow light activated by the bale size switch to a solid yellow light. At this point, forward motion of the tractor should be stopped.

A—Twine Arm Switch

Fig. 48 — Twine Arm Switch

Continued on next page   OUO1082,0002D16 -19-15OCT12-5/13

If the tractor is not stopped and the bale is permitted to grow to the maximum possible diameter, the oversize bale arm (B) will pivot and depress the contact on the microswitch (Fig. 49). The red light on the monitor will light and the alarm will sound to alert the operator that baling must be stopped immediately.

A—Oversize Bale Switch   B—Oversize Bale Arm

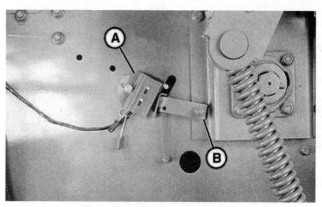

Fig. 49 — Oversize Bale Switch

Continued on next page   OUO1082,0002D16 -19-15OCT12-6/13

The shape of the bales is monitored by a potentiometer (B) mounted on each outside belt on the rear of the baler (Fig. 50). Each potentiometer uses a bell crank (A) that pivots to monitor the slack in the belt. Signals are sent to the left and right bale shape indicators (Fig. 45), which tell the operator how evenly hay is entering the baler. The pointers on the two indicators should be kept as nearly the same as possible so as to obtain an evenly shaped bale.

TROUBLESHOOTING

Red light comes on, solid yellow light did not come on, and twine arm did not cycle.

• Twine trip bell crank arm is out of adjustment.
• Twine trip rod clevis is out of adjustment.
• Red light switch is not adjusted properly.

Solid yellow light on; twine arm is in home position.

• Switch is not adjusted properly.
• Switch is defective.
• White wire from twine arm switch is shorted to baler or tractor frame.

No flashing yellow light, yellow light comes on solid and twine arm goes through its normal cycle.

• Switch is not adjusted properly.
• Extra light bulb inside of monitor box is burned out.
• Flasher is defective or connection is loose.
• Switch is defective.
• Voltage is too low.

Green light does not come on when gate is closed.

• Gate lockout lever is engaged.
• Gate switch is not adjusted properly.
• Bulb or switch is defective.
• Wire is broken or not connected properly.

Green light goes out while baling.

• Gate latch switch is not adjusted properly.
• Hydraulic system has air in it.
• Gate hydraulic cylinder has an internal leak.

Gauges read low or uneven with tight, well-shaped bale.

• Gauge sending units are not adjusted properly.
• Gauge or sending unit is defective.

Gate is not latched; green light is on.

• Switch is defective.

Bale shape gauges will not function; lights are all right.

• Polarity is reversed on hookup.

CHECKS AND ADJUSTMENTS

Checks and adjustments consist of:

• Checking wire continuity.
• Adjusting switches and potentiometers.

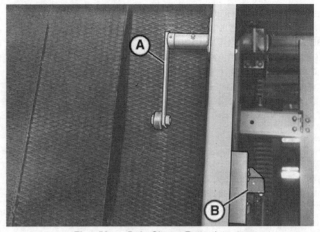

Fig. 50 — Bale Shape Potentiometer

A—Bell Crank   B—Potentiometer

• Checking switches, potentiometers, and gauges.

Checking Wire Continuity

The first thing that should be checked in this or any other electrical system if it is not working properly is continuity of the wires and wiring harness. Because if a switch is not receiving current, it certainly will not work. Perform the following steps to check wire continuity. Also, refer to the applicable technical manual.

1. Disconnect the baler wiring harness at the connector on the tractor.

2. Using a volt-ohm meter, check the continuity from each switch to the connector. Refer to the technical manual for wire colors and connector pin numbers.

3. If continuity is present from switch to connector, check continuity from connector to monitor inside the tractor cab.

4. If continuity is present from the connector to the monitor, connect the two halves of the wiring harness and check continuity from switches to the monitor inside the tractor cab.

5. If continuity is still present, this indicates that all wiring and the connector are good. If continuity is not present, the connector is at fault. Chapter 9 discusses servicing and repair of connectors.

6. If a broken wire is suspected, connect a volt-ohm meter to wire end and connector end of harness. Starting at one end, flex harness while watching the volt-ohm meter and work along entire length of harness. A reading on the volt-ohm meter will indicate that the wire is broken in that approximate area.

Adjustments

Continued on next page   OUO1082,0002D16 -19-15OCT12-7/13

PN=557

The switches and potentiometers on the round baler can be adjusted. For example, you know that the gate is closed but the monitor in the tractor cab is not telling you that it is. Or the monitor is indicating that the bales are correctly shaped when in fact they are not. More than likely the problem is that a potentiometer or switch needs adjustment. The monitor itself is probably in good working order.

Adjusting the switches and potentiometers is a mechanical operation and usually involves loosening the mounting hardware of the switch, repositioning the switch, and tightening the screws and nuts.

OUO1082,0002D16 -19-15OCT12-8/13

As an example, (Fig. 51) shows a gate latch switch. When the gate that releases the finished bale is closed, the switch arm (A) should be contacting the switch body (B) so that the switch roller (D) is centered on the short leg of the ramp (E). But if the mounting cap screw (C) had come loose allowing the switch bracket to pivot, the switch arm would not contact the switch and the green light would not indicate that the gate was closed when in fact it was. See applicable technical manuals for proper adjustment procedures and dimensions.

Checking Switches, Potentiometers, and Gauges

A volt-ohm meter can be used to check the switches and potentiometers. A known good potentiometer and a battery can test the two gauges on the monitor. Use the following procedures for these electrical checks.

Checking Switches

1. Unplug baler-to-tractor harness connection.

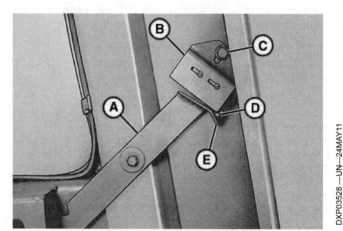

Fig. 51 — Adjusting Gate Latch Switch

A—Switch Arm
B—Switch Body
C—Mounting Cap Screw
D—Switch Roller
E—Short Leg of Ramp

Continued on next page   OUO1082,0002D16 -19-15OCT12-9/13

2. Using a volt-ohm meter, check across COMMON (A) and NORMALLY OPEN (B) (Fig. 52) with switch contact in closed position (E). If the volt-ohm meter (C) does not register, replace switch. If it does register, go to step 3.

3. Check across COMMON (A) and NORMALLY CLOSED (D) (Fig. 53) with contact switch in open position (F). If volt-ohm meter (C) does not register, replace switch.

A—Common
B—Normally Open
C—Normally Closed
D—Ohmmeter
E—Closed
F—Open

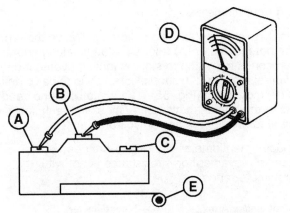

Fig. 52 — Checking Switch in Closed Position

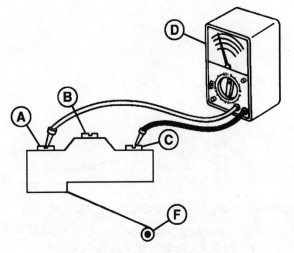

Fig. 53 — Checking Switch in Open Position

Continued on next page
OUO1082,0002D16 -19-15OCT12-10/13

Checking Potentiometers

1. Attach volt-ohm meter to potentiometer. Move the arm of the potentiometer (A) (Fig. 54) slowly, taking about five seconds from stop to stop. Needle movement on the volt-ohm meter (D) should correspond to bell crank arm (B) movement (Fig. 55). There should be no dead spots in the needle movement. Check the technical manual for proper reading on volt-ohm meter.

2. Replace potentiometer (C) if there are dead spots in needle movement or if resistance is not within approximate range.

A—Potentiometer Arm
B—Bell Crank Arm
C—Potentiometer
D—Volt-Ohm Meter

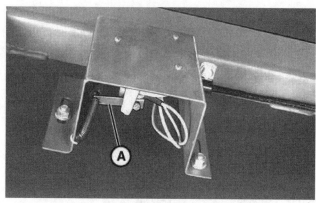

Fig. 54 — Checking Potentiometer

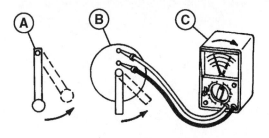

Fig. 55 — Bell Crank Arm and Volt-Ohm Meter Move With Potentiometer

OUO1082,0002D16 -19-15OCT12-11/13

Checking Bale Shape Indicator Gauge

1. Connect a known good potentiometer (A), 12-volt battery (C), and the indicator gauge (B) as shown in (Fig. 56).

A—Potentiometer
B—Indicator Gauge
C—12 V Battery

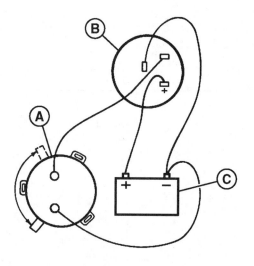

Fig. 56 — Checking Bale Shape Indicator Gauge

Continued on next page

OUO1082,0002D16 -19-15OCT12-12/13

2. Move potentiometer arm slowly taking about five seconds from stop to stop. Needle on the gauge should correspond to movement of the potentiometer arm (Fig. 57). If it does not, replace the gauge.

A—Gauge
B—Potentiometer

C—Battery

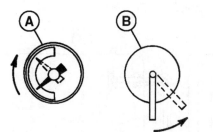
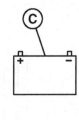

Fig. 57 — Gauge Needle Movement Should Correspond to Potentiometer Arm Movement

OUO1082,0002D16 -19-15OCT12-13/13

FORAGE HARVESTERS
METAL DETECTION SYSTEM

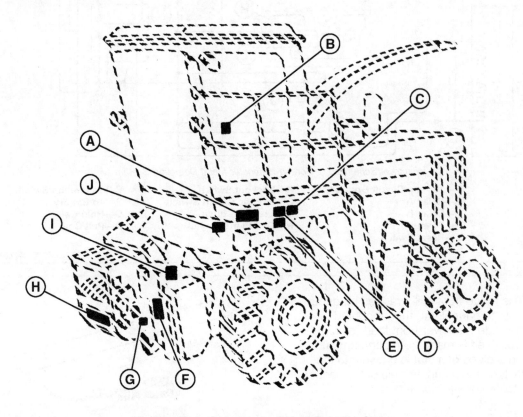

Fig. 58 — Components of Metal Detection System

A—Electronic Module
B—Rocker Switch and Alarm

C—10-Amp Circuit Breaker
D—Relay B
E—Relay A

F—Solenoid
G—Lockout Switch
H—Sensor
I— Electric Clutch

J— Reset Switch

The metal detection system (Fig. 58) is designed to prevent material containing iron from entering the cutterhead area of the forage harvester. This reduces the possibility of cutterhead damage and hardware disease in livestock. The system consists of a metal detector sensor located inside the lower front feed roll, a metal detector module, a relay module, a solenoid and stopping mechanism, an electric clutch, warning lights and alarm, and wiring harnesses.

Continued on next page

OUO1082,0002D17 -19-15OCT12-1/6

An electrical diagram is shown in Fig. 59.

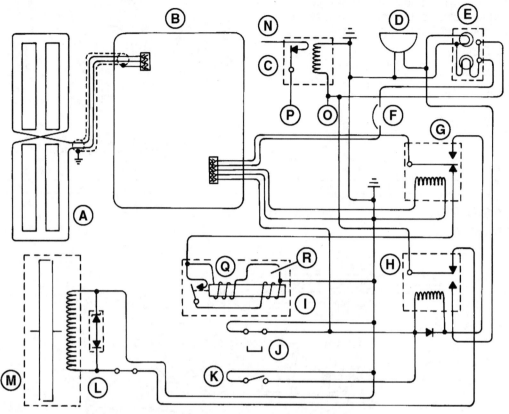

Fig. 59 — Electrical Schematic of Forage Harvester Metal Detection System

A—Detecting Sensor	F—10-Amp Circuit Breaker	K—Lockout Switch	O—To Ignition Switch
B—Electronic Module	G—Relay A	L—Electric Clutch Switch	P—To Battery
C—Cab Relay	H—Relay B	M—Electric Clutch	Q—Hold Call
D—Alarm	I— Solenoid	N—To Other Circuits	R—Pull Coil
E—Detector Switch	J— Reset Switch		

OUO1082,0002D17 -19-15OCT12-2/6

The sensor (Fig. 60) is made from coil-wrapped magnets encased in an aluminum channel and then mounted on a stationary shaft inside the lower front feed roll (A) (Fig. 61). The feed roll itself is made from nonmagnetic stainless steel. When a piece of metal is drawn into the feed roll, the metal distorts the magnetic field of the sensor (B), which then creates a voltage signal.

A—Feed Roll   B—Sensor

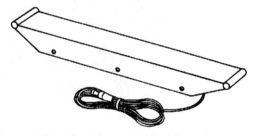

Fig. 60 — Sensor in Metal Detector

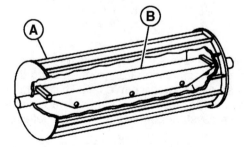

Fig. 61 — Sensor Inside Feed Roll

Continued on next page

OUO1082,0002D17 -19-15OCT12-3/6

B
A
C
D
E
F
12V
12V
DXP03539 —UN—24MAY11

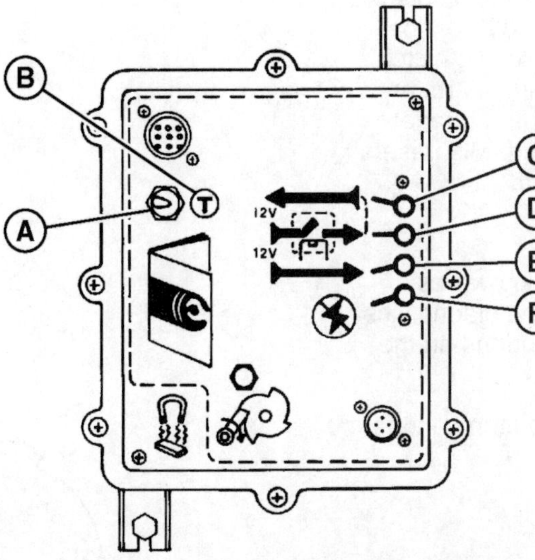

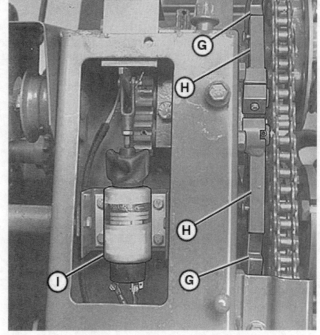

Fig. 62 — Metal Detector Module in Metal Detection System

This signal goes directly to the metal detector module (Fig. 62), which stops the flow of electricity to the solenoid (I), deactivating it (Fig. 63).

A—Test Toggle Switch
B—Test Push Button Switch
C—Relay Power-Out Indicator Light
D—Relay Power-In Indicator Light
E—Main Power Indicator Light
F—Low Voltage Indicator Light
G—Ratchet Plate (2 used)
H—Stopping Pawl (2 used)
I— Solenoid

G
H
H
I
G
DXP03540 —UN—10APR12

Fig. 63 — Solenoid on Metal Detector

Continued on next page OUO1082,0002D17 -19-15OCT12-4/6

When the solenoid is deactivated, it drops the stopping pawls (H) (Fig. 64) into the ratchet plates (G) to stop the feed rolls (Fig. 65). At that time the electric clutch is deactivated and the red warning light and alarm are activated. The operator then shuts down the forage harvester, removes the metal from the feed rolls, resets the metal detector, and resumes operation.

TESTING THE METAL DETECTOR

The metal detection system has what is known as on-board diagnostics—it will test itself. The diagnostics are performed using the lights and test buttons on the metal detector module and relay module.

The metal detector module has two test buttons and four power lights (Fig. 62).

• Test push button switch (A)
• Test toggle switch (B)
• Relay power-out indicator light (C)
• Relay power-in indicator light (D)
• Main power indicator light (E)
• Low voltage indicator light (F)

When the power to the metal detector module falls below 10 volts, low voltage light will come on. At the same time, the metal detector will "trip." The light will stay on until the metal detector is reset. This light also indicates a power interruption.

Main power indicator light (E) will be on as long as there is at least 10 volts power to the metal detector module and will be on during normal operation. Both the low voltage indicator light (F) and main power indicator light monitor power at the same point. The power supply is protected by a 10-amp circuit breaker in the relay module.

Relay power-in indicator light (D) indicates that there is power to the relay in the metal detector module. The light is on during normal operation.

Relay power-out indicator light (C) indicates that there is power to the coil in the metal detector module relay. The light is on during normal operation.

Test push button switch (A) (Fig. 62) induces a voltage into the metal detector module. When this button is pushed, power relay indicator lights should go out and the system should trip, causing the stopping pawls (H) (Fig. 65) to fall into the ratchet plates.

Test toggle switch (B) (Fig. 62) checks the reset coil assembly. When it is pushed, power is sent to the relay

Fig. 64 — Stopping Pawls

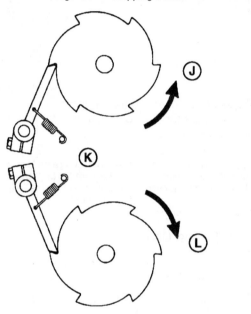

Fig. 65 — Stopping Pawls Engaging Ratchets

G—Ratchet Plate (2 used)
H—Stopping Pawl (2 used)
J— Upper Feed Roll Ratchet Plate
K—Return Springs
L—Lower Feed Roll Ratchet Plate

coil in the metal detector module, bypassing all the logic circuits and amplifier. At this time the relay power-out light should be on.

Continued on next page

OUO1082,0002D17 -19-15OCT12-5/6

The relay module has one test button and four indicator lights (Fig. 66).

- Test push-button (A)
- Reset indicator light (B)
- Solenoid indicator light (C)
- Clutch shift indicator light (D)
- Pawl/solenoid light (E)

METAL DETECTION SYSTEM TROUBLESHOOTING CHART

Detector will not reset.

- Reset switch is not working properly.
- Lockout switch is closed.
- Loose connections or defective wiring.
- Detector is resetting, but solenoid is not releasing stopping pawls.
- Reset switch, lockout switch, or electronic module has failed.

Stopping pawls do not disengage.

- Pawls are trapped by ratchet plate.
- Pawls do not move freely.
- Voltage at solenoid is low.
- Pawl clearance not adjusted.
- Detector not resetting.
- 10-amp circuit breaker, solenoid, or relay A has failed.

Detector trips immediately after setting.

- Plunger of solenoid unable to retract completely.
- Pull coil not switched to hold. High amperage opens circuit breaker.
- Metal is lodged in or wrapped around feed roll.

Metal detector does not trip.

- Metal does not contain iron
- Improper test procedure.
- Detecting sensor harness damaged.
- Poor electronic module connections.
- Detecting sensor not installed correctly.
- Failure of detecting sensor, electronic module, or relay A.

Numerous false trips.

- Loose connections or intermittent short at pawl solenoid.
- Detected metal is too small to find easily.
- Metal is lodged in or wrapped around feed roll.
- Detector sensor harness is damaged.
- Loose connections or damaged wire in power supply circuit.
- Stopping pawls improperly adjusted.
- Upper or lower front feed roll assembly damaged, or worn bearings.

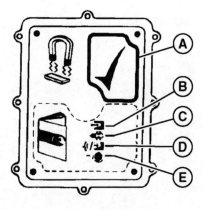

Fig. 66 — Relay Module

A—Test Push-Button
B—Reset Indicator Light
C—Solenoid Indicator Light
D—Clutch Shift Indicator Light
E—Pawl/Solenoid Light

- Repair welds using ferrous metal have been made on front feed rolls.
- Detecting sensor is picking up a strong outside signal.
- A feed roll shaft or one of the rear rolls is magnetized.
- Failure of detecting sensor, electronic module, circuit breaker, or rocker switch.

Green pilot light does not come on.

- Ignition or detector switch not in ON position.
- Loose connections at detector switch.
- Battery voltage low, poor connections.
- Faulty detector switch.

Alarm and red light do not come on.

- Feed roll shift lever is in reverse position.
- Reset switch not positioned correctly.
- Failure of relay A, relay B, circuit breaker, alarm, detector switch, or reset switch.

Alarm and red light remain on with feed rolls reversed.

- Pawls locked out. Lockout bail not in position under spring clip retainer.
- Feed roll shift lever is not between reset switch and magnet in reverse position.
- Failure of reset switch, lockout switch, or relay B.

Electric clutch does not engage.

- Loose connections, damaged wiring.
- Retaining pin for electric clutch field is loose.
- Failure of relay B.

OUO1082,0002D17 -19-15OCT12-6/6

TRACTORS
GENERAL INFORMATION

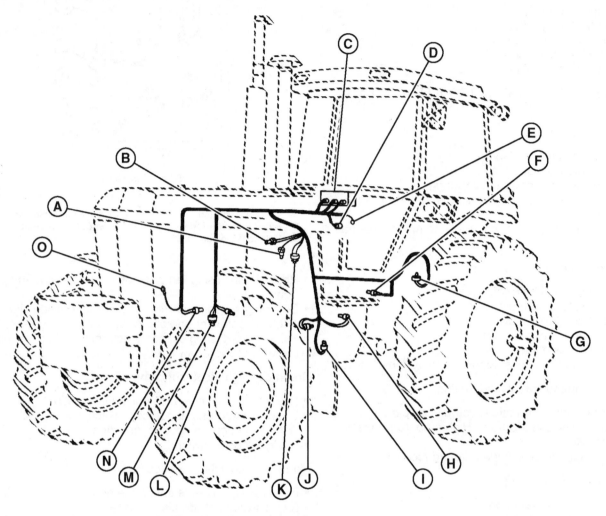

Fig. 67 — Components of Tractor Monitoring System

A—Cylinder Head Temperature
    Sensor
B—Coolant Temperature Sensor
C—Instrument Console
D—Warning Horn
E—To Circuit Breaker Panel

F—Ground Speed Sensor
G—PTO Speed Sensor
H—Hydraulic Oil Temperature
    Sensor
I— Transmission Oil Pressure
    Sensor

J—Transmission Oil Filter
    Restriction Pressure Sensor
K—Air Filter Restriction Sensor
L—Clutch Temperature Sensor

M—Engine Oil Pressure Sensor
N—Engine Speed Sensor
O—Fuel Level Sensor

Tractor monitoring systems (Fig. 67) monitor two main functions:

- Engine, hydraulic, and power train systems.
- Speed functions.

Speed functions include engine rpm, PTO rpm, and ground speed. To perform these functions, the system uses two electronic modules, indicator lights, and numerous electronic sensors.

Continued on next page   OUO1082,0002D18 -19-05APR12-1/12

ENGINE ANALYSIS

One electronic module (Fig. 68) analyzes the condition of the engine and power train and indicates where problems exist. The unit also indicates whether the problem is critical (requiring immediate engine shutdown) or is noncritical (requiring attention soon). The unit consists of four gauges—voltmeter, fuel, oil pressure, and coolant—and seven indicator lights, which will be explained later.

A—Warning Indicator Lamps   C—Performance Monitor
B—Tachometer

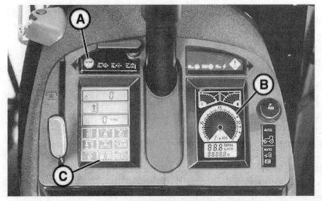

Fig. 68 — Electronic Modules for Tractor Monitor

OUO1082,0002D18 -19-05APR12-2/12

Critical and noncritical problems are indicated by a red stop engine light or amber warning light and a horn (Fig. 69). A critical problem is indicated by a steady horn sound, a flashing stop engine light, and a lighted indicator light or gauge needle in the warning or red scale of the gauge. A noncritical problem is indicated by a steady service message light, an indicator light or gauge needle in warning or red scale and, on some systems, by a beeping horn.

A—Stop Engine Light   C—Horn
B—Warning Light

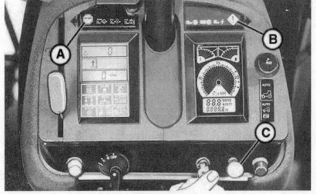

Fig. 69 — Warning Lights and Horn

Continued on next page   OUO1082,0002D18 -19-05APR12-3/12

GAUGES

Most older tractors use four gauges: voltmeter, fuel, coolant temperature, and oil pressure.

Newer tractors use indicator lights combined with a tachometer module to indicate voltage, fuel level, engine speed, rated speed, and ground speed. They also include an hour meter, a stop engine light, a service alert signal, and a warning horn or buzzer.

The voltmeter (Fig. 70) indicates tractor system voltage when the key switch is on and while running. The bands on the meter indicate various voltages.

In the fuel gauge circuit (Fig. 71), a float and potentiometer mechanism causes fuel level sensor resistance to increase as level rises. So as the tank is filled with fuel, resistance at the sensor increases, causing the needle in the gauge to move toward the full mark.

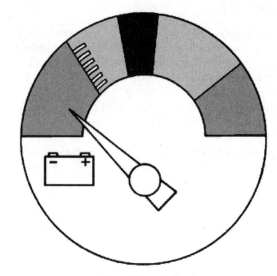

Fig. 70 — Voltmeter

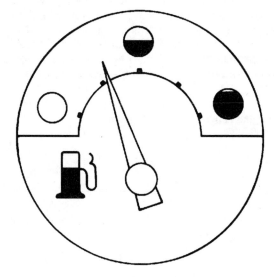

Fig. 71 — Fuel Gauge

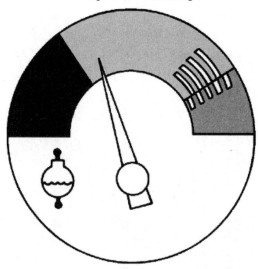

Fig. 72 — Water Temperature Gauge

Continued on next page   OUO1082,0002D18 -19-05APR12-4/12

Coolant temperature (Fig. 72) is measured by a variable resistance temperature sensor in the cylinder head. Increasing temperature increases sensor resistance values.

Engine oil pressure (Fig. 73) is sensed by a pressure sensor that indicates decreasing voltage with decreasing pressure. When the pressure drops below the predetermined pressure for the particular engine rpm, the gauge needle moves to the lowest band, engine oil pressure indicator light comes on, stop engine light flashes, and the horn sounds. Low or no engine oil pressure is a critical problem.

A—Engine Oil Pressure

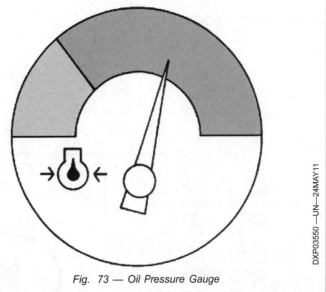

Fig. 73 — Oil Pressure Gauge

DXP03550 —UN—24MAY11

OUO1082,0002D18 -19-05APR12-5/12

INDICATOR LIGHTS

The indicator lights (Fig. 74) give priority to a critical problem over a noncritical problem. Two or more lights may signal a noncritical warning at the same time. However, if any one of the functions becomes critical, all noncritical warnings are cancelled and a critical problem is signaled by the appropriate indicator light, stop engine light, service alert signal, horn, and gauges, if equipped.

On tractor start-up, the module conducts a lamp test (all lamps light) for five seconds and a horn sound for two seconds.

The seven indicator lights alert the operator of critical and noncritical problems pertaining to:

- Transmission control pressure
- Engine oil pressure
- Voltage level
- Hydraulic oil temperature
- Air filter
- Transmission oil filter
- Transmission tube pressure (on early-model 4-wheel drive)

COMMON TROUBLESHOOTING

All indicator lights come on and stay on.

- The 37-pin connector lost ground at pin 4.

Indicator lights, stop engine light, and service alert light will not activate.

- The 37-pin connector lost ground at pin 22.

Filter indicator light, stop engine light, and horn are on when key switch is on and engine is off.

- Transmission pressure sensor and transmission filter sensor F2 wires are switched.

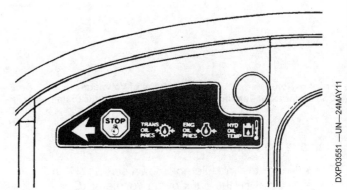

Fig. 74 — Indicator Lights

DXP03551 —UN—24MAY11

Filter indicator light and service alert light are on when key switch is on and engine is off.

- Transmission pressure sensor and transmission filter sensor F1 wires are switched.

Transmission pressure indicator light, stop engine light, and horn come on.

- The 37-pin connector lost ground at pin 17.

Only service alert light comes on.

- Alternator diode is faulty.

CALIBRATIONS AND CHECKS

Procedures follow for:

- Calibration of voltmeter.
- Low voltage warning check.
- High voltage warning check.
- Speed monitoring.

Continued on next page OUO1082,0002D18 -19-05APR12-6/12

CALIBRATION OF VOLTMETER

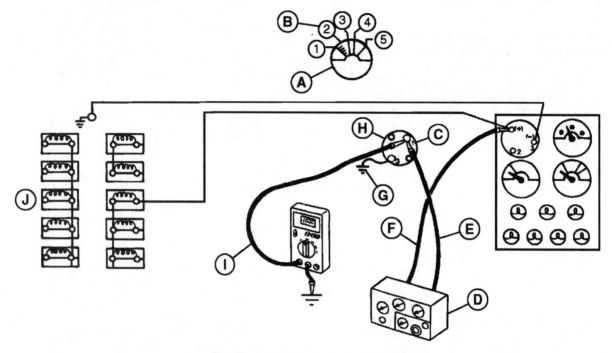

Fig. 75 — Voltmeter Calibration Test Setup

A—Front of Voltmeter
B—Checkpoints for Testing
C—Back of Voltmeter
D—Universal Gauge Tester
E—Green
F—Black
G—Jumper Lead
H—Hold-Down Screws
I— Red
J— Circuit Breakers

1. Remove the voltmeter.

2. Place two of the module hold-down screws (H) in holes 1 and 3 on the back of the voltmeter (C) as shown in Fig. 75.

3. Connect a jumper lead from hole 3 of voltmeter to ground.

4. Connect green (E) and black (F) leads of universal gauge tester (D) between voltmeter and hole 1 of voltmeter socket.

5. With key switch on and engine at 1,000 rpm, adjust 50-ohm potentiometer on the universal gauge tester so as to position voltmeter needle on each of the five

checkpoints one at a time as shown at the top of Fig. 75.

6. Read volts on multimeter and compare the readings as follows:

Table 12 — Multimeter Readings

Checkout	Volts
1	11.2 + 0.35
2	11.8 + 0.35
3	12.6 + 0.35
4	13.2 + 0.35
5	15.5 + 0.35

Continued on next page   OUO1082,0002D18 -19-05APR12-7/12

LOW VOLTAGE WARNING CHECK

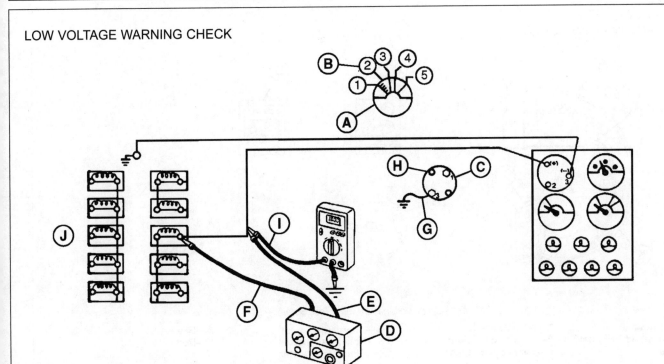

Fig. 76 — Low Voltage Warning Test Setup

A—Front of Voltmeter
B—Checkpoints for Testing
C—Back of Voltmeter
D—Universal Gauge Tester
E—Black
F—Green
G—Jumper Lead
H—Hold-Down Screws
I— Red
J—Circuit Breakers

1. Connect universal gauge tester in series with the lead at third right-hand circuit breaker (Fig. 76).

   Connect red lead to circuit breaker as shown.

2. Connect digital multimeter as shown in Fig. 76.

3. Turn key switch ON. After automatic lamp test cycle is completed, hold test button on gauge tester down and

adjust the 25-ohm potentiometer so that the service alert light comes on. The digital multimeter should show 10.5 to 11.5 volts. The tractor voltmeter needle should be at checkpoint 1 (Fig. 76).

Continued on next page   OUO1082,0002D18 -19-05APR12-8/12

HIGH VOLTAGE WARNING CHECK

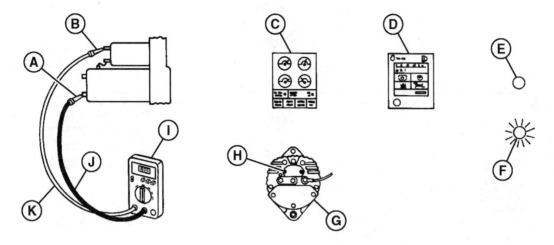

Fig. 77 — High Voltage Warning Test Setup

A—Ground Terminal
B—Starter Solenoid Terminal
C—Voltmeter

D—RPM Readout
E—Stop Engine Light
F—Service Alert Light

G—Alternator
H—Hole in Alternator
I— Digital Multimeter

J—Black
K—Red

1. Connect red lead of digital multimeter to starter solenoid battery terminal and ground the other lead (Fig. 77).

2. With key switch ON, run engine at 1500 rpm.

3. One person should observe the service alert light and multimeter reading. The other person should ground the alternator field circuit through the hole in the rear of the alternator frame.

⚠ CAUTION: Make sure you know how to perform this procedure. If not, check the applicable technical manual.

IMPORTANT: Do not ground voltage regulator longer than necessary to observe the warning lamp or reach a maximum of 18 volts.

4. The service alert light should light above 16 volts. The tractor voltmeter needle should be in the right-hand amber band (top of Fig. 76).

OUO1082,0002D18 -19-05APR12-9/12

SPEED MONITORING

As we mentioned earlier, the system also monitors functions pertaining to speed. A six-function digital tachometer (Fig. 78) displays engine rpm, rated speed, and ground speed of the tractor. It also includes an hour meter, an engine coolant temperature gauge, and a fuel gauge.

At start-up, engine rpm is automatically displayed both in miles per hour and in rpm (Fig. 78).

Fig. 78 — Speed Monitoring Module (Tachometer)

Continued on next page

OUO1082,0002D18 -19-05APR12-10/12

The tachometer was designed to accommodate different tire sizes when measuring ground speed. Eight small rocker switches (A) (Fig. 79) on the back are used to program the tachometer according to tire size.

A—Rocker Switch (8 used)

Fig. 79 — Programming Tachometer to Tire Size

OUO1082,0002D18 -19-05APR12-11/12

Another module (Fig. 80), the performance monitor, contains touch switches that indicate the engine speed and the distance traveled in feet or meters. It has an adjust touch switch that indicates the position of an implement and also displays various values (and increases them in increments) during preset.

To preset a desired distance, touch the distance switch repeatedly until the digit to be changed flashes. Pressing the adjust switch as the digit is flashing causes the digit to increase. Then, press the distance switch again for the next digit.

Fig. 80 — Performance Monitor

OUO1082,0002D18 -19-05APR12-12/12

MOTOR GRADERS
AUTOMATIC BLADE CONTROL SYSTEM

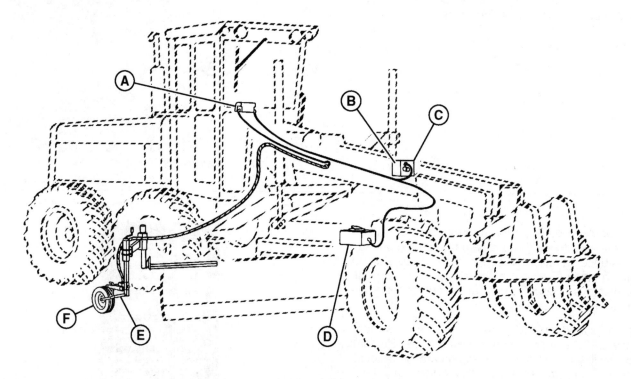

Fig. 81 — Components of Automatic Blade Control System

A—Control Console
B—Solenoid Valves

C—Servo Valves
D—Slope Control Unit

E—Grade Sensor
F—Follower Wheel

The purpose of the automatic blade control system in a motor grader is to sense changes in grade and slope of the ground so that the blade lift cylinders can adjust the blade accordingly (Fig. 81).

The system consists of:

• Control console (A)

• Solenoid valves (B)
• Servo valves (C)
• Slope control unit (D)
• Grade sensor (E)
• Wiring harnesses

Continued on next page   OUO1082,0002D19 -19-15OCT12-1/23

The slope control unit (Fig. 82) is mounted on the draft frame of the grader. The slope sensor (Fig. 83), mounted inside the slope control unit, electromagnetically measures the deviation of the sensor and its mount from a gravity reference. That is why it is so important that the motor grader be leveled first and then the slope control unit leveled and installed parallel to the main frame. See the applicable technical manuals for these procedures.

The slope sensor (Fig. 83) consists of a pendulum (A) and a blade angle switch (D). The pendulum is suspended from a shaft mounted on ball bearings so that it can rotate with respect to the gravity reference.

A—Pendulum
B—Timing Belt
C—Position Feedback
   Transducer

D—Blade Angle Switch
E—Terminal Board

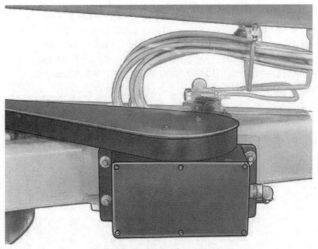

Fig. 82 — Slope Control Unit

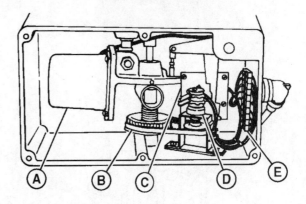

Fig. 83 — Slope Sensor

Continued on next page

OUO1082,0002D19 -19-15OCT12-2/23

The grade sensor assembly (Fig. 84) attaches to the blade of the motor grader. It senses changes in grade by means of the contact tube (C). Either this tube can follow a pre-leveled string line attached to stakes, or a wheel can be attached (Fig. 85) to follow a curb, previously cut surface, or pavement.

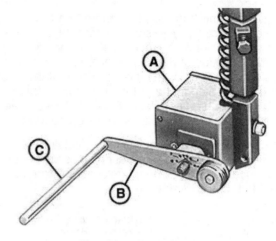

Fig. 84 — Grade Sensor

A—Grade Sensor   C—Contact Tube
B—Grid

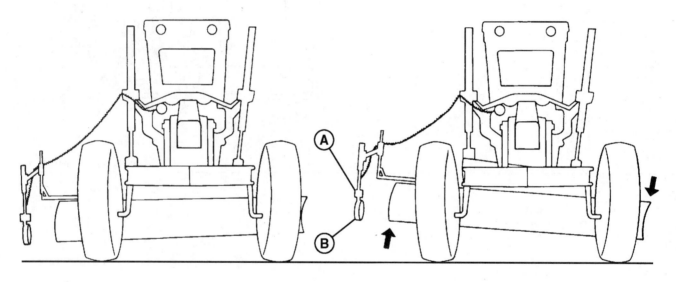

Fig. 85 — Grade Sensor With Wheel Attached

A—Grade Sensor   B—Follower Wheel

Continued on next page   OUO1082,0002D19 -19-15OCT12-3/23

The function of the servo valves (Fig. 86) is to provide electrical interface with the hydraulic system. The servo valves, of which there are two (one for each lift cylinder), are mounted on the hydraulic manifold. The manifold contains integral check and shutoff valves that isolate the automatic blade control system from the manual blade control hydraulics.

A—Spool Valve   B—Torque Motor

Fig. 86 — Servo Valve

OUO1082,0002D19 -19-15OCT12-4/23

The control console (Fig. 87) receives signals from the sensors and in turn causes the servo valves to actuate the lift cylinders.

A—Slope Deviation Meter   F—Power Switch
B—Slope Set Point Dial   G—Power Indicator Light
C—Left-Right Function Switch H—10-Amp Fuse
D—Grade Deviation Meter   I— 1-Amp Fuse
E—Grade Set Point Dial

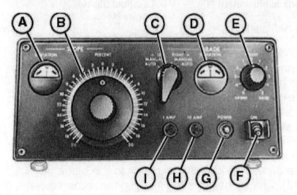

Fig. 87 — Control Console

Continued on next page   OUO1082,0002D19 -19-15OCT12-5/23

OPERATION

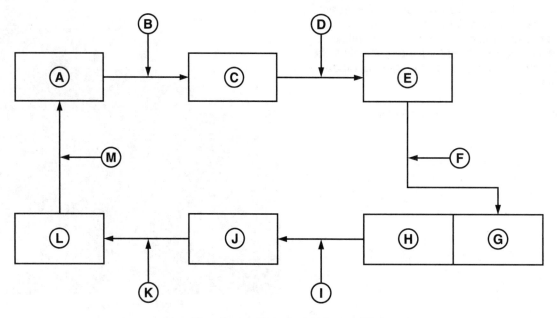

Fig. 88 — How a Blade Control System Works

A—Sensor Actuator
B—Mechanical Movement (1)
C—Sensor
D—Electrical Signal (2)

E—Amplifier (Control Console)
F—Electrical Signal (3)
G—Torque Motor

H—Servo Valve
I— Hydraulic Fluid Flow (4)
J— Blade Lift Cylinder
K—Mechanical Movement (5)

L—Blade
M—Mechanical Movement (6)

The relationships between the servo valves (H), sensors (C), and amplifier or control console (E) can best be described by the block diagram of Fig. 88. As the sensor actuator (A) moves because of a mechanical motion (1) (B) such as the grid arm raising or lowering, a sensor electrical signal (2) (D) is transmitted to the control console. The control console then sends an electrical signal (3) (F) that powers the servo valve. The servo valve then allows hydraulic flow (4) (I) to the blade lift cylinder (J), which positions the lift cylinder in the proper direction. The lift cylinder then positions the blade (L). As the blade is positioned, the sensor actuator returns to its normal position and is again ready to sense a change in grade or slope.

TROUBLESHOOTING

Automatic blade control system operates, but with a loss of accuracy.

• Tire pressure on motor grader is uneven.
• Blade is not centered under draft frame.
• Grade sensor bracket is not tight in its mount.
• Grade sensor is too far from the blade.
• Rear tires are running in loose material.
• Servo valves are not centered.
• Wear points are not tight (circle support shoes, moldboard side shift, blade lift, blade tilt, and center shift linkages).

Left or right cylinder loses action with automatic blade control system on.

• Hydraulic system has a malfunction.
• Servo valves are defective.
• Automatic blade control system has an electrical malfunction.

Automatic blade control system is completely inoperative even though power is on.

• One-amp fuse in control console is blown.

Slope meter consistently reads off center in same direction.

• Servo valve is out of adjustment.

SYSTEM TESTING

Three different test procedures are used on the automatic blade control system:

• System check under controlled conditions.
• Component substitution.
• Use of specialized test set.

The purpose of these tests or checks is to verify that the system is working properly.

System Check Under Controlled Conditions

Four system checks are performed:

• Manual control lever check.
• Slope only check.
• Grade only check.
• Grade and slope full system check.

Continued on next page   OUO1082,0002D19 -19-15OCT12-6/23

These checks are normal operational procedures and should be performed with the motor grader sitting on a flat and level concrete floor such as a shop service area. Also, the engine must be running so that the operation of the blade lift cylinders, blade pitch, and circle can be observed in relation to the particular settings on the control console.

Component Substitution

The second test procedure is used when the first one indicates that something is not performing as it should. This procedure involves changing electronic boards and meters in the control console in an attempt to isolate a failed component.

The slope amplifier and grade amplifier are identical printed circuit boards and can be interchanged to verify a defective board. The boards are easily interchanged by removing the two screws in the corners of the boards and gently pulling and rocking the boards up and out of the console. Fig. 99 shows one board removed from the console.

Check slope amplifier board in the following manner:

1. With engine off turn key switch to ACC and control console (Fig. 89) to ON.

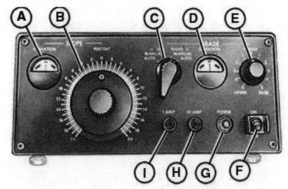

Fig. 89 — Control Console

A—Slope Deviation Meter
B—Slope Set Point Dial
C—Left-Right Function Switch
D—Grade Deviation Meter
E—Grade Set Point Dial
F—Power Switch
G—Power Indicator Light
H—10-Amp Fuse
I— 1-Amp Fuse

OUO1082,0002D19 -19-15OCT12-7/23

2. Place left/right function switch (Fig. 90) in manual left position.

A—Left
B—Right
C—Auto
D—Manual

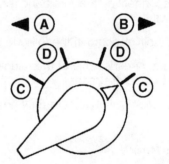

Fig. 90 — Set Function Switch

OUO1082,0002D19 -19-15OCT12-8/23

3. Rotate slope set point dial left to 2 degrees slope (Fig. 91). Slope deviation meter should deflect to the left. If it does not, the slope amplifier circuit board inside the control console is probably defective.

Fig. 91 — Rotate Dial to Two Degrees of Slope

Continued on next page

OUO1082,0002D19 -19-15OCT12-9/23

110112

PN=579

4. Interchange the two amplifier boards and repeat the procedure (Fig. 92).

A—Slope Amplifier Circuit
   Board

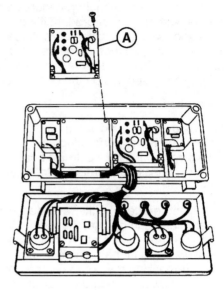

Fig. 92 — Changing Amplifier Boards

OUO1082,0002D19 -19-15OCT12-10/23

5. If the slope deviation meter still does not deflect, the meter is probably defective. This can be verified by interchanging the slope and grade deviation meters (Fig. 93) by disconnecting the wires and removing the attaching screws.

Check the grade amplifier board in the following manner:

1. Disconnect grade sensor cable at the middle of the main frame of the motor grader.

2. Set left/right function switch to auto right position (Fig. 90).

A—Slope Deviation Meter

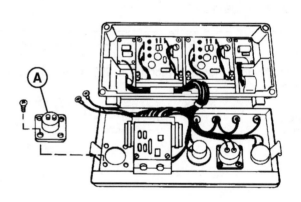

Fig. 93 — Changing Deviation Meters

OUO1082,0002D19 -19-15OCT12-11/23

3. Rotate grade set point dial (Fig. 94) up and down from 0 position.

A—Rotate   D—Lower
B—Height   C—Raise

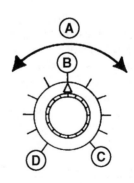

Fig. 94 — Rotate Set Point Dial Up and Down

Continued on next page   OUO1082,0002D19 -19-15OCT12-12/23

4. The grade deviation meter should deflect to the left and right (Fig. 95). If it does not, the grade amplifier board is probably defective.

5. Interchange the two amplifier boards and repeat the procedure.

6. If the grade deviation meter still does not deflect, the meter is probably defective. Verify by interchanging the slope and grade deviation meters.

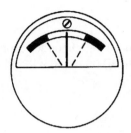

Fig. 95 — Grade Deviation Meter Should Deflect

OUO1082,0002D19 -19-15OCT12-13/23

Use of Specialized Test Set

The third test procedure uses a special test set (Fig. 96) that provides a means of quickly performing resistance continuity and ground defect checks on sensors, valves, slope control unit, and interconnecting wiring. The test set is used with a standard volt-ohm meter.

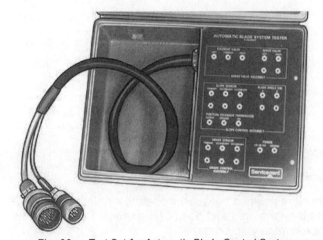

Fig. 96 — Test Set for Automatic Blade Control System

OUO1082,0002D19 -19-15OCT12-14/23

To use the test set (B), disconnect the cable connectors from the left and right sides of the control console (Fig. 97). Reconnect the cables to matching cables on the test set. The test set can be used to check the following:

• Power
• Solenoid valves
• Servo valves
• Grade control sensor
• Slope sensor
• Position feedback transducer
• Blade angle switch

When running these tests, be sure to check the applicable technical manuals for the exact specifications pertaining to voltage and resistance readings.

A—Connect to Test Set Cables   C—Control Console
B—Test Set   D—Disconnect From Console

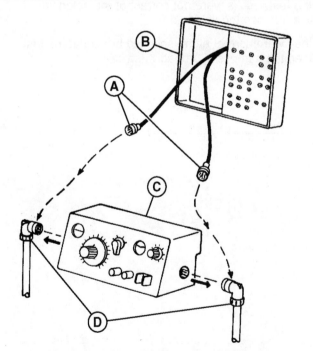

Fig. 97 — Connect Test Set to Control Console

Continued on next page   OUO1082,0002D19 -19-15OCT12-15/23

POWER

1. Turn key switch to ACC.

2. Using the volt-ohm meter, check for proper voltage (see technical manual) on the test panel between the points indicated in Fig. 98.

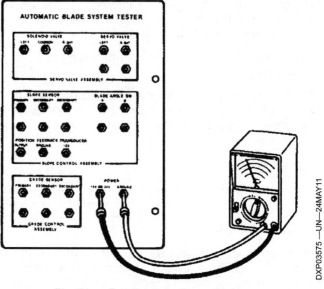

Fig. 98 — Test Points for Power Check

OUO1082,0002D19 -19-15OCT12-16/23

SOLENOID VALVES

1. Turn key switch to OFF.

2. Check resistance between the left test points (Fig. 99) and then the right test points. The reading should be approximately 25 ohms.

3. If not, disconnect wiring to the solenoids and make the same test.

4. If the test results were not correct at the solenoid valve, replace the solenoid.

5. If they were correct at the solenoid but not at the test panel, the harness is probably defective.

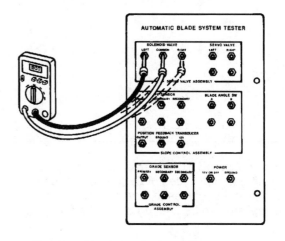

Fig. 99 — Test Points for Solenoid Valves

Continued on next page   OUO1082,0002D19 -19-15OCT12-17/23

SERVO VALVES

1. Check for resistance (see technical manual) between the two left test points (Fig. 100) and then the two right test points.

2. If the readings at the test panel are not correct, disconnect the wires at the servo valves and test at the valves.

3. If the reading at the servo valves is not correct, replace them.

4. If the reading is correct, but not at the test panel, then the harness is probably defective.

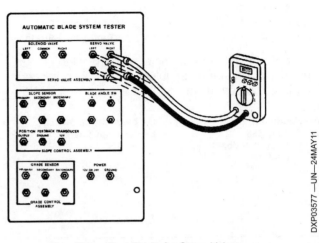

Fig. 100 — Test Points for Servo Valves

OUO1082,0002D19 -19-15OCT12-18/23

GRADE CONTROL SENSOR

1. Check for resistance (see technical manual) between the primary test points (Fig. 101) and between the two secondary test points.

2. If results of any of the test points were not correct, disconnect the grade sensor cord at the mainframe and check the cord and sensor.

3. If the readings still are not correct, disconnect the cord from the sensor and check the sensor.

4. If the sensor reads incorrect, replace it.

5. If sensor reads correct but incorrect at the cord, replace the cord.

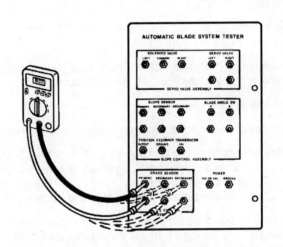

Fig. 101 — Test Points for Grade Sensor

OUO1082,0002D19 -19-15OCT12-19/23

SLOPE SENSOR

1. Check for resistance (see technical manual) between the primary test points (Fig. 102) and between the two secondary test points.

2. If any of the checks were incorrect, disconnect the connector at the slope control unit and make the same checks at the unit itself. Pins A and B are the primary, pins C and D are one secondary, and E and F are the other secondary.

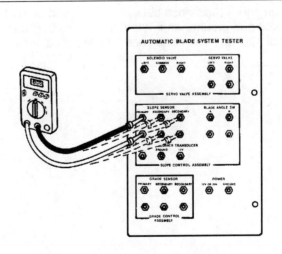

Fig. 102 — Test Points for Slope Sensor

Continued on next page

OUO1082,0002D19 -19-15OCT12-20/23

3. If readings at slope control unit are incorrect, the pendulum (A) (Fig. 103) or the wiring from the pendulum to the slope control connector is defective.

4. Test wiring with an ohmmeter with the wiring disconnected at the pendulum. If the wiring is good, replace the pendulum.

A—Pendulum
B—Timing Belt
C—Position Feedback
    Transducer
D—Blade Angle Switch
E—Terminal Board

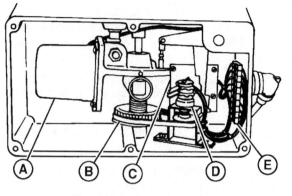

Fig. 103 — Slope Sensor

OUO1082,0002D19 -19-15OCT12-21/23

POSITION FEEDBACK TRANSDUCER

1. Turn key switch ON.

2. Check for voltage (see technical manual) between output and ground (Fig. 104).

3. If no voltage is present, either the wiring harness or feedback transducer (Fig. 103) is defective.

4. Turn key switch OFF.

5. Disconnect the connector at the slope control unit.

6. Check resistance between output and ground, 12-volt and ground, and output and 12-volt as shown in Fig. 104. Resistance should be high (infinity). If there is a resistance reading, there is a short in the harness.

7. If a high reading was obtained, place jumper wires in terminals V, M, and L of the wiring harness at the slope control unit end.

8. Tie the three wires together making sure a good electrical connection is made.

9. Again check resistance between output and ground, 12-volt and ground, and output and 12-volt. There should be very little resistance (see technical manual).

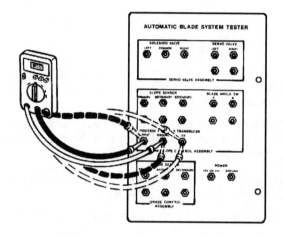

Fig. 104 — Test Points for Position Feedback Transducer

If any pair of terminals does not read near zero, the wiring harness is open.

10. If the harness checks out and the initial voltage check between output and ground did not read the correct voltage (see technical manual), replace the position feedback transducer.

Continued on next page

OUO1082,0002D19 -19-15OCT12-22/23

BLADE ANGLE SWITCH

NOTE: Check the technical manual for correct readings in steps 2, 3, 4, 5, and 6..

1. Start the motor grader and position the blade perpendicular to the main frame.

2. Check resistance between the two terminals of switch A (Fig. 105) and switch B.

3. Circle the blade 15 degrees in either direction. Repeat step 2.

4. Circle the blade to 30 degrees. Resistance should be about 25 ohms.

5. Circle the blade to 45 degrees. Resistance should increase to about 45 ohms.

6. Run the blade back to perpendicular. The resistance should return to zero.

7. Circle the blade in the other direction and repeat steps 3 through 6. Readings should be the same.

8. If only one or two resistances are incorrect, the blade angle switch (Fig. 103) is defective.

9. If there was no resistance reading on one or both sets of terminals in any degree of blade angle, the switch or wiring harness could be at fault.

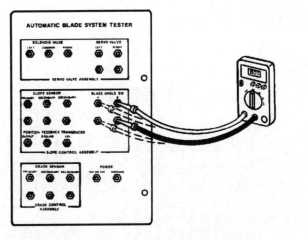

Fig. 105 — Test Points for Blade Angle Switch

DXP03582 —UN—10APR12

10. Repeat steps 2 through 7, but connect the ohmmeter to the connector pins on the slope control unit. Use pins G and K for switch A, and H and J for switch B.

11. If the readings are incorrect, the blade angle switch is defective. If the readings are correct at the slope control unit and incorrect at the test panel, the wiring harness is defective.

OUO1082,0002D19 -19-15OCT12-23/23

SCRAPERS
AUTOMATIC TRANSMISSION CONTROL SYSTEM

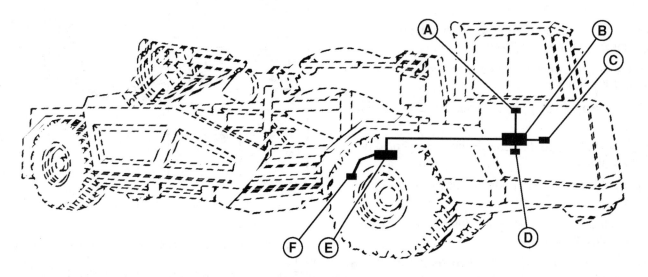

Fig. 106 — Components of Automatic Transmission Control System

A—Gear Selector Switch
B—Transmission Controller
C—Hold Switch
D—Downshift Switch
E—Solenoid Valve (6 used)
F—Magnetic Pickup

The automatic transmission control system (Fig. 106):

• Transmission controller (B)
• Gear selector switch (A).
• Magnetic pickup (F).
• Six solenoid valves (E).
• Hold switch (C).
• Downshift switch (D).
• Elevator switch.

A neutral start switch and reverse warning alarm switch are contained in the circuitry of the transmission controller.

The elevator circuit on the scraper is also connected to the transmission controller since the position of the elevator determines the gear that the controller selects.

The transmission can be operated in either manual or automatic mode, depending on the position of the mode switch on the transmission controller.

OUO1082,0002D1A -19-05APR12-1/7

When the transmission is in automatic mode, ground speed of the scraper determines whether the transmission shifts up or down. As the scraper slows, the transmission shifts down, and as speed increases, the transmission shifts to a higher gear just as your car does. However, the transmission will not shift any higher than the gear that the gear selector lever is in, just as your car will not shift into high if you have the lever in second gear. A magnetic pickup (Fig. 107), located on the transmission housing, senses ground speed.

A—Cover (Disconnected)
B—Magnetic Pickup
C—Harness Connector

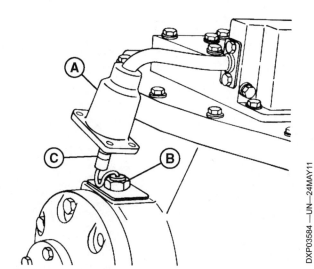

Fig. 107 — Magnetic Pickup on Transmission Housing

Continued on next page

OUO1082,0002D1A -19-05APR12-2/7

The transmission controller (J) (Fig. 108) switches different combinations of six solenoid valves (C) (Fig. 109) on and off. These solenoid valves in turn control two clutch and four brake packs in the transmission to obtain six forward speeds, one reverse speed, and torque converter lockup. Table 13 gives solenoid and brake and clutch pack engagement for each gear. Solenoid number 3 is on in all gears. When this solenoid is off, the transmission is in neutral. Solenoid number 4 controls torque converter lockup and number 6 is on only in reverse.

In the manual mode, even though the signal still goes through the transmission control box, the gear is selected by the position of the gear selector lever. The speed signal (from the magnetic pickup) is used to provide automatic control of the torque converter lockup clutch.

Table 13 — Transmission Gear Engagement Chart		
Gear	**Solenoids**	**Clutch and/or Brake Packs**
Reverse	3, 5, 6	B2, B3
Neutral	—	B4
1	2, 3, 5	B1, C2
2	3, 5	B2, C2
3	2, 3	B1, B4
4	3	B2, B4
5	1, 2, 3, 5	C1, C2
6	1, 2, 3	C1, B4
TC (Lockup)	4	Converter Clutch

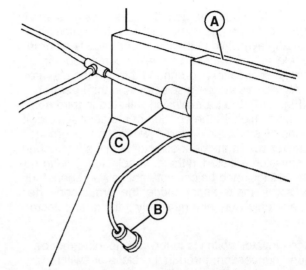

Fig. 108 — Transmission Controller

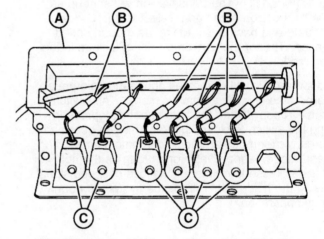

Fig. 109 — Solenoid Valves for Transmission Controller

A—Cover (Open)
B—Harness Connectors (6 used)

C—Solenoid Valve (6 used)

Continued on next page   OUO1082,0002D1A -19-05APR12-3/7

In the automatic mode, the gear the transmission starts in is determined by the position of the elevator switch and gear selector lever. When the elevator switch is off or in reverse (elevator in transport mode), a certain portion of the control box circuitry is grounded through the elevator switch. As long as the gear selector is in third gear or higher (Fig. 110), the transmission will start in third gear and shift up as high as the position of the gear selector if ground speed is adequate, and down to third as ground speed decreases. If the gear selector is in first or second, the transmission will start in the gear selected. The torque converter will lock and unlock automatically in gears four, five, and six. In the transport mode, the torque converter will lock and unlock in third gear only if the gear selector is in third.

When the elevator switch is in forward (loading mode), the ground connection, through the elevator switch, is removed, which causes the transmission to start in first gear (Fig. 111). The transmission will shift up as high as the position of the gear selector if ground speed is adequate and back down to first as ground speed decreases. The torque converter will not lock up in the loading mode.

A hold switch (Fig. 112), located above the hold pedal, is incorporated into the automatic mode. This switch is normally open. When the hold pedal is depressed causing the switch to close, the transmission gear and torque converter mode are "locked in" into their existing gear and mode, respectively, for as long as the hold pedal is de-pressed and there is no loss of speed signal. Releasing the hold pedal returns the system to normal automatic operation.

Fig. 110 — *Transmission Will Start in third and Shift Up to fifth With Elevator Switch in Off or Reverse*

Fig. 111 — *Transmission Will Start in first and Shift Up to fifth with Elevator Switch in Forward*

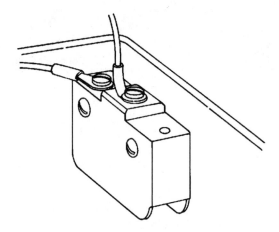

Fig. 112 — *Transmission Hold Switch*

Continued on next page   OUO1082,0002D1A -19-05APR12-4/7

A transmission downshift switch (A) (Fig. 113) is activated by the throttle linkage. It is normally closed. At about 1200 rpm, the switch is activated. When the foot throttle is released, the switch is closed and the transmission downshifts from sixth to fifth to fourth with the torque converter locked up, and then down to third with the torque converter unlocked when the scraper is in the transport mode.

A—Transmission Downshift
Switch

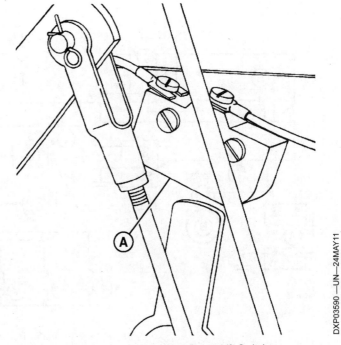

Fig. 113 — Transmission Downshift Switch

Continued on next page

OUO1082,0002D1A -19-05APR12-5/7

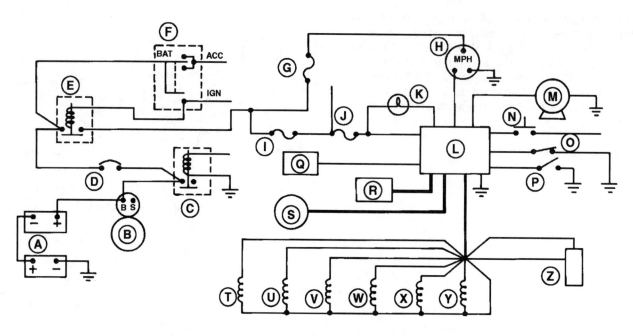

Fig. 114 — Automatic Transmission Control Circuit

A—Batteries
B—Starting Motor
C—Start Circuit Relay
D—Main Circuit Breaker
E—Accessory Relay
F—Key Switch
G—Gauge Fuse
H—Speedometer

I— Controls Fuse
J—Transmission Fuse
K—Automatic Shifting Indicator
L—Transmission Control Box
M—Reverse Warning Alarm
N—Start Switch

O—Transmission Downshift
   Switch
P—Transmission Hold Switch
Q—Elevator Switch
R—Gear Display Circuit Board
S—Gear Selector Switch
T—Solenoid No. 6

U—Solenoid No. 5
V—Solenoid No. 4
W—Solenoid No. 3
X—Solenoid No. 2
Y—Solenoid No. 1
Z—Magnetic Pickup

In Fig. 114 is shown the circuitry of the automatic transmission control system.

TESTING THE TRANSMISSION CONTROL CIRCUIT

Two different diagnostic procedures are used to check the scraper transmission control circuit. The first is a self-diagnostic system built into the transmission control box. The second uses a special scraper transmission/elevator diagnostic test set.

The second test procedure is used only when the first test procedure does not reveal the problem in the transmission control circuit.

NOTE: The first test procedure will check only the solenoids and their associated wiring and not other components of the transmission control circuit.

Self-Diagnostic Test

The first diagnostic procedure is initiated every time the scraper is started. The control box does not check itself but automatically checks all solenoids and leads for short or open circuits.

Place the gear selector lever in neutral. Check the gear display for a neutral (0) indication.

If the gear display is flashing a sequence of gears, the control box has diagnosed one or more of the solenoid valve circuits as defective. The flashing sequence shows the remaining usable gears.

NOTE: The transmission gears are represented by the numbers 1 through 6 (1 for 1st gear, etc.). Reverse is represented by a negative (–) and neutral by a zero (0).

Table 14 — Scraper Troubleshooting Chart

TEST	RESULTS[a]	CAUSE
Scraper batteries.	Between 18 and 30 volts.	Battery, cable, or fuse is defective.
Transmission hold switch key (key off)	Meter should indicate open circuit.	Switch or cable is shorted.
Transmission hold switch key (key on)	Meter should indicate less than 10 ohms.	Switch or cable is open.
Elevator switch (key off, switch in F)	Meter should indicate less open circuit.	Switch or cable is shorted.
Elevator switch (key off, switch in N or R)	Meter should indicate less than 10 ohms.	Switch or cable is open.
Transmission downshift switch (key off, full throttle)	Meter should indicate less open circuit.	Switch or cable is shorted.

Continued on next page   OUO1082,0002D1A -19-05APR12-6/7

Table 14 — Scraper Troubleshooting Chart

TEST	RESULTS[a]	CAUSE
Transmission downshift switch (key off, throttle released)	Meter should indicate less than 10 ohms.	Switch or cable is open.
Gear selector switch (repeat for each gear)	Meter should indicate less than 10 ohms.	Switch or cable is open.
Solenoids (repeat for each)	Meter should indicate more than 5 but less than 12 ohms.	Less than 5 ohms, valve or cable is shorted. More than 12 ohms, they are open.
Gear display circuit board (repeat for each display)	Meter should indicate more than 25 but less than 250 ohms.	Less than 25 ohms, display or cable is shorted. More than 250 ohms, they are open.
Gear selector switch (in N)	Meter should indicate less open circuit.	Switch is defective.
Gear selector switch (in all other gears)	Meter should indicate less than 10 ohms.	Switch is defective.
Magnetic pickup (key on, engine off)	Meter should indicate more than 1 but less than 6 volts.	Pickup or cable is shorted if less than 1 volt; open if more than 6 volts.
Speedometer output (key off)	Meter should indicate more than 1,000 but less than 10,000 ohms.	Speedometer or cable is shorted if less than 1,000 ohms; open if more than 10,000 ohms.
Start circuit relay (key off, push starter button)	Meter should indicate more than 10 but less than 20 ohms.	Start circuit relay or cable is shorted if less than 10 ohms; open if more than 20 ohms.
Reverse warning alarm (key on, engine off) (Press button on test set.)	Horn should sound.	Cable or alarm is defective if horn does not sound.

[a]*Volts and ohms listed in this column are typical. Check the applicable technical manual for the exact specifications for your machine.*

Uses for Diagnostic Test Set

When the self-diagnostic test fails to reveal the problem, then a special diagnostic test set must be used. In Fig. 115 is shown how the test set is connected to the transmission controller.

The test set will test the following components:

- Scraper battery
- Transmission hold switch
- Elevator switch
- Downshift switch
- Gear selector
- Transmission solenoids
- Gear display
- Gear selector switch
- Magnetic pickup
- Speedometer output
- Starter relay
- Reverse warning horn

Table 12 lists the tests, the results that should be expected from the tests, and the probable cause if the test results are not met.

SUMMARY

As we said earlier, no attempt was made to present every application of electronics and microprocessors in agricultural and industrial equipment. Our primary aim was to show you how vastly different and varied the uses are and to present the fundamentals of service on these systems.

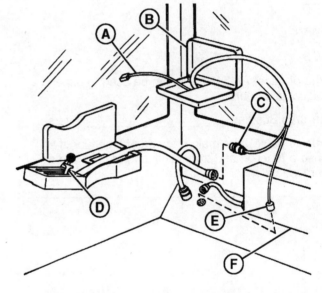

Fig. 115 — Connecting Test Set to Transmission Controller

A—Elevator Harness Connector
B—Test Set
C—35-Pin Connector
D—Shift Lever
E—19-Pin Connector
F—Transmission Controller

One final note: Do not be intimidated by the electronic systems on a machine. They were installed on the machine for one main purpose—to improve productivity of the machine.

OUO1082,0002D1A -19-05APR12-7/7

TEST YOURSELF

QUESTIONS

1. What is the difference between a monitor and a controller?

2. (True or False) Most microprocessors have a control register.

3. (True or False) All microprocessors have internal data and address buses.

4. (True or False) The accumulator holds the results of a mathematical or logical operation of the X and Y registers.

5. (True or False) The RS-232 Serial Bus is limited to not more than 100 feet in length.

6. (True or False) Ports of a microprocessor are usually groups of 10 pins for DIO.

7. Identify the following abbreviations:

    a. NMI

    b. RD

    c. WR

    d. CS

8. (True or false) An 74HC237 can be used to expand a digital input port.

9. The CAN Bus has _____ layers.

10. (True or False) The main purpose of a sensor is to sense a function and transmit this information to a microcontroller.

11. What three components do practically all monitoring systems have in common?

12. The sensor in a metal detector is _____ (optical or magnetic).

13. (True or False) The sensor in a planter monitoring system is of the magnetic type.

14. The _____ monitor indicates with lights and a buzzer when a combine straw chopper, straw walker, conveyor auger, grain elevator, or tailings elevator are operating at less than _____ percent of their designed speed.

15. (True or False) The grain loss monitor does not monitor the straw walker on a combine.

16. The lowest ground speed the digital tachometer can display is _____ mph.

17. (True or False) To display engine hours on a digital tachometer, you press the ground speed and rpm buttons at the same time.

18. The five sensors on the low shaft speed monitor are the straw chopper, straw walker, _____ clean grain elevator, and _____

19. (True or False) The bale size monitoring system on a round baler monitors only four functions.

20. (True or False) There are seven indicator lights on early four-wheel drive tractors.

(Answers on page B-4 in back of text.)

OUO1082,0002D1B -19-16AUG12-1/1

Hybrid Systems

DXP02718 —UN—23FEB11

18

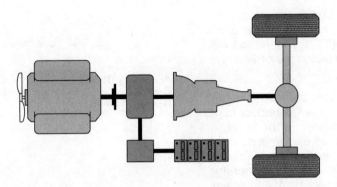

DXP03840—UN—16AUG12

As the demand for more efficient vehicles increases, so do the variations of hybrids being developed. In general, hybrids use two motors, an internal combustion engine, and an electric motor, to make the vehicle run. The designs in hybrids may differ, but the result in each case is that the electric motor provides some type of power. This relieves the internal combustion engine from fuel consumption.

Hybrids also incorporate regenerative braking to further improve the efficiency of the system. Regenerative braking can be used to help recharge batteries or to help run hydraulics. In both cases the electric motor becomes a generator and captures the kinetic energy that would be lost as heat when the vehicle's brakes are applied.

MM61211,00012C8 -19-16AUG12-1/1

Ground Drive Systems

Hybrids are classified by the division of power sources;

- Series Drive Train
- Parallel Drive Train
- Series/Parallel Drive Train

Current hybrids use both an internal combustion engine (ICE) and a battery/electric drive system

The following are the most common hybrid drive train configurations:

SERIES DRIVE TRAIN

This is considered the simplest hybrid configuration. A series hybrid will have an electric motor and in general a small internal combustion engine (ICE). The vehicle will get its main power from only the electric motor that is connected to drive wheels.

The internal combustion engine's only purpose is to run a generator creating power to recharge the battery bank and supply power to the electric motor. So the power required from the internal combustion engine is minimal to run at a constant rpm also, the need for a transmission can be eliminated with an electric motor. The generator may simultaneously charge the battery bank and power the driving electric motor that moves the vehicle.

Advantage

The series hybrid can function as a fully electric vehicle on short trips, reserving the internal combustion engine to produce extra power on extended trips. This configuration is optimal for continuous city, stop and start driving, generating high mpg's and low emissions.

Disadvantage

Series hybrid can travel only a short distance before exhausting their electrical reserves, making them best for drivers who travel short distances. Typically the electric motor will only run up to about 15-25 miles before the internal combustion engine starts running, lowering the efficiency. Long highway use will more than likely not benefit from this type of hybrid.

The stages are as follows:

Off — Vehicle is stopped. No power is being generated (Fig. 1).

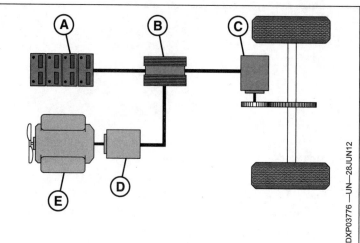

Fig. 1 — Basic Series Drive Train (Off)

A—Battery Bank
B—Inverter
C—Electric Motor
D—Generator
E—Internal Combustion Engine

Continued on next page

MM61211,00012CA -19-29OCT12-1/15

Slow — Driving at slow speeds, power is drawn from the battery bank (A), through the inverter (B), powering the electric motor (C) (Fig. 2).

A—Battery Bank
B—Inverter
C—Electric Motor
D—Generator

E—Internal Combustion Engine
F—DC Voltage
G—AC Voltage

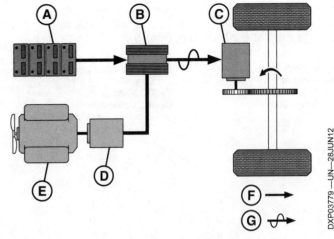

Fig. 2 — Driving at Slow Speeds

MM61211,00012CA -19-29OCT12-2/15

Acceleration — During acceleration, the internal combustion engine (E) will run, turning the generator (D), sending power through the inverter (B). At the same time, power from battery bank (A) is also sending power through the inverter (B) simultaneously, to create energy to the electric motor (C) turning the wheels (Fig. 3).

A—Battery Bank
B—Inverter
C—Electric Motor
D—Generator

E—Internal Combustion Engine
F—DC Voltage
G—AC Voltage

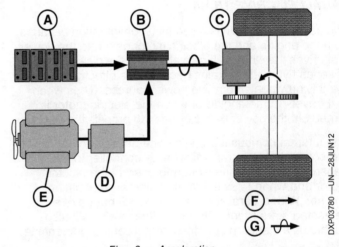

Fig. 3 — Acceleration

MM61211,00012CA -19-29OCT12-3/15

Cruise — During cruising speeds, the internal combustion engine (E) is running, creating power from the generator (D) to the electric motor (C) and recharging battery bank (A) simultaneously (Fig. 4).

A—Battery Bank
B—Inverter
C—Electric Motor
D—Generator

E—Internal Combustion Engine
F—DC Voltage
G—AC Voltage

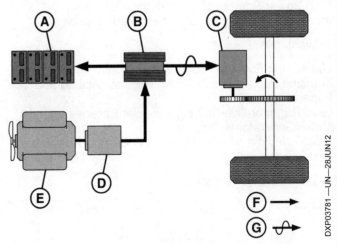

Fig. 4 — Cruising Speed

Continued on next page

MM61211,00012CA -19-29OCT12-4/15

Regenerative Braking — While braking, energy is created from the braking wheels and sent back to recharge the battery bank (A), (Fig. 5).

A—Battery Bank
B—Inverter
C—Electric Motor
D—Generator
E—Internal Combustion Engine
F—DC Voltage
G—AC Voltage

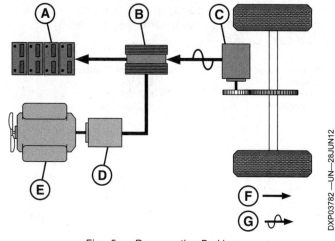

Fig. 5 — Regenerative Braking

MM61211,00012CA -19-29OCT12-5/15

PARALLEL DRIVE TRAIN

The parallel drive train is a common configuration because both the engine and the electric motor generate the power that drives the wheels. It also alleviates the disadvantages of series hybrid drive trains because it is directly coupling the driving wheels from two power sources. Thus when fuel travels to the engine or when the electric motor is turned on, the power that is generated propels the vehicle.

The internal combustion engine and an electric motor are connected to a transmission. A controller in the transmission determines when to operate the electric motor and when to switch to the internal combustion engine. With a parallel drive train, it will not have a dedicated starter motor; the motor/generator will also double as a starter to start the internal combustion engine.

Advantages

• Increased Power
• Smaller, Affordable Battery Packs
• Both Power Sources Can Work Simultaneously
• Increased Highway Efficiency and Performance

Disadvantages

• Lower Fuel Economy Than a Series Drive Train
• Transmission and Drive Trains are Complicated and Expensive
• Less Regenerative Braking Potential Because the Motor/Generator Is Smaller
• Electric Motors Are Not Powerful Enough to Accelerate the Vehicle

The stages are as follows:

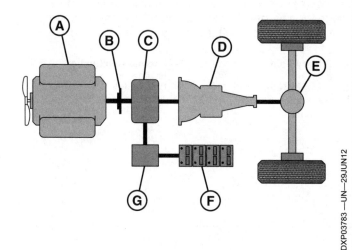

Fig. 6 — Basic Parallel Drive Train (Off)

A—Internal Combustion Engine Is Off
B—Clutch Is Engaged
C—Motor/Generator in Standby Mode
D—Transmission
E—Output
F—Battery Bank Ready to Send Voltage
G—Inverter

Off — Vehicle is stopped and no power is being generated, but the system is ready in standby mode (Fig. 6).

Continued on next page   MM61211,00012CA -19-29OCT12-6/15

Start-Up — This will happen each time the vehicle stops and at initial start-up. The battery bank (F) sends voltage to the motor/generator (C), in turn starting the internal combustion engine (A), (Fig. 7).

A—Internal Combustion Engine Is Starting
B—Clutch Is Engaged
C—Motor/Generator Sending Power to Engine
D—Transmission

E—Output
F—Battery Bank (DC Voltage Out)
G—Inverter (Converting DC to AC Voltage)

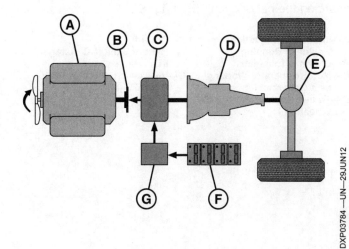

Fig. 7 — Parallel Drive Train (Starting)

MM61211,00012CA -19-29OCT12-7/15

Acceleration — As the internal combustion engine (A) sends power to the wheels through the motor/generator (C) and the transmission (D), it also receives assistance from the battery bank (F), (Fig. 8).

A—Internal Combustion Engine is Running
B—Clutch is Engaged
C—Motor/Generator Sending Power to Transmission
D—Transmission Propels the Vehicle

E—Output
F—Battery Bank (DC Voltage Out)
G—Inverter (Converting DC to AC Voltage)

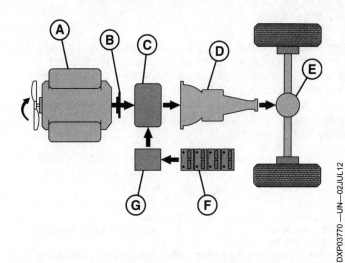

Fig. 8 — Parallel Drive Train (Acceleration)

Continued on next page   MM61211,00012CA -19-29OCT12-8/15

Cruise — During cruising speeds, the internal combustion engine (A) runs, creating power to the motor/generator (C) through the transmission (D) sending power to the wheels. It simultaneously sends power to the inverter (G), recharging the battery bank (F), (Fig. 9).

A—Internal Combustion
   Engine is Running
B—Clutch is Engaged
C—Motor/Generator Working
   as a Generator
D—Transmission Powering the
   Wheels

E—Output
F—Battery Bank (DC Voltage
   IN)
G—Inverter (Converting AC to
   DC Voltage)

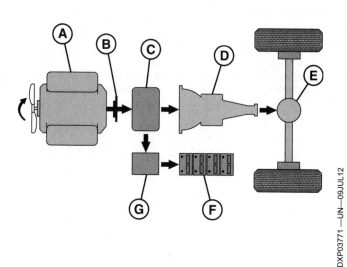

Fig. 9 — Battery Recharging Mode

MM61211,00012CA -19-29OCT12-9/15

The following figure is an example of the basic operation of a hybrid using regenerative energy.

NOTE: Motor/Generator and Transmission may be one unit.

Regenerative Braking — The motor/generator acts as an electric generator whenever the brakes are applied. this causes the motor/generator to create a drag or torque to the drive train and counteracts the forward momentum, thus stopping the vehicle. As this happens, it will also create energy (voltage), sending it back to recharge the battery bank, (Fig. 10).

NOTE: In some cases where hybrids have no traditional energy storage, regenerative braking can be used in assisting with hydraulic operations.

A—Internal Combustion
   Engine Is Off
B—Clutch Is Disengaged
C—Motor/Generator Receiving
   AC Voltage
D—Transmission

E—Input
F—Battery Bank (DC Voltage
   In)
G—Inverter (Converting AC to
   DC Voltage)

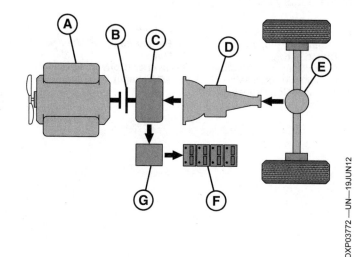

Fig. 10 — Regenerative Braking

Continued on next page

MM61211,00012CA -19-29OCT12-10/15

SERIES/PARALLEL DRIVE TRAIN

The series/parallel or power split merges the parallel and series drive trains. Combining these two configurations allows the internal combustion engine to either power the wheels (as a parallel drive train) or to be disconnected from the wheels, and by doing so the vehicle can run strictly from the electric motor (as a series drive train). Or power from the two can be shared to drive the wheels with the help of a power split device, that is similar to a planetary gear. The electric motor can also double as a generator when charging the battery bank is needed.

When highway use or when maximum power is required, the internal combustion engine will be the primary source of power, and the electric motor would assist the internal combustion engine to maximize the available power for short periods.

For stop and go driving such as in the city, the internal combustion engine shuts off to reduce emissions.

The stages are as follows;

Off — In standby mode, the vehicle is stopped and no power is being generated through the system (Fig. 11).

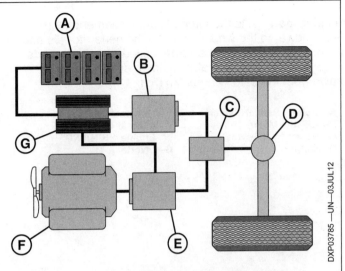

Fig. 11 — Basic Series/Parallel Drive Train (Off)

A—Battery Bank
B—Electric Motor
C—Power Split Device
D—Output
E—Generator
F—Internal Combustion Engine
G—Inverter

MM61211,00012CA -19-29OCT12-11/15

Slow — Driving at slow speeds, power is drawn from the battery bank (A), through the inverter (G), powering the electric motor (B), and converting to mechanical power with the power split device (C) sending it to output (D) (Fig. 12).

A—Battery Bank, Sending DC Voltage
B—Electric Motor Receiving AC Voltage
C—Power Split Device Mechanical to Output
D—Output
E—Generator
F—Internal Combustion Engine
G—Inverter Converting DC Voltage

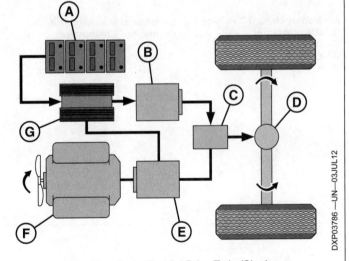

Fig. 12 — Series/Parallel Drive Train (Slow)

Continued on next page   MM61211,00012CA -19-29OCT12-12/15

Hybrid Systems

Acceleration — As the internal combustion engine (F) sends power to the wheels through the generator (E) and power split device (C), the power split device also sends power back to the generator, supplementing the power drawn from the battery bank (A) (Fig. 13).

A—Battery Bank DC Voltage
B—Electric Motor
C—Power Split Device
D—Output
E—Generator Voltage Out
F—Internal Combustion Engine "RUNNING"
G—Inverter

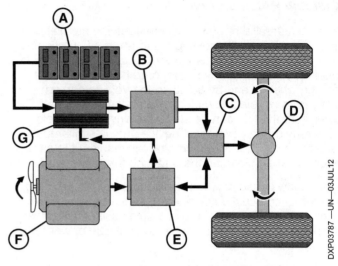

Fig. 13 — Series/Parallel Drive Train (Acceleration)

MM61211,00012CA -19-29OCT12-13/15

Cruise — At steady speeds, the internal combustion engine (A) sends power to the wheels through the generator (E) and power split device (C). The power split device also sends power back to the generator, creating voltage to recharge the battery bank (A) (Fig. 14).

A—Battery Bank DC Voltage
B—Electric Motor
C—Power Split Device
D—Output
E—Generator Voltage Out
F—Internal Combustion Engine Running
G—Inverter

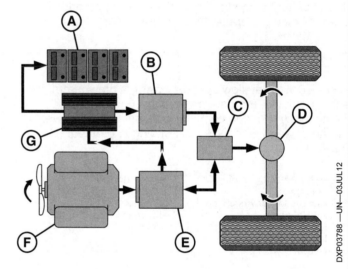

Fig. 14 — Series/Parallel Drive Train (Cruise)

Continued on next page
MM61211,00012CA -19-29OCT12-14/15

18-8

110112
PN=600

The following figure is an example of the basic operation of a series/parallel hybrid using regenerative energy.

Regenerative Braking — This happens while braking or the vehicle is decelerating. Energy is sent back from the power split device (C) through the electric motor (B), generating voltage recharging the battery bank (A) during braking, (Fig. 15).

A—Battery Bank
B—Electric Motor
C—Power Split Device
D—Output

E—Generator
F—Internal Combustion
   Engine
G—Inverter

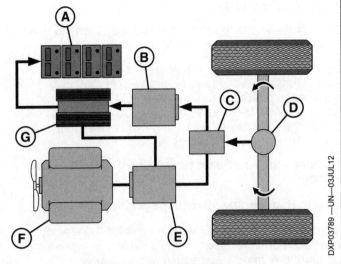

DXP03789 —UN—03JUL12

Fig. 15 — Regenerative Braking

MM61211,00012CA -19-29OCT12-15/15

Regenerative Braking

Engineers have managed to come up with a way to use brakes to generate energy or regenerative braking.

In the simplest of terms, regenerative braking is when kinetic energy is recaptured from a vehicle motion and converted to another source of energy. This converted energy can now be used as a power source; for example, to recharge batteries or assist in a hydraulic system, in each case improving efficiency.

The Following Are Some Examples of Regenerative Braking:

General Regenerative Braking System

Regenerative braking is a system in which the electric motor that normally drives a hybrid vehicle is essentially operated in reverse (electrically) during braking or coasting. This energy is reclaimed during braking by recharging the batteries and used to power the motor when the vehicle calls for an electric power source.

Instead of consuming energy to propel a vehicle, the motor acts as a generator that charges the on-board batteries with electrical energy that would normally be lost as heat through traditional mechanical friction brakes.

Storage — As brakes are applied on a hybrid car, kinetic energy is converted to electrical energy and sent back to the battery bank, thus recharging these batteries and increasing the efficiency.

This type of regenerative braking is mostly found on hybrid cars. The motor/generator acts as an electric generator whenever the brakes are applied. This causes the motor/generator to create a drag or torque to the drive train and counteracts the forward momentum, thus stopping the vehicle. As this happens, it will also create energy (voltage) back to the battery pack, (Fig. 16).

Hydraulic Regenerative Braking

The general function of hydraulic regenerative braking is when a vehicle decelerates or slows down. Kinetic energy is now converted to pressure instead of electrical energy, as previous discussed to recharge a battery bank. This

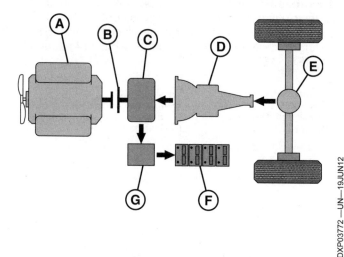

Fig. 16 — Regenerative Braking Mode

A—Internal Combustion Engine is "OFF"
B—Clutch is Disengaged
C—Motor/Generator Receiving AC Voltage
D—Transmission
E—Input
F—Battery Pack (DC Voltage IN)
G—Inverter (Converting AC to DC Voltage)

is done using an electric controller, pump/motor, and an accumulator to create hydraulic energy.

As the vehicle accelerates, pressure will release from the accumulator, thus sending mechanical energy to the driveshaft propelling the vehicle, and still allowing the engine to remain idle. As pressure is released from the accumulator, the need to keep a constant velocity or if acceleration is needed, the internal combustion engine will engage, suppling the vehicle with the added energy needed. This system relies on an electronic controller to send the correct signal at a specific time to each component to function correctly.

Continued on next page   MM61211,00012CB -19-19JUL12-1/3

Storage — As the vehicle decelerates or slows, down kinetic energy turns the gearbox and pump/motor sending a signal to the electronic controller. As the controller receives this signal, it tells the pump/motor to act as a pump, which starts to send fluid into the accumulator, increasing the pressure in the accumulator, thus storing energy (Fig 17).

A—Low Pressure Reservoir
B—Pump/Motor
C—Electronic Controller
D—Accumulator
E—Output
F—Control Valve
G—Gearbox
H—Transmission
I— Internal Combustion Engine

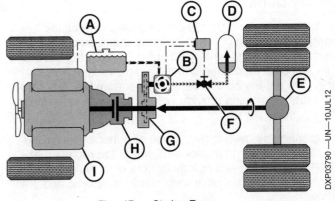

Fig. 17 — Storing Energy

MM61211,00012CB -19-19JUL12-2/3

Using Stored Energy — As the vehicle accelerates, the electronic controller sends a signal to the engine and the pump/motor. The controller now sends this signal, telling the pump/motor to act as a motor using the pressurized fluid in the accumulator to create torque. This energy assists the internal combustion engine in propelling the vehicle, keeping constant velocity of acceleration or when torque is needed (Fig 18).

A—Low Pressure Reservoir
B—Pump/Motor
C—Electronic Controller
D—Accumulator
E—Output
F—Control Valve
G—Gearbox
H—Transmission
I— Internal Combustion Engine

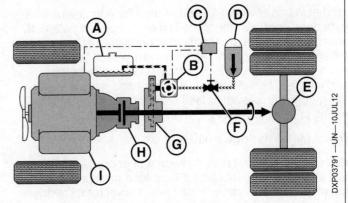

Fig. 18 — Using Stored Energy

MM61211,00012CB -19-19JUL12-3/3

Battery Bank

A battery bank consists of several small, low-voltage batteries called cells. These cells are connected together to form high-voltage battery modules. Combining several of these battery modules creates a high-voltage battery bank. The battery bank receives power from the generator when recharging and provides power to the electric motor when needed.

The technology used in the design of batteries for hybrid vehicles continues to improve. Some of the factors that drive the changing technology include cost, weight, size, service life, run time, environmental friendliness, and safety.

Battery Types

Lead Acid

Lead acid batteries have been around for a long time and were developed as one of the first rechargeable batteries. Lead acid batteries are the most economical rechargeable batteries for power applications where weight is not a significant concern. When compared to newer battery technologies, however, lead acid batteries have a lower energy density, providing less energy by volume which results in a higher weight in a given application.

Nickel Metal Hydride (NiMH)

NiMH batteries are a reliable source of energy for hybrids and are a major improvement from lead acid batteries that most conventional vehicles use. Nickel metal hydride batteries have a higher energy density, providing more energy by volume than lead acid batteries. NiMH batteries also use more environmentally friendly materials.

NiMH batteries still have some significant disadvantages such as higher cost, and higher self-discharge. As a result, engineers continue to develop more powerful and lighter batteries.

Lithium Ion (Li-ion)

Lithium ion (Li-ion) batteries for hybrids have emerged. Li-ion batteries have a higher energy density than lead-acid or nickel-metal-hydride batteries. Li-ion batteries can have an energy density close to three times that of a nickel-metal hydride battery, and are capable of producing a higher output. Higher efficiency makes Li-ion batteries a great improvement over NiMH batteries.

Another advantage is that Li-ion batteries have no memory effect, which means the battery does not have to completely discharge before recharging.

There are several varieties of lithium ion battery. Lithium ion batteries vary by the type of chemical composition used for the anode and cathode. The anode in all varieties is typically made of graphite. The cathode, however, may be made of cobalt dioxide, nickel-cobalt-manganese (NCM), nickel-cobalt-aluminum (NCA), manganese oxide spinel (MnO), or iron phosphate (FePo). The type of material used is determined by the manufacturer based on the cost, performance, and service life for a specific application.

Lithium Ion Polymer (Li-Poly)

Lithium ion polymer (Li-Poly) batteries use technology evolved from Li-ion technology. The primary difference is that the newer Li-Poly batteries use a solid polymer composite material for the electrolyte compared to the liquid lithium salt electrolyte used in Li-ion batteries.

This improvement offers two primary advantages. Li-Poly batteries offer the same attributes of the Li-ion battery but in a smaller package, and Li-Poly batteries are less hazardous if mishandled since the solid polymer electrolyte is nonflammable.

Zinc-Air

Zinc-air battery technology is currently being researched as a power source for hybrid vehicles. Zinc-air batteries are non-rechargeable batteries that have a higher energy density than other types of batteries and are relatively inexpensive to manufacture since zinc is more abundant than lithium. Zinc-air batteries use a zinc-based porous electrode as a "fuel." When the zinc is exposed to oxygen from the air, oxidation occurs and the chemical reaction provides electrical energy. The speed of the oxidation process can be controlled by controlling the amount of air flow to the zinc.

Challenges to be overcome for using zinc-air batteries commercially in hybrid vehicles include replacing the spent non-rechargeable batteries in the application, and the cost to recycle the spent zinc material. These challenges have led to research on rechargeable technology for zinc-air batteries.

DA78623,5F5E5E8 -19-18JUL12-1/1

Test Yourself

QUESTIONS

1. This is known as what, when braking or deceleration occurs?

2. What is the disadvantage of a series hybrid?

3. What configuration requires the internal combustion engine and the electric motor to generate power to the wheels?

4. Which configuration is optimal for continuous city stop and start driving, generating high mpg's and low emissions?

5. Which configuration uses a power split device?

6. Instead of consuming energy to propel a vehicle, the motor acts as a _____?

7. Typically the electric motor will only run up to about _____ before the internal combustion engine starts running in a series drive train.

8. What has these components: electric controller, pump/motor, and an accumulator?

9. When the controller receives a signal and fluid is sent to the accumulator, the pump/motor is acting as a _____?

10. A battery bank consists of several small, low-voltage batteries called what?

11. What is the primary difference between the electrolyte used in Li-Poly batteries and the electrolyte used in Li-ion batteries?

12. The amount of energy by volume characteristic of a battery is called what?

(Answers are in the back of the textbook.)

MM61211,00012CF -19-15AUG12-1/1

Definitions Of Terms

A

ACTUATOR SOLENOID—The solenoid in the actuator housing on the back of the injection pump which moves the control rack as commanded by the engine controller.

ALTERNATOR—A device which converts mechanical energy into electrical energy. For additional information, see Chapter 6, "Charging Circuits."

ALTERNATING CURRENT (AC)—A flow of electrons which reverses its direction of flow at regular intervals in a conductor.

AMBIENT TEMPERATURE—The temperature of the surrounding medium, such as gas, air or liquid, which comes into contact with a particular component.

AMMETER—An instrument for measuring the flow of electrical current in amperes. Ammeters are always connected in series with the circuit to be tested.

AMPERE—A unit of measure for the flow of current in a circuit. One ampere is the amount of current flow provided when one volt of electrical pressure is applied against one ohm of resistance. The ampere is used to measure electricity much as "gallons per minute" is used to measure water flow.

AMPERE-HOUR—A unit of measure for battery capacity. It is obtained by multiplying the current (in amperes) by the time (in hours) during which current flows. For example, a battery which provides 5 amperes for 20 hours is said to deliver 100 ampere-hours.

AMPLIFIER—A device of electronic components used to increase power, voltage, or current of a signal.

AMPLITUDE—A term used to describe the maximum value of a pulse or wave. It is the crest value measured from zero.

ANALOG IC—Integrated circuits composed to produce, amplify, or respond to variable voltages. They include many kinds of amplifiers that involve analog to-digital conversions and vice versa, timers, and inverters. They are known as Operational Amplifier Circuits or OP-Amps.

ANALOG GAUGE—A display device utilizing a varying current to cause a mechanical change in the position of its needle.

ARMATURE—The movable part of a generator or motor. It is made up of conductors which rotate through a magnetic field to provide voltage or force by electromagnetic induction. The pivoted points in generator regulators are also called armatures.

ARTIFICIAL MAGNETS—A magnet which has been magnetized by artificial means. It is also called, according to shape, a bar magnet, or a horseshoe magnet.

ATOM—A particle which is the smallest unit of a chemical element. It is made up mainly of electrons (minus charges) in orbit around protons (positive charges).

AUXILIARY SPEED SENSOR—The engine speed sensor located on the engine timing gear cover. It serves as a backup to the primary engine speed sensor.

OUO1082,0002D2F -19-10JAN12-1/1

B

BENDIX DRIVE—One type flywheel engaging device for a starting motor. It is said to be mechanical because it engages by inertia. For additional information, see Chapter 7, "Starting Circuits."

BREAK—See "Open."

BRUSH—A device which rubs against a rotating slip ring or commutator to provide a passage for electric current to a stationary conductor.

OUO1082,0002D30 -19-10JAN12-1/1

19-1

PN=606

C

CALIBRATION—The determination or rectification of the graduations used on a testing instrument.

CAPACITOR—A device which stores electrical energy. Commonly used for filtering out voltage spikes.

CHARGE—To restore the active materials in a storage battery by the passage of direct current through the battery cells in a direction opposite that of the discharging current.

CIRCUIT—A continuous, unbroken path along a conductor through which electrical current can flow from a source, through various units, and back to the source.

CIRCUIT BREAKER—A device used to protect an electrical circuit from overloads. The breaker acts as a switch and opens when the current passing through the circuit exceeds the rated level. Some circuit breakers must be reset manually; others may reset automatically after a period of time or when the current drops to the rated capacity. Also see "Fuse."

COIL—A number of turns of wire wound on an iron core. When current flows through the wire, the assembly becomes an electromagnet.

COIL (IGNITION)—An electrical device with two coil windings, whereby, through electromagnetic induction of one coil to another, the input voltage is stepped up to produce a high voltage ignition spark.

COLD RATING—The cranking load capacity of a battery at low temperatures.

COMMUTATOR—A device for assuring a one direction (DC) flow of current from a generator.

CONDENSER—An automotive term which describes a capacitor.

CONDUCTOR—A substance or body through which an electrical current can be transmitted. Elements which are good conductors have less than four electrons in the outer rings of their atoms. Also see "Insulator."

CONTROL CIRCUIT—The circuit of a control device or system which carries the electrical signals directing the performance of the controller, but does not carry the main power circuit.

CONTROLLER—An electronic device consisting of necessary circuitry, sensors, console, and wiring harnesses to automatically control a function of a machine.

CONVENTIONAL THEORY—The theory which states that the direction of current flow is from positive to negative in a circuit. This manual follows this theory regarding the direction of current flow.

COVALENT BONDING—The joining of electrons in the outer ring of one silicon atom with the electrons of other silicon atoms so that the atoms share electrons in their outer rings. This forms silicon crystal which is then "doped" by adding other materials and which creates a very good insulator.

CURRENT—Movement of electricity along a conductor. Current is measured in amperes.

CURRENT FLOW—The flow or movement of electrons from atom to atom in a conductor.

CYCLE—The change in an alternating electrical sine wave from zero to a positive peak to zero to a negative peak and back to zero.

CYCLING—The process by which a battery is discharged and recharged.

OUO1082,0002D31 -19-10JAN12-1/1

D

DIAGNOSTIC CODE—A number which represents a problem detected by the engine controller. Diagnostic codes are transmitted for use by on-board displays or a diagnostic reader so the operator or technician is aware there is a problem and in what part of the fuel injection system the problem can be found.

DIFFERENTIATOR CIRCUIT—A circuit that consists of resistors and capacitors designed to change a DC input to an AC output. It is used to make narrow pulse generators and to trigger digital logic circuits. When used in integrated circuits it is known as an inverter.

DIGITAL IC—Integrated circuits that produce logic voltage signals or pulses that have only two levels of output that are either ON or OFF (yes or no). Some component output examples are: Diagnostic Codes Output, Pulse-Width-Modulated (PWM) Throttle Output, Auxiliary Speed Output, and Fuel Flow/Throttle Output.

DIODE—An electrical device that will allow current to pass through itself in one direction only. Also see "Zener Diode."

DIRECT CURRENT (DC)—A steady flow of electrons moving steadily and continually in the same direction along a conductor from a point of high potential to one of lower potential. It is produced by a battery, generator, or rectifier.

DISCHARGE—To remove electrical energy from a charged body such as a capacitor or battery.

DISTRIBUTOR (IGNITION)—A device which directs the high voltage of the ignition coil to the engine spark plugs.

DISTRIBUTOR LEAD CONNECTOR—A connection plug in the wires that lead from the sensor in the distributor to the electronic control unit.

DYER DRIVE—One type of flywheel engaging mechanism in a starting motor. For additional information, see Chapter 7, "Starting Circuits."

OUO1082,0002D32 -19-10JAN12-1/1

E

ELECTRICAL FIELD—The region around a charged body in which the charge has an effect.

ELECTRICITY—The flow of electrons from atom to atom in a conductor.

ELECTROCHEMICAL—The relationship of electricity to chemical changes and with the conversions of chemical and electrical energy. A battery is an electrochemical device.

ELECTRO-HYDRAULIC VALVE—A hydraulic valve actuated by a solenoid through variable voltage applied to the solenoid coil.

ELECTROLYTE—Any substance which, in solution, is dissociated into ions and is thus made capable of conducting an electrical current. The sulfuric acid-water solution in a storage battery is an electrolyte.

ELECTROMAGNET—A core of magnetic material, generally soft iron, surrounded by a coil of wire through which electrical current is passed to magnetize the core.

ELECTROMAGNETIC CLUTCH—An electromagnetic device which stops the operation of one part of a machine while other parts of the unit keep on operating.

ELECTROMAGNETIC FIELD—The magnetic field about a conductor created by the flow of electrical current through it.

ELECTROMAGNETIC INDUCTION—The process by which voltage is induced in a conductor by varying the magnetic field so that lines of force cut across the conductor.

ELECTRON—A tiny particle which rotates around the nucleus of an atom. It has a negative charge of electricity.

ELECTRON THEORY—The theory which explains the nature of electricity and the exchange of "free" electrons between atoms of a conductor. It is also used as one theory to explain direction of current flow in a circuit.

ELECTRONICS—The control of electrons (electricity) and the study of their behavior and effects. This control is accomplished by devices that resist, carry, select, steer, switch, store, manipulate, and exploit the electron.

ELECTRONIC CONTROL UNIT (ECU)—General term for any electronic controller. See "Controller."

ELECTRONIC GOVERNOR—The computer program within the engine controller which determines the commanded fuel delivery based on throttle command, engine speed, and fuel temperature. It replaces the function of a mechanical governor.

ELECTRONIC IGNITION SYSTEM—A system in which the timing of the ignition spark is controlled electronically. Electronic ignition systems have no points or condenser, but instead have a reluctor, sensor, and electronic control unit.

ELEMENT—Any substance that normally can not be separated into different substances. or The completed assembly of a battery consisting of negative plates, positive plates, and separators mounted in a cell compartment.

ENGINE CONTROLLER—The electronic module which controls fuel delivery, diagnostic outputs, backup operation, and communications with other electronic modules.

OUO1082,0002D33 -19-10JAN12-1/1

F

FIELD EFFECT TRANSISTOR (FET)—A transistor which uses voltage to control the flow of current. Connections are the source (input), drain (output) and gate (control).

FIXED RESISTOR—A resistor which has only one resistance value.

FREQUENCY—The number of pulse or wave cycles that are completed in one second. Frequency is measured in Hertz, as in 60Hz (hertz) per second.

FUNDAMENTAL LAW OF MAGNETISM—The fundamental law of magnetism is that unlike poles attract each other, and like poles repel each other.

FUSE—A replaceable safety device for an electrical circuit. A fuse consists of a fine wire or a thin metal strip encased in glass or some fire-resistant material. When an overload occurs in the circuit, the wire or metal strip melts, breaking the circuit. Also see "Circuit Breaker."

OUO1082,0002D34 -19-10JAN12-1/1

G

GATE—A logic circuit device which makes a YES or NO (one or zero) decision (output) based on two or more inputs.

GENERATOR—A device which converts mechanical energy into electrical energy. For additional information, see Chapter 6, "Charging Circuits."

GRID—A wire mesh to which the active materials of a storage battery are attached.

GROUND—A ground occurs when any part of a wiring circuit unintentionally touches a metallic part of the machine frame.

GROUNDED CIRCUIT—A connection of any electrical unit to the frame, engine, or any part of the tractor or machine, completing the electrical circuit to its source.

GROWLER—A device for testing the armature of a generator or motor.

OUO1082,0002D35 -19-10JAN12-1/1

H

HYDROMETER—An instrument for measuring specific gravity. A hydrometer is used to test the specific gravity of the electrolyte in a battery.

OUO1082,0002D36 -19-10JAN12-1/1

I

IGNITION CONTROL UNIT—The module that contains the transistors and resistors that controls the electronic ignition.

INDUCTANCE—The property of an electric circuit by which an electromotive force (voltage) is induced in it by a variation of current either in the circuit itself or in a neighboring circuit.

INDUCTOR—A coil of wire wrapped around an iron core.

INSULATED GATE FIELD EFFECT TRANSISTOR (IGFET)—A diffused transistor which has an insulated gate and almost infinite gate-channel resistance.

INSULATOR—A substance or body that resists the flow of electrical current through it. Also see "Conductor."

INTEGRATED CIRCUIT (IC)—An electronic circuit which utilizes resistors, capacitors, diodes, and transistors to perform various types of operations. The two major types are Analog and Digital Integrated Circuits. Also see "Analog IC" and "Digital IC."

INTEGRATOR CIRCUIT—A circuit that consists of resistors and capacitors and functions as a filter which can pass signals only below a certain frequency.

INVERTER—A device with only one input and one output; it inverts or reverses any input.

ION—An atom having either a shortage or excess of electrons.

ISOLATION DIODE—A diode placed between the battery and the alternator. It blocks any current flow from the battery back through the alternator regulator when the alternator is not operating.

OUO1082,0002D37 -19-10JAN12-1/1

L

LIGHT EMITTING DIODE (LED)—A solid-state display device that emits infrared light when a forward-biased current flows through it.

LINES OF FORCE—Invisible lines which conveniently illustrate the characteristics of a magnetic field and magnetic flux about a magnet.

LIQUID CRYSTAL DISPLAY (LCD)—A display device utilizing a special crystal fluid to allow segmented displays.

OUO1082,0002D38 -19-10JAN12-1/1

M

MAGNET—A body which has the property of attracting iron or other magnets. Its molecules are aligned. For additional information, see Chapter 2, "Electricity—How it Works."

MAGNETIC FIELD—That area near a magnet in which its property of magnetism can be detected. It is shown by magnetic lines of force.

MAGNETIC FLUX—The flow of magnetism about a magnet exhibited by magnetic lines of force in a magnetic field.

MAGNETIC INDUCTION—The process of introducing magnetism into a bar of iron or other magnetic material.

MAGNETIC LINES OF FORCE—Invisible lines which conveniently illustrate the characteristics of a magnetic field and magnetic flux about a mag net.

MAGNETIC MATERIAL—Any material to whose molecules the property of magnetism can be imparted.

MAGNETIC NORTH—The direction sought by the north pole end of a magnet, such as a magnetic needle, in a horizontal position. It is near the geographic north pole of the Earth.

MAGNETIC PICKUP ASSEMBLY—The assembly in a self integrated electronic ignition system that contains a permanent magnet, a pole piece with internal teeth, and a pickup coil. These parts, when properly aligned, cause the primary circuit to switch off and induce high voltage in the secondary windings.

MAGNETIC SOUTH—The opposite direction from magnetic north towards which the south pole end of a magnet, such as a magnetic needle, is attracted when in a horizontal position. It is near the geographic south pole of the Earth.

MAGNETIC SWITCH—A solenoid which performs a simple function, such as closing or opening switch contacts.

MAGNETISM—The property inherent in the molecules of certain substances, such as iron, to become magnetized, thus making the substance into a magnet.

MICROPROCESSOR—An integrated circuit combing logic, amplification and memory functions.

MILLIAMPERE—1/1,000,000 ampere.

MOLECULE—A unit of matter which is the smallest portion of an element or compound that retains chemical identity with the substance in mass. It is made up of one or more atoms.

MONITOR—An electronic device that through sensors, gauges, console, and wiring harnesses keeps constant watch on functions of machines and alerts the operator of possible trouble.

MOTOR—A device which converts electric energy into mechanical energy. For additional information, see Chapter 7, "Starting Circuits."

MULTIMETER—A testing device that can be set to read ohms (resistance), voltage (force), or amperes (current) of a circuit.

MUTUAL INDUCTION—Occurs when changing current in one coil induces voltage in a second coil.

OUO1082,0002D39 -19-10JAN12-1/1

N

NATURAL MAGNET—A magnet which occurs in nature, such as a lodestone. Its property of magnetism has been imparted by the magnetic effects of the Earth.

NEGATIVE—Designating or pertaining to a kind of electricity. Specifically, an atom that gains negative electrons is negatively charged.

NEUTRON—An uncharged elementary particle. Present in all atomic nuclei except the hydrogen nucleus.

NON-MAGNETIC MATERIAL—A material whose molecules cannot be magnetized.

NORMALLY OPEN and NORMALLY CLOSED—These terms refer to the position taken by the contacts in a magnetically operated switching device, such as a relay, when the operating magnet is de-energized.

OUO1082,0002D3A -19-10JAN12-1/1

O

OHM—The standard unit for measuring resistance to flow of an electrical current. Every electrical conductor offers resistance to the flow of current, just as a tube through which water flows offers resistance to the current of water. One ohm is the amount of resistance that limits current flow to one ampere in a circuit with one volt of electrical pressure.

OHMMETER—An instrument for measuring the resistance in ohms of an electrical circuit.

OHM'S LAW—Ohm's Law states that when an electric current is flowing through a conductor, such as a wire, the intensity of the current (in amperes) equals the electromotive force (volts) driving it, divided by the resistance of the conductor. The flow is in proportion to the electromotive force, or voltage, as long as the resistance remains the same.

OPEN OR OPEN CIRCUIT—An open or open circuit occurs when a circuit is broken, such as by a broken wire or open switch, interrupting the flow of current through the circuit. It is analogous to a closed valve in a water system.

OPERATIONAL AMPLIFIER—A high-voltage gain, low-power, linear amplifying circuit device used to add, subtract, average, etc.

OVERRUNNING CLUTCH—One type of flywheel engaging member in a starting motor. For additional information, see Chapter 7, "Starting Circuits."

OUO1082,0002D3B -19-10JAN12-1/1

P

PARALLEL CIRCUIT—A circuit in which the circuit components are arranged in branches so that there is a separate path to each unit along which electrical current can flow.

PERMANENT MAGNET—A magnet which retains its property of magnetism for an indefinite period.

PIEZO-ELECTRIC DEVICE—A device made of crystalline materials, such as quartz, which bend or distort when force or pressure is exerted on them. This pressure forces the electrons to move.

PLATE—A solid substance from which electrons flow. Batteries have positive plates and negative plates.

POLARITY—A collective term applied to the positive (+) and negative (-) ends of a magnet or electrical mechanism such as a coil or battery.

POLE—One or two points of a magnet at which its magnetic attraction is concentrated.

POLE SHOES—Iron blocks fastened to the inside of a generator or motor housing around which the field or stator coils are wound. The pole shoes may be permanent or electro-magnets.

POSITIVE—Designating or pertaining to a kind of electricity. Specifically, an atom which loses negative electrons and is positively charged.

POTENTIOMETER—A variable resistor used as a voltage divider.

POWER SWITCH TRANSISTOR—The part responsible for switching off the primary circuit that causes high voltage induction in the secondary winding in an electronic ignition system.

PRIMARY SPEED SENSOR—An engine speed sensor located inside the actuator housing on the back of the injection pump.

PRINTED CIRCUIT BOARD—A device used to hold integrated circuit components in place and provide current paths from component to component. Copper pathways are etched into the board with acid.

PROTON—A particle which, together with the neutron constitutes the nucleus of an atom. It exhibits a positive charge of electricity.

PULSE—A signal that is produced by a sudden ON and OFF of direct current (DC) within a circuit.

PULSE-WIDTH-MODULATED (PWM)—A digital electronic signal which consists of a pulse generated at a fixed frequency. The information transmitted by the signal is contained in the width of the pulse. The width of the pulse is changed (modulated) to indicate a corresponding change in the information being transmitted, such as throttle command.

OUO1082,0002D3C -19-10JAN12-1/1

R

RECTIFIER—A device (such as a vacuum tube, commutator, or diode) that converts alternating current into direct current.

REGULATOR—A device which controls the flow of current or voltage in a circuit to a certain desired level.

RELAY—An electrical coil switch that uses a small current to control a much larger current.

RELUCTANCE—The resistance that a magnetic circuit offers to lines of force in a magnetic field.

RELUCTOR—A metal cylinder, with teeth or legs, mounted on the distributor shaft in an electronic ignition system. The reluctor rotates with the distributor shaft and passes through the electromagnetic field of the sensor.

RESISTANCE—The opposing or retarding force offered by a circuit or component of a circuit to the passage of electrical current through it. Resistance is measured in ohms.

RESISTOR—A device usually made of wire or carbon which presents a resistance to current flow.

RHEOSTAT—A resistor used for regulating a current by means of variable resistance; rheostats allow only one current path.

RIGHT-HAND RULE—A method used to determine the direction a magnetic field rotates about a conductor, or to find the north pole of a magnetic field in a coil. For additional information, see Chapter 4, "Electromechanical Components."

ROTOR—The rotating part of an electrical machine such as a generator, motor, or alternator.

OUO1082,0002D3D -19-10JAN12-1/1

S

SELF-INDUCTION—Voltage which occurs in a coil when there is a change of current.

SEMICONDUCTOR—An element which has four electrons in the outer ring of its atoms. Silicon and germanium are examples. These elements are neither good conductors nor good insulators. Semiconductors are used to make diodes, transistors, and integrated circuits.

SENDING UNIT—A device, usually located in some part of an engine, to transmit information to a gauge on an instrument panel.

SENSOR—A small coil of fine wire in the distributor on electronic ignition systems. The sensor develops an electromagnetic field that is sensitive to the presence of metal. In monitors and controllers, they sense operations of machines and relay the information to a console.

SEPARATOR—Any of several substances used to keep one substance from another. In batteries a separator separates the positive plates from the negative plates.

SERIES CIRCUIT—A circuit in which the parts are connected end to end, positive pole to negative pole, so that only one path is provided for current flow.

SERIES-PARALLEL CIRCUIT—A circuit in which some of the circuit components are connected in series and others are connected in parallel.

SHORT (OR SHORT CIRCUIT)—This occurs when one part of a circuit comes in contact with another part of the same circuit, diverting the flow of current from its desired path.

SHUNT—A conductor joining two points in a circuit so as to form a parallel circuit through which a portion of the current may pass.

SLIP RING—In a generator, motor, or alternator, one of two or more continuous conducting rings from which brushes take, or deliver to, current.

SOLENOID—A tubular coil used for producing a magnetic field. A solenoid usually performs some type of mechanical work.

SOLID-STATE CIRCUITS—Electronic (integrated) circuits which utilize semiconductor devices such as transistors, diodes and silicon controlled rectifiers. SPARK PLUGS—Devices which ignite the fuel by a spark in a spark-ignition engine. SPECIFIC GRAVITY—The ratio of a weight of any volume of a substance to the weight of an equal volume of some substance taken as a standard, usually water for solids and liquids. When a battery electrolyte is tested the result is the specific gravity of the electrolyte.

SPRAG CLUTCH DRIVE—A type of flywheel engaging device for a starting motor. For additional information, see Chapter 7, "Stating Circuits."

STARTER MOTOR—A device that converts electrical energy from the battery into mechanical energy that turns an engine over for starting.

STATOR—The stationary part of an alternator in which another part (the rotor) revolves.

STORAGE BATTERY—A group of electrochemical cells connected together to generate electrical energy. It stores the energy in a chemical form. For additional information, see Chapter 5, "Storage Batteries."

SULFATION—The formation of hard crystals of lead sulfate on battery plates. The battery is then "sulfated."

SWITCH—A device which opens or closes electrical pathways in an electrical circuit.

SYNCHROGRAPH—An all-purpose distributor tester.

OUO1082,0002D3E -19-10JAN12-1/1

T

TACHOMETER—An instrument for measuring rotary speed; usually revolutions per minute.

TEMPORARY MAGNET—A magnet which loses its property of magnetism quickly unless forces act to re-magnetize it.

THERMISTOR—A temperature-compensated resistor. The degree of its resistance varies with the temperature. In some regulators, it controls a Zener diode so that a higher system voltage is produced in cold weather, when needed.

TRANSFORMER—A device made of two coil windings that transfers voltage from one coil to the next through electromagnetic induction. Depending upon the number of windings per coil, a transformer can be designed to step-up or step-down its output voltage from its input voltage. Transformers can only function with alternating current (AC).

TRANSIENT VOLTAGE PROTECTION (TVP) MODULE—A device which protects the engine controller electronics against high energy voltage transients such as alternator load dumps.

TRANSISTOR—A device constructed of semiconductors that is used in circuits to control a larger current by using a smaller current for operation. Its function is the same as a relay.

TRIMMER RESISTOR—A resistor used in applications where only a small resistance change is needed.

TURNING FORCE—Magnetic force acting on a current carrying conductor to create movement of an armature, such as in an electric motor. For additional information, see Chapter 4, "Electromechanical Components."

OUO1082,0002D3F -19-10JAN12-1/1

V

VACUUM FLORESCENT DISPLAY (VDC)—An anode controlled display which emits its own light. It works like a television tube, directing streams of electrons to strike phosphorescent segments.

VARIABLE RESISTOR—A resistor that can be adjusted to different ranges of value.

VISCOSITY—The internal resistance of a fluid, caused by molecular attraction, which makes it resist a tendency to flow.

VOLT—A unit of electrical pressure (or electromotive force) which causes current to flow in a circuit. One volt is the amount of pressure required to cause one ampere of current to flow against one ohm of resistance.

VOLTAGE—That force which is generated to cause current to flow in an electrical circuit. It is also referred to as electromotive force or electrical potential. Voltage is measured in volts.

VOLTAGE REGULATOR—A device that controls the strength of a magnetic field produced by a generator or alternator. It prevents the battery from being over or under charged during high or low speed operation of the generator or alternator.

VOLTMETER—An instrument for measuring the force in volts of an electrical current. This is the difference of potential (voltage) between different points in an electrical circuit. Voltmeters are connected across (parallel to) the points where voltage is to be measured.

OUO1082,0002D40 -19-10JAN12-1/1

W

WATT—A unit of measure for indicating the electrical power applied in a circuit. It is obtained by multiplying the current (in amperes) by the electrical pressure (in volts) which cause it to flow. That is: watts = amperes x volts.

WATT-HOUR—A unit of electrical energy. It indicates the amount of work done in an hour by a circuit at a steady rate of one watt. That is, watt-hours = ampere-hours x volts.

WAVE—A signal that is produced by varying a continuous flow of current within a circuit. Waveforms can be created by either AC or DC current.

WAVEFORM—A graphical representation of electrical cycles which shows the amount of variation in amplitude over some period of time.

WINDING—The coiling of a wire about itself or some object.

WIRING HARNESS—The trunk and branches which feed an electrical circuit. Wires from one part of the circuit enter the trunk, joining other wires, and then emerge at another point in the circuit.

OUO1082,0002D41 -19-10JAN12-1/1

Z

ZENER DIODE (Reverse Bias Direction Diode)—A semiconductor device that will conduct current in the reverse direction when the voltage becomes higher than a predetermined voltage.

OUO1082,0002D42 -19-10JAN12-1/1

SUGGESTED READINGS

Sensors and Circuits, Sensors, Transducers, and Supporting Circuits for Electronic Instrumentation, Measurement and Control; Joseph J. Carr, Prentice Hall, Englewood, New Jersey 07632, 1993

Basic Electronics: Sixth Edition; Bernard Grob; Mcgraw-Hill

Instrumentation and Measurement for Environmental Sciences; Second Edition; Bailey W. Mitchell, Editor; American Society of Agricultural Engineers, 2950 Niles Road, St. Joseph, Michigan 49085, 1983

Your Guide to the Electronic Control of Fluid Power; National Fluid Power Association; 3333 N. Mayfair Road, Milwaukee, Wisconsin 53222-3219, 1992

Agricultural Sensors; Glen E. Vanden Berg; American Society of Agricultural Engineers, 2950 Niles Road, St. Joseph, Michigan 49085, 1988

Agricultural Electronics — 1983 and Beyond; Volume 1, Field Equipment, Irrigation and Drainage; Proceedings of the National Conference on Agricultural Electronics Applications, December 11-13, 1993, Chicago, Illinois; American Society of Agricultural Engineers, 2950 Niles Road, St. Joseph, Michigan 49085, 1983

OUO1082,0002D43 -19-10JAN12-1/1

MEASUREMENT CONVERSION CHART

MEASUREMENT CONVERSION CHART	
METRIC TO ENGLISH	**ENGLISH TO METRIC**
Length	**Length**
1 millimeter = 0.03937 inches (in)	1 inch = 25.4 millimeters (mm)
1 meter = 3.281 feet (ft)	1 foot = 0.3048 meters (m)
1 kilometer = 0.621 miles (mi)	1 mile = 1.608 kilometers (km)
Area	**Area**
1 meter² = 10.76 square feet (sq. ft)	1 square foot = 0.0929 meter² (m²)
1 hectare = 2.471 acres (acre) (1 hectare = 10 000 m²)	1 acre = 0.4047 hectare (ha) (1 hectare = 10 000 m²)
Mass (Weight)	**Mass (Weight)**
1 kilogram = 2.205 pounds (lb)	1 pound = 0.4535 kilograms (kg)
1 tonne (1000 kg) = 1.102 ton (tn)	1 ton (2000 lb) = 0.9071 tonnes (t)
Volume	**Volume**
1 meter³ = 35.31 cubic feet (cu ft)	1 cubic foot = 0.02832 meter³ (m³)
1 meter³ = 1.308 cubic yards (cu yd)	1 cubic yard = 0.7646 meter³ (m³)
1 meter³ = 28.38 bushel (bu)	1 bushel = 0.03524 meter³ (m³)
1 liter = 0.02838 bushel (bu)	1 bushel = 35.24 liter (L)
1 liter = 1.057 quart (qt)	1 quart = 0.9464 liter (L)
	1 gallon = 3.785 liters (L)
Pressure	**Pressure**
1 kilopascal = 0.145 pounds per square inch (psi) (1 bar = 101.325 kilopascals)	1 psi = 6.895 kilopascals (kPa) 1 psi = 0.06895 bars (bar)
Stress	**Stress**
1 megapascal =145 pounds per square inch (psi) (1 megapascal = 1 newton/millimeter²)	1 psi = 0.006895 megapascal (MPa) 1 psi = 0.006895 newton/millimeter² (N·mN/mm²)
Power	**Power**
1 kilowatt = 1.341 horsepower (hp) (1 watt = 1 Nm/s)	1 horsepower (550 ft-lb/sec) = 0.7457 kilowatt (kW) (1 watt = 1 Nm/sec)
Energy (Work)	**Energy (Work)**
1 joule + 0.0009478 British thermal units (Btu)	1 British thermal unit = 1055 joules (J)
Force	**Force**
1 newton = 0.2248 pounds force (lb-force)	1 pound = 4.448 newtons (N)
Torque or Bending Moment	**Torque or Bending Moment**
1 newton-meter = 0.7376 pound-foot (lb-ft)	1 pound-foot = 1.356 newton-meters (N·m)
Temperature	**Temperature**
°F = °C x 1.8 + 32	°C = (°F − 32) / 1.8

OUO1082,0002D44 -19-10JAN12-1/1

ANSWER TO TEST YOURSELF QUESTIONS

ANSWERS TO CHAPTER 1 QUESTIONS

1. Bypass, start
2. Gasses.
3. Safety goggles.
4. Grounded.
5. Danger, warning, and caution.
6. Current path
7. 0.006 ampere
8. False. The maximum sound level exposure in an 8 hour period is 85 dB
9. 13.5

OUO1082,0002D5B -19-06JUN12-1/1

ANSWERS TO CHAPTER 2 QUESTIONS

1. Meter.
2. First blank—"electons." Second blank—"conductor".
3. "conductors".
4. First blank—"repel." Second blank—"attract."
5. First blank—"amperes." Second Blank—"volts." Third blank—"ohms."
6. First blank—"electrons." Second blank—"behavior." Third blank—"effects."
7. "Opposition."
8. First blank—"Series". Second Blank—"Parallel." Third blank—"Series-Parallel".
9. True
10. First blank—"field." Second blank—"Force."
11. True.
12. First blank—"stronger." Second blank—"current."
13. A coil of wire wound over a soft iron core.
14. a-3; b-1; c-2.

OUO1082,0002D5C -19-10JAN12-1/1

ANSWERS TO CHAPTER 3 QUESTIONS

1. Silver
2. Copper
3. A circuit breaker is a protective switch which trip when excess current passes through its circuit, and is reset manually or automatically. A fuse is a protective element which blows out when current gets too high. Circuit breakers are used where heavy loads are instantly placed on the current, while fuses are normally replaced after they activate.
4. "Control, selection, and sensing"
5. True
6. "Amperage"
7. First blank—resistance. Second Blank—ohms
8. 10,000 ohms ±5%
9. Store
10. Diodes and transistor
11. One direction
12. D. All of the above
13. B. Electrical overload
14. Circuit breaker can be reset and used again while a fuse cannot
15. True
16. Step-down or buck converter

OUO1082,0002D5D -19-11JUL12-1/1

ANSWERS TO CHAPTER 4 QUESTIONS

1. First Blank—"small". Second blank "large".
2. True.
3. Solenoids.
4. False. The commutator converts the generator's output to DC.
5. True.
6. D. All of the above.
7. C. Both a and b.
8. D. Diodes.
9. C. Both a and b.
10. True.
11. Motor/generator
12. Regenerative brakes

OUO1082,0002D5E -19-11JUL12-1/1

ANSWERS TO CHAPTER 5 QUESTIONS

1. False. Specific gravity readings must be adjusted for temperature.
2. Battery electrolyte is made up of water and sulfuric acid.
3. False. They are activated in the field by the dealer or customer just made prior to use.
4. Recharge the battery. Then test it again.
5. Recharge the battery. The difference between cells is less than 0.05 points, so the battery is probably good. However, two cells are below 1.195, showing a need for recharging.
6. The two methods of charging batteries are slow charging and fast charging.
7. Slow charging.
8. First blank—"series." Second blank—"20."
9. First blank—"50%." Second blank—"cold cranking ampere."
10. Several small, low-voltage batteries called cells
11. From the motor/generator

OUO1082,0002D5F -19-12JUL12-1/1

ANSWERS TO CHAPTER 6 QUESTIONS

1. Recharge the battery, and 2) Generates current to power electrical, electromechanical and electronic components during operation.
2. False. Both circuits generate an alternating current (AC). The difference is in the way they rectify the AC current to DC current.
3. a-2; b-1 c-3
4. Anarmature and magnetic poles (or field).
5. By moving the armature or conductor though the magnetic field.
6. First blank—"alternator." Second blank—"generator."
7. Rotor assembly, stator assembly, and rectifier assembly.
8. The rectifier assembly.
9. The diodes convert AC to DC current.
10. True. This might damage the rectifier unit.
11. The transistorized model.
12. After.
13. Diode trio.

OUO1082,0002D60 -19-10JAN12-1/1

ANSWERS TO CHAPTER 7 QUESTIONS

1. First blank—"battery." Second blank—"starting motor." Third blank—"switch."
2. Series-wound, compound-wound, parallel-wound, and series-parallel wound.
3. False. The coaxial mounting is enclosed in the motor housing.
4. The no-load test.
5. 1/2.
6. b. No. 00 sandpaper.
7. First blank—"overheating." Second blank—"30 seconds."

OUO1082,0002D61 -19-10JAN12-1/1

ANSWERS TO CHAPTER 8 QUESTIONS

1. The spark which ignites the engine fuel.
2. Ignition coil, distributor points and the condenser, distributor, and spark plug.
3. a-2; b-1.
4. Time the sparks to occur at the correct time for the engine speed and piston cycles.
5. False. Remove and hone them or clean with a lint-free cloth and lighter fluid.
6. Fouled plugs have dirty deposits on their tips, while eroded plugs have badly burned tips. Too much heat causes eroded plugs, while lack of heat causes fouled plugs.

OUO1082,0002D62 -19-10JAN12-1/1

ANSWERS TO CHAPTER 9 QUESTIONS

1. Reluctor, sensor, and ignition control unit.
2. Any three of the following:
   a. No problems with distributor points and condenser.
   b. Quicker starts in all kinds of weather.
   c. Hotter spark of long duration will ignite marginal air-fuel mixutres under adverse weather conditins
   d. More complete combustion.
   e. Increases spark plug life.
3. False. They must be replaced.
4. The reluctor teeth may break or wear and result in hard starting
5. All components (including the coil) are inside the distributor.
6. Frequency.
7. Electronic.
8. All-speed.
9. Smoke.

OUO1082,0002D63 -19-10JAN12-1/1

ANSWERS TO CHAPTER 10 QUESTIONS

1. 25
2. False. Sealed beam lights are most commonly used for headlights.
3. Low power consumption and high efficiency
4. Lasers
5. False. Halogen bulbs must be allowed to cool, handled by the base, and should not be dropped or scratched.
6. False. Current is required to activate and deactivate an electromagnetic clutch.
7. False. Small DC electrical motors are used to perform auxiliary functions on some machines.
8. Variable resistance
9. True.
10. True.
11. Electric current.
12. Voltage.
13. Starting aid.
14. Satellite-Based Positioning Systems
15. Navstar
16. Control segment of GPS

OUO1082,0002D64 -19-12JUL12-1/1

ANSWERS TO CHAPTER 11 QUESTIONS

1. Pass current from one set of wires to another.
2. The Microscopic roughness or peaks and valleys on the surfaces of pin contacts which causes resistance.
3. Mating half locking mechanism, safeguard against being connected wrong, and design for individual pin contact replacement.
4. True. But vacant cavities should be plugged.
5. False. After stripping, the wire should not be twisted before installing in the terminal.

OUO1082,0002D65 -19-10JAN12-1/1

ANSWERS TO CHAPTER 12 QUESTIONS

1. Positive.
2. False. Never polarize an alternator. On the other hand, a DC generator-equipped system MUST be polarized.
3. Faulty wiring or poor connections cause high resistance and excessive voltage drop. Batteries will not charge properly, and spark plugs may not fire.
4. Acid film and dirt on the battery will allow current to leak between terminals. Corrosion will impede current flow to the system.

OUO1082,0002D66 -19-10JAN12-1/1

ANSWERS TO CHAPTER 13 QUESTIONS

1. Seven basic steps:
   ☐ Know the System
   ☐ Ask the Operator
   ☐ Inspect the System
   ☐ Operate the Machine
   ☐ List the Causes
   ☐ Reach a Conclusion
   ☐ Test your Conclusion
2. Test Your Conclusion
3. Battery

OUO1082,0002D67 -19-29OCT12-1/1

ANSWERS TO CHAPTER 14 QUESTIONS

1. Voltage between points A and D—"24 VDC." Voltage between points B and D—"16 VDC." Voltage beween points C and D—"2.67 VDC."
2. Voltsge between points A and D—"16 VDC." Voltage between points B and D—"8 VDC." Voltage between points C and D—"1.33 VDC."
3. True.
4. 5.276 VDC.
5. 400 Hz.
6. 5.236
7. 377 RPS.
8. 3E8h (hexidecimal)
9. 8h (hexidecimal)
10. True.
11. 85.
12. False. 0 OR 1 = 1
13. False. 0 AND 1 = 0
14. True.

OUO1082,0002D68 -19-10JAN12-1/1

ANSWERS TO CHAPTER 15 QUESTIONS

1. False. Low voltage can still kill.
2. True.
3. False. ESD susceptible equipment and parts are identified with the ESD susceptibility symbol or be in special packaging.
4. First blank—Binary." Second blank—"Logic."
5. Gates.
6. 8 VDC.
7. False. A chip can receive inputs when the ENABLE input is active.
8. True.
9. D5.
10. False. LCDs must be illuminated from behind if used at night.

OUO1082,0002D69 -19-10JAN12-1/1

ANSWERS TO CHAPTER 16 QUESTIONS

1. True.
2. True.
3. False. An NTC thermistor's resistance decreases with an increase in temperature.
4. False. Inductive proximity sensors can only be used in metal-sensing applications.
5. First Blank—"magnetic field." Second blank—"motion."
6. Light source, light detector, lens and the output switching device.
7. First blank—"wheatstone bridge." Second blank—"electrical signal.
8. True.

OUO1082,0002D6A -19-10JAN12-1/1

ANSWERS TO CHAPTER 17 QUESTIONS

1. A controller causes a function of the machine to operate in a programmed and automatic manner. A monitor keeps track of a particular function on the machine.
2. True.
3. True.
4. True.
5. False. The RS-232 serial bus is limited to about 50 feet in length.
6. False.
7. Identify the following abbreviations:
   a. NMI—non-maskable interupt.
   b. RD—read command.
   c. WR—write command.
   d. CS—chip select.
8. False.
9. Seven.
10. True.
11. Monitor or control console, sensors and wiring harness.
12. Magnetic.
13. False. It is an opto-electric sensor.
14. First blank—"low shaft speed." Second blank—"70."
15. False.
16. 0.5.
17. True.
18. First blank—"tailing elevator." Second blank—"conveyer auger."
19. False. The bale size monitoring system monitors five functions.
20. True.

OUO1082,0002D6B -19-10JAN12-1/1

ANSWERS TO CHAPTER 18 QUESTIONS

1. Regenerative Braking
2. Can only travel a short distance
3. Parallel drivetrain
4. Series hybrid
5. Series/parallel drivetrain
6. Generator
7. 15-25 miles
8. Hydraulic regenerative braking
9. Pump
10. Cells
11. Li-Poly batteries have a solid electrolyte; Li-ion batteries have a liquid electrolyte
12. Energy density

MM61211,00012C9 -19-19JUL12-1/1

110112
PN=620

Index

Continued on next page

Continued on next page

Continued on next page